D0889449

All Men Are Brothers

[SHUI HU CHUAN]

TRANSLATED BY PEARL S. BUCK

ILLUSTRATED BY MIGUEL COVARRUBIAS

IN TWO VOLUMES:

OF WHICH THIS IS VOLUME TWO

THE TEN FOOT GREEN SNAKE CAPTURES WANG THE DWARF TIGER

All Men Are Brothers

[SHUI HU CHUAN]

TRANSLATED FROM THE CHINESE BY PEARL S. BUCK

WITH AN INTRODUCTION BY LIN YUTANG

AND ILLUSTRATIONS BY MIGUEL COVARRUBIAS

FOR THE MEMBERS OF

The Limited Editions Club

NEW YORK: 1948

All Men Are Brothers

[SHUI HU CHUAN]

TRANSLATED BY PEARL S. BUCK

ILLUSTRATED BY MIGUEL COVARRUBIAS

Chapter 37

THE OPPORTUNE RAIN MEETS
THE MAGIC MESSENGER
THE BLACK WHIRLWIND
FIGHTS WITH
WHITE STRIPE IN
THE WAVES

IT IS SAID: At the time that Sung Chiang parted from the warden and went out from the writing room he came to the Hall Of Examination and there he looked about him. He saw the chief gaoler who had taken a bench and who sat there at the front of the hall and the man shouted in a great voice, "Which is the newly come prisoner?"

A guard pointed to Sung Chiang and said, "This one is he."

Then the chief gaoler cursed him, saying, "You short, black fellow who ought to be killed, by whose authority do you not send me the gift according to custom?"

Sung Chiang replied, "A favor should be given according to one's own desire, and will you compel a man's money by force? How mean a likeness of a man!"

Now the two men on either side of him heard this and they burst into a sweat. Then was that gaoler filled with fury and he shouted and cursed, "You cursed criminal, how dare you be so lawless and turn about and call me mean? You guards, bind him for me! I shall have him beaten a hundred strokes for torture!"

Now the men in the court were all good friends with Sung Chiang and when they heard he was to be beaten they all went away together and there were left only the chief gaoler and Sung Chiang. That man seeing them all gone, was all the more angry within himself. He took up the club he had and he leaped forward to beat Sung Chiang. But Sung Chiang asked, "If you beat me for what fault is it?"

The gaoler shouted in a loud voice, "You accursed prisoner, you are but a thing in my hands! If you so much as whisper a cough it is a crime!"

Sung Chiang replied, "Even though you fix my crime it is not one for which I ought to die."

Then that gaoler exclaimed in his anger, "You say you ought not to die—but if I wish to kill you it will not be hard to do it, either. It will be but killing a fly."

Sung Chiang smiled chilly and he replied, "Then because I did not send you a bribe I ought to die? And what about those who are friends with Wu Yung in the great lair?"

When the man heard these words he dropped in the greatest haste the club he held and he asked Sung Chiang, saying, "What is it you say?"

And Sung Chiang replied, "I am only speaking to myself of those who are friends with Wu Yung. Why do you ask me?"

But now the gaoler was in a confusion of fear and he laid hold on Sung Chiang and he asked, "Who are you in truth? Where have you heard such talk as this?"

Then Sung Chiang laughed and he said, "This humble one is a man of Yün Ch'en in the province of Shantung."

When the gaoler heard this he was full of great fear and in great haste he made obeisance and he said, "If you, Elder Brother, are indeed The Opportune Rain, Sung Chiang—"

And Sung Chiang said, "What is there to be talking of it all the time?"

Then that gaoler said, "Elder Brother, this is no place to talk. I do not dare to bow my head to the ground here before you. Let us go together into the city. Pray let my elder brother come with me."

So Sung Chiang said, "Good, but pray wait a little for me here. Let me go and lock the door of my room and I will come."

In much haste Sung Chiang went to his room and he brought out the letter from Wu Yung and he fetched some silver also. He came out then and locked the door of his room and he bade the warden guard it. Then he went away with that gaoler and they went toward the city of Chiang Chou, and they entered into the upper storey of a wine shop that opened upon the street.

There the gaoler asked him, saying, "Elder Brother, where did you see Wu Yung?"

Sung Chiang brought the letter out of his bosom and he gave it to the gaoler and the gaoler tore open the envelope and he read it from the beginning and then he put it into his sleeve. He rose up then and he looked at Sung Chiang and bowed himself to the ground before him. In great haste Sung Chiang returned the courtesy and he said, "My words just now were very offensive —do not blame me—do not blame me!"

That gaoler replied, "This humble brother had only heard it told that there was one surnamed Sung who had been sent to the gaol. Formerly every prisoner sent there must according to old custom send me a gift. Now more than ten days passed and I saw the gift was not sent and today being an idle day I went to seek the one who had not sent it. But I did not think it would be you, my Elder Brother. Truly did I offend in my words that I spoke a little while past in the gaol. A thousand thousand times do I beg for pardon."

Then Sung Chiang said, "The warden has told me often of your great name, and I had the desire to pay my respects before one so honorable, but I did not know where you lived and I had no reason otherwise to come to the city. Therefore I could but wait for you to come that I might meet you. For this reason did I delay these many days. It was not that I grudged the few ounces of silver and would not send them, but I thought you would surely come yourself to fetch them and I waited for this on purpose. Today luckily we have met and I have what I have hoped for my life long."

Now who was this man who spoke? It was that very one whom Wu Yung had commended to Sung Chiang. He was surnamed Tai and named Chung and he was head of the two gaols in Chiang Chou and he was called chief of all the gaols of the cities of the Yangtse river in that time of the Sung Dynasty; all of the keepers of the gaols toward the southwest called him chief also.

Now this Gaoler Tai had a certain magic skill he had learned from the Taoists and when he went out to take some urgent message of war he would tie about his legs the painted pictures of two paper gods and he would by his magic skill walk nearly two hundred miles in a day. If he tied four such pictures on his legs he could walk nearly three hundred miles in a day. For this he was called The Magic Messenger.

When they had finished telling each other what was in their hearts they were pleased with each other and they sat there in a corner and called to the wine seller to come and to prepare wine and fruits and some small meats for them and they drank on in the upper storey of that wine shop. And Sung Chiang told how he had met many fine fellows all along his way and of all that had happened when they met. Tai Chung also told all that was in his heart and how he came to be friends with Wu Yung and all that had happened.

Thus the two talked until they had become warm friends. But they had drunk but two or three cups of wine when they heard an uproar suddenly break forth down the stairs, and a vendor came running to their corner in haste and he said to Tai Chung, "This man who makes the turmoil can be rebuked by none but the head gaoler. There is no way but to ask the head gaoler to go and settle the matter."

Then Tai Chung asked, saying, "Who is that man who makes such an uproar below?"

The vendor replied, "It is he who walks about often with the head gaoler, and he is nicknamed Li The Iron Ox. He is downstairs asking the innkeeper to lend him money."

Then Tai Chung laughed and said, "It is that thing again behaving lawlessly. I wondered what sort of a man it was. Brother, pray wait for me a little while here."

Then Tai Chung rose and went downstairs. In a short time he came back leading a great black fellow up the stairs. Sung Chiang saw him and he gave a start and he asked, saying, "Gaoler, who is this great brother?"

Tai Chung answered, "This is a lesser guard out of my gaol and his surname is Li and his name is K'uei. His ancestors have always been men of I Chou in Shantung, and of The Village Of Thousand Feet. He has a strange name in his own village. He is called The Black Whirlwind Li K'uei but in this country men call him The Iron Ox. Because he beat a man to death he had to run away and although he met with the Emperor's pardon he drifted here to Chiang Chou and he cannot return to his village. He is of a very evil temper when he is drunken, and so everyone fears him. He can swing two great axes and he can wield a club. Now he has a place in the gaol."

Li K'uei stared at Sung Chiang and he asked Tai Chung, saying, "Elder Brother, who is this black fellow?"

Then Tai Chung laughed to Sung Chiang and said, "Sir, you see how coarse and rude this thing is! He knows not a whit of manners."

Li K'uei said, "How was what I asked rude?"

Tai Chung said, "Brother, you should ask, Who is this honorable official? That is the right way. But you said, Who is this black fellow? If this is not rude then what is? I will tell you now. This honored brother is the merciful one to whom you have always wished to go."

Li K'uei said, "Is it The Opportune Rain, black Sung Chiang of Shantung?"

Tai Chung shouted out, "Ha, how great impudence is this! How dare you call his name straight out! You do not know anything at all of high and low! And still you do not hasten to bow your head—to what time will you wait to do it?"

But Li K'uei said, "If it is truly Sung Chiang, then I will get down and knock my head. If it is but some idler, why should I bow before such an accursed? Elder Brother, do not fool me into bowing and then laugh at me!"

Then Sung Chiang said, "I am truly black Sung Chiang of Shantung."

Then Li K'uei clapped his hands and called out, "Ah, my Father! Why did you not say it sooner, and so make The Iron Ox happy?" And he fell to the ground and made obeisance.

In much haste Sung Chiang returned his obeisance and he said, "Brave Brother, pray seat yourself."

And Tai Chung said, "Younger Brother, come hither beside me and sit down and drink wine."

Then Li K'uei said, "I cannot be troubled with such a small cup. Change it for a big bowl!"

After a while Sung Chiang asked, saying, "Who was it who downstairs just now angered you, Brother?"

Li K'uei replied, "I had pawned a big piece of silver at a man's house for ten small ounces of silver to use, and I asked the keeper of this inn to lend me ten ounces of silver so that I could redeem my piece of silver and then I would pay him back and have some to use too. But this accursed keeper would not lend it to me. Even as I was about to fight the thing and beat him into powder this elder brother called to me to come up."

And Sung Chiang asked, "If you need the ten ounces to redeem the piece of silver, must there be interest money given also?"

Li K'uei replied, "I have the interest money here. I need only the ten ounces to redeem it."

When Sung Chiang had heard this he felt in his person and brought out ten ounces of silver and he gave it to Li K'uei and he said, "Elder Brother, take it and redeem your silver and use it."

Tai Chung would have prevented it but Sung Chiang had already brought the money out and Li K'uei took it and he said, "This is very well. Do you wait a little for me here, Elder Brothers. When I have redeemed my silver I will come then and pay this back, and then I will go with my elder brother Sung outside the city to drink a bowl of wine."

Sung Chiang said, "Pray sit awhile and drink a few bowls and then go."

Li K'uei said, "I will go and then come back." And he pushed aside the curtain and went down the stairs.

Then Tai Chung said to Sung Chiang, "Brother, it would have been better if you had not lent him the silver. I would have prevented you but you had already given it into his hand."

Sung Chiang asked, "And why?"

Tai Chung answered, "Although he is a straightforward person, yet he loves wine and gambling. Where did he have any big piece of silver to pawn at someone's house? You have been deceived by him and your silver is lost. He went out in such haste and surely it was to gamble. If he wins he will bring some back and return it to you, Elder Brother. But if he loses from whence can he get these ten ounces of silver to return to you? It makes a bad appearance for me."

But Sung Chiang laughed and said, "Honored Brother, do not look upon me as a stranger. Of what use is it to mention so small a bit of silver?

Let him go and lose it at gaming. I see this man is an honest, loyal fellow."

To this Tai Chung replied, "This thing has some ability but his heart is coarse and his courage is too ready and this is his fault. In the gaol in Chiang Chou when he is drunken he does not ill treat the prisoners but he attacks the more harsh among the wardens. I have been troubled with him sorely, for wherever he sees anything untoward by the way he wants to fight the oppressor. Because of this everyone in the city of Chiang Chou fears him."

Sung Chiang said, "Let us drink a couple of bowls more and then go outside the city and idle away the morning."

But Tai Chung replied, "I had forgotten—let us go and look at the view over the river."

And Sung Chiang said, "I would see what is here in Chiang Chou also. This will be best."

Let us not tell of how they again drank wine. But let it be told of how when Li K'uei had this silver he thought to himself, "It is not often that I meet such an one as Elder Brother Sung Chiang—he is not an old friend with me, either, and yet he has lent me ten ounces of silver! He is truly kind and he looks lightly on silver—it is not an empty name he has. Now he has come hither. But it is unlucky I have lost at gaming the last few days and I have not a penny with which to be a good fellow and invite him. But I have these ten ounces of silver of his and I will take them and game a little. If I win a few strings of cash then I will invite him and it will look very well, too."

Thus did Li K'uei run in great haste outside the city to the gaming house of Little Chang I. He went into the gaming room and threw the ten ounces down upon the ground and he cried out, "Give me the first chance at gaming!"

Now Little Chang I knew of old that Li K'uei played an honest game and so he said, "Elder Brother, rest awhile. When this game is over you shall game."

But Li K'uei cried, "I will game first."

Little Chang I said, "Well and you may take a chance from the side, too."

But Li K'uei said, "I will not take a chance from the side. I will lead this game. Five ounces is the stake!"

Now the men were on the point of gaming again but Li K'uei stepped forward and snatched their stakes away and he shouted out, "Who games with me?"

Little Chang I said, "Game the five ounces with me, then."

Li K'uei shouted out once, "Quick! For luck!"

The dice clattered, and he had lost. Little Chang I reached for the five ounces of silver. Then Li K'uei said, "I have ten ounces of silver."

Little Chang I replied, "Game with me five ounces more. Quick—for luck! If you win I will return the money."

Li K'uei took the stakes again and shouted, "Quick!"

The dice clattered, again he had lost! Little Chang I laughed and said, "I told you not to seize the stakes and to wait until the game was over. But you would not hear me. Now you have lost twice together."

Li K'uei said, "This silver of mine belonged to someone else."

And Little Chang I said, "Whose ever it is, it is no use to him now. If you have lost it, what more can you say?"

Then Li K'uei said, "I have no way—pray lend me a little! Tomorrow I will return it to you."

But Little Chang I replied, "What idle talk is this? It has been said from ancient times that in gaming there is neither father nor son even. If a game is lost the money must be paid. You have plainly lost. Why do you come to quarrel?"

Then Li K'uei took up his long robe and knotted it about him and he shouted out, "You will not return it to me?"

Little Chang I said, "Brother Li, you do always play a very honest game and you say nothing if you lose. Why is it you are so evil this day?"

Li K'uei did not answer him but he snatched up the silver from the floor and he snatched the silver also with which the others gamed and he thrust it all into the pocket of his cotton robe. Then he opened wide his two eyes and he said, "This lord has always played an honest game but today I will not be honest at all!"

Now Little Chang I rushed forward to seize his money but Li K'uei thrust at him with his finger and he fell backward. The twelve or thirteen gamblers all rose against him then and they would fain have taken the silver by force from him. But Li K'uei pointed north and struck south and he pointed east and struck west until he had beaten them to such a place they did not know where to hide and then he went to the gate. The gateman asked him, saying, "Good Fellow, and whither do you go?"

But Li K'uei kicked him aside and with one kick he kicked open the gate and went on. The crowd of men rushing out pursued him and they all shouted from the gate, saying, "Brother Li, you are too lawless and you have robbed us of all our silver!"

But they did no more than shout at the gate and not one dared to come forward and take the silver from him.

Now as Li K'uei was going along he heard a man coming up to him from behind him and the man seized his arm and shouted out, "You thing, why have you robbed others of their money?"

Li K'uei answered, "What cursed business is it of yours?" But when he turned his face around to see, it was Tai Chung and behind him stood Sung Chiang. When Li K'uei saw them shame covered his face and he said, "Elder Brother, do not blame me. I, The Iron Ox, have always gambled very honestly, but I did not think today I would lose my elder brother's silver and I had no money wherewith to invite my brother. I was so upset that in the moment I went and did this crooked deed."

Sung Chiang heard this and he laughed loudly and said, "Good Brother, if you want silver to use only come and ask me for it. Today very clearly you lost, and therefore return the silver to them quickly."

So Li K'uei could but take the silver out of his bosom and he poured it all into Sung Chiang's hand. Then Sung Chiang gave it over to Little Chang I to give to all the others. Little Chang I took it and he said, "Sirs and two lords, I will only take my own. These first ten pieces of silver, although my brother Li did lose it to me in two games, yet I do not want what is his so that I may be spared his hatred."

But Sung Chiang said, "Take it and forget the matter."

But how could Little Chang I be willing to do it? At last Sung Chiang said, "He has not struck you and wounded you, has he?"

Little Chang I replied, "The man who gathers the stakes and the man who sets out the tables and the gateman—he has knocked them all down."

Then Sung Chiang said, "If this be so, give it to them for a fee to refresh themselves. He of course does not dare to come himself. I will tell him to go."

So Little Chang I received the silver and he gave his thanks and returned and Sung Chiang said, "Let us go and drink three bowls with brother Li."

And Tai Chung said, "Near the river ahead of us is the wine shop called The Lute Pavilion. It is an ancient house made by Po Chü I of the T'ang Dynasty. Let us go thither and drink three cups and while we drink we can see the view over the river."

And Sung Chiang said, "Can we buy some meats and foods in the city to take with us?"

Tai Chung replied, "It is not needful. There is someone now in that pavilion who sells wine."

And Sung Chiang said, "If it be so, it is very well."

The three then went toward The Lute Pavilion. When they had come into it and looked about they saw one side of it faced the Ching Yang river, and the other side was the innkeeper's house. There were more than ten tables in this pavilion, and the gaoler chose one that was clean and he let Sung Chiang take the highest seat. He sat opposite and below him sat Li K'uei.

When the three were seated thus, they called to the serving man to bring out meats and fruits and cakes and foods from the sea and such things as will cool the mouth from wine when it is drunk. The serving man brought two jars of Jade Spring wine. It was the best, the most famous wine of Chiang Chou and he broke the clay seals. Then Li K'uei said, "Bring big bowls for the wine! It is too troublesome to drink from these small cups."

At this Tai Chung shouted out, "Brother, how coarse you are! Be silent! Drink your wine and it is enough!"

But Sung Chiang commanded the serving man, saying, "Place two usual wine cups before the two of us, but before this brother place a large bowl."

The serving man agreed and he went to fetch the bowl and he put it before Li K'uei. Then he poured out wine and he spread out the meats, and Li K'uei laughed and said, "Truly it is a good brother Sung! Men have spoken truly. He knows what my temper is. It would not be vain to swear brother-friends with an elder brother like this!"

And the serving man poured out wine and he poured out five or seven rounds, and Sung Chiang seeing his two companions, was pleased in his heart and he drank several cups. Suddenly he bethought himself that he would like to eat a peppery fish soup and he asked the head gaoler, saying, "Are there good fresh fish here?"

Tai Chung laughed and said, "Brother, do you not see the river is full of fishing boats? This is the very place for fish and rice. Why should there not be fresh fish?"

Sung Chiang said, "To have some peppery fish soup to dispel drunkenness is the best possible thing."

Tai Chung then called the serving man and he said, "Make three bowls of red pepper whitefish soup and with more pepper than usual."

In a short time the soup was there. Sung Chiang, seeing it, said, "A thing of beauty is yet better than a thing good to eat. Although this is but a wine shop yet this bowl is beautiful."

He took up his chopsticks and he urged Tai Chung and Li K'uei to eat. He himself ate also and he dipped up several mouthfuls of soup. Now Li K'uei would not use his chopsticks, but he took his hand and dipped up the fish out of the bowl and he chewed it up bones and all. Sung Chiang could no longer restrain his laughter. He drank two mouthfuls of soup and he put his chopsticks down and ate no more. He said, "I like to drink a little of such fish soup after I have drunk wine. But this fish truly is not very good."

Tai Chung answered, saying, "I also cannot eat it. It has been salted and it is not fit to eat."

But Li K'uei chewed all the fish in his own bowl and then he said, "If you two elder brothers will not eat I will eat it for you." And he reached out his hand and put it into Sung Chiang's bowl and he dipped the fish up and ate it. So he dipped into Tai Chung's bowl also and dipped the fish up and ate it, and the table was covered with the dripping of the soup.

When Sung Chiang saw Li K'uei had eaten all three bowls of fish, and even to the bones, he called the serving man and commanded him, saying, "This elder brother of mine I think is hungry. Bring a large piece of meat here, two catties, and in a little while I will pay for all."

The serving man replied, "This humble one sells only sheep's flesh here and no cow's flesh. If you want fat sheep's flesh, I have a plenty."

Li K'uei heard this and he threw what was left of the fish soup into the serving man's face and wet the man all over. Tai Chung shouted out, "What is it you do now?"

Li K'uei answered, saying, "This cursed fellow is so lawless! He thinks to fool me and that I will only eat cow's meat and so will not sell me sheep's meat to eat!"

But the serving man replied, "This humble one does only ask and I have said very little."

Then Sung Chiang commanded him, saying, "Do you but go and cut it and bring it hither. I will pay for it myself."

The serving man held down his anger then and he was silent. He went and cut off two catties of sheep's meat and he put it on a plate and he brought it and set it upon the table. When Li K'uei saw it he asked no more. He seized the great lump of meat and fell to eating it. In the click of thumb and finger he had eaten down those two catties of meat. When Sung Chiang saw it he said, "Ha, brave, ha, Good Fellow—truly—"

And Li K'uei said, "This brother Sung Chiang knows my cursed feelings. Is it not better to eat meat than fish?"

Then Tai Chung called the serving man and he said, "The bowls in which just now you put the fish soup were truly beautiful, but the fish had been salted and was not good to eat. Have you any other fresh fish? Make some other peppery soup of it, and bring it hither to this lord to dispel the fumes of his wine."

The serving man answered, "I do not dare deceive the head gaoler. This fish was truly caught last night. Today's live fish are still in the boats. We wait for the middleman of the fish market before we dare to buy and because of this we have no good fresh fish."

Then Li K'uei leaped up and said, "I will go myself and find two live fish for my elder brother to eat!"

But Tai Chung said, "You shall not go. Let the serving man go and borrow a fish and return it later."

Li K'uei said, "The fishermen on the boats will not dare not give me fish. What does this matter?"

Nor could Tai Chung restrain him. Li K'uei went straightway and Tai Chung said to Sung Chiang, "Elder Brother, do not blame me, that I bring such a man to meet you. He is without any grace at all, and he is shameful enough to kill one."

But Sung Chiang said, "This is his temper by nature. How can he be told to change it? I honor him because he has no falseness in him."

The two of them then sat there in The Lute Pavilion, and they talked and laughed and sought their joy.

Let it be told on. When Li K'uei had walked to the river's edge and looked about he saw the fishing boats there in a row, and there were eighty or ninety of them and they were tied to the green willow trees. The fishermen on the boats were all lying every way, their heads propped upon their boats. Some were making their nets, and some were bathing in the waters. Now this was the time of the middle of the fifth moon, and the red sun was about to sink into the west. The fish middleman was not to be seen anywhere.

Li K'uei went to the side of the boats and he shouted, saying, "Give me two of such fresh fish as you have on your boats!"

The fishermen answered, saying, "We do not see the middleman coming and we do not dare to open our holds. You see all those waiting there on the shore to buy our fish!"

But Li K'uei said, "What accursed middleman do they await? Give me two fish first!"

Again the fishermen answered, saying, "We have not burned incense before our gods yet; how dare we open up our holds? How can we dare open up and give a fish to you first?"

Li K'uei, seeing that none of them were willing to give him fish, leaped upon a boat. How could the fishermen restrain him? But Li K'uei did not understand the matters on the boat. He jerked aside the bamboo frames. The fishermen were on the shore and they cried out, "Well, well, let be, then!"

Then Li K'uei thrust his hand down under the boards of the boat and he felt about in the hold. But there was not a fish there. Now it was the custom for those fishing boats on the great river to have a great hole opened at the back so that the river's water could pass to and fro. There fresh fish were kept and a frame of bamboo was made in which to keep the fish. Thus the water passed in and out where the live fish were put and thus it was that Chiang Chou had good fresh fish.

But Li K'uei did not know this and he drew up the bamboo curtain and the whole lot of fresh fish all escaped. Then he leaped to another boat and lifted that bamboo curtain also. Then those seventy or eighty fishermen all hastened on to their boats and took up their bamboo poles to beat Li K'uei. Li K'uei was in a fury of anger and he tore off his long cotton robe. Under this he wore only a kerchief knotted about his loins. When he saw the poles descending from every direction he threw up his two hands and he grasped five or six in his hands. He twisted them like onion leaves and they were all broken.

When the fishermen saw this they were startled and they loosened the ropes that held their boats and moved out into the river. But Li K'uei was crazed with his wrath and all naked then he took the broken bamboos and came ashore and beat the fish mongers waiting there. In great confusion they took up their loads and went away.

In the midst of all this a man was seen to come near by a small road. When the people saw him they cried out, saying, "The master has come! This big black fellow is here robbing us of our fish! He has chased away all the fishing boats."

That man said, "What big black fellow? How dares he be so lawless as this?"

Then everyone pointed at Li K'uei with their fingers, and they said, "That thing is there still on the river's bank seeking for someone to beat."

That man rushed over and he shouted out, "You—even though you have eaten a leopard's heart and a tiger's gall still you shall not come and disturb this lord's way!"

Now Li K'uei when he looked at this man saw

that he was some six and a half feet tall and he was thirty-two or -three years of age and he had three parted whiskers. On his head he wore a kerchief of sky-blue muslin folded in a swastika. Inside the kerchief could be seen dimly in the coil of his hair a dash of red. He wore a white robe and his girdle was of thin silk. Below on his feet was a pair of hempen shoes. In his hand he held a pair of scales such as are used for buying and selling.

Now that man had come to buy and sell fish and when he saw Li K'uei, a great naked fellow, beating everyone, he gave his scales to some other in the business and he rushed forward and said in a great shout, "You thing, whom do you seek to beat?"

But Li K'uei made no answer. He took his bamboos and lunged toward that man to strike him also. The man charged forward and he had soon seized the bamboos. Li K'uei then grasped the man's hair. The man tried to strike some part of Li K'uei's person below his waist to overthrow him. But how could he move strength such as Li K'uei had, a very water buffalo's strength? Li K'uei pushed the man over and the man could not come near. He beat his fists a few times against Li K'uei's ribs but Li K'uei scarcely felt it. Then the man's feet flew up to kick but Li K'uei pushed his head steadily down and he lifted up his fist that was like an iron hammer and he beat it down with a sound of thunder and drums upon the man's shoulders. That man could not extricate himself in any way.

Even as Li K'uei was beating him a man came from behind and grasped him about the waist and another came and seized his hands and shouted out, "You cannot—you cannot!"

When Li K'uei turned his head to look, it was Sung Chiang and Tai Chung. Then Li K'uei loosened his hands and only then did the man he held escape and he went quickly away. And Tai Chung blamed Li K'uei, saying, "I told you not to come out and seek fish. Here you are again fighting with someone! Suppose you had killed a man with a blow of your fist? Would you not have paid for it with your life?"

Li K'uei answered, saying, "You are only afraid I will drag you into it. Even though I did beat a man to death I would suffer for it myself."

Then Sung Chiang said, "Brother, do not speak wildly. Take your robe and let us go and drink wine."

Then Li K'uei went to the foot of a willow tree and he took up his robe and he hung it upon his arm and he went with Sung Chiang and Tai Chung. They had not gone more than ten-odd paces when they heard someone behind them calling and cursing and he called, "You black ought-to-die! Today I will fight with you to the end, gain or lose!"

When Li K'uei turned his head to look it was that same man. He had stripped himself stark naked except for a pair of such trousers as are worn in the water and his flesh shone forth like white silk. He had taken the sky-blue kerchief from his head and the coil of hair stood revealed with its dash of red cord. He had a pole and he stood alone on a fishing boat poling. Now he rushed forward and he cursed mightily, saying, "A thousand knives shall cut you—into ten thousand slices shall you be cut, you black ought-to-die! If this lord who am I, fears you, then am I not to be counted a good fellow! If you go away then it is you who are not a good fellow."

When Li K'uei heard this he was mightily angry and he roared out once. He cast aside his cotton robe and he rushed back. The man brought the boat gradually nearer the shore and he put it close. With one hand he fixed the boat by the pole and he cursed mightily. And Li K'uei cursed also thus, "If you are a good fellow then come ashore!"

But that man thrust his bamboo pole at Li K'uei's legs and thus he stirred up Li K'uei's temper so that with a leap he jumped upon the boat. To tell of it is slow but the doing was swift. That man had trapped Li K'uei into coming on the boat and now he pushed the boat away with his pole and he thrust away with his feet at the same moment and the fishing boat darted into the middle of the river like an arrow. Now Li K'uei, although he knew a little of swimming unfortunately did not know much and so he began to feel afraid and confused. That man no longer shouted and cursed. He called out once, "Today I shall surely either win or lose over you." Then he seized Li K'uei's arm and he said, "I will not fight with you first. No, first I shall make you drink some water."

THE BLACK WHIRLWIND FIGHTS WITH WHITE STRIPE IN THE WAVES

Then with a foot on each side of the boat he began to rock it back and forth. The bottom of the boat turned to heaven and the two heroes fell into the water! Both the good fellows turned over with a splash and they were both in the river. Sung Chiang and Tai Chung in great agitation rushed to the river bank. But there the boat was turned over in the river and the two on the bank could only call, "Ah, bitter!"

Now soon there gathered on the bank some three to five hundred people and they watched from the shadows of the willows and they said, "This big black fellow has the worst of it this time. Even if he gets out with his life he will have drunk a bellyful of water."

And even as Sung Chiang and Tai Chung watched from the shore they saw the waters of the river parted and the man lifted Li K'uei up and again he thrust him down under. There the two of them were in the clear waves of the river, one his whole body black, the other as white as winter frost. There the two of them fought, knotted together in the water and struggling. The three to five hundred people on the river bank all applauded the sight.

Then Sung Chiang and Tai Chung, watching from the shore, saw that man hold Li K'uei under the water until his eyes were rolled so that nothing but the white showed. He lifted him up but to thrust him under again and Li K'uei suffered bitterly. Sung Chiang implored Tai Chung to find someone to save Li K'uei and Tai Chung asked the crowd, saying, "Who is this big white fellow?"

There were some who knew him and they said, "This good fellow is the master of the fish market here and he is named Chang Shun."

When Sung Chiang heard this he thought to himself in his heart and he suddenly remembered and said, "Is it not he who is called White Stripe In The Waves Chang Shun?"

Everyone answered, "It is he—it is he!"

Then Sung Chiang said to Tai Chung, "I have a letter from his brother and it is in the gaol."

Tai Chung heard this and he shouted out from the river's bank, "Brother Chang The Second, do not put forth your hand! There is a letter here from your own brother Chang Heng. This big black fellow is our brother. Pray forgive him and come hither to the bank to talk!"

Chang Shun from the middle of the river, seeing it was the head gaoler Tai Chung who shouted, knew him very well and he let Li K'uei go free and he swam to the bank. When he had climbed up and had seen Sung Chiang and Tai Chung he called a greeting and he said, "Gaoler, do not blame me for my lawlessness."

Tai Chung replied, "Pray consider my honor and go and save my brother and bring him hither to the bank. Then there is someone for you to meet."

So Chang Shun leaped down into the water again and he swam away from the bank. Now Li K'uei was there struggling and pretending to swim in the water and every now and again thrusting his head up. Chang Shun soon came to his side and caught one of his hands and then he tread the water as though he walked upon flat ground. The water was but up to his waist. One hand he swung empty and with the other he dragged Li K'uei to the shore. All the people on the river's bank applauded the deed. When Sung Chiang saw it he was dazed for half a day. And Chang Shun and Li K'uei both came up on the bank. Li K'uei panted for a while and he vomited clear water and Tai Chung said, "Pray come to The Lute Pavilion to talk."

So Chang Shun found his cotton robe and put it on and Li K'uei also put on his robe and the four then went to The Lute Pavilion and there Tai Chung asked Chang Shun, "Second Brother, do you know me?"

Chang Shun replied, "This humble one does know the head gaoler. But I—"

Then Tai Chung pointed to Li K'uei and he asked Chang Shun, saying, "Sir, have you ever known this one? Today he has offended you."

And Chang Shun replied, "And how could this humble one not recognize my elder brother Li? But we have never quarreled before."

But Li K'uei said, "And you have already drowned me enough!"

And Chang Shun retorted, "And you have beaten me very well, too!"

Then Tai Chung said, "Now you two had better become brother-friends. The proverb says, 'If two never quarrel they can never know each other well enough to be friends.' "

But Li K'uei said, "But you had better not come against me on dry land!"

And Chang Shun said, "I will just wait for you in the water, then!"

Then the four of them all began to laugh and they all made obeisances of apology. Tai Chung, pointing at Sung Chiang, said to Chang Shun, "Second Brother, do you know this brother of ours?"

Chang Shun looked at him and said, "This humble one does not know him. I have not seen him hereabouts."

Then Li K'uei leaped up and cried, "This elder brother is the black Sung Chiang!"

Chang Shun said, "Can it be The Opportune Rain, Sung Chiang of Yün Ch'en and Shantung?"

Tai Chung said, "It is that very elder brother, Sung Chiang."

Then Chang Shun bowed his head to the ground and he said, "Long have I heard his great name but I did not think to meet him on this day. I have heard those who travel to and fro by river and lake speak of his worth and goodness that he helps those who are weak and looks lightly on silver."

To this Sung Chiang made reply, saying, "But what is there to mention about so small a one as I? The other day I lived for a few days in the home of Li Chün. Afterwards I came to the river of Ching Yang and there I met with Mu Hung and your elder brother, Chang Heng, who wrote a letter home to give to you, Sir. But it is still in the gaol and I have not brought it hither with me. Today I came here with the head gaoler Tai Chung and with my brother Li to The Lute Pavilion to drink a few cups and to look out over the view of the river. But suddenly after I had drunk wine I thought to drink a soup of fresh fish, and how could we hold this one? Both of us could not hold him back and we heard a great noise and shouting upon the river banks. When we told the serving man to see what was amiss he said it was the big black fellow fighting with the people. In great haste we rose then to come and exhort and explain, but we did not think to meet with you, Brave Sir. Today has Sung Chiang had the good fortune to meet with three of the best of fellows. Is not such fortune from Heaven itself? Pray come and sit with us here, and we will drink a little of this poor wine together."

Then he commanded the serving man to change the wine cups and the dishes and again to prepare meats and side dishes.

And Chang Shun said, "If my elder brother wants good fresh fish to eat, this younger brother can go and find a few."

Sung Chiang said, "Nothing could be better."

And Li K'uei said, "I will go with you to get them."

But Tai Chung shouted out, "Here is he again! You must drink water or you are not happy!"

Chang Shun began to laugh and he clasped Li K'uei's hand and said, "I will go with you today and find the fish and we will see what the others say."

The two then left The Lute Pavilion and they went to the river's edge and Chang Shun whistled shrilly and all the fishing boats poled into the shore, and Chang Shun asked them, saying, "Which boat has golden fish?"

Then one answered here, "I have them on my boat," and another answered there, "Here on my boat I have them," and altogether they were able to give more than ten golden fish. And Chang Shun chose out four large ones and he plucked a willow twig and strung them upon it. He bade Li K'uei take them and go first to The Lute Pavilion and prepare them, and he himself would count for the fish market. Then he commanded his underling to go and fetch the scales for selling fish. After this Chang Shun went himself also to The Lute Pavilion to be company for Sung Chiang.

Then Sung Chiang thanked him, saying, "Why did you bring so many? If there were only one it would be enough."

But Chang Shun answered, saying, "But why put such a small thing in front of the teeth to talk about it? If you cannot eat them all, my Elder Brother, take them back with you to your honorable temporary abode."

And the two, Chang Shun and Li K'uei sat down in such rank as befitted their ages, and Li K'uei said, "My age is greater," and so he took the third seat. And Chang Shun sat in the fourth seat.

Then they commanded the serving man to bring again the Jade Spring wine of the highest quality and some sea food and some fruits and cakes and the like, and Chang Shun commanded the serving man to take one of the fish to make the peppery fish soup and to steam it in wine fumes. Another fish he commanded the serving man to chop into small bits.

Now when the four of them were in the midst of their wine drinking each one spoke out what was in his heart and when they were at the height of their good talk and words were fitted to the ear, they saw suddenly a girl about sixteen years old, wearing summer garb, and she came into their presence, and she made four very deep obeisances, and she opened her throat and began to sing. Now Li K'uei at this moment had been just on the point of telling all his great doughty deeds to the other three, and this singing turned the attention of all away from him. The other three all listened now to the singing and interrupted the flow of his talk. The anger rose up in Li K'uei's heart and he leaped up and he took his two fingers and pushed upon that girl's brow. The girl gave a great scream and fell suddenly upon the ground.

When everyone began to push forward to see what had happened they saw the girl's peach-bloom cheeks had turned the deathly color of clay and her little mouth was speechless. The keepers of the wine shop all came to restrain the four men and they made ready to go and report to the magistrate. Truly was it

> To have no heart to love a fragrant jade-like maid,
> To brew a noble heron upon a fire burning a harp.

How did these four escape from this wine shop? Pray hear it told in the next chapter.

Chapter 38

SUNG CHIANG WRITES A REVOLUTIONARY POEM IN THE CHING YANG INN. TAI CHUNG OF THE ROBBERS' LAIR BRINGS A FALSE LETTER

IT IS SAID: At the time when Li K'uei took his two fingers and pushed down that maid, the keeper of the wine shop laid hold on him and said, "Sirs, how is this come about?" And he was frightened in his heart, and he told the serving men and the vendors all to come and rescue the maid.

Then they came and took water into their mouths and sprayed it out upon the maid's face, and as they watched her she came slowly to life again. When they supported her they saw that a piece of skin was scraped away from her forehead and this was why she had fainted and fallen. But now she was brought to herself again and there were many exclamations of pleasure. The maid's parents had heard that she had been attacked by The Black Whirlwind and they were terrified into a daze for a long time and how could they dare to say one word? They looked at the maid and saw that she could speak again, and the mother took a kerchief and bound up her daughter's head and set aright again the ornaments in her hair and the rings in her ears and Sung Chiang asked, saying, "What is your surname? And what is your place?"

The old woman answered, "I will not deceive the lord when I say we old two are surnamed Sung, and we were once people of the capital. We have but this one daughter and her small name is Jade Lotus. Her father himself taught her a few songs and he told her to come anyhow to this Lute Pavilion and sell her singing for a living. But because she is of an impatient heart and she does not look to see how things are and she did not heed whether you lords were talking but only went on with her singing, this elder brother today put forth his hand and wounded her. Shall we because of this accuse you before the magistrate and write out our plea and trouble you in such a fashion?"

Sung Chiang, seeing how honestly she spoke, then said, "Whom will you send to go with me to the gaol? I will pay him twenty ounces of silver with which to restore your daughter. And give her to some husband and so she need not sell her songs here."

Then the old couple made obeisance to thank him and they said, "How dare we hope for so much?"

Sung Chiang said, "If I speak a thing then it is a thing done. I cannot tell a lie. Bid this old man go himself with me to fetch the money."

Again did the old pair bow in thanks and they said, "Greatly do we thank the lord for helping us."

Then Tai Chung blamed Li K'uei, saying, "You thing that you are, you will forever be quarreling with people and now you have made our elder brother waste a deal of money!"

But Li K'uei cried, "Yet I only touched her a little with my fingers, and down she fell! I never did see such an accursed female and so tender and dainty an one as this! If you beat with your fist on my face a hundred times it would not trouble me."

Then Sung Chiang and all the others began to laugh, and Chang Shun commanded the serving man to go and tell the keeper of the wine shop, "The money for the wine I will pay."

When the serving man heard this he said, "Do not trouble—do not trouble—only go your way."

But how could Sung Chiang be willing for this? He said, "Brother, I implored these two Honorable Ones to come and drink wine, and how can I have you pay for it?"

But Chang Shun would by every means pay the money and he said, "It is not often I can see your face. When I was in Shantung we two brothers would have come to our elder brother. Today by the fortune of Heaven I have met you. Let me show forth my slight purpose, and do not count it an occasion."

And Tai Chung exhorted Sung Chiang also, saying, "Elder Brother Sung, if this is the heart of brother Chang to do you reverence, then indeed you must let him."

Then Sung Chiang said, "If my brother pays for the wine then on another day must I ask you to drink again with me in return."

Chang Shun was greatly rejoiced at this and he took the two fresh fish and with the head gaoler and Li K'uei and with the old man Sung and with Sung Chiang he left The Lute Pavilion and they came to the gaol. The five of them all went in the Hall Of Scribes. Sung Chiang then brought forth two pieces of silver, each of ten ounces, and he gave them to the old man Sung, and the old man made an obeisance of thanks and went his way, and of this no more need be said.

Now the sky had darkened to night and Chang Shun presented the two fish and Sung Chiang took out Chang Shun's letter and gave it to Chang Shun and they parted. After this Sung Chiang took out a great piece of silver, fifty ounces, and he gave it to Li K'uei and said, "Brother, take this and use it."

Then Tai Chung said farewell and he went away with Li K'uei to the city.

Let it be told then of Sung Chiang. He took one of the fish and presented it to the warden of the gaol, and one he left for himself to eat. Now Sung Chiang, seeing how fresh the fish was, felt the taste of it comforting upon his tongue and he ate the more of it therefore. In the fourth watch of the night he felt as though his intestines were wrung together in his belly and scraped with a knife. When it was dawn he had already passed his excrement more than twenty times and he was faint and giddy and he fell down and lay there in the middle of the floor.

Now Sung Chiang always treated people very well and all the people in the gaol came and made gruel for him and boiled hot water for him and cared for him and nursed him. On the next day Chang Shun, seeing that Sung Chiang loved to eat fish, again found two good golden fish and brought them to give him to thank him for bringing the letter. But when he found Sung

Chiang with his belly ill and he was lying on his bed and all the prisoners in his room tending him, Chang Shun would have asked a physician to come and cure him. But Sung Chiang said, "It was I who desired to please my mouth and my belly. I ate the fresh fish and I have spoiled my belly. Do you then but go to the medicine shop and buy me a packet of six-herbs medicine and brew a broth of it and I shall be well." And he bade Chang Shun to take the two fish and give one to the warden and the other to the guard in the gaol. Chang Shun presented the fish and then he bought the packet of six-herbs medicine and gave it to Sung Chiang and then he went away again. Of this no more need be said.

In the gaol there were many prisoners who cared for Sung Chiang and tended him and brewed him the medicine. Tai Chung prepared wine and meat and Li K'uei came with him and they came into the Hall Of Scribes to see Sung Chiang. There they found Sung Chiang just better of his great illness and he could not yet drink the wine or eat the meat. The two then ate it themselves and they did not part until night came and of this also no more need be told.

Let it be told then of Sung Chiang in the recovering from his illness. After some five or six days he felt that there was nothing wrong with his body and his illness was well and he thought to himself that he would go to the city to seek out Tai Chung. But he let a day pass and when not one of them came, on the second day when he had eaten his early meal and when it was not yet mid-morning he thrust some silver into his bosom and he locked the door of his room and he left the gaol and he let his feet go as they would to the street. He went straight into the city and he went to the left of the court and asked concerning the home of the head gaoler Tai Chung. There was a man who said, "He has no wife and no sons and he lives next to the temple of the city God of Devils in a little temple to the Goddess of Mercy."

Sung Chiang heard this and he sought the place straightway, but Tai Chung had already locked his door and gone out. Then again did Sung Chiang ask concerning The Black Whirlwind Li K'uei and there were many who said, "He is a fellow without a head and he has no home or relatives and he lives in the gaol and he has no regular way of going. He stops a couple of days to the east and lays himself down awhile in the west and indeed we do not know where his home is."

Then again did Sung Chiang ask where the middleman of the fish market lived and again there were some who said, "He lives in a village outside the city and when it is time to sell fish he is still outside the city beside the river's edge. He does not come into the city unless he wants a debt paid that one owes him."

When Sung Chiang heard this he could but go outside the city and he would have asked his way thither for he was somewhat downcast by himself alone. So he walked outside the city and there he saw the view of the river was such that he could not have done with looking at it. He had just come to a wine selling shop and when he looked about him he saw a flag pole beside him, and upon it hung a sky-blue flag and upon it was written, "The Treasury Of The Ching Yang River," and upon the carved eaves was a tablet on which was written in three letters the name of the shop, and the letters were written by the famous Su Tung P'o. Sung Chiang saw this and he said, "When I was in Yün Ch'en I heard it said that in Chiang Chou there was a very fine shop such as this and that it was here. Although I am alone yet I cannot make the mistake of passing it by. Why shall I not go upstairs and myself see it awhile?"

When Sung Chiang came to the front and looked about him he saw two red painted pillars on either side of the door and two tablets painted white. On each were written five large letters and these were, "Of all things on earth none can compare to wine; of all shops on earth the best is this one." Then Sung Chiang went upstairs and he went into a corner that faced upon the river and sat down and he leaned his arms on the table and lifted his head and stared about him and he could not but cry out in praise. And the serving man came upstairs and asked him, saying, "Does my lord await guests or will he spend a little time here alone?"

Sung Chiang answered, "I wait for two guests but they are not come yet. Bring out first a jar of good wine and bring meats and cakes and such things. But bring no fish."

The serving man heard this and he went down the stairs and in a short time he brought up a tray and on it was a wine called Wine Of The Southern Wind And Moon, and he brought meats also and all kinds of cakes and fruits. Then he poured out wine. He placed also dishes of fat sheep's meat, tender chicken, goose cooked in the lees of wine and good meat. They were all on dishes red as blood. When Sung Chiang saw these he was secretly pleased in his heart and he praised them to himself, saying, "Such delicate meats as these and such fine ware—truly this is a fine city! Although I have committed a crime and have been exiled, yet I have seen true mountains and true waters. Although I have seen some famous and storied mountains yet they are not to compare to these."

Thus sitting alone and leaning upon the balustrade he drank a cup of wine slowly and then more and more and without knowing it he became very drunken. There came thoughts into his heart then and he pondered and said to himself, "I was born in Shantung and I grew up in Yün Ch'en and I learned to be a scribe in a court. Many good fellows have I met by river and lake and although I have achieved some empty fame yet now I am more than thirty years old and I have neither fame as a scholar who has passed the examinations nor have I money from being in trade. On the contrary, there is the brand of a criminal on my cheeks and I am exiled hither. My old father and my brother in my home too—how can I ever see them again?"

Without his being aware of it the fumes of his wine rose up in him and his tears began to flow. The winds and the view seemed to press upon his eyes and moved him to a deep sadness of heart. Suddenly he thought of a verse to the tune of "Moon On The Western River." Then he called the serving man and bade him bring brush and inkstone and he rose and looked about. He saw there were many who had already written poems on the northern wall and to himself Sung Chiang thought, "Why should I not just write it there? If later I become famous and if at some other time I pass here and see it again, I will remember in what year and what month I was here and wrote it, and I will remember the bitterness of this day."

So he took the advantage of his wine drinking and he ground the ink very thick and filled the brush with the ink. Then he went to the northern wall and he wrote thus,

"In youth I learned the classics,
In manhood I knew wiles.
A tiger on a bare hill
Am I, claws drawn, teeth hid.
Blighted am I, branded,
How bear this exile here?
Later, when I seek revenge,
Blood shall dye the river's mouth."

When Sung Chiang had written this he looked at it with great pleasure and he laughed loudly. He drank yet several more cups of wine and without being aware of it joy arose in him and he grew hilarious and he shook his hands and stamped his feet. Again he took up the pen and after the verse he had written he wrote four more sentences thus,

"Heart in Shantung, flesh in Wu,
Sad I pass the waters through.
Later if I reach great heights,
Ancient braves shall be but wights."

When Sung Chiang had finished this poem he wrote after this still more and he wrote five great letters which said, "Written by Sung Chiang of Yün Ch'en." When he had finished this he threw the pen upon the table and then he sang for a while and he drank again several cups of wine and without knowing it he became exceedingly drunken. Even his strength could not overcome the wine and he called to the serving man to come with his account. He took out some silver to pay what he owed and with what was over he rewarded the serving man and throwing his arms out he went down the stairs stumbling and staggering, and he followed the road and returned to the gaol.

When he had opened the door to his room he fell upon the bed and he slept without waking until the fifth watch. When he had awakened from his drunkenness he did not remember at all that the day before he had written the verses in the wine pavilion of Ching Yang. On that day he suffered from his drinking of wine and he lay alone in his room and slept and of this no more need be said.

Let it be told that on the opposite shore of the river there was another city and it was named Wu Wei Chün. It was a place somewhat lawless, and in it was a certain official whose surname was Huang and his double name was Wen Ping. This man, although he had studied the classics, was a servile, flattering man and his heart was very narrow. He hated all who were better than he or more able. Better men than himself he injured, and lesser men than himself he made to suffer and he did nothing but injure people in that whole countryside. He knew the magistrate Ts'ai in Chiang Chou that he was the son of the premier of that time and he came constantly to bring him some gift, and he constantly crossed the river to inquire after him, for he hoped to be sent out by the premier to a higher place as an official.

Now it was in Sung Chiang's fate that he must eat bitterness and he came up against a misfortune. For one day when this Huang Wen Ping sat idle in his house and he was weary with his idleness he took two of his serving men and he bought some fresh gifts and he took his own swift boat and crossed over the river and he entered the court to see and inquire after the magistrate. By ill luck he chanced upon a feast and he did not dare to go in and so he returned to his boat. The boatman had already tied the boat just below the Ching Yang Pavilion. Huang Wen Ping, seeing that the day was very hot, thought to go upstairs to idle there for a time. He went to the wine-drinking hall and he looked about and then he turned to go upstairs. There he leaned his arms on the balustrade and looked out to pass the time away.

He saw then that there were many verses written upon the wall. There were some very well done and there were some written any way. Huang Wen Ping looked at them and smiled coldly. Then he saw the verse that Sung Chiang had written to the tune of "Moon On The Western River" and the verse after it and he gave a start of great fear and said, "Is this not a verse of revolution? Who dares to write thus here?"

Then he looked at the end and there were written the five great letters "Written by Sung Chiang of Yün Ch'en." Huang Wen Ping read the verses again, and he read,

"In youth I learned the classics,
In manhood I knew wiles,"

and he smiled coldly and said, "This man praises himself overmuch!"

Again he read,

"A tiger on a bare hill
Am I, claws drawn, teeth hid,"

and he put his head on one side and said, "That thing is not one who does his proper duty!"

Again he read,

"Blighted am I, branded,
How bear this exile here?"

and once more he laughed and said, "Nor is he a man of any lofty sort. He is nothing but a criminal exiled."

Again he read,

"Later, when I seek revenge,
Blood shall dye the river's mouth."

Then he shook his head and said, "And upon whom will this thing revenge himself that he thinks to make a disturbance here? He is but an exile, and what can he do?"

Then he read the verse,

"Heart in Shantung, flesh in Wu,
Sad I pass the waters through."

He nodded his head and said, "These two lines can be forgiven him."

Again he read,

"Later if I reach great heights,
Ancient braves shall be but wights."

He stuck out his tongue and shook his head and he said, "This thing is lawless! He would be more fierce than those of old! If this is not revolution, what is it?"

Again he read, Written by Sung Chiang of Yün Ch'en," and he thought and said, "I have many times heard of this name. Doubtless that man has some small official position."

Then he called the serving man and asked him, "Who in truth wrote this song and verse?"

The serving man answered, "Last night a man came here and he sat alone by himself and drank a jar of wine. He wrote it here."

Then Huang Wen Ping asked, "And what sort of a man was he in general?"

The serving man replied, "There were two gilt letters branded on his cheeks and doubtless he was a man out of the gaol. In body he was black and short and fat and plump."

Huang Wen Ping said, "It is he!"

And he asked the serving man to lend him a pen and inkstone and he took out a sheet of paper and he copied the verses and put them away on his person, and he commanded the serving man that the words were not to be scraped away. Then he came downstairs and went into his boat and there he slept the night.

On the next day after he had eaten his servant took the box which held his gifts and again he went straight to the court of the magistrate. It was just after the hour of audience. A man was sent in to announce his coming and after a long time the magistrate Ts'ai sent one out and invited him to come to the inner hall and that he, the magistrate Ts'ai, would soon come out.

After the magistrate had exchanged courteous speeches with Huang Wen Ping and the gifts had been presented, they sat down according to the rank of host and guest. Then Huang Wen Ping made bold to say, "In the night I crossed the river and I came to the court to present my respects. I heard that there was a feast within and so I did not dare to come in. Today I have come again to pay my respects."

Magistrate Ts'ai said, "You and I are very great friends and if you had come straight in and feasted with us what would it have mattered? This humble official, who am I, has lost that opportunity to welcome you."

Then the servants to right and left of them presented tea. When the tea was tasted Huang Wen Ping said, "Most Noble, I do not dare to ask and I do not know whether or not the Most Gracious, Your Father The Premier, today has sent or has not sent a messenger."

The magistrate replied, "A letter came just the day before yesterday."

Then Huang Wen Ping said, "I do not dare to ask again whether or not there is any news in the city now."

And the magistrate replied, "The head of my home wrote to me in a letter, saying, 'Today in the Court of History the Lord Of The Weather said to the Emperor, that in the night he looked on the stars in the heavens and that the thirty-six stars of war stirred themselves and settled over the kingdoms of Wu and Ts'u. If there are rebellious persons about, then in everything take care. Besides this, the children in the streets are rumored to be singing thus,

'The curse of the country is home and wood,
The head of the rebellion is water and work.
Thirty-six invincible braves
Scatter rebellion in Shantung.'

Because of this he has commanded me to exercise watchfulness over my domain."

Now Huang Wen Ping thought to himself for a while and he laughed and said, "Most Gracious, this is a sudden thing and no common one." Then he took out of his sleeve the verses he had copied and presented them with both hands to the magistrate, saying, "I had not dreamed that this person was here."

Then magistrate Ts'ai read the paper and he said, "These are revolutionary verses. Where did you get them?"

And Huang Wen Ping replied, "This humble one did not dare to enter the court last night and so I went back to the river's edge. There I was idle and had nothing wherewith to amuse myself, and so I went into the Ching Yang Wine Shop to escape the heat and to find pleasure, and I looked at the verses idlers had written on the walls and on the northern wall these verses I saw freshly written."

The magistrate asked, "What sort of a man was it who wrote these verses?"

Huang Wen Ping answered, saying, "Most Noble, the name is written plainly there and it says 'Written by Sung Chiang of Yün Ch'en.' "

The magistrate asked, "And who is this Sung Chiang?"

And Huang Wen Ping replied, "He says there plainly, 'Blighted am I, branded, How bear this exile here?' The eye can see he is an exile and a criminal in the military gaol."

The magistrate asked, "And what can an exiled criminal do?"

Huang Wen Ping replied, "The magistrate must not despise him. The words which you did just now read from your most noble father's letter told of the rumors of the children and they point exactly to this very person."

The magistrate asked, "And how do you see this?"

Huang Wen Ping replied, " 'The curse of the country is home and wood.' This means he who shall lay waste the country, his name is made up of the home radical and the letter for wood underneath and this is, very clearly, the character Sung. The second line: 'The head of the rebellion is water and work.' The man who is to rouse the rebellious soldiers is he whose name is made up of the water radical and the letter for work. Clearly this is the character Chiang. This man here is surnamed Sung and named Chiang and he has written also this revolutionary poem. It is Heaven's decree that he fall into your hands and the millions of people are thus blessed."

Again the magistrate asked, "But who are the thirty-six scattering rebellion in Shantung?"

Huang Wen Ping answered, saying, "It is the six times six year of the Emperor or it is six times six number of men. As for the fourth line, Yün Ch'en is in Shantung. These four lines of rumor are all fulfilled."

Again the magistrate said, "I do not know whether this man is here now or not."

And again Huang Wen Ping answered, saying, "This humble one asked the serving man last night and he said, 'This man wrote it only day before yesterday.' It is not difficult. The record of names in the gaol can be examined and it will be seen if his is there."

Then the magistrate said, "How high is your vision and how clear your foresight!"

So he called one of his underlings to bring out of the closet the book of records of the gaol and the man brought the record out of the closet and magistrate Ts'ai examined it himself and in the back he found a record that in the fifth moon there was a prisoner newly come from Yün Ch'en in Shantung and his name was Sung Chiang. When Huang Wen Ping saw it he said, "It is the very one who fulfills the rumor. This is no small slight matter. If you are too slow this matter will flare forth. Men must be sent quickly to bring him hither and put him fast into this city gaol. Then we can take further counsel."

The magistrate said, "You have spoken very truly."

At once he went to the Hall Of Audience and he sent men out to call the head gaoler, Tai Chung, to him. And Tai Chung came and made his obeisance in the hall and the magistrate said, "Take my retainers and go quickly to the military gaol and arrest that criminal who wrote the revolutionary verses in the Ching Yang Wine Shop, Sung Chiang of Yün Ch'en, and bring him hither. You are not to delay an instant."

When Tai Chung heard this he gave a start of fear and in his heart he could but cry bitterness. Straightway he went out of the court and he gathered together the guards of the gaol and he said to each one, "Let each man go to his home and fetch his weapons of war and we will meet together in the temple across the street from where I live."

When Tai Chung had commanded thus, each man went back to his home and Tai Chung used his magic and came at once to the military gaol. He went straight into the Hall Of Scribes and when he pushed the door open and looked in Sung Chiang was there. When Sung Chiang saw Tai Chung was come, he rose in haste to welcome him and he said, "I went into the city the day before yesterday and where did I not look for you! But because my good brother was not there, I was listless alone and so I went to the Ching Yang Wine Shop and drank a bottle of wine. These two days my head has been muddled from it and I am here recovering from my wine."

Then Tai Chung said, "Elder Brother, what words did you write the other day in the wine shop?"

Sung Chiang replied, "Who remembers the wild words written after wine?"

Tai Chung said, "But just now the magistrate called for me and in the audience hall he commanded me, saying, 'Take plenty of men and arrest that revolutionist who wrote the rebellious verses in the Ching Yang Wine Shop, Sung Chiang of Yün Ch'en. This is my own command.' I gave a start of fear and I went first and bade the guards to meet me at the temple. Now I have come on purpose to tell the news to you first. Elder Brother, what is the best thing to do? How shall we save you?"

When Sung Chiang had heard this, he scratched his head anyhow without knowing where it itched and he could but cry out bitterness, and he cried, "Surely this time I am to die!"

But Tai Chung said, "I will teach you a way

of escape, but I do not know if it be good or not. I do not dare to delay now. I must return at once and lead the men here to capture you. Do you scatter your hair every which way and spill out your urine and excrement upon the ground and lie in it and pretend you are a madman. When I come with the others then speak wildly as though you were a brainless idiot. Then I can go back and tell the magistrate."

And Sung Chiang answered, "Thank you, my good Brother, for thus telling me. A thousand thousand times do I hope you will help me to pass through this trouble."

In great haste then did Tai Chung take his leave of Sung Chiang and he returned to the city and ran straight to the temple. He called all the guards together and they went at once and in haste to the military gaol. Tai Chung shouted out in false questioning, "Which is the newly come Sung Chiang?"

A sergeant there then led them to the Hall Of Scribes. There they saw Sung Chiang, his hair torn in all ways, fallen and rolling in urine and excrement. When he saw Tai Chung and the guards come he said, "What accursed men are you?"

Then Tai Chung falsely gave a great shout, "Seize this thing!"

And Sung Chiang rolled the whites of his eyes and began to strike out wildly and he spoke at random, saying, "I am the son-in-law of the Emperor Of Heaven! My father-in-law commanded me to lead ten thousand heavenly soldiers hither and kill all of you Chiang Chou people! The King Of The Devils is to lead us out, and the Prince Of Evil is to follow behind. The Emperor Of Heaven has given me a great golden seal! It is more than eight hundred pounds in weight. I shall kill you cursed people!"

All the guards said, "He is a true madman! What is the use of taking him?"

And Tai Chung said, "You have spoken well. Let us go back with this report and if we are to take him we can come again."

So they all went with Tai Chung and they went back to the city court. Now magistrate Ts'ai was in his hall waiting especially for their report and Tai Chung and the guards then made their report thus: "Sung Chiang is a true madman. Urine and filth he does not mind. He speaks wildly from his mouth and the filth and vileness of his person is beyond telling. For this we did not dare to bring him hither."

Even as the magistrate was about to ask the reason Huang Wen Ping hastened out from behind the screen and he said to the magistrate, "Do not believe this talk! The words and the script that this man wrote are not those of a madman. There is some falsehood here. Good or ill he must be brought hither. If he cannot walk and must be carried, yet must he be carried hither."

And the magistrate Ts'ai said, "My comrade, you have spoken well." And he sent Tai Chung out again, saying, "I do not care how he is you must bring him to me."

Then Tai Chung led his guards, crying bitterness to himself, and again he took them to the military gaol and he said to Sung Chiang, secretly, "Brother, the thing cannot be done. You must go at once."

And he took a great bamboo cage and they carried Sung Chiang straight to the court in the city and put him down before the hall. The magistrate said, "Bring that thing here!"

The guards then held Sung Chiang at the entrance, but how could he be willing to kneel? He opened wide his eyes and seeing the magistrate he said, "What accursed man are you? How dare you ask me anything? I am the son-in-law of the Emperor Of Heaven! He told me to lead out ten times ten thousand heavenly soldiers to kill all you Chiang Chou people, and the King Of Hell is to be our vanguard and the Prince Of Evil is to bring up our rear! There is a golden seal a hundred pounds in weight. Hide yourself quickly! If you do not, I shall cause you all to be killed!"

Now magistrate Ts'ai looked at him and he did not know what to do. Again Huang Wen Ping said to him, "Bring the wardens and gaolers of the military gaol here and inquire of them and see whether this man was mad when he came, or whether he has only been mad today. If he was mad when he came then it is a true malady. If he was taken mad today, then it is a false madness."

And the magistrate said, "Your words are fitly spoken." So he sent men to call the gaoler and the warden and when he asked the twain, how dared they answer falsely? They could only speak the truth.

"When this man came we did not see that he was ill with a madness. It has only come on him today."

When the magistrate heard this he was mightily angered and he called all the prison guards and bade them to bind Sung Chiang and to beat him fifty continuous blows. They beat him then so that he was breathless and half dead. His skin was flayed open and his flesh was torn and the red blood streamed. When Tai Chung saw this he could but cry bitterness, for there was no way whereby to save him. At first Sung Chiang still talked wildly but after a while he could not bear the blows longer and he could but confess and say, "I should not have written wrongly the rebellious verses when I was drunken with wine. Besides this I have no revolutionary plans."

The magistrate caused this to be written down and a rack twenty-five catties in weight was set on Sung Chiang's neck, such a rack as those wear who are condemned to die, and then he was thrust into gaol.

Now Sung Chiang had been so beaten that he could not walk and they had fastened irons on his ankles also, and he was guarded and taken into the gaol where those condemned to death are kept. Fortunately Tai Chung helped him with all his strength and he commanded all throughout the gaol that they were to tend him well. He himself prepared food for Sung Chiang. Of this no more need be told.

Let it be told again. The magistrate left the hall and invited Huang Wen Ping to come to the inner hall, and there he thanked him, saying, "If it had not been for such wisdom and such high foresight this humble magistrate would have been deceived by them."

And Huang Wen Ping spoke again, saying, "Lord high above me, this matter ought not to be delayed. A letter should be written immediately and one should take it by night and day to the capital and announce the matter to the Most Gracious, your father. Thus will it be shown how great a service you have performed for the nation. And at the same time tell him if he wants the man alive, then send a prisoner's cart for him. If he does not want him alive, lest he escape on the way, then he can be killed here and his head set up publicly for all to see. Thus will the great danger be averted. Even though the Emperor himself hear of it he will surely be pleased."

The magistrate replied, "What you have said has reason. In a few days I had planned to send one to my home and in my letter I shall tell of your noble deed so that my father can tell of it to the Emperor face to face. Thus will you be soon raised to a high and wealthy place, and there will you secure your glory and your power."

Huang Wen Ping bowed himself to the ground in thanks and he said, "I shall stay at your gates my whole life long. Surely will I return with some offering of thanks in return for your mercy."

Then Huang Wen Ping urged the magistrate to hasten to write his letter home and the magistrate set his seal to it, and Huang Wen Ping asked, saying, "Most Noble, which trusty man shall you send?"

The magistrate replied, "We have a head gaoler here and he is called by the name of The Magic Messenger, for he can use a magic way of walking and he can walk nearly three hundred miles in a day. Tomorrow I will bid him go straight to the capital. In ten days he will come and go."

Huang Wen Ping said, "If it can be as swift as this, then good—better than anything!"

Then the magistrate had a feast spread in the inner hall and he entertained Huang Wen Ping. On the next day Huang Wen Ping took his leave and he returned to his own seat of office.

Let it be told further. The magistrate Ts'ai prepared two caskets and he prepared gold and jewels and treasure and fine wares and put them inside. And he sealed the caskets and the morning of the next day he called for Tai Chung to come to the inner hall and he commanded him, saying, "I have these gifts and letter to be taken to my home. I want them sent to my father the premier in the eastern capital for his birthday on the fifteenth of the sixth moon. The day draws near and it is only you who can go. Do not refuse because of the fatigue, but travel by night also. When you have the answer, then return and I will reward you heavily. Every step of your way is on my heart, and I have set a certain day for your return. I do only wait for the answering letter. Above all you must not delay on the road and so delay my affairs."

Tai Chung heard this and he did not dare to do otherwise than consent. He could but take the letter and the caskets and bow his farewell to the magistrate, and he carried them out. When all was arranged he went into the gaol and he said to Sung Chiang, "Elder Brother, let your heart rest. The magistrate has sent me to the capital and in ten days I shall return, and I shall use ways I have in the court to save you, my Elder Brother. The charge of the food for each day I have left upon Li K'uei and he is to prepare it and bring it and you shall lack for nothing. Brother, enlarge your heart and be patient for a few days."

Sung Chiang said, "Ten thousand times do I look to my brother to save my life."

And Tai Chung called Li K'uei and before Sung Chiang's face he commanded him, saying, "Your elder brother, because he wrote a revolutionary verse, is suffering here in the gaol and we do not know how it will end. I have now been sent to go to the eastern capital and traveling by day and night I shall soon return. Our elder brother's food is wholly upon you to care for."

Li K'uei answered, saying, "And what does it matter if he wrote a revolutionary verse? Thousands of times have rebels turned over and become great officials. You let your heart rest and go to the eastern capital. Who in the gaol dares to come and trouble him? If they treat him well, I will treat them well. If they do not treat him well, I will take my great war axe and strike that one a blow or two!"

As Tai Chung was about to depart he again commanded Li K'uei, saying, "Brother, be careful. Do not guzzle wine and forget the food for our elder brother. Do not go out and get drunken and starve our elder brother."

And Li K'uei said, "Elder Brother, let your heart rest and go on. If you doubt me like this I will break off my wine drinking from this very day and I will not begin again until you come back. Day and night I will only stay in the gaol and tend to our elder brother Sung Chiang, and what is there about it that I cannot do?"

Tai Chung heard this with much pleasure and he said, "Brother, if you will have such a heart to protect him as this, then you will care for him all the better."

And taking farewell he went his way.

Truly enough, Li K'uei drank no more wine and day and night he did but stay in the gaol and tended Sung Chiang. He did not leave him by a foot or an inch.

It will not be told more of how Li K'uei tended Sung Chiang. Let it be told of Tai Chung. He changed the cloths upon his legs and put on hempen shoes and put on an apricot-yellow robe and he tied his girdle about him. Into his girdle he thrust the tablet of his name and position. He changed his hat also and into his bag he put the letter and money he needed, and he took the caskets on his shoulders. He went outside the city. There he took from his person his four magic letters and he tied two about each leg. In his lips he muttered the sacred words and in an instant he was away from Chiang Chou.

He went the whole day until night and then he rested in an inn. He took off his magic letters and then he burned some gold paper money to escort away the god who had helped him. After the night had passed he rose early the next morning. When he had eaten food and drunk wine he left the inn and again he tied on his magic signs and took up the caskets and he let his strides out freely and went on his way.

The wind roared past his ears and his feet did not touch the earth. He took a little vegetable food by the way, and on he went again. When he saw it was already night he rested early and again he went to an inn and spent the night there. On the next day he rose at the fifth watch to go by the coolness of the morning and he tied on his magic letters and took up the caskets and again he went his way.

When he had gone a hundred miles or so it was about ten o'clock and he saw no clean inn. This was during the first ten days of the sixth moon and the weather was hot and his sweat fell like rain so that his whole body was dripping and he was afraid of being overcome with heat when he was both thirsty and hungry. Soon he saw among some trees to one side an inn beside a stream and a pool of water. In an instant as Tai Chung went to see it, he saw it was clean and neat and there were some twenty tables all painted red. The whole inn was opened half way to the roof.

Carrying the caskets Tai Chung went inside and chose a convenient and suitable seat and he put the caskets down. Then he loosened his girdle, and he took off his apricot-yellow robe and since it was wet with his sweat he took a mouthful of water and sprayed it on the robe and hung it to dry.

Then Tai Chung sat down and he saw a serving man come and ask him, "Most Noble, how many measures of wine shall I pour for you? And what meats will you have to send it down, pork or cow's flesh or sheep's flesh?"

Tai Chung replied, "I do not wish much wine. Make me a mouthful of rice and bring it to me."

Again the serving man said, "I sell wine here and I sell rice. I have bread too, and bean vermicelli."

Tai Chung said, "I will eat no meat. What vegetable soups have you?"

The serving man replied, "Fine bean curd stewed with pepper and with sesame oil—how is that?"

Tai Chung said, "Best of all—best of all!"

The serving man was not long gone and he stewed a bowl of bean curd and he brought also two saucers of vegetables. Besides this he poured three large bowls of wine out. Now Tai Chung was truly athirst and hungry and in a movement of his hand he had taken up the wine and the bean curd and swallowed it. But even as he was about to dip up rice to eat he saw the heavens begin to whirl and the earth to turn. His head grew giddy and his eyes befogged and he fell over the side of the bench.

The serving man cried out, "He is fallen!"

Then a man came out from the inn and it was Chu Kuei from the robbers' lair and he said, "Take the caskets in first and then search his person and see what he has."

So two apprentices searched over his person to see what was there and they found in his girdle a paper packet in which was wrapped a letter. This they took out and gave to Chu Kuei to see and Chu Kuei tore it open and it was a letter to someone's home. Upon the envelope was written, "A Peaceful Home Letter. It Is Presented To The Great One, My Father, With A Hundred Obeisances. Sealed With Care By Your Son, Ts'ai Tê Chang."

Then Chu Kuei opened it and read it from beginning to end and he saw written thus: "I have already captured the one who fulfills the rumors of rebellion, a writer of revolutionary verse, Sung Chiang of Shantung. I have locked him in gaol and I await your commands."

When Chu Kuei had finished reading the letter he was frightened into a daze and he could not speak a word. Even as the apprentices were about to lift up Tai Chung and carry him into the butchering room, they saw his wide girdle hanging to the ground from one end of the bench. Upon it were hung two signs of red the hue of pig's blood. When Chu Kuei took them up to look at them he saw carved upon them in white these letters, Tai Chung, Head Gaoler Of The Two Gaols in Chiang Chou."

When Chu Kuei saw this he said to himself, "Do not touch him. I have long heard Wu Yung say that there was a head gaoler named Tai Chung in Chiang Chou who used magic to walk and he calls him a dear friend. It must be this very man But why does he take a letter to injure Sung Chiang? This letter must surely be sent into my hands by Heaven itself." And he called to the apprentices, "Pray free him from his stupor! Then we will question him as to what he is."

So the apprentices mixed the medicine in water and they lifted Tai Chung up and forced the draught down his throat. In a short time Tai Chung was seen to lift his eyebrows and open his eyes and he scrambled up. When he saw Chu Kuei had torn open the letter, Tai Chung shouted out, "Who are you? How bold you are to give me a drug to confuse me and now you tear open the magistrate's letter and you have torn the envelope! What punishment ought you to have?"

But Chu Kuei laughed and replied, "And what does this accursed letter matter? Not only dare we tear open such a letter but we here will even rebel against the great Sung Emperor himself!"

When Tai Chung heard this he was vastly frightened and he asked, "Good Fellow, who are you indeed? I beg to know your great name."

Chu Kuei answered, saying, "I am a good fellow from Liang Shan P'o and I am named Chu Kuei."

Then Tai Chung said, "If you are a chief from that robbers' lair, then surely you know Wu Yung."

And Chu Kuei said, "He is the advisor of battles in our lair. He has the power in his hand over our fighting men. How is it you know him?"

And Tai Chung said, "We are very dear friends, he and I."

Then Chu Kuei said, "Brother, are you he of whom Wu Yung often speaks, the head of all the gaols in Chiang Chou?"

Tai Chung said, "This humble one is he indeed."

Again Chu Kuei asked, "Formerly there was a Sung Chiang exiled to Chiang Chou and he passed our lair. Our Wu Yung sent a letter by him to you. Why then do you go today and do something against his very life?"

Tai Chung said, "Sung Chiang and I are loved brother-friends, but because he wrote a revolutionary poem I cannot save him, and I am even now on my way to the capital to find a way to save him. How would I be willing to injure his life?"

Chu Kuei said, "If you do not believe it, then read this letter from the magistrate."

And Tai Chung read the letter and he gave a start of fear and he told in detail the story of Wu Yung's letter and of the writing of the revolutionary poem and Chu Kuei said, "If it is like this, pray let the head gaoler go himself to the lair to take counsel with our chiefs and think of some good plan by which we can save Sung Chiang's life."

Then Chu Kuei in great haste sent men ahead to prepare a feast of welcome to honor Tai Chung, and he let fly a singing arrow from the pavilion by the water side, and this arrow was a signal to the lair. Soon from the place to which the arrow flew a boat was seen to come forth rowed by the robbers. Chu Kuei and Tai Chung took the letter and the caskets and went into the boat and went to the beach of Golden Sands where they came ashore, and from thence he led Tai Chung to the great lair.

When Wu Yung was told that the head gaoler Tai Chung was there he came forth in great haste to meet him and when he had seen Tai Chung he made an obeisance and said, "Many days have I been separated from you and what wind has blown you hither today? Pray come into the great lair and meet with all the chieftains."

Chu Kuei then told the reason for Tai Chung's coming and how Sung Chiang was locked in the gaol. Ch'ao Kai heard this and in great haste he invited Tai Chung to be seated and he asked in great detail why it was that Sung Chiang had come before the officials. Then Tai Chung told the tale of the revolutionary poem and when Ch'ao Kai had heard it he was very fearful and he rose to tell off men and horses to go down the mountain to attack Chiang Chou and to save Sung Chiang and bring him up the mountain. When Wu Yung saw this he said, "Elder Brother, you may not do this. Chiang Chou is a long way from here and if men and horses go forth there may arise some evil thing. It will be but beating the grass and driving the snake away, and Sung Chiang will lose his life for it. We cannot use force, we must use guile. I am but a worthless person, but I would use a small plot and if Tai Chung will take it upon himself, Sung Chiang's life can be saved."

Then Ch'ao Kai said, "I would hear this excellent plot."

And Wu Yung said, "Now the magistrate Ts'ai has commanded the head gaoler Tai Chung to take this letter and to wait there for an answer from the premier. We will use his plan in this letter for our own and we will write a false answer and bid Tai Chung return. In the letter we will say with all urgency that this prisoner Sung Chiang is assuredly not to be killed, but that he is to be entrusted to a trustworthy man to escort to the capital. There he is to be questioned in the matter most closely, and assuredly if he be killed he is to be publicly killed. Thus will the children's prophecy be stopped. We will wait until Sung Chiang is sent past us here and then I will send men down from the mountain to bring him here. How is this plan?"

Then Ch'ao Kai said, "If he does not pass by here then will not this stir up a great trouble?"

But Kung Sun Sheng said, "What is there hard about this? We will send men to spy far and near and wherever he passes we will surely be waiting there for him. Good or ill we will seize him. I do but fear he will not be sent to the capital."

And Ch'ao Kai said, "Good—yes, it is good

enough. But there is no one who can write in the style of the premier."

Again Wu Yung said, "I have already thought of this. In this whole empire now the styles that men most like to learn are those of four men. These are the styles of Su Tung P'o, of Huang Lu Chi, of Mi Yuen Chang, and of the premier himself, these four, and these four are unexcelled both before and during the Sung Dynasty. This humble one, who am I, was formerly friend to a scholar of highest degree in Chi Chou. His surname is Siao and his name is Jang. Because he can write in the style of all these four he is called The Magic Scribe. He can wield weapons also and he can fence and he can use a double-edged sword and hold a knife. I know he can write in the style of the premier. We had better ask Tai Chung to go quickly to his house and deceive him, saying, 'The temple in T'ai An wants a copy for a stone tablet,' and then give him first fifty ounces of silver for his family to use while he is gone, and we will ask him to come at once. Later we will send men to trick his wife and children into coming up the mountain and so we will have him join us."

Ch'ao Kai said, "If he can write the letter it will be well enough. But there must be a seal at the end of the letter."

Again Wu Yung said, "I have yet another plan, for I have already thought of all this in my heart. There is a man who is peerless in skill in our whole region. He lives now in the city of Chi Chou. His surname is Ching and he has a double name and it is Ta Chien. He can carve upon stone most excellently well and he can carve a good seal and a good sign upon any stone or jade. He understands, too, the use of weapons and staff in fighting. Because he can cut stone and jade so well everyone calls him The Jade Armed Warrior. Let us give him fifty ounces of silver also, and let us trick him hither to cut a seal, and when he is half way with us we will do with him as we did with the other. We can use these two men, too, in the lair."

Then Ch'ao Kai cried, "Excellent!"

On that day a feast was prepared to entertain Tai Chung and when night came they rested.

On the next day after they had eaten their early meal they invited Tai Chung to come in and they disguised him to look like the abbot of a temple and they gave him a hundred or two ounces of silver. Then he tied his magic letters about his legs and went down the mountain, and went into a boat at The Golden Sands and was ferried across. When he was ashore on the other side he let his strides free and he hastened to Chi Chou. In less than four hours he had already come to the city and there he asked where it was that Siao Jang, The Magic Scribe, lived.

A man pointed and said, "He lives to the east of the court in front of the Confucian temple."

Then Tai Chung went straight to his door and he coughed once and asked, "Is the Teacher Siao there?"

And he saw a scholar of high degree come out from within, who when he saw Tai Chung did not know him, and he asked, saying, "From whence does the priest come? What business have you to tell me?"

When Tai Chung had made an obeisance he said, "This humble one is the abbot of the temple to the King Of Hell in T'ai An. In our temple we are now repairing the Hall Of The Five Sacred Mountains. All the wealthy persons of our city wish a stone tablet to be inscribed and they have sent me hither especially to bring these fifty ounces of silver to give for the use of your family while you are gone. Pray let the scholar of high degree come quickly now and come with me to the temple to do this thing. The day has already been set and it cannot be delayed."

Siao Jang answered, "This humble one can only write essays and red ink characters, and besides this I am good for naught. If you wish to use a stone tablet you must seek out one to cut the stone."

Tai Chung said, "I have fifty more ounces of silver and I am going now to invite Ching Ta Chien, The Jade Armed Warrior, to come and cut the letters into the stone. The good day is set and a thousand times do we hope you will point the way and when I have found him we will go on together."

Then Siao Jang received the fifty ounces of silver and so he went with Tai Chung to seek Ching Ta Chien. They had but just passed the Confucian temple when Siao Jang lifted his hand and pointed and said, "He who comes ahead there is Ching Ta Chien, The Jade Armed Warrior."

And Siao Jang called Ching Ta Chien and called to him to come and meet Tai Chung and he said to him, "The temple to the King Of Hell in T'ai An is repairing its Hall Of The Five Sacred Mountains and all the wealthy people thereabouts wish to erect a stone tablet. This priest has come especially to present us each with fifty ounces of silver and he has come to invite you and me to go."

Ching Ta Chien saw the silver and in his heart he was pleased. Both of them then invited Tai Chung to a wine shop to drink three cups of wine and they caused some dishes to be prepared to entertain him. Then Tai Chung gave Ching Ta Chien the fifty ounces of silver for his household use and he said again, "The geomancer has already chosen a lucky day. Pray let your honored selves set forth today."

But Siao Jang answered, "The day is already very hot. If we set forth today we cannot go far and there is no place to rest that we can reach. Let us rise tomorrow morning at the fifth watch and go out the instant the city gate is open."

And Ching Ta Chien said, "Let it be indeed as you have said."

So the two then arranged to set forth the next morning and each returned to his home to prepare for the journey. Siao Jang would have Tai Chung to rest in his home and on the next day at the fifth watch Ching Ta Chien brought his bundle and his tools and came thither and he set out with Siao Jang and Tai Chung.

They left the city of Chi Chou and they had not gone more than a little above three miles when Tai Chung said, "Pray walk slowly. I dare not press you to hasten. This humble one will hasten ahead and make report to our wealthy patrons that they may come to meet you two honored ones."

And he let his strides out and rushed ahead, and the other two carrying their bundles went along slowly. When they saw they had walked until the middle of the afternoon they had walked some twenty-five miles. Suddenly they heard a whistle blow ahead of them and down the slope of the mountain rushed a band of good fellows. There must have been forty or fifty men and the one in front was Wang The Dwarf Tiger. He gave a great shout and said, "What two men are you? Whither do you go? Children, seize these two men and dig out their hearts to eat when we drink wine!"

Then Siao Jang said humbly, "We two lowly ones are going to the temple at T'ai An to carve a stone tablet and we have not a penny on our persons. We have only a few garments."

But Wang The Dwarf Tiger shouted, saying, "We do not want your money or your clothes. We only want the hearts and livers of you two clever men to eat with our wine!"

At this Siao Jang and Ching Ta Chien grew very angry and each man did his best and they took their staffs and charged at Wang The Dwarf Tiger. Wang The Dwarf Tiger also took up his knife to make combat and each man used the weapon he had in his hand and they fought five or seven rounds. Then Wang The Dwarf Tiger turned himself about to go. The other two were just about to give pursuit when they heard the sound of a gong being beaten on the mountain and they saw come forth on the left the robber chieftain called Guardian God In The Clouds, Sung Wan. On the right came out the Eagle Who Flutters Against The Sky, Tu Ch'ien. Behind them came The White Faced Goodman, Chen T'ien Shou. Each of them led more than thirty men and they all came forward and they pulled Siao Jang and Ching Ta Chien willy-nilly into the wood.

And these four good fellows said, "You two let your hearts rest. We have the command of Ch'ao Kai and we have come especially to invite you two honored ones to go up the mountain and join with us."

But Siao Jang said, "And what use have they for us in the mountain lair? We two have not strength enough in our hands to tie a chicken fast. We can only eat."

Then Tu Ch'ien answered, "In the first place, our chief Wu Yung knows you. In the second place you two have skill at weapons and so Tai Chung was sent especially to your homes to invite you."

Siao Jang and Ching Ta Chien looked at each other speechless for they could not speak. They could but go then to Chu Kuei's wine shop, and there a feast of welcome was prepared. In the night a boat was called and they were sent up the mountain.

When they had reached the great lair Ch'ao

Kai and Wu Yung and all the robber chieftains met them and a feast of wines and meats was prepared for their welcome, and they were told of the matter of writing a letter to answer the magistrate's letter and that for this they were invited to join the robbers in their lair. Thus it had been decided by all in general meeting. When the twain heard this they laid hold on Wu Yung and said, "We are willing to serve you here and think nothing of it. But we grieve because we each have wives and children. Tomorrow when it is known to the magistrates then surely will evil come upon them."

But Wu Yung replied, "Let the two honorable brothers not grieve for this. It will all be made clear to you at dawn."

That night they did naught but feast and then sleep. On the next day at dawn they heard the lesser robbers make report, saying, "They have all come."

Then Wu Yung said, "Pray let the two good brothers go themselves to meet their families."

Now Siao Jang and Ching Ta Chien heard this and half they believed and half they did not believe. But they went part way down the mountain and there they saw several sedan chairs bringing their two families up the mountain. The pair were frightened into a daze and they questioned their families closely. The answer was, "After you left home yesterday we saw all these men bringing chairs and they said, 'The lords of your houses lie unconscious with a stroke of heat in the inn outside the city wall. Their wives and children are called to go at once to see them.' When we came outside the city they would not let us down out of our chairs, but they carried us straight hither."

Thus both families spoke. When Siao Jang heard this he and Ching Ta Chien closed their mouths and had nothing to say. All hope of return died in their hearts and they could but go and join the robbers at the lair. There they settled their two families.

Then Wu Yung invited Siao Jang to come out to consult with him and write the answering letter that was to save Sung Chiang, and Ching Ta Chien said, "For a long time I have known how to cut the seal of the premier, the seal of his name and also of his nickname."

And the two put forth their hands and worked until they had finished, and thus made ready the false answer. Then a feast was prepared and Tai Chung was speeded upon his way and he was told in detail what the letter said. When Tai Chung had bade farewell to all the chiefs and come down the mountain, the robbers in all haste ferried him across from The Golden Sands and brought him to Chu Kuei's wine shop. In great haste he took out his four magic letters and tied them upon his legs and took his farewell of Chu Kuei. Then he let his strides out freely and hastened to the city.

Let it now be told that when Wu Yung had sent Tai Chung across on the ferry he went back with all the other robber chiefs to the lair to feast. Even as they were in the midst of their drinking of wine they suddenly heard Wu Yung give a cry, "Bitterness!" But they did not know yet for what he called out, and the chiefs asked him, saying, "Why does the noble chief call out for bitterness?"

Then Wu Yung said, "None of you understand. In this letter I have made Tai Chung and Sung Chiang lose their lives."

The chieftains were all in terror at this and in greatest haste they asked, saying, "What was written wrongly in the letter?"

And Wu Yung answered, "I only thought of what was before and not of what was behind. There is a great mistake in the letter."

Then Siao Jang said, "But this humble one copied it exactly like the noble one's, and there was not one mistake in the style of address from father to son. Pray let the noble one tell me where the mistake is."

And Ching Ta Chien said, "The seal this humble one cut did not have a hairbreadth's mistake. How can there be aught wrong?"

Then Wu Yung held up his two fingers and he told them where the mistake was. Because of this the good fellows made a great commotion in Chiang Chou and created a turmoil in the Temple To The White Dragon. Truly was it

> The clouds of horses and arrows braved,
> Sung Chiang and Tai Chung their bare lives saved.

What then was the mistake of which Wu Yung spoke? Pray hear it told in the next chapter.

Chapter 39

THE HEROES FROM THE ROBBERS' LAIR MAKE A RESCUE FROM THE EXECUTION GROUNDS. THEY GATHER AT THE TEMPLE TO THE WHITE DRAGON

IT IS SAID: When Ch'ao Kai and all the chiefs heard this they asked Wu Yung, saying, "What mistake is there in this letter?"

To this Wu Yung answered, "The answering letter Tai Chung took this morning had a mistake that I overlooked for the moment and I did not see it. Did we not use the four characters on the seal signifying the personal name and the degree of the premier? It is this seal which will cause the arrest of Tai Chung."

Then Ching Ta Chien said, "But I have constantly seen the premier's letters and his essays and the seal is always thus affixed. There is not the least mistake to what I cut. How can there be anything wrong?"

But Wu Yung replied, "None of you understand. The letter purported to be from father to son. How then could the seal have his personal name? This is what is wrong. It is what I did not foresee. When this man reaches Chiang Chou he will be closely questioned and they will find out the truth, and it will go ill with him."

Then Ch'ao Kai said, "Quickly send someone and call him back! Then we can write another letter."

But Wu Yung said, "How can we catch him? He is using his magic and in this one day from dawn to dark he has already gone nearly two hundred miles. Yet the matter cannot be delayed. There is but one way to save the two of them."

Ch'ao Kai asked, "How can we go and save them? What good way can we use?"

Then Wu Yung leaned forward and said beside Ch'ao Kai's ear, "Thus—and then—and like this—" and he said, "You are the chief. Do you send out secret commands so that all may know. But we must start at once and not delay the day."

All the good fellows received the command and each prepared his goods for the journey. That night they went down the mountain and went toward Chiang Chou. Of this there is no more to be said.

Let it be told further how Tai Chung had a fixed day on which he must reach Chiang Chou and when he was come he brought the answer he had to the Hall Of Justice. When the magistrate saw Tai Chung was come back on the day appointed he was exceedingly glad. He first brought out wine and rewarded him with three bowls and he himself took the letter and he asked, "Did you see my father yourself?"

Tai Chung replied humbly, "This lowly one did but stay a night and then I came back and I did not see the Most Gracious."

The magistrate tore open the letter and he saw it said in the beginning, "All the many gifts in the letter caskets I have received." In the middle of the letter it said, "The Emperor himself wishes to see the trickster Sung Chiang. A prisoner's cart must be called and he placed in it. Let trustworthy men be chosen as guards and let him be sent night and day to the capital. Nor can he be allowed to escape by the way." At the end of the letter it said, "As for the matter of Huang The Magistrate I will tell it to the Emperor and assuredly he will soon be a high official."

When the magistrate Ts'ai had seen this he was very pleased but he said nothing, except he commanded that a piece of stamped silver weighing twenty-five ounces should be brought out as a reward for Tai Chung. At the same time he ordered a prisoner's cart to be made, and he planned how Sung Chiang should be guarded on the way.

Tai Chung thanked the magistrate and came away. He bought some wine and meat and he went to the gaol to inquire after Sung Chiang. Of this no more need be said.

Let it be told then of the magistrate Ts'ai and how he hastened the making of the prisoner's cart. When a day or two had passed and they were on the point of starting upon their journey the gateman was seen to come to report thus, "Huang Wen Ping of Wu Wei Chün has come especially to see the magistrate."

The magistrate commanded that he was to be invited into the inner hall and Huang Wen Ping came bringing gifts of fresh fruit and wine and cakes. The magistrate thanked him and said, "Ever I have this goodness of yours thus shown me. How can I be worthy of it?"

Huang Wen Ping said, "These poor fruits of a wilderness need not even be mentioned."

The magistrate said, "I congratulate you. Soon you will attain to a high official position."

Huang Wen Ping said, "How does the magistrate know this?"

The magistrate said, "Yesterday the messenger returned with the answering letter and it said, 'The trickster Sung Chiang is commanded to be sent to the capital, and in a short time my father will ask the Emperor for a high official place for you.' My father's answering letter said this very clearly."

Huang Wen Ping said, "Deeply do I thank the Most Gracious for this. That messenger is truly a magic one."

The magistrate said, "If my comrade does not believe it I will let you see my father's letter, and you will see I speak truly."

Huang Wen Ping said, "I feared I might not see it, since it is a letter from your home. But if you trust me, then pray let me see it."

And the magistrate said, "We are not common friends. Our friendship is of the heart. What harm can come of it?"

Therefore he commanded one to go and fetch the letter and give it to Huang Wen Ping to see, and Huang Wen Ping took the letter into his hand and read it over from beginning to end. Then he turned it over and looked at the envelope. There he saw the seal to be very fresh and clear, and he shook his head and said, "This letter is not a true one."

But the magistrate said, "You are mistaken. This is the pen style of my father's own hand. It is his own way of writing. How can it not be true?"

Huang Wen Ping said, "Most Noble, allow me to speak. Formerly when letters have come from your home did they have this seal?"

The magistrate said, "The letters that have come from my home before did not have this seal. This seal must have been taken at random by my father. His box of seals must have been beside him and he took this one by chance."

But Huang Wen Ping said, "Most Noble, do not blame this humble one for his many words. In this letter someone has deceived the most noble. There are many now in the empire who imitate the four great masters of style. Who cannot learn to write in this way? This seal is one which your father might have used in the time when he first took his scholar's high degree. On his model writings and on his essays many have seen this seal. But now your father has become a premier. How could he take out his scholar's seal again? More than this, when a father writes to a son he should not use a seal that has cut upon it his personal name. Your most illustrious father is one who can comprehend the whole universe; how could he use a seal so wrongly? If the most noble does not believe my humble words let him question the messenger closely and ask whom he saw in the palace. If he speaks inaccurately, then truly is this letter a false one. Do not reproach me that I have spoken too much, for because I have received your unmerited affection I dare to speak thus freely."

The magistrate heard this and he said, "It will not be hard. This man has never before been to the eastern capital. As soon as I question him I can know whether it is true or false."

So the magistrate let Huang Wen Ping sit behind the door and immediately he ascended into the hall and he commanded that the head gaoler be called, for he had something for him to do, and the retainers received the command and sent out runners everywhere to find Tai Chung.

Let it be told thus. As soon as Tai Chung returned to Chiang Chou he went first to the gaol to see Sung Chiang and he put his mouth to Sung Chiang's ear and told him the whole story. Sung Chiang was secretly much pleased in his heart.

On the next day there was one who invited Tai Chung to drink wine. As he was in the midst of his wine drinking in the inn he saw the court retainers coming from all four directions to find him and they called to him to go at once to the court. There the magistrate asked him, "You suffered great weariness for me the other day and for all you did for me I have not yet rewarded you heavily enough."

Tai Chung answered, saying, "I am but one whose duty it is to fulfill the commands of the most gracious. How can I grow bold?"

The magistrate said, "I have been truly too busy these few days and I have not questioned you closely. When you went to the capital the other day which city gate did you enter?"

Tai Chung replied, "When this humble one went to the eastern capital the day was already turned to night and I do not know what the gate was."

Again the magistrate asked, "And who met you at the gate of the palace, my home? Where did they put you to rest?"

Tai Chung answered, "When I reached the palace I found a gateman and he took the letter and went in. In a little while he came back and he received the letter and caskets and he told me to go myself to an inn and stop there and to return the next morning early, at the fifth watch. When I waited there at the gate to the palace I saw the gateman come out with the answering letter. I was afraid also lest I miss the day set for me to return and how then did I dare to ask any detail? In greatest haste and at one bound I returned."

Again the magistrate asked, "Which gateman did you see in the palace? How old a man was he? Was he thin and dark, or was he fat and pale and large? Was he short and small and bearded, or was he beardless?"

Tai Chung replied, "When this humble one went to the palace it was dark. The next morning when I went back it was the time of the fifth watch and the light was still dim and cloudy. I could not see clearly, but I thought he was not very tall, of a middle stature, and perhaps he did have a little beard."

Then did the magistrate grow mightily angry and he shouted out, "Take him out of the hall!"

And some ten-odd of the prison guards dragged Tai Chung down, although Tai Chung implored the magistrate, saying, "This humble one is without sin!"

But the magistrate shouted, saying, "You ought to die, such as you! The old gateman Wang at the palace has been dead for several years. It is a younger Wang who watches the gate now. How can you say he is old and has a beard? Moreover, the gateman Little Wang could not go into the palace where my father lives. All letters and messages must be sent to the outer superintendent of the palace Chang, and then he must go to the inner superintendent Li. Only then can it be sent within and received. If you want an answer you must wait three days. As for my two caskets of gifts, how is it that no trusted person came and asked you in detail of them? Did they receive them in such a haphazard fashion? I was a little confused yesterday for the moment and I was deceived by such as you. Now confess exactly; from whence did you receive this letter?"

Tai Chung said, "My heart was excited for the time because I was in such haste. Because of this I did not see clearly."

But the magistrate shouted out, "You speak like a fool! You bone of a robber! If I do not beat you how will you confess? You to the right and left, beat him with all your strength!"

Now all the wardens and guards of the gaol knew there was something wrong and so they could not consider who he was. They bound Tai Chung and they beat him until his skin was split and his flesh torn and the red blood streamed out. Tai Chung could not endure such beating and he could but confess and say, "This letter is indeed false."

Then the magistrate asked, "How did such as you get this false letter?"

Tai Chung said humbly, "This humble one passed by Liang Shan P'o, the robbers' lair, and a crowd of robbers came forth and they seized me, and they tied me and took me up the mountain and they wanted to cut open my side and dig out my heart. They felt upon my person and took out the letter and read it. They seized the letter casket too. But they pardoned me. I knew, nevertheless, that I could not come back and so I wished them to kill me there on the mountain. They wrote this letter then and bade me return and so escape my crime. Because I was afraid the most gracious would blame me, I deceived."

The magistrate said, "What you have said sounds well enough. But there is still some foolish talk there. I can see with my own eyes you have been with the robbers and you joined together and made this plan. How can you then speak thus? Beat him again!"

Tai Chung suffered himself to be thus questioned and beaten, but he would not confess that he was allied with the robbers' lair in the mountain. Again the magistrate questioned and beat him, but all he said was what he had said before. Then the magistrate cried, "It is useless to ask more. Bring a great rack and set it on him! Put him in the gaol!" And the magistrate came down out of his hall and he thanked Huang Wen Ping, saying, "If it had not been for your great insight, I would all unknowingly have brought about great trouble."

And Huang Wen Ping said again, "The eye can see clearly enough that this man has dealings with the robbers' lair, and they joined together to make this plot and they have joined together to make revolution. If we do not wash them clean away now, surely great evil will come about later."

And the magistrate said, "Let the confessions of these two be written down for proof and then let them be taken into the busiest street and there let them be beheaded. After that we will write a report of it and send it to the throne."

Huang Wen Ping said, "The magistrate's foresight is great and his name is mighty. If this is done, the Emperor will bestow his favor. He will know this glorious deed has been done, in the first place. In the second place, the plan of the robbers to help the prisoner escape from gaol will be foiled."

And the magistrate said, "Your sight is very far. I will myself write a testimonial that shall guarantee that you will go out to a high official place."

On that day he entertained Huang Wen Ping and escorted him outside the court gates, and from there Huang Wen Ping returned to his own city.

On the next day the magistrate ascended to his hall and he commanded a court scribe to come forward and he bade him write down the report of this matter with all speed, and he commanded that all the head gaoler's confession and Sung Chiang's also should be attached to it. On the other hand the accusation against them was to be written out with the order that on the next day the pair should be beheaded in the streets. From ancient times there need be no delay in killing a revolutionist, and if these two were killed it would spare all later trouble.

Now the scribe was one named Huang and he was a close friend of Tai Chung. But he had no way to save him and he could but cry out bitterness for him. On this day, however, he said humbly to the magistrate, "Tomorrow is a memorial day for the nation. The day after is the fifteenth day of the seventh month, and it is the mid-festival. On these two days men may not be killed. On the third day is a national holiday. Only on the fifth day may men be killed."

Outside of this the scribe Huang had no other good way, except to give Tai Chung a few days longer to live. This was, moreover, a common habit with him when men were condemned to death. When the magistrate heard it he did according to these words.

But on the morning of the sixth day he sent men to the cross roads and he commanded them to sweep and put in order the execution grounds. After the early morning the magistrate appointed soldiers and armed guards and executioners, in all some five hundred men, and they all waited at the gate of the great gaol. It was mid-morning. The chief warden of the gaol then said that the magistrate himself would come to be the supervisor of the execution. The scribe Huang had no recourse, therefore, except to present to the magistrate the accusation he had written upon two tablets and the magistrate set upon each the sign "Behead." The tablets were then fastened to a reed mat.

Now all the wardens and guards in the gaol were friendly to Sung Chiang and to Tai Chung but there was no way by which they could now save them. They could but cry bitterness for them, and the prisoners were prepared to come forth and they were tied with ropes and bound. Their hair was pasted close to their heads and knotted upon their crowns in the shape of a horn. Into each knot was thrust a red flower. Then they took the pair and brought them before the blue-faced god of the gaol and there by the altar they gave to them the bowl of rice for eternal rest and the cup of wine for eternal farewell.

When they had eaten and drunk they left the altar and they were turned about and forced along. Some fifty or sixty soldiers of the gaol surrounded Sung Chiang in front and Tai Chung behind and thus they pushed them to the front of the gaol. Sung Chiang and Tai Chung, the pair of them, stared at each other and neither could speak a word. Sung Chiang could but stamp his foot from time to time and Tai Chung hung his head and sighed. All the people of Chiang Chou who came to watch were pressed breast to back and shoulder to shoulder and there were many more than a thousand or two.

Thus the two were forced to the cross roads where the place of execution was and they were walled about by the weapons of the soldiers. Sung Chiang they placed with his face to the south and his back to the north, and Tai Chung they placed with his face to the north and his back to the south. Then they forced them to sit and they waited for the time after noon when the executioner was to come to kill them.

And the crowd lifted their heads to read the tablets whereon were written the accusation against the two and it said, "The revolutionist in Chiang Chou, Sung Chiang, who wilfully wrote a poem to overturn the state and stirred up wild talk to make people afraid, who joined himself to the robbers in the lair at Liang Shan P'o that they might all join together in revolution. According to law, he is to be beheaded."

For Tai Chung the accusation read, "The prisoner, Tai Chung, who secretly wrote his own letter for Sung Chiang, and who went and enticed out the robbers at Liang Shan P'o that joined together they might all cause revolution. According to law he is to be beheaded. The superintendent of the execution is the one surnamed Ts'ai."

And the magistrate reined in his horse and waited for one to tell him when the hour of death was come.

Now there were certain beggars there who were snake charmers and with their snakes they were bent upon forcing a way through the crowd to see what was to be seen and although the soldiers beat them they would not go away. In the midst of the confusion there was to the west of the execution ground a group of wandering medicine vendors and tricksters with weapons also forcing their way in. The soldiers shouted out, "Such as you do know nothing at all! What sort of a place do you think this is that you come forcing your way in to see?"

Then those tricksters answered, "You are accursed fools yourselves! To what town and city and place have we not run? We have seen men killed everywhere. Even if the Emperor killed men in the capital we could see it! In this little small city of yours you think because you kill two men that you shake the whole earth! And if we push in to see, well, and what of it?"

Even as they were thus quarreling with the soldiers the master of the execution grounds shouted out, "Drive them away—do not let them in!"

Before the confusion was over there was seen to come from the south of the execution grounds a group of porters bearing loads and also pushing their way into the crowd. The soldiers shouted, "This is a place where men are to be killed—what are you doing here carrying loads?"

The men answered, "We are carrying things for the magistrate. How dare you stop us?"

The soldiers said, "Even though it were the men out of the court itself they must needs pass by another way than this today."

Then the men put their loads down and they freed their carrying poles from the ropes and each man held his pole in his hand and they stood among the crowd and stared.

Then to the north of the execution ground a party of merchants was seen to come with two carts of goods and they, too, were bent on pushing their way into the beheading place. And again the soldiers shouted out, "Whither do you men go?"

And the travelers answered, saying, "We are passing on our journey. Pray make a way for us."

But the soldiers said, "This is a place where men are to be killed. How can we let you pass? If you are on your journey, pass by another way."

The travelers laughed at this, saying, "You speak well, truly! We are men from the capital and we do not know your accursed roads and we will pass by this highway."

But how could the soldiers allow them to

pass? The travelers, however, stood solidly together and did not move. The confusion on the four sides was now without bounds and the magistrate himself could not control it. Then the travelers were seen to climb up upon their carts and there they fixed themselves to see.

In a short time the people in the center of the beheading place divided and one man came forth and said in one shout, "Half after noon!"

The master of the execution said, "When they are killed, then report to me."

Then the soldiers who stood on guard with their weapons and the executioners went to the prisoners to unlock their racks, and the executioners held their swords ready. To tell of it is slow. But when the travelers on the cart heard the magistrate say the word "Behead" there was one among them who took out of the bosom of his robe a small drum and he put it down upon the cart and beat it twice or thrice resonantly. On all four sides movement began, and it was swift. For there was seen in the upper storey of a tea house there at the cross roads a great black tigerish fellow who was stark naked and who held in either hand a curved broadaxe. He gave a loud bellow and it was as though a crack of thunder burst from the sky. He leaped down out of midair and lifted his arms and brought the axes down and the two executioners lay dead. Then he turned toward the magistrate's horse.

When the soldiers rushed forward to attack him with their spears, how could they withstand him? The magistrate and those who surrounded him had already run for their lives. Then the snake charmers to the east were seen to bring knives out of their girdles and when they saw a soldier they killed him. Those who were weapon tricksters and to the west ran shouting wildly, and they killed everywhere. In the shortest possible time the soldiers and the gaol guards were killed.

The porters to the south lifted up their carrying poles and struck upright and crosswise blows and they knocked over soldiers and onlookers. The travelers to the north all leaped down from their carts and pushed the carts so to form a barricade. Two of the travelers pushed their way into the crowd and one took Sung Chiang on his back and the other took up Tai Chung. As for the others, they drew out their bows and arrows and there were some who had stones and threw them and there were some with darts.

Now these who were travelers were Ch'ao Kai and Hua Yung, Huang Hsin, Lü Fang, and Kao Shen. The ones who were tricksters with weapons were Yien Shun, Liu T'ang, Tu Ch'ien and Sung Wan. The porters were Chu Kuei, Wang The Dwarf Tiger, Chen T'ien Shou and Shih Yung. The ones who were snake charmers were Juan The Second, Juan The Fifth, Juan The Seventh and Pei Sheng. Sixteen chiefs of the robbers' lair were there and with the robbers they led there were more than a hundred men, and they fell to killing on all four sides.

Then that great black fellow was seen in the crowd swinging his broadaxes this way and that heedlessly. But Ch'ao Kai and his comrades did not know him; only they saw he put forth more strength than any one of them and killed more than any of them. Then Ch'ao Kai suddenly thought to himself, "Tai Chung once spoke of The Black Whirlwind Li K'uei and that he was a good friend of Sung Chiang's. He is a coarse fellow, too." And Ch'ao Kai called out, "Is not that good fellow there in front The Black Whirlwind?"

But how could that fellow be willing to answer? Leaping like a flame of fire he fell upon men here and there and everywhere. Then Ch'ao Kai called to the two robbers who carried Sung Chiang and Tai Chung that they were to follow that big black fellow.

So they all left the cross roads and as they went they did not care whether they met soldiers or officials or people, they felled them all to the earth. The blood ran in a river and the ones that were speared and felled were beyond counting. The chieftains left their carts and their burdens and the whole crowd followed after the big black fellow and they slaughtered their way out of the city.

Behind them were Hua Yung and Huang Hsin, Lü Fang and Kao Shen, and they held their bows and let their arrows fly behind them like a flock of locusts. Of the soldiers and the people of that city of Chiang Chou, which one dared to come near them?

And the big black fellow killed his way straight to the river's edge and his body was covered with blood. Yet even there at the river's edge he still killed on. Then Ch'ao, holding his sword, cried out, "This matter has naught to do with the people! Do not keep on killing them, therefore!"

But how could that fellow be willing to hear what Ch'ao Kai called? With every blow of an axe he struck a man down. He had gone thus some miles along the river's edge when ahead of him suddenly stretched the expanse of the river, its waters rough, and there was no further road upon the land. Ch'ao Kai, seeing it, could but cry out bitterness. Only then did the big black fellow call out, "Do not fear! Bring our elder brothers hither into the temple!"

When they all came to see, there was a great temple there beside the river and the two sides of the gate were closely fastened shut. The big black fellow struck it open with a blow of his two axes and he rushed inside. As Ch'ao Kai and the others watched they saw on both sides very ancient juniper and pine trees which cast their shade over the temple, and above the gate were four great characters written in gold, and they said, "Temple To The White Dragon."

And the robbers carried Sung Chiang and Tai Chung into the temple and there put them down. Only then did Sung Chiang dare to open his eyes. He saw Ch'ao Kai and the others and he began to weep and to say, "Elder Brother, are we not meeting in a dream?"

Then Ch'ao Kai exhorted him, saying, "Gracious Brother, you would not stay in our mountain and so you have met today's bitterness. Who is this strong, murderous fellow?"

Sung Chiang said, "This is The Black Whirlwind Li K'uei. Several times he would have freed me out of the gaol but I was afraid I could not escape and I would not let him have his way."

Ch'ao Kai said, "It would be hard to find a man like this, he has put forth such mighty strength and he does not fear knife or axe or arrow or dart."

Hua Yung then shouted, "Let us first put some clothing upon our two elder brothers!"

Even as they met together here Li K'uei was seen coming out of the veranda bearing his two axes and Sung Chiang called out, saying, "Brother, whither do you go?"

Li K'uei answered, saying, "I am seeking the priests of this temple that I may kill them all together. The cursed things, afraid of every god and devil, went and locked the cursed temple gates in the day! I will drag them hither and sacrifice them to the gate! But I cannot find the things!"

But Sung Chiang said, "Pray come first and meet with my elder brothers the chiefs."

Now Li K'uei heard this and he dropped his two axes and came and knelt before Ch'ao Kai and he said, "Elder Brother, do not blame the coarse and stupid Iron Ox." And then he met them all. He recognized Chu Kuei as a man of his own region and the two of them were mightily pleased. Then Hua Yung said, "Elder Brother, you told us all only to follow our brother Li K'uei. Now we have come here and ahead of us a great river prevents us and there is no way to go, nor is there a ship come to meet us. What if the soldiers come out of the city to pursue and kill us? How can we then withstand them? How can we reinforce ourselves?"

Then Li K'uei said, "Do not hurry. I will go with you and kill our way into the city again and we will kill that accursed Ts'ai magistrate and all his men, and then our hearts can be happy."

Now Tai Chung came to himself again and he called out, "Brother, your coarse temper will not do here. There are five or seven thousand horsemen in the city. If you slaughter your way back into the city, surely all will be lost."

Then Juan The Seventh said, "We can see several boats in the distance across the river. We three brothers will swim across the water and seize those boats and bring them here and ferry you all over. How is this?"

And Ch'ao Kai answered, "This is the best way of all."

Then the three Juan brothers stripped themselves free of their clothing except their girdles and into this each man thrust a dagger and they leaped into the water. When they had swum perhaps a sixth of a mile they saw up the river three row boats approaching them. As they came the boatmen whistled and called, and the boats flew swift as the wind. As they all watched they saw on each boat some ten-odd men and they all held weapons in their hands. They all began to be stirred in fear.

LI K'UEI SWINGS HIS BROADAXES

Now Sung Chiang heard this inside the temple and he said, "How can my life be so destined for such bitterness as this!" and as he hastened out of the temple to see, he saw sitting upon the foremost boat a huge fellow who held downwards a glittering five-pronged fork. About his head was wound into the knot of his hair a red cord. Upon his lower person were trousers of white silk to use in the water. He blew a whistle in his mouth. Sung Chiang, seeing this, knew he was no other than Chang Shun and in great haste Sung Chiang beckoned to him and called, "Brother, save me!"

When Chang Shun and the others with him saw it was Sung Chiang he cried out loudly, "Truly it is well!" and as though they flew they rowed to the shore.

When the three Juans saw them they swam back and everyone came from the boats and went to the temple, and Sung Chiang saw Chang Shun and the ranks of good strong men with him. On the other boat's prow was Chang Heng, leading Mu Hung and Mu Ch'un and Hsüeh Yung and some ten-odd villagers and all on one boat.

On the third boat Li Chün led Li Li, T'ung Wei, T'ung Meng and they also had with them some ten-odd salt smugglers, and each man with his weapon or staff came ashore. Chang Shun saw Sung Chiang and his happiness was as though it had dropped down from Heaven, and weeping he made obeisance and he said, "Ever since my elder brother was under court arrest I have not sat or stood in peace. Yet I had no way whereby to save you. Today I heard that Tai Chung was also taken, and I did not meet Li K'uei either. I could but go and seek out my elder brother and take him to the village of the old lord Mu. There we called many such as we knew and today we were just about to fight our way to Chiang Chou and were going to force our way into the gaol and rescue you. I did not dream that you, our Elder Brother, had already good fellows to save you and bring you hither. I do not dare to ask who all these braves are, but must this not be that righteous one of Liang Shan P'o, The Heavenly King Ch'ao?"

And Sung Chiang pointed to the one standing above and said, "This one is indeed our elder brother Ch'ao Kai. All of you come hither into the temple and do him reverence."

Chang Shun and those eight with him, Ch'ao Kai and the sixteen with him, Sung Chiang, Tai Chung and Li K'uei in all were twenty-nine persons, and they all went into The White Dragon Temple to meet together. This can be considered the first lesser joining together of the righteous robbers at The White Dragon Temple.

At this time these twenty-nine good fellows each performed the rites of courtesy. Then a robber was seen coming in the greatest haste to the temple to make report, saying, "Drums are beating and gongs sounding in the city of Chiang Chou, and horses and men are prepared to come in pursuit! Far, far off we can see the great flags hiding the sun, and swords and arrows are like flax standing in the field. Before are horsemen on armored horses and behind are the soldiers with weapons and their captains. They have great knives and great axes and they are coming to do battle at The White Dragon Temple!"

Li K'uei heard this and he gave a great shout, "We will go and kill them!" And he took up his two broadaxes and rushed out of the temple.

Then Ch'ao Kai called out, "Since the first step is taken the second must follow! All of you good fellows help me who am surnamed Ch'ao! We must kill every soldier and horse of Chiang Chou! Only then can we return to our lair!"

And all the heroes rose together and answered, "We will all obey your command!"

And the hundred and forty or fifty men all shouted together and they rushed to the shore of the river.

Because of this the waves were dyed red and the dead men heaped up like mountains.

> Leaping over the waves, the sky-blue dragons
> sent forth their fiery breath,
> Mountain-climbing tigers, the fierce ones,
> breathed out their windy gales of death.

How then did Ch'ao Kai and all these good fellows leave Chiang Chou? Pray hear it told in the next chapter

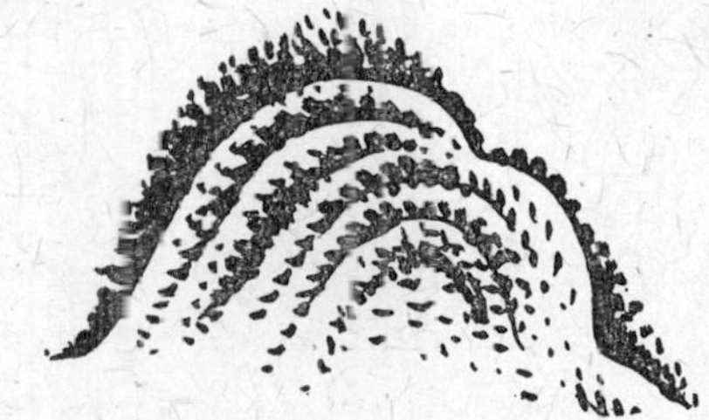

Chapter 40

SUNG CHIANG BY GUILE CAPTURES THE CITY OF WU WEI CHÜN. CHANG SHUN CAPTURES HUANG WEN PING ALIVE

IT IS SAID: In The White Dragon Temple outside of the city of Chiang Chou the good fellows from the robbers' lair stormed the beheading grounds and they saved Sung Chiang and Tai Chung. These good fellows were indeed Ch'ao Kai, Hua Yung, Huang Hsin, Lü Fang, Kao Shen, Liu T'ang, Yien Shun, Tu Ch'ien, Sung Wan, Chu Kuei, Wang The Dwarf Tiger, Chen T'ien Shou, Shih Yung, Juan The Second, Juan The Fifth, Juan The Seventh and Pei Sheng, in all seventeen, and they led some eighty or ninety fierce, brave, strong men. The good fellows who came down the river Ching Yang to help them were Chang Shun, Chang Heng, Li Chün, Li Li, Mu Hung, Mu Ch'un, T'ung Wei, T'ung Meng, and Hsüeh Yung, nine good fellows, and they led also more than forty men, who were salt smugglers upon the river, and they brought three large boats here to the rescue. From the city there was The Black Whirlwind Li K'uei, who led them all, killing as he went to the river's edge, and with those who came with him there were in all a hundred and forty or fifty men. They all met together in The White Dragon Temple, and they heard what the robber reported, that soldiers from the city of Chiang Chou were waving their flags and beating their drums and coming in pursuit.

Now when that Black Whirlwind Li K'uei heard this he gave a great roar and he lifted his two broadaxes in his hands and he went first out of the temple gate. And all the good fellows shouted in unison and holding aloft the weapons they had, they all rushed out of the temple together to meet the enemy. Liu T'ang and Chu Kuei first protected Sung Chiang and the head gaoler and took them on to the boats and Li Chün and Chang Shun and the three Juans prepared the boats. As they looked to the shore they saw that the imperial soldiers who came out were, including horsemen, some five or seven thousand in number. Those in front wore helmets and armor and they carried bows and many arrows and in their hands they held spears. Around them were the soldiers on foot and they waved flags and shouted their war cry and they came forward ready to kill.

On the other side Li K'uei was in front holding his two broadaxes and he came flying toward the enemy stark naked. Behind him were Hua Yung, Huang Hsin, Lü Fang and Kao Shen, and they surrounded him to protect him. Now Hua Yung, seeing that the horsemen in front all had their spears poised, only feared that Li K'uei would be wounded, and he freed one hand and took out his bow and arrows. He fitted the arrow to the string and pulled wide his bow and he aimed at the one who led the horsemen and he let fly an arrow with a singing noise. The horseman was seen to tumble under his horse. Then all the horsemen were startled and each man thought to run for his life. They turned their horses' heads and knocked over many of the soldiers on foot.

Then all the good fellows on the other side charged forward and they killed the imperial soldiers so that the dead lying every way were trampled to pieces and the river was dyed red. They killed them all the way to the city, where there were soldiers to succor the defeated, and these had early begun to roll down beams and great stones from the city wall as the soldiers outside rushed into the city. Then they locked the city gates and for several days they did not dare to come out.

All the good fellows then dragged The Black Whirlwind away and they returned to the front of The White Dragon Temple where they prepared to embark on the boats. And Ch'ao Kai counted over the men and bade them divide and come aboard, and they set sail and left the shore.

And they met opportune winds and they put sail. And so the three great boats, filled with many men, horses, and the robber chieftains, went toward the village of the old lord Mu, and all the way they had the favorable wind. Soon they came to the shore and the place where they might come out of the boats, and so all of them came on land.

Then Mu Hung invited them all to come to the guest hall of his home and the old lord Mu came out to welcome them, and Sung Chiang and all the others met him and the old lord said, "All of you, Sirs and Chieftains, have been wearied the night through. Pray come into the guest hall and rest your honorable persons."

So each man went into the hall and rested awhile and straightened his garments and mended his weapons.

On that day Mu Hung commanded the villagers to kill a cow and to kill ten-odd pigs, sheep, chickens, geese, fish and ducks and all such dainty meats and fine dishes and to prepare a feast with which to entertain the robber chieftains. In the midst of their feasting they talked of many things, and Ch'ao Kai said, "If it had not been for the two elder brothers and the others who brought the boats to save us, we must assuredly have been captured and put into gaol."

The old lord Mu asked, "But why did you come out by that road?"

Li K'uei said, "At that time wherever I saw people thickest I went to kill them! They came with me of themselves—I did not tell them to!"

When the others heard this they laughed heartily and Sung Chiang rose and said to them all, "This humble one Sung Chiang, if it had not been that you good fellows had come and saved Tai Chung and me, we would have met an untimely end. Such mercy as you have shown today is deeper than the deepest sea. How can I repay you all? I can but hate that thing Huang Wen Ping, who would dig me up by the roots and pick my very teeth out. Several times has he set others on to harm us. Upon such hatred how can we not take revenge? How can I again ask a favor from you as wide as Heaven so that we can go and attack the city of Wu Wei Chün and kill that thing Huang Wen Ping, and so vent me this revenge in my heart? Only then can I go back to the lair; what think you of this?"

Then Ch'ao Kai said, "We can only once attack an enemy secretly. How can we do it again? This time the treacherous thief has already a plot. Better that we return first to our lair and gather together a great army of men and horses and take with us Wu Wung and Kung Sun Sheng, these two honored ones, and Ling Ch'ung and Ch'ing Ming, and let all of them come and take revenge with us. Nor will that be too late, either."

But Sung Chiang said, "If we return to the mountain, we cannot come again. In the first place, the mountain is distant and the road long. In the second place, they will send out letters to every small place to be on guard. We must not be fools. Let us take this good chance and put forth our hands at once. Let us not wait until they have prepared."

And Hua Yung said, "Elder Brother, you have seen aright. Yet although it is thus, there is not one of us who knows the road. We do not know what the lie of the land of that place is. We must first send a spy to that city to see what is true and false, and he must see what the ways are which lead in and out of that city. And beyond this he must know clearly where that thief Huang Wen Ping lives. Only then can we begin."

Then Hsüeh Yung rose and said, "I have traveled far by river and lake and I know this city of Wu Wei Chün very well. I will go and spy the once—how is that?"

And Sung Chiang said, "If this good brother will go once, that is best of all."

On that day therefore Hsüeh Yung took leave of all the others and he went out alone.

Let it now be told only how Sung Chiang and all the chiefs in the village of Mu Hung consulted together how they could attack Wu Wei Chün. They ordered their soldiers and horses and weapons for battle and they prepared their bows and arrows and they chose out boats both large and small and all such things they made ready. When all was finished and Hsüeh Yung had been gone two days he returned bringing with him a man to come and meet Sung Chiang. Then Sung Chiang asked, saying, "Brother, who is this brave fellow?"

Hsüeh Yung answered, saying, "This man's surname is Hou and his name is Chien and his ancestors were natives of the province of

Kiangsi. He is the finest of tailors and his needle seems to fly and his thread to run. Beyond this he is skilled in weapons, and he formerly reverenced me as his teacher. Men see how black and thin his face is and how light and swift his body and so he is nicknamed The Strong Armed Gorilla. He is now in the city of Wu Wei Chün and working in the home of Huang Wen Ping. Because I saw him I invited him to come hither."

Then Sung Chiang was greatly pleased and he told Hou Chien to sit with them to take counsel. Now The Strong Armed Gorilla was destined to be one of the seventy-two stars and therefore his temper and nature were in accord with these others. Sung Chiang then asked for news of Chiang Chou and he asked how the roads were to Wu Wei Chün and Hsüeh Yung answered, "The magistrate Ts'ai now has counted the number of soldiers and people who have been killed and there are five hundred and more. Of those wounded and those struck by arrows the number is beyond counting, and messengers have been appointed to travel by night and by day to report the matter to the Emperor. The gates of the city are locked after the hour of noon and all who come in and out are questioned most severely. But this trouble that you, Elder Brother, fell into had nothing to do with the magistrate Ts'ai. It was all because of that thing Huang Wen Ping who time and again urged the magistrate and pointed out where he might injure you. Now seeing that you have escaped from the gaol, the city is all in confusion and day and night they are on guard. This humble one has also gone to Wu Wei Chün to listen about the city and there I met this brother as he came out to eat and because of this I found out all these details.

Then Sung Chiang asked, "Elder Brother Hou, how did you know?"

And Hou Chien answered, "This humble one has ever loved to learn of fencing and I have learned much of my master Hsüeh and for this I dared not forget his mercy. During these last few days Huang Wen Ping asked me to come especially to his house to make garments and when I came I met my master, and when he mentioned the great name of the well-loved elder brother and told me all concerning this matter, this humble one desired to know you, loved Elder Brother, and so I came especially to tell you all. Now this Huang Wen Ping has an own brother and he is named Huang Wen Yi, and they are sons of one mother. But this Huang Wen Yi is by nature one who does good deeds. He mends bridges and smooths roads and wherever a god is broken he mends him and he gives food to priests. Those in danger he delivers, those in need he helps and he saves the poor. In the city of Wu Wei Chün they all call him The Yellow Faced God. But Huang Wen Ping although he is an official of this city in his heart only wishes to injure people and he loves always to do evil. The people call him Sting Of The Wasp. These two brothers have divided their house and they live in separate courts but they come in and go out of one street. The door to the north is the good brother's. Huang Wen Ping lives next the city wall; Huang Wen Yi is next the main street. There I have been working and I heard the official Huang come home and tell of this matter. 'Again the magistrate has been deceived. It is I who told the magistrate to kill them first and then report the matter to those above.' When Huang Wen Yi heard him talk thus he could but curse him behind his back and say, 'Again he is doing this sort of fierce thing which will cut his own days short.' And to Huang Wen Ping he said, 'It has nothing to do with you. Why are you determined to injure him? If Heaven punishes him then your revenge will be quickly come. Are you not inviting disaster?' These last two days Huang Wen Ping has heard that you have rescued the revolutionaries and he has been very fearful. Last night he went to see the magistrate and they have taken counsel together concerning this matter and he is still there and he has not come back."

Then Sung Chiang asked, "And how far is Huang Wen Ping's home from his brother's?"

Hou Chien answered, "It was formerly one house and it is now divided. There is but a vegetable garden between."

Again Sung Chiang asked, "And how many people are there in Huang Wen Ping's home? How many families in the household?"

Hou Chien answered, "Men and women together there are forty or fifty of them."

Then Sung Chiang said to the others, "Heaven bids me take revenge and so it has sent me this man especially. Although this be so, I must trust to you, all my brothers, to support me."

Then they all said together, "Surely will we spend our very lives in pressing forward so that we may indeed put an end to this grasping, fawning, treacherous, ruthless man, and we will take revenge for you and wipe out the hatred from your heart."

And again Sung Chiang said, "But I hate only Huang Wen Ping, this one man, and it has nothing to do with the people of Wu Wei Chün, and if his brother is so compassionate and good a man we must not for anything injure him. Do not let men under Heaven curse me for one who does not love mercy. When you all go, my Brothers, you are not to do one least injury to the people. When you have reached that place, I have a plan, and I only look to you all to help and support me."

Then all the chiefs promised together, "We will hear only what our elder brother says."

And Sung Chiang said, "I must trouble the old lord Mu to give me eighty or ninety sacks and I want also a hundred-odd bundles of reeds. I must use five large boats and two small boats and I will ask Chang Shun and Li Chün to row these two small boats. On the five large boats I will use Chang Heng, the three Juans, T'ung Wei, and all those who can walk under water. Only thus can I carry out my plan."

Then Mu Hung replied, "We have here the reeds, oil, sacks and fuel—we have them all. The villagers can all walk under water and handle boats. Pray let Elder Brother proceed."

And Sung Chiang said, "Then we will use this brother Hou to lead Hsüeh Yung and Pei Sheng, and let them first go into the city of Wu Wei Chün and there hide and in the second part of the third watch of the night of the second day they are to listen for the whistle fastened in a pigeon's tail as it flies outside the city wall. Then Pei Sheng is to come up on the city wall to help us. He is to put up first a signal of white silk and it must be near to Huang Wen Ping's house and it must be the place where we are to climb the city wall. Then Shih Yung and Tu Ch'ien are to garb themselves as beggars and they are to go to the city gate and there hide. When you see flames, it will be the sign for you to begin. You are to kill the guards of the city gate. Li Chün and Chang Shun must go to and fro upon the river's edge and see who needs succor and go quickly to his aid, and so wait for us."

When Sung Chiang had fixed his commands upon each one, Hsüeh Yung, Pei Sheng and Hou Chien went first alone. After them came Shih Yung and Tu Ch'ien, garbed as beggars, and in their clothing they hid short knives and secret weapons and they went out together. Then the others carried sand and sacks and the reeds, the oil and the fuel, and they went on the boats and filled the sacks with the sand.

When the appointed time was come each of these good fellows girded himself and prepared and made ready his weapons. They hid themselves in the cabins of the boats and the chieftains divided and went aboard the boats also. Ch'ao Kai, Sung Chiang and Hua Yung went on to T'ung Wei's boat. Yien Shun, Wang The Dwarf Tiger and Chen T'ien Shou all went on Chang Heng's boat. Tai Chung, Liu T'ang and Huang Hsin were on Juan The Second's boat. Lü Fang, Kao Shen and Li Li were on Juan The Fifth's boat. Mu Hung, Mu Ch'un and Li K'uei were on Juan The Seventh's boat. There were only Chu Kuei and Sung Wan and they were left in the old lord Mu's village and they were to spy and to hear the news of Chiang Chou. Then T'ung Meng was told to row out a swift fishing boat and to go ahead and spy out the road. The robbers and the soldiers all hid in the cabins. Their underlings and the villagers and the boatmen poled and managed the boats and that night they went secretly to Wu Wei Chün.

Now this time of the year was the end of the seventh moon and the night was cool but windless. The moonlight fell white upon the clear water of the river, and the shadows in the river repeated the mountains on the land. It was perhaps at the beginning of the first watch when the boats, large and small, came to the shores of Wu Wei Chün, and they chose a spot where the reeds were deep and there they anchored their boats in a row.

Then T'ung Meng was seen to turn his boat about and come back to make report, saying, "There is not a sound in the city."

Therefore Sung Chiang bade the men under his command to take the sand and sacks and reeds and the fuel and throw them on the shore nearest the city, and he listened then and he heard the watchman's drum beat the second watch. Then he told each man to drag a sack of sand and a load of reeds and they piled them up beside the city wall, one upon the other. Each man held in his hand his weapon of war. Only Chang Heng, the three Juans, and the two T'ungs were left on the boats to meet them when they came back. All the other chieftains hastened to the city wall. As they looked at the city they saw they were a sixth of a mile from the north gate and there Sung Chiang told them to free the pigeon with the whistle. Then they saw upon the city wall a bamboo pole wrapped around with the white signal and the wind rose and waved it to and fro.

When Sung Chiang saw this he bade the men to pile the sacks there and he told them to carry the fuel and the reeds and the oil up the wall with them. There they saw Pei Sheng waiting for them and he pointed and said, "There in that neighborhood is where Huang Wen Ping lives."

Then Sung Chiang asked Pei Sheng, saying, "Where are Hsüeh Yung and Hou Chien?"

Pei Sheng replied, "They have already gone secretly to Huang Wen Ping's house, and they wait until Elder Brother comes."

Again Sung Chiang asked, "And have you seen Shih Yung and Tu Ch'ien?"

And Pei Sheng answered, "They are both at the city gate, and wait near there."

When Sung Chiang had heard this he led all the good fellows and they went into the city and they went straight to Huang Wen Ping's gate. There they saw Hou Chien hiding in the shadow of the eaves, and Sung Chiang called to him to come and he put his mouth to his ear and said in a low voice, "You go and open the gate of the vegetable garden and let the men put the reeds and the oil and fuel in there, and you may tell Hsüeh Yung to come and set fire to it. Then you are to go and knock on Huang Wen Ping's gate and say, 'The lord's house next door is on fire. There are boxes and furniture and goods to be brought in.' When you have knocked the door open, surely will I have a plan."

Then Sung Chiang divided his men into two parts to guard the ends of the street and Hou Chien went first and opened the garden gate and the men brought the reeds and fuel in and piled it there. Then Hou Chien started a flame on a torch and he gave the torch to Hsüeh Yung, and he darted out and he ran out and knocked on the gate and called out, "The great lord next door has his house afire! There are boxes and baskets here to be brought in! Open quickly, therefore!"

When those within heard this and they rose to see, they saw fire rising from next door and in great haste they opened the door and came forth. Then Ch'ao Kai and Sung Chiang and all the others shouted in chorus, "Kill the way in!"

Each good fellow rushed forward and everyone they saw they killed, and every pair they saw they killed the pair. The whole house of Huang Wen Ping, outside and inside, old and young, forty or fifty people, they killed them all clean. Not one was left. Only Huang Wen Ping himself was not seen. But all these good fellows collected out of his courts the gold and the silver that he had robbed in times past from the people. Then they blew a great blast on their bugles and they carried away the treasure and the boxes and they hastened again to the city wall.

Let it now be told of Shih Yung and Tu Ch'ien. When they saw the fire rise each took out his pointed sword and they killed the guards of the city gate. Then they saw the neighbors of the first street coming out with buckets of water and ladders and they were all hastening to the fire. But Shih Yung and Tu Ch'ien shouted out in great voices, "Ha, you people, you are not to go forward! There are countless thousands of us good fellows from the mountain lair here, and we have come to kill the house of Huang Wen Ping and all his wives great and small! We do it to take revenge for Sung Chiang and Tai Chung! It has nothing to do with you who are the people. Quickly return to your homes and hide. Do not come out and manage what is none of your affair!"

But some of the people would not believe them and they stood still to stare. Then they saw The Black Whirlwind Li K'uei whirl up his two axes and strike them along the earth. Only then did they cry out in chorus and lifting up their ladders and water buckets, they all ran away in a rush. In the neighborhood behind the gate there were a few more gate guards and they led some men out and they brought ropes and hooks and they all came rushing forth to put out the fire.

But Hua Yung soon put up his bow and let fly an arrow and one of these soldiers fell, and Li K'uei said in a great shout, "He who wants to die, let him come and put out the fire!"

Those soldiers also all retreated. And Hsüeh Yung was seen holding a torch and he set fire to Huang Wen Ping's house, both front and back, and from this place and that the flames burst forth. Li K'uei then with his axe split open the iron lock on the city gate and he opened the gate wide. Half of the robbers came down over the wall and half came out through the gate, and the three Juans, Chang Heng, and T'ung Wei all came to succor them and they joined into one group and carried the booty on to the boats.

Now the people of Wu Wei Chün knew already that the city of Chiang Chou had been robbed of the prisoners by these good fellows of the robbers' lair, and that countless numbers of the people had been killed, and so how could they dare to come out to pursue them? They could but close their eyes to it, and Sung Chiang and all the good fellows grieved only because they had not taken Huang Wen Ping. They all went on the boat and rowed off and they went toward the village of Mu Hung's family, and of this no more will be told.

Let it be told then that when those in the city of Chiang Chou saw flames rise in Wu Wei Chün so that the whole sky was red, the whole city began to talk and they could only go and report the matter to the magistrate. Now Huang Wen Ping was at that very time in the court on business and when he heard what had been reported, in greatest haste he came to plead before the magistrate and he said, "My humble city is on fire and I am anxious to return home to it."

The magistrate Ts'ai heard this and in great haste he commanded the city gates to be opened and he commanded an official boat to ferry Huang Wen Ping across the river. Huang Wen Ping thanked the magistrate and in great haste he came out and with his retainers he went to the boat with all speed. When the boat had left the shore and was on the face of the river and turned to Wu Wei Chün, the boatman saw how fierce the fire was and that the whole river was red with its glow, and he said, "This fire is inside the north gate."

Now when Huang Wen Ping heard him say this, his heart grew yet more anxious, and when they had rowed to the middle of the river he saw there a small boat that was being rowed past. In a little while yet another small boat was seen also rowed along. But it did not pass the official boat; instead it turned straight toward it. Then his retainers shouted out, "What boat is this? How dares it come at us straight like this?"

Then they saw a great tall fellow leap out on the boat and he held in his hand a barbed hook, and he answered, "We are the boat that goes to Chiang Chou to report the fire."

Then Huang Wen Ping crawled out of his boat cabin and he asked, "Where is the fire?"

That big fellow answered, "The good fellows from the mountain lair have killed everyone in the house of the official Huang and they have taken all his treasure and now the house is burning still."

Cries of bitterness burst from Huang Wen Ping and he did not know how it was with the affair. The fellow heard him and with one fling of his hook he had caught the official boat and he leaped over into it.

Now Huang Wen Ping was a clever, tricky man and he had already seen there was something wrong and he turned instantly and ran out the back of the boat and jumped into the heart of the river. But suddenly he saw another boat come out before his face and a man crawled into the water beneath him and seized him about the waist. With his other hand he seized Huang Wen Ping's knot of hair and dragged him upon the boat, and the tall fellow on the other boat had early come to aid and he took a hempen rope and bound Huang Wen Ping.

The one who walked under the water and who caught Huang Wen Ping alive was White Stripe In The Waves Chang Shun. The one on the boat with the hook was The Dragon Who Roils Rivers Li Chün. These two good fellows stood fast upon the official boat and the boatman could but knock his head before them and Li Chün said, "I will not kill you. I only wish to seize this Huang Wen Ping. Do you only go back. Tell that robber and donkey of a magistrate, 'We good fellows of the mountain lair will for the present leave that ass's head of his where it is. But sooner or later we will come for it.' "

The boatman, all of a tremble, said, "This—this—this hum-hum-ble one will—will go t-tell."

Then Li Chün and Chang Shun took Huang Wen Ping on to their own small boat and they let the official boat go, and the two good fellows on the two boats went straight to the village of Mu. They soon came to shore and there they saw the company of chieftains all waiting there for them and they helped to bring the booty ashore. When they heard it said Huang Wen Ping was captured Sung Chiang could not restrain his joy, and all the good fellows felt their hearts filled with joy and they said, "Truly did we wish to meet this man face to face."

Now Li Chün and Chang Shun had soon brought Huang Wen Ping ashore. And all of them watched and stood on guard, and at last they withdrew from the shores of the river and turned to the village of the old lord Mu. Chu Kuei and Sung Wan met them and they entered the village and there in the central hall they sat down.

And Sung Chiang took the wet garments from Huang Wen Ping and he bound him to a green willow tree. Then he asked the chieftains to sit in a circle about him and he cried out, "Fetch hither a jug of wine and pour it out for all!"

From Ch'ao Kai at the top to Pei Sheng at the end there were in all thirty good fellows and when each had drunk wine Sung Chiang cursed Huang Wen Ping mightily, saying, "You thing that you are! In the times past I had no quarrel with you, I have never done you ill, and why have you harmed me? Thrice and many times have you urged the magistrate to kill the two of us. If you have ever read the books of the sages, then why will you do such fierce and poisonous deeds as these? You needed not to revenge yourself on me for killing your father, then why did you at any cost seek some way to harm me? Your elder brother, Huang Wen Yi, was born of one mother with such a thing as you—then how is it he is so assiduous in virtue? I have long heard that in that city of yours they all call him a god. Last night I did not injure him in the least. But you thing, you do nothing in this whole countryside except to injure men. You join yourself to the powerful and the strong, you curry favor with the officials and you cheat and oppress good people. I know that all the people of Wu Wei Chün call you Huang The Wasp's Sting. But today I shall take the sting out of you!"

Then Huang Wen Ping made humble reply, saying, "This lowly one knows already his fault. I can only ask that you let me die soon."

Ch'ao Kai shouted out, "You thief and ass! Can you fear you will not die? You thing! If you knew this day must come you should have repented long since of your evil."

Then Sung Chiang asked, saying, "Which brother will put forth his hand for me?"

At this The Black Whirlwind Li K'uei leaped up and he said, "I will put my hand forth and chop this thing up for my elder brother! I see he is fat and plump and he looks good enough to fry and eat!"

And Ch'ao Kai said, "He speaks rightly." Then he commanded, "Bring hither a brazier of coals and slice this thing up in small pieces. Then throw the flesh on the coals and bring wine to eat with the meat, and thus we can cool the anger of revenge in my elder brother's heart."

And Li K'uei took up the pointed knife and he looked at Huang Wen Ping and he laughed and said, "You thing, you were behind the magistrate's guest hall and you told lies about this and about that and you stirred up harm for everyone! Where there was no harm you made it and you urged him on to evil. Today you would die quickly but I the lord would have you die slowly!"

Then he with his pointed knife first began to cut the flesh from Huang Wen Ping's legs, and he chose the good meat and there before Huang Wen Ping's eyes he heated the flesh on the coals and ate it with wine. Cutting piece after piece and broiling it thus on the coals in a short time he had cut away all of Huang Wen Ping's flesh from his bones. Only then did Li K'uei open the breast and take out the heart and liver and he took these and made a broth of them for the chieftains to drink when they were drunken.

When the good fellows had seen Huang Wen Ping thus cut to pieces they came to the great hall to congratulate Sung Chiang. There they saw Sung Chiang kneeling first upon the ground. Then all the chiefs made haste to kneel also and together they said, "Elder Brother, what is it that troubles you? Speak and no harm will come. Which of us your brothers dares not to hear you?"

Then Sung Chiang answered, "I am but an ignorant man and from childhood I learned nothing except to be a scribe. But from the time I came out among men I have longed to be with the good fellows under Heaven. Yet my strength has been feeble and my learning very scanty, and I do not know how to receive such good fellowship. Thus the whole hope of my life has been lost. Ever since I was exiled to Chiang Chou I have been grateful to the chieftains and the good fellows of the mountain lair that you have so earnestly entreated me to stay among you. But because I did not dare to disobey my father's command, I could not stay among you. Yet Heaven has truly given me a good opportunity for as I came along the road to Chiang Chou I have met many men greater than ten thousand. But I did not think that I could be so ignorant even as I am, that in the little time after I drank wine I could write those few wild words so that Tai Chung would be concerned in it even to the point of death. I do thank all of you great and good men that you did not shrink from this fierce and evil thing but that you went to the tiger's lair and to the dragon's den to save this life of mine, and that through your help I am revenged. Because of this great crime two cities have been put to turmoil, and surely the magistrate will report it to the Emperor. Today whether I will or not I must go to the mountain lair and I must come now for refuge to you, my Elder Brothers. But I do not know whether your wills are the same as mine, you who are not yet joined to the great lair. If so, then prepare and let us all go together. If there be any who do not wish to join, then go whither you will. I fear only that what you have done must come out and you will be—"

But before he finished speaking Li K'uei first leaped up and he yelled out, "We all go—we all go— If there is one who does not go he will taste this cursed axe of mine! I will cut him in two and there will be an end on it!"

But Sung Chiang said, "Such coarse talk as this! It depends entirely on the hearts of these brothers before it can be done."

Then they decided among themselves that since now they had killed so many of the imperial soldiery, both men and horses, and they had disturbed the courts of two cities how could it be that it would not be told to the Emperor? Surely the Emperor would send many soldiers out to seize them, and they said, "If we do not therefore go with our elder brother, to die and to live with him, then whither shall we go?"

Sung Chiang was mightily pleased then and he thanked them all.

On that day Chu Kuei and Sung Wan were commanded to go first to the mountain lair and report. Then the men and horses were to be divided into five groups. The first group were Ch'ao Kai, Sung Chiang, Hua Yung, Tai Chung and Li K'uei. The second group were Shih Yung, Liu T'ang, Tu Ch'ien, Hsüeh Yung and Hou Chien. The third group were Li Chün, Li Li, Lü Fang, Kao Shen, T'ung Wei and T'ung Meng. The fourth group was Chang Heng, Huang Hsin, Chang Shun and the three Juans. The fifth group was Mu Hung, Mu Ch'un, Yien Shun, Wang The Dwarf Tiger, Chen T'ien Shou and Pei Sheng. In the five groups there were thirty chieftains, and they led all of their men with them, and the booty they had taken from the house of Huang Wen Ping they divided and put upon carts. Mu Hung took with him the old lord Mu and the people of the household, and the money and treasure they had in the house they took upon the carts also.

Among the villagers there were some who did not wish to go and to these were given some money and they went themselves to other places to work. Such as did wish to go they took with them. One group after the other they went their way and the first had already started. When Mu Hung had put in order everything in his village he set alight several torches and he burned the village and he left such lands and fields as he had and he himself then went to the robbers' lair.

Let it not be told further of the five groups of men and horses as they went forward each in place, each five miles from the other. Let it be told rather of the first group, Ch'ao Kai, Sung Chiang, Hua Yung, Tai Chung, Li K'uei and five horses. They led men and carts and went on their way for five days and they came to a place ahead whose name was The Mountain Of The

Yellow Gate. Then Sung Chiang on horseback said to Ch'ao Kai, "The shape of the mountain is strange and fierce and there must be great wild robbers in there. Send one back to hasten the groups behind and let us cross over the mountain all together."

But before he had finished speaking gongs were heard to beat and drums to sound upon the mountain in front. Then Sung Chiang said, "Do you believe what I said? Pray let us not move but wait until the men and horses behind come up to us and we will fight together."

Hua Yung took his bow and fitting an arrow to it, he held it in his hand. Ch'ao Kai and Tai Chung each took his sword. Li K'uei took his two axes and they all surrounded Sung Chiang. Then each one urged his horse forward. Suddenly out of a slope of the mountain some three or five hundred robbers were seen to come forth and they surrounded four good fellows who led them out. And every man held his weapon in his hand and they shouted in loud voices, saying, "You who have turned Chiang Chou upside down and you who looted Wu Wei Chün and who have killed many of the state's soldiers and people, now you seek to return to the mountain lair at Liang Shan P'o. We four have waited long for you. If you are wise you will leave Sung Chiang alone with us, and all others shall be forgiven your lives."

Now Sung Chiang heard this and he came out from among the others and he knelt on the ground and said, "This small one Sung Chiang has been injured by men and there was no way for me to get revenge. Then many good men came from everywhere to save me. But I, small as I am, do not know where or how I have offended the four honorable heroes. Ten thousand times do I hope you will lift your hands high to give me this remaining life I have left to me."

The four good fellows seeing Sung Chiang kneeling in front, made haste to leap down from their saddles and they threw aside their weapons and flew forward and knelt down in obeisance upon the ground and they said, "We four brothers have only heard the great name of The Opportune Rain, Sung Chiang. Although we longed ourselves near to death yet we could not meet with you. Then we heard our elder brother was in Chiang Chou and that for something he suffered from the officials. We brothers had decided among ourselves that we would come and free you out of the gaol but we could hear no certain news. The other day we sent a robber to Chiang Chou to hear what he could and he returned and said, 'There were many good fellows who stirred up the city mightily and they saved him off the execution grounds and they have saved him and taken him to the village of Mu. Then they burned Wu Wei Chün and they robbed the house of Huang Wen Ping.' We thought our elder brother then must surely pass this way and time after time we sent men upon the road to see, and we feared even yet that you were not those we truly sought. So we turned our words about and seemed to question you and thus we have offended our elder brother. Ten thousand times do we hope to escape your reproof. But today we have the great fortune to see you and in our humble lair we have prepared at random a little poor food and coarse wine to be a welcome for you. Pray let all the good fellows go to our lowly lair and there spend a little idle time."

Then was Sung Chiang mightily pleased and he lifted up the four good fellows and one after the other he asked their high names. The one at the front was surnamed Ou and his name P'eng and his ancestors lived as men of Hang Chou and he was a guard upon the river. But because he offended the man above him he escaped into the wilds and in the green woods with the robbers this name was given him and he was called Eagle In The Clouds. The second good fellow was surnamed Chiang and his name was Ching, and his ancestors lived in T'ang Chou in the province of Hunan. He was one who failed to pass in the examinations in the state halls. Therefore he cast aside his books and took up military life and he was a man skilled in guile and skilled in writing characters and in counting on the abacus. Even though he reckoned up thousands and tens of thousands of pieces of money he would not make a penny's mistake. Staff and weapon of war he could wield and he could marshal soldiers in rank for battle and for this men called him The God Of Accounting. The third good fellow was surnamed Ma and his name was Ling, and his ancestors were men of Nanking. He was an idler by habit and he could blow the double metal flute and he was greatly skilled in the use of the long sword. Because of this men called him The Magic Iron Flautist. The fourth good fellow was surnamed T'ao and his name was Chung Wang. His ancestors were men of Kuan Chou and they were farmers and he himself could wield an iron spade, and he had great strength. Staff and sword he could use also, and for this men all called him The Nine Tailed Turtle.

And what of these four good fellows? They welcomed Sung Chiang and the robbers and presented the boxes of comfits and a great jug of wine and two great plates of meat and they presented them upon the palms of their hands, first to Ch'ao Kai and Sung Chiang, then to Hua Yung, Tai Chung, and Li K'uei, then to all the others. Then they presented the wine also. In less than two watches the second group of chiefs arrived and one by one they were met. When all had drunk wine they invited them all to go up the mountain and the ten chiefs first came to the lair of The Mountain Of The Yellow Gate. Then the four good fellows commanded that cows and horses were to be killed for a feast of entertainment and they told off robbers to go down one after the other to meet the three later groups of eighteen chiefs and bring them up the mountain to feast.

Before half a day had passed the three groups of good fellows had also all come and they entered the Hall Of Meeting and there met at the feast. And in the midst of the wine drinking and in the midst of the idle talk of the feast Sung Chiang said to the four chieftains of the mountain, "Today since I have come to join my elder brother Ch'ao The King Of Heaven, and I go to the mountain lair at Liang Shan P'o to become one of them, I do not know whether you four good fellows are willing to quit this place and go with us all thither to the great lair."

Then the four good fellows all answered together, "If the charity of you two honorable ones does not despise such poor ones as we are, we will come as servants to you, to hold the whip and walk by the stirrups of your saddles."

And Sung Chiang and Ch'ao Kai were greatly pleased and they said, "If you four honored ones are willing to come with us then pray prepare at once and let us set forth."

All the chieftains were rejoiced and they lived one day in the lair and when the night was passed on the next day Sung Chiang and Ch'ao Kai went ahead down the mountain. After them the others came in the old order, and they separated some six or seven miles apart. And the four good fellows prepared their treasure and their silver and the like and they led out their robbers, some three or five hundred in all, first burning the houses in the lair. They formed themselves then into the sixth group.

Thus Sung Chiang gathered in these four good fellows also and he was truly glad in heart, and on the road as he went upon his horse he said to Ch'ao Kai, "These several times that I have traveled abroad by river and lake, although I have suffered some terrors, yet I have met also with all these good fellows. Today I go up the mountain with my elder brother, and now my heart is fixed in quietness for I will live and die with you."

They talked idly along the road therefore and before they knew they were already come to Chu Kuei's wine shop.

Let it then be further told. The four chiefs who kept the lair, Wu Yung, Kung Sun Sheng, Ling Ch'ung, Ch'ing Ming and the two newly come, Siao Jang and Ching Ta Chien, had already heard the news of the return and every day they sent out small captains with boats to wait at the wine shop for everyone came to shore at The Golden Sands. Drums beat and flutes blew and all the good fellows either riding horses or sedan chairs went up the mountain. When they came to the first pass Wu Yung and the others poured out the wine of welcome and they all came to the Hall Of Meeting and there they burned a censer full of good incense.

There did Ch'ao Kai invite Sung Chiang to be the lord of the lair and to sit in the highest seat. But how could Sung Chiang be willing? He said, "Elder Brother, you make a mistake. I thank you good brothers that you did not try to escape from the sword and the battle axe and that you saved Sung Chiang's life and seized me out of danger. Elder Brother, from the beginning you have been lord of the lair. Why do you give the place to one so worthless as I am? If you force me to it then I would rather die."

But Ch'ao Kai said, "Good Brother, why do you speak like this? If it had not been that you burdened yourself heavily as with a sea of blood and saved the lives of the seven of us and sent us to the mountain how would there have come this day? Truly you are the gracious lord of the lair; if you will not be lord, then who may be?"

Sung Chiang answered, "Brother, according to years you are ten years older than I. It will be a shame to me if I am lord."

After arguing thus one with the other Ch'ao Kai was given the first place, and Sung Chiang took second place, Wu Yung the third, and Kung Sun Sheng, the fourth. Then Sung Chiang said, "Let us not judge this one by his greater glory or that one by his lesser glory, but let all the former chieftains go to the left and sit in the seats of the hosts. Then let the newly come chiefs go to the right and take the seats of guests. Later we will see who puts forth more strength than others and we can then arrange the seats."

Then all said together, "These words are fitly spoken."

Upon the left sat Ling Ch'ung, Liu T'ang, Juan The Second, Juan The Fifth, Juan The Seventh, Tu Ch'ien, Sung Wan, Chu Kuei and Pei Sheng. Upon the right these sat in order of age and each gave way to the other in all courtesy, Hua Yung, Ch'ing Ming, Huang Hsin, Tai Chung, Li K'uei, Li Chün, Mu Hung, Chang Heng, Chang Shun, Yien Shun, Lü Fang, Kao Shen, Siao Jang, Wang The Dwarf Tiger, Hsüeh Yung, Ching Ta Chien, Mu Ch'un, Li Li, Ou P'eng, Chiang Ching, T'ung Wei, T'ung Meng, Ma Ling, Shih Yung, Hou Chien, Chen T'ien Shou, T'ao Chung Wang. In all there were forty chieftains who so seated themselves and there was the sound of many drums and horns as they ate the feast of mutual congratulations.

And Sung Chiang told the tale of the magistrate Ts'ai and how he made trouble when there was none and he told of it to all the chiefs thus, "That accursed thing Huang Wen Ping, although this affair had nothing to do with him, yet told the magistrate the meaning of the song the children sang in the streets of the capital,

'The curse of the country is home and wood.'

That is, the man who is to destroy the country has for his name character the sign for home and beneath that the sign for wood. Is this not a Sung?

"The second line is,

'The head of the rebellion is water and work.'

That is, the man who stirs up the war of revolution has for his name character the sign for water and beside it the sign for work. Is this not a Chiang? Truly this points to me, Sung Chiang. The last two lines say,

'Thirty and six invincible braves,
Scatter rebellion in Shantung.'

These four lines put together mean that Sung Chiang will make a revolution in Shantung. Because of this was I seized. Nor did I dream that Tai Chung would bring back the false letter. Because of this that thing Huang Wen Ping urged on the magistrate to behead us first and then make all known to the Emperor. If it had not been that all you good fellows came to save us, how could we have come to this place?"

Then Li K'uei leaped up and he said, "Good Elder Brother, truly you have fulfilled the prophecy of Heaven. Although you have suffered bitterness from that thing, yet that Huang Wen Ping has also suffered my slicing, for which my heart is made glad. Now we have a host of soldiers and horses and even if we make a revolution why should we be afraid? Then Ch'ao Kai Elder Brother will be the great Sung Emperor, and Elder Brother will be the Little Sung Emperor and Teacher Wu will be premier and the Taoist Kung Sun Sheng will be premier also. We will all be generals and we will kill our way to the eastern capital and seize that accursed throne. There we will be happy and will that not be well? Is it not better by much than this accursed watery lair?"

In great haste Tai Chung shouted out, "Iron Ox, you speak like a fool! You are here now and you cannot act as you used in Chiang Chou. You must hear the good commands of our two elder brother chiefs and indeed you may not speak wildly and foolishly and talk while others are speaking. If you interrupt like this again then we will cut off your head for a warning to others!"

Then Li K'uei cried, "Ah-yah! But if you cut off this head of mine how long must it be before

I can grow another one out? I will just drink wine and there will be an end of it."

And all the good fellows laughed.

Then Sung Chiang spoke again of how to fight the imperial soldiers and of like matters and he said, "At that time when I had just heard this news, I was in much terror and I did not think such a day as today was to come to me."

And Wu Yung said, "Elder Brother, if at that time you had followed my words, you would have been living happily upon the mountain and you would never have gone to Chiang Chou and would not this have saved you much trouble? But this has all been so decided by Heaven."

Then Sung Chiang asked, "That thing Huang An—where is he today?"

Ch'ao Kai replied, "That thing had not lived but two or three months when he died of an illness." And Sung Chiang murmured pity.

On that day when these chiefs drunk wine together their happiness was complete. Ch'ao Kai first settled the whole family of the old lord Mu and he commanded that the booty from Huang Wen Ping's house be brought and he rewarded those robbers who had put forth their strength. Then he took out the former letter caskets that Tai Chung had borne and gave the contents to him to use for himself. But how could Tai Chung be willing to take it? He would have it put into the treasure house to be used equally by all. And Ch'ao Kai commanded all the robbers to come and meet the new chieftains and make obeisance to them and so they did to Li Chün and to all of them. Day after day they killed cows and horses in the lair to make feasts of congratulation. Of this no more need be told.

Again it is said: Ch'ao Kai commanded that each should choose his house at the front and at the back of the mountain, and they built new houses in the lair, and they repaired the walls round about. On the third day of the feasting Sung Chiang rose and he said to all the chieftains, "Sung Chiang has yet one matter of importance to bring before all the brethren. Today I wish to go down the mountain and I ask leave for a few days' absence. But I do not know whether those present are willing or no."

Then Ch'ao Kai asked, saying, "Good Brother, where is it you go today? And what important affair have you?"

Then without hurry and without haste Sung Chiang told where he would go. Because of this again he barely escaped with his remaining life out of a forest of spears and swords. Out of the wood by the mountain he was given and he received the glory of a thousand years. Truly,

> The goddess gave him three books there,
> From these he made his history fair.

Where then in truth did Sung Chiang wish to go that morning so early? Pray hear it told in the next chapter.

Chapter 41

IN A VILLAGE THREE BOOKS ARE RECEIVED FROM HEAVEN. SUNG CHIANG SEES THE GODDESS OF THE NINTH HEAVEN

IT IS SAID: At that time Sung Chiang spoke to the good fellows at the feast, saying, "Since you saved me and brought me hither to the mountain, I, this lowly Sung Chiang, have been happy in these days of joy. But I do not know how it will fare with my old father at home. The magistrate of Chiang Chou will soon tell the Emperor and a proclamation will be sent to Chi Chou that all those of my house at Yün Ch'en are to be seized in order to reveal the true criminal. Whether my old father is dead or alive cannot be said surely. Thus have I thought in my heart: if I go to my home and help my old father to come hither it will ease my constant anxiety. I do not know whether my brothers will so allow me."

Then Ch'ao Kai replied, "Good Brother, the

relation of father to son is one of the chief among the five relationships of men. Shall I keep you here to make merry and leave your old father at home to suffer? Why should we not then allow our good brother this? Except these other brothers have suffered somewhat these last days, nor have we settled finally the men and horses in our lair. Stay, therefore, two days more and wait until we have counted out the horses and the men in the lair and then you may go straightway and bring him hither."

So Sung Chiang said, "Good Brother, it matters not if a few more days pass. But I fear only that Chiang Chou will send a proclamation to Chi Chou to seize my household, and because of this there should not be delay. Nor do I desire many men to go with me. I will go alone and secretly and with my brother Sung Ch'ing we will bring my old father up the mountain by night, so that in our village neither spirit nor devil may know of it. If I take many men with me it will frighten the countryside and inconvenience will surely come of it."

But Ch'ao Kai said, "Good Brother, but if some mistake come to pass by the way there will not be one man to save you."

Then Sung Chiang replied, "Even though I die for my father it will not matter."

On that day, therefore, he would go forth at all costs and they could not stay him. He put on a fur cap and he took a short staff and fixed his girdle knife to his waist and he went down the mountain, and all the chiefs escorted him to The Golden Sands and then they returned.

Let it then be told that Sung Chiang ferried across the ford and he went ashore at Chu Kuei's wine shop. There he took the highway for the city of Yün Ch'en. The necessities of the road were that he hungered and ate, he thirsted and drank, and at night he was weary and rested. One day he thought to hasten to his village but it grew too late and he could not reach it by nightfall and so he turned to an inn to rest. On the next day as he hastened on it was still very early and he hid for a while in the wood and waited until night. Then he went to the village and knocked upon the back door. Those within the village heard and Sung Ch'ing came out to open the gate. When he saw his elder brother he gave a start of fright and in great haste he asked, "Elder Brother, how is it you have come home?"

Sung Chiang replied, "I came especially to take out my father and you."

But Sung Ch'ing said, "Elder Brother, that which you did at Chiang Chou is now known hereabouts too. Our city has appointed two guards to come every day to try to seize you. They guard us and do not let us move and they do but wait for messages from Chiang Chou when we also are to be seized, father and son, and we are to be put into gaol and held until they find you. Day and night a hundred or two soldiers search for you. There can be no delay—quickly return to the robbers' lair! Ask all the chiefs to come and save your father and brother."

When Sung Chiang heard this he was so frightened he was all in a cold sweat and he did not dare to enter the gate. He turned himself about and went away and he hastened along the road again to the robbers' lair. But the light of the moon that night was misted and he could not see the road clearly and he had perforce to choose a small and lonely road. When he had gone about two hours upon his way he heard men behind him begin to shout. Sung Chiang turned his head to listen and it was less than a mile away. There he saw a mass of lights and torches and he heard the shouts saying, "Sung Chiang, do not go on!"

But Sung Chiang went on and he thought to himself, "I did not listen to Ch'ao Kai and now I have this sudden woe. O Heaven, pity me! Save this Sung Chiang!"

In the far distance he saw a place and he went on to it. Soon the wind blew away the faint clouds from the sky and the clear moon appeared. Then only did Sung Chiang know where he was and he cried out bitterness for he did not know what to do. When he saw that place he knew it was a place called the Village Of One Way.

Now this place was encircled on all sides by high mountains and on three sides at the foot of these mountains were streams. There was but one road into that place. For all who came from right or left to this village there was but this one road and there was none second to it. Sung Chiang knew this way to the village and when he thought to go back he turned about. But those who pursued him blocked the road and the light of their torches flamed like the light of the bright sun and Sung Chiang could do nothing but hasten into the village and seek for a place to hide. He passed swiftly by a wood and he soon saw an old temple. He pushed the gate open with his two hands and by the light of the moon he went into the temple, that he might find some hiding place. He looked into the inner hall and into the outer hall of gods and he pondered for a while but there was no place for him to rest. His heart grew the more fluttered then for he heard someone outside say, "Captain, he went into this temple."

And Sung Chiang heard this to be the voice of Chao Len and in his agitation he could find no place to hide. But he saw in the hall a niche where a god was placed and Sung Chiang pulled aside the curtain and he crept in behind the god, and put his staff down beside him. There he hid, curled into a knot, but he could not stop the trembling of his body for he saw the glare of the torches coming from outside. He trembled and peered out secretly and he saw Chao Len and Chao Teh leading some forty or fifty men and carrying torches and they went everywhere searching. Looking every step they came at last into the hall. Then trembling, Sung Chiang said to himself, "This time I have gone into a blind alley and I pray the god to protect me. O God, protect me—O God, protect me!"

One by one his pursuers passed by him and not one looked into the god's niche, and at last Sung Chiang's trembling ceased and he murmured, "Ah, pitying Heaven!"

But suddenly he saw Chao Teh, bearing his torch, come again to search the niche. This time Sung Chiang trembled until he nearly lost his consciousness. Chao Teh took his sword in his other hand and with its hilt he pushed aside the curtain and he moved his torch up and down. The smoke rushed up from the torch and a cloud of black dust came down and it fell straight into Chao Teh's eyes and blinded him. He threw the torch down and stamped it out with his foot and went outside the gate of the hall and he said to the soldiers, "This thing is not in the temple. What other road is there? Whither could he have gone?"

The soldiers replied, "Doubtless this thing went into the wood. We need not fear his escape from this place. This village has but the one road and there is none other by which to come and go. Although there are these high mountains and woods yet there is no road by which they can be ascended. Captain, do you but guard the entrance to the village. Even though he could thrust wings into himself yet he could not fly away. When dawn is come let us go into the village and search closely."

And Chao Teh said, "Well spoken!"

So he led the soldiers out of the temple and again Sung Chiang's trembling ceased and he said to himself, "Is this not the god who has protected me? If I have my life safe again then surely will I return and repair this temple and make new—"

Suddenly he heard a few soldiers cry out at the gate of the temple, "Captain, he is here!"

Then Chao Len and Chao Teh and all the others rushed forward, and again Sung Chiang could not check his trembling. And Chao Len came to the front of the temple and he asked, "Where is he?"

The soldiers said, "Captain, come and see! There are two dusty prints upon the temple gate! He has certainly but even now pushed open the temple gate and he is surely hiding inside."

Chao Len replied, "Well spoken! Search closely and see."

Those men came again into the temple to search and then indeed did Sung Chiang tremble nearly to the point of death. The men went to the back and to the front of the temple and they looked everywhere and they did all except turn over bricks. Again they searched and they flashed the light of their torches over the temple and Chao Len said, "He must be there in that niche. Just now, my Brother, you must not have looked closely. I will go myself and see."

A soldier carried the torch and Chao Len put aside the curtain and five or six men thrust forward their heads to see. If they had not looked there would have been no trouble. But even as they looked they saw a fierce wind blow out of the niche and it blew out all the torches and a heavy darkness fell upon the temple. Face could not see face. Then Chao Len said, "Here is a strange thing! How can a fierce wind blow suddenly out of a peaceful place? It must be that the god is angry with us that we come again and again with our torches, and he has shown forth this miracle and sent out this fierce wind. Let us go and only guard the village pass. When it is dawn let us come again to search."

But Chao Teh said, "Only in this niche of the god we have not searched closely. Let us thrust our spears in."

And Chao Len said, "Well spoken!"

Yet even as they went forward to do this they heard again the sound of a strange great wind in the front of the temple and it blew with such might that sand and stones were loosened and rattled down and the temple rocked back and forth and a black cloud came down and filled that temple. The chill entered into the very flesh of the men and the hair of their heads and bodies stood erect in terror. Then Chao Len knew it was an evil omen and he called to Chao Teh and said, "Brother, let us go quickly! The god is displeased!"

In a great rush the men all hastened out of the temple and ran out of the gate. There were some who fell down and there were some who twisted the muscles of their legs and they all scrambled up and ran for their lives. When they were out of the gate they heard someone call in the temple, "Forgive us!"

When Chao Len went back to see, there were two or three soldiers fallen in the court and there they were caught by their clothing upon the roots of trees and however they pulled they could not pull themselves free. They had thrown down their swords and they dragged at their garments and yelled, "Forgive—forgive!" And Sung Chiang heard it in the god's niche and he trembled and laughed together.

But Chao Len freed the soldiers' clothing and led them outside the temple gate. There were a few soldiers at the front and they said, "We told you already that this god was very lively, but you would stay inside and quarrel with him, and now you have roused even the little devils who guard him. We can only go and guard the village pass and wait for him, for surely he cannot fly away."

And Chao Len and Chao Teh said, "Well spoken. We must only guard all four sides of the pass."

All of the men then went to the village pass.

Let it now be told of Sung Chiang in the god's niche. He could but exclaim and say, "Although I have not been seized by those things, yet how can I come out by the village pass?"

As he was there in the niche so thinking to himself he thought of a hundred ways and not one was good, when he heard someone come by the veranda behind. Once more Sung Chiang fell to trembling and he said to himself, "Again it is bitterness for me! Lucky am I that I did not go out!"

Then he saw two youths in sky-blue robes and they came to the niche and said to him, "We have received the commands of the goddess to come to the Lord Of The Stars and speak."

But how could Sung Chiang dare to speak in answer? Again the youths spoke from outside the niche, saying, "The goddess has commanded and you may go free."

Again Sung Chiang did not dare to answer. Again the youths spoke: "Lord Of The Stars, do not doubt and delay. The goddess has waited for long."

To Sung Chiang it seemed their voices were sweet as those of maids, like nightingales and swallows, and not the voices of men, and so he came up out of the niche, and there were two virgins garbed in sky-blue and they stood on either side of the god's throne. And Sung Chiang gave a start, for he saw they were but two figures made of clay. Then he heard the voices speaking from outside and they said, "Lord Of The Stars, the goddess invites you."

Sung Chiang parted the curtains and he came forth. There he saw two blue-garbed serving maids, and their hair was coiled high upon their heads. Together they bowed their foreheads to the ground. Sung Chiang asked, saying, "From whence have you two come, who are maids of the goddess?"

The serving maids answered, "We fulfill the commands of the goddess to invite the Lord Of The Stars to go to the palace."

Sung Chiang said, "Holy maids, you are mistaken. I am but one who is surnamed Sung and named Chiang, and I am no lord among the stars."

But the maids answered, "How are we mistaken? Pray let the Lord Of The Stars set forth at once. The goddess waits."

SUNG CHIANG SEES THE GODDESS OF THE NINTH HEAVEN

Sung Chiang said, "What goddess? I have never worshipped before her. How dare I go, then?"

The maids said, "Lord Of The Stars, when you are come there you will understand. It is not meet that you should ask."

Then Sung Chiang asked, "Where is the goddess?"

The maids answered, "She is in the inner hall."

Then the maids went before to lead him on and Sung Chiang followed behind them and so left the hall. They passed into the inner hall and in a side wall was a door, and the maids said, "Lord Sung Of The Stars, enter by this door."

Sung Chiang went with them into this small door and as he looked about he saw the heavens full of stars and there was the moon, and the winds wafted waves of fragrance to him. On all four sides were deep woods and tall bamboos. Sung Chiang thought to himself, "Then there was such a place as this behind the temple! If I had known this before I could have come here to hide, nor would I then have suffered all that great fright."

As Sung Chiang went along he saw beside low walls two large pine trees, so large that two men with their arms outstretched could not reach about their trunks. Between these walls was a path curved like a turtle's back. When Sung Chiang saw this he said to himself secretly, "I never thought there was so good a road as this behind the old temple!"

He went with the two maids and they had not gone more than the third of a mile when he heard the sound of gurgling water. When he looked ahead he saw a bridge made of blue stones and on either side was a red balustrade. On the banks were planted strange flowers and grasses, green pines and many bamboos, willows of tender green and pink flowering peach trees. Beneath the bridge the water ran rolling silver and whirling snow and it ran down into a cave in the rocks. When he went over the bridge and looked about him there were two rows of curious trees and in the center a red latticed gate. And he went to the gate to see and he lifted his head and he saw a temple hall and to himself he thought, "I was born in Yün Ch'en but I never heard there was such a place as this."

And he feared in his heart and he did not dare to move his foot. But the maids urged him on from behind and they said, "Lord Of The Stars, pray go on."

And they led him into the very gate and into a dragon tiled court. On both sides there were red pillared verandas and they were hung with embroidered curtains. In the center was a great temple and it was filled with the light of many candles. The maids led him step by step out of the dragon tiled court onto the terrace before the temple and he heard in the entrance to the temple and upon the temple steps the voices of several other holy maids and they said, "The goddess invites the Lord Of The Stars to enter."

Then Sung Chiang went into the great temple and without his knowing it his flesh trembled and the hair on his body stood erect. The tiles beneath his feet were all carven with dragons and phœnixes. The maids coming within the temple spoke thus to the goddess behind her curtain, "The invited one, the Lord Of The Stars, stands at the entrance."

Then Sung Chiang came before the curtain and by the sacred dais, and he bowed himself and knocked his head upon the ground and he lay upon the ground and he said, "Your subject is but a low and filthy thing upon the earth and I do not know the holy one. I do but pray for your heavenly mercy to descend in pity upon me."

Then a voice came out from behind the sacred curtain and it said, "Let the Lord Of The Stars be seated."

But how did Sung Chiang dare so much even as to lift his head? Then the voice commanded that the holy maids support him and seat him upon a porcelain seat. So forced, Sung Chiang could but sit, and a voice sounded throughout the temple, "Roll up the curtain!"

Several maids quickly came and rolled up the jeweled curtain and placed it upon two gold hooks. Then the goddess asked, saying, "Lord Of The Stars, and has it been well with you since we two parted?"

Again Sung Chiang rose and again he made obeisance and he said, "I am but a common subject and I dare not look upon your face."

But the goddess said to him, "Lord Of The Stars, now that you have come here you need not be so full of these courtesies."

Only then did Sung Chiang dare to lift up his head and to look. There on all sides he saw the glitter of gold and of jade and he saw dragon lamps and phœnix candlesticks alight. On either side were maids in sky-blue robes and they held the sacred scepters and they held flags and behind the goddess a great fan. In the very center upon a throne made of nine dragons and seven precious materials sat the goddess. Upon her person she wore a red silk woven with gold, and in her hand she held a scepter of white jade. Her eyes were of the most natural beauty and her face was of a very noble fearless dignity. She spoke thus, "Pray let the Lord Of The Stars come hither," and she commanded her maids to present wine to him.

Then the maids on both sides brought a precious bottle of a lotus shape and they brought the wine in it and poured it into a bowl. The first of the maidens brought the wine and presented it to Sung Chiang, and Sung Chiang stood up and he dared not refuse it. He received the cup and facing the goddess he knelt and drank the cup clean. And Sung Chiang perceived the wine was very fine and fragrant and it ran through his whole body and made him glad, and it was like dew upon his heart.

Again a maiden came forward and she presented a plate of sacred dates and she exhorted Sung Chiang to eat. Then with the most meticulous care and fearing lest he lose his manners, he put out his fingers and took up one date and put it to his mouth and ate of it and he hid the pit in his hand. And the maiden again poured out a cup of wine and presented it to Sung Chiang and again Sung Chiang took it and drank it, and the goddess commanded that once more he was to be asked to drink, and once more a maiden poured a cup of wine and presented it and she exhorted Sung Chiang to drink of it. Once more did Sung Chiang drink and a maiden presented the dates and again he took two. In all he drank three cups of sacred wine and he ate three of the sacred dates. After drinking thus Sung Chiang perceived himself to be a little drunken, and he feared lest if he were drunken he might behave without propriety, and so he made obeisance to the goddess and he said, "I can drink but a little wine, and I pray the goddess to give me no more."

Then the command came forth into the temple, "If the Lord Of The Stars cannot drink more, let the wine cease," and the goddess commanded those who waited upon her, "Bring out the three sacred books and give them to the Lord Of The Stars."

Then the maidens went behind the screens at the back of the temple and upon a blue plate they bore a packet wrapped in yellow silk and within this were the three sacred books and these they presented to Sung Chiang. When Sung Chiang looked at them he saw a packet some five inches long and about two inches wide, but he did not dare to open them and see them. He made two more obeisances and raising his hands he received them and put them into his sleeves. Then the goddess sent forth her command and she said, "Sung, Lord Of The Stars, I do pass to you these three sacred books that you may work for Heaven the ways of virtue. If you become a leader among men you are with all your might to be a help to the helpless. If you are to be a statesman, you are to protect the people and bring peace to the state. You are to leave false ways and come back to the true. Do not forget and do not tell anyone."

Then again Sung Chiang made obeisance twice, and reverently he received the words. Again the goddess commanded, saying, "The Emperor Of Heaven, because the evil in your heart is not yet cut off, and because the way of virtue you have not yet completed, has now punished you by sending you to this earth. But in no great while you shall return to the halls of the gods and there must be no smallest point then in which you fail, for if when you die your soul cannot ascend into Heaven and must descend into Hell even I may not save you. These three books you are to read continually, but you may only read them in company with that one whose star is called The Decree Of Heaven. No other may see them. When your virtue is complete then you are to burn these sacred books, for they must not be left upon the earth. What I command you are to remember. Now am I in Heaven, you upon earth, and we are separate though it is hard for me to leave you so long. Quickly return, therefore."

Then she commanded the maidens, "Speedily escort the Lord Of The Stars that he may return.

We shall meet again in the palace of red jade beside the gates of gold."

And Sung Chiang thanked the goddess and he went with the maidens and out of the temple and they passed through the latticed gate. The maidens escorted him to the stone bridge and they said, "Just now when you suffered your great fright, if the goddess had not protected you, they would have seized you. When the dawn comes assuredly you will have passed out of this difficulty. Lord Of The Stars, look under the bridge and you will see two dragons playing."

Then Sung Chiang leaned upon the balustrade and he looked and suddenly he saw two dragons sporting in the water. The two maids, when they saw him watching, gave him a push. Sung Chiang gave a great shout and started—and there he was in the god's niche! He had waked from a miraculous dream.

Then Sung Chiang crawled up and as he looked about the moon was at its very height and he guessed it to be midnight and the hour when if one dreams, the dream comes true. Sung Chiang felt in his sleeve and there in his hand were three date pits, and in his sleeve was a packet of the three sacred books wrapped in silk. When he brought them out to look at them they were indeed the three sacred books. Moreover he tasted the fragrance of wine in his mouth. Then he thought to himself, "Truly this dream was a very curious one; it is like a dream and yet it is no dream. If I take it for a dream then why have I these sacred books in my sleeve? And why is there the fragrance of wine in my mouth? And why the date pits in my hand? All the words she spoke to me I remember and I have not forgotten one word. But if I do not take it for a dream, why then, here I am still here in the niche without moving and I fell into it and what is there hard to see in that? I think it must be this goddess is very lively that she has so appeared like this to me. Only I do not know what goddess it is."

When he pulled aside the curtain to see, there upon a nine dragon throne sat a beautiful goddess and he thought, "She is exactly like the one I saw even now." And he pondered on and he said to himself, "This goddess called me Lord Of The Stars, and I think in the life before this I must have been no common man. These three sacred books have surely some use and I have not forgotten any of the heavenly commands I heard. The blue-garbed maidens said, 'When the dawn comes surely you will pass out of this difficulty.' Now the dawn comes faintly and I will therefore go forth."

Then he put out his hand and felt in the niche for his staff and he girdled his garments about him and step by step he came out of the temple. He passed by the left veranda and out to the front of the temple and as he looked on both sides he saw an old tablet upon which four letters were inscribed in gold and they said, "Temple Of The Dark Goddess." Then Sung Chiang folded his hands upon his forehead and he gave thanks and he said, "Divine fortune—this was then The Goddess Of The Ninth Heaven who gave me the sacred books and who saved my life also. If I can come once more out of this present darkness into the light of the sun surely will I repair this temple and build anew the great hall of the gods. Descend upon me, O Goddess, as here I kneel, and protect me!"

When he had thus given thanks he crept secretly out toward the village pass. Before he was far from the temple he heard far ahead of him a shout of voices rising to very Heaven. To himself Sung Chiang said, "Again it will not do! I must stay my feet for I cannot go out now. If I go before them surely I shall suffer being captured by them. Better it is if I hide here by the roadside behind these trees."

But when he had only just hidden himself behind the trees he saw several soldiers panting and coming in the greatest haste and leaning upon their weapons as they staggered step by step and they all cried out together voice by voice, "Save us, O gods, save us our lives!"

When Sung Chiang saw this from behind the trees to himself he thought, "Here again is some strange thing! They guarded the village pass and they waited for me to come out to seize me. Why then have they come running here?"

When he looked again he saw Chao Len come rushing also and he cried out, "Save me, O gods!"

Sung Chiang said, "Why are these things in such haste?"

Then he saw a great tall fellow behind pursuing them. That great fellow had not a stitch on his upper body and his strange devilish flesh was all showing. In his hands he held two steel and iron battle axes and he shouted, saying, "You cursed, you are not to go!"

What is distant cannot be seen, but what is near is evident. It was truly The Black Whirlwind, Li K'uei. Sung Chiang thought, "Must this not be the midst of a dream?" And he did not dare to come out.

Now that Chao Len had just come to the front of the temple when he stumbled upon the root of a pine tree and he fell to the ground, and Li K'uei caught up to him and he took this chance and with one foot he pinned him down. Then he lifted his great axes and he was about to bring them down when again two good fellows caught up from behind and they threw back their caps and each bore aloft a sword. The one in front was Ou P'eng, the one behind was T'ao Chung Wang. Li K'uei, seeing these two hastening forward, feared they came to rob him of his glory and so spoil their brotherhood and so he let his axe fall upon Chao Len and cut him into two halves. He cut open even his breast and his belly. Then he leaped aside and pursued the soldiers and killed them and they scattered in all four directions. Still Sung Chiang did not dare to come out. Then he saw three more good fellows come up from behind, and they killed as they came. The ones in front were The Redheaded Devil Liu T'ang and the second one was The Stone Warrior Shih Yung. The third one was The Pursuing God Of Death Li Li and the six good fellows said to each other, "These are all killed and scattered but still we cannot find our elder brother. Now what shall we do best?"

Then Shih Yung cried out, saying, "Ha, there is one standing behind the pine trees!"

Only then did Sung Chiang dare to stand erect and come out, and he said, "I thank all my brothers that again you have come and saved my life and how can I return such mercy?"

When the six good fellows saw Sung Chiang they were greatly rejoiced and they said, "We have found our elder brother. Quickly go and tell our chieftain Ch'ao Kai!"

And Shih Yung and Li Li parted from them to go. Then Sung Chiang asked Liu T'ang, saying, "How did you know to come hither to save me?"

Liu T'ang answered, saying, "When your feet had scarcely reached the foot of the mountain the chieftains Ch'ao Kai and Wu Yung could not let their hearts rest and they told Tai Chung to come down straightway and to hear where our elder brother was. And the chieftain Ch'ao could not even then let his own heart rest and he sent us ahead to come and meet you, fearing some ill fortune might befall Elder Brother. Halfway we met Tai Chung and he said, 'There are two thievish asses who pursue our elder brother to seize him.' Our chieftain Ch'ao was greatly wroth then and he commanded Tai Chung to go into the lair and leave there only Wu Yung and Kung Sun Sheng and the three Juan brothers, Lü Fang, Kao Shen, Chu Kuei and Pei Sheng to guard the lair. All the other brothers he commanded to come hither to seek out Elder Brother. We heard men say that they had pursued Sung Chiang to the pass of this village and these all guarded the pass. But we have killed them all and we have not left one. There were only these few who rushed into the village and straightway Elder Brother Li pursued them. Then all of us hastened here but we did not think Elder Brother was here—"

Before he finished speaking Shih Yung came bringing Ch'ao Kai, Hua Yung, Ch'ing Ming, Huang Hsin, Hsüeh Yung, Chang Ch'ing, Ma Ling and they all came thither. Li Li brought Li Chün, Mu Hung, Chang Heng, Chang Shun, Mu Ch'un, Hou Chien, Siao Jang and Ching Ta Chien, and all the good fellows greeted one another. And Sung Chiang gave thanks to all the great chiefs and Ch'ao Kai said, "I told my good brother he should not go down the mountain himself. But he would not listen to his foolish brother's words and very nearly a great trouble has come again."

Sung Chiang said, "I have felt my anxiety for my father hanging this long time upon my very entrails and sitting or sleeping I had no peace, and you could not stay me from coming."

Ch'ao Kai replied, "But I can make you happy now. Your honorable old father and your honorable brother and all their household I did first command Tai Chung to lead to the lair, and he took with him Tu Ch'ien, Sung Wan, Wang The Dwarf Tiger, Chen T'ien Shou, T'ung Wei and T'ung Meng to escort them. They have already reached the lair."

When Sung Chiang heard this he was filled with great joy, and he made obeisance and he thanked Ch'ao Kai and he said, "Since I have received such mercy as this, even though I die it will be without regret."

Then each chief mounted his own horse and they left the village pass and Sung Chiang, sitting upon his horse, forked his hands together and he made obeisance to the heavens and he gave thanks to the goddess for this protective power and he vowed, saying, "On a day to come I will return and fulfill the vow of my heart."

Then all the men and horses returned straightway to the lair. Wu Yung led out those who had been left to guard the lair and they went to The Golden Sands and there they met. They went first to the great Hall Of Meeting and there all the good fellows gathered together, and Sung Chiang asked with anxiety, "Where is my old father?"

Ch'ao Kai then commanded, "Invite the old lord Sung to come hither!"

In no great while The Iron Fan Sung Ch'ing came there holding to a mountain sedan in which the lord Sung sat. Everyone went forward to help the old lord descend and they came into the hall. Sung Chiang met his father and his joy seemed to drop from the heavens. His face opened into wide smiles and he made obeisance and said, "Old Father, you have suffered fear—Sung Chiang has been an unfilial son. I have troubled my father and made him suffer fear and fright."

But the old lord Sung replied, "That cursed thing Chao Len, those two brothers, they sent men to guard us every day until the command came from Chiang Chou and they were going to seize the two of us, father and son, and send us to gaol. When you beat at the gate behind the village, there were seven or eight soldiers in the hall. But suddenly we did not see them and we did not know how they were driven away. In the time of the third watch again more than two hundred men opened the village gate and they led me to a sedan and they told your younger brother to prepare our boxes and baskets and then burn the village. At that time they would not let me ask for a reason and we came straight hither."

Sung Chiang said, "Today we, father and sons, are all together and we lack not one, and we trust to the strength of these our brethren."

Then he told his brother Sung Ch'ing to make obeisance to thank all the chiefs. Ch'ao Kai and all the others all came and made obeisance to the old lord Sung and when this was finished they killed cows and horses and they all ate together for a feast of congratulation because the father and son were united. That day they feasted until all were drunken before they separated.

On the next day again they prepared a feast of rejoicing and the chieftains great and small all made merry.

On the third day Ch'ao Kai prepared a feast of his own and he invited Sung Chiang's father and the sons, and in the midst of the feast there was a thought stirred up in Kung Sun Sheng. He thought of his old mother in Chi Chou and that he had been long away from his home and he did not know how she did. And as they all drank their wine they saw Kung Sun Sheng rise and he said to the assembly of chieftains, "I do thank all you mighty ones that for so long you have treated me well, and you have treated me as might my own flesh and blood. But ever since I, this humble Taoist, came with the chieftain Ch'ao up the mountain we have feasted every day and made merry. Not one time have I returned to my home to see to my old mother. And I fear too that my old teacher in magic looks for me. I think therefore to return to my home and visit my mother and my teacher and therefore I will part from you for three or five months. But I will return and meet with you again when I have fulfilled my desire and assuaged the anxiety of my old mother."

Then Ch'ao Kai said, "I have heard you speak of this before, Sir, and your honored mother is in the north without one to care for her. Now that you have thus spoken, I cannot easily stay you. Yet I do not wish to part from you; although you would go, yet wait until tomorrow and we will escort you."

And Kung Sun Sheng gave thanks. On that day they all drank again until they were drunken before they separated and each went to his own room to rest. And early the next morning a feast was prepared at the pass to send Kung Sun Sheng on his way.

Let it now be told that Kung Sun Sheng again garbed himself as a Taoist wandering as a cloud. His girdle bag and his belly bag he put on, and he thrust into the back of his robe a pair of magic daggers, one male and one female. On his shoulder he hung a hat of palm bark, and in his hand he held a fan curved like a tortoise's back. Then he went down the mountain. All the chiefs escorted him and prepared the feast there at the pass and each one drank a parting cup to him, and when each had so done Ch'ao Kai said, "Sir and Teacher, this time you go we can ill urge you to stay. But you are to do as you say. We were fain not to let you go except that you have your old mother to hold first and we dare not stop you. After a hundred days I hope you will return to us riding like a god upon the sacred crane. Above all you are to keep your word."

Kung Sun Sheng replied, "Long have I received benefit from all the mercies of you, my Chieftains, and how would this lowly Taoist, who am I, dare not to do as I promise? When I have returned and seen mine own teacher and have placed my mother well and safely somewhere I will return then to the mountain lair."

And Sung Chiang said, "Sir, why do you not take some men with you and with them bring your old mother hither? Then at any time you can care for her as you are able."

But Kung Sun Sheng answered, "My mother has all her life loved a lonely peaceful life and she cannot bear fright and fear. For this I do not dare to bring her hither. There are fields and mountains and villages at my home and my mother can manage her own affairs. I will go and see to her once and I will return and meet again with you all."

Sung Chiang said, "If it is thus, I will let it be as you will. I only hope you will return soon."

And Ch'ao Kai brought a plateful of gold and silver to present, and Kung Sun Sheng said, "I do not need much, and only enough to come and to go."

But Ch'ao Kai would have him take one-half and he bid him put it in his girdle bag. Then Kung Sun Sheng made his bow of farewell and he parted from them all and he passed by The Golden Sands and went toward Chi Chou.

When all the chieftains had feasted and scattered and were about to go up the mountain, they saw The Black Whirlwind Li K'uei suddenly let out a great roar and begin to weep there by the pass. In great haste Sung Chiang asked him, "Brother, and why are you so troubled?"

Li K'uei, weeping, replied, "And is this cursed thing not enough to anger a man? This one goes and finds his father and that one goes and sees his mother, and was The Iron Ox born of a hole in the ground?"

Then Ch'ao Kai asked, saying, "What is it you wish to do now?"

Li K'uei answered, "I have only an old mother at home, and my elder brother is hired out in another man's house. How can he care for my mother and make her happy? I want to go and find her and bring her here and let her be happy, and then all will be well."

Ch'ao Kai said, "Brother, you have spoken rightly. I will appoint several men to go with you and bring her up and this will be a very good thing."

Then Sung Chiang said, "It cannot be. The temper of our brother Li is not good. If we let him go back surely some trouble will arise out of it. If men are told to go with him that also is not well. His temper is like a smouldering fire ready to flame, and whomever he comes upon by the way he will offend. Also he has killed many persons in Chiang Chou, and who does not know him for The Black Whirlwind? Why has not the magistrate sent a command for his arrest long ago to this home? Surely he will send now because of the trouble stirred up in Chiang Chou. Moreover the look on his face is fierce and evil and if anything untoward comes about that place is very far from here and it will be hard for us to know it here. Wait for a while, then, and wait until we hear all is peaceful and then it will not be too late to go."

But Li K'uei fell into a great wrath and he shouted out, "Elder Brother, you are an unjust man, too! You would have your father come up the mountain and be happy, but you would let my mother stay in the village and suffer! Is it not enough to tear my belly open with wrath?"

But Sung Chiang replied, "Brother, do not be so wrathful. If you want to go and find your mother then but hear these three things and we will let you go."

And Li K'uei said, "Then tell me those three things what they are!"

And Sung Chiang put up his two fingers and he told off these three things. Because of these things did Li K'uei

> Put forth his great hands to shake the heights of Heaven, of Earth the deeps,
> To fight with a wild beast climbing cliffs from stream to stream it leaps!

What three things then did Sung Chiang tell to Li K'uei? Pray hear it told in the next chapter.

Chapter 42

THE FALSE LI K'UEI ROBS LONELY TRAVELERS IN THE WILDERNESS. THE BLACK WHIRLWIND KILLS FOUR TIGERS ON THE MOUNTAIN I NING

IT IS SAID: Li K'uei asked, "Elder Brother, say what three things," and Sung Chiang answered, "You wish to go to I Chou to the county of I Suei to fetch your mother. The first thing is that you are to go straight thither and drink no wine by the way. The second thing, because your temper is so swift, who is willing to go with you? You must go secretly and alone and bring your mother here. The third thing, you are not to take with you those two axes you use. Take care upon the road and set forth soon and come back soon."

Then Li K'uei said, "What is there in these three things that I cannot do? Elder Brother, rest your heart. I will set forth today and I will not stay long."

At that very moment Li K'uei straightened his garb and set all in order and he took only a girdle knife and a sword and he took one large piece of silver and three or five small pieces. Then he drank several cups of wine and cried out a loud farewell and thus he parted from them all and he went down the mountain and passed by The Golden Sands.

Ch'ao Kai, Sung Chiang, and all the chieftains when they had escorted him a way, returned to the lair and they met in the hall and seated themselves according to rank. But Sung Chiang could not let his heart rest, and he said to all of them, "This brother Li K'uei will certainly rouse some trouble. I do not know whom among you here is a man of his own village and can go thither and find the news about him."

Then Tu Ch'ien said, "There is but Chu Kuei who is a man of I Chou and he is a village man of Li K'uei's."

When Sung Chiang heard this he said, "I had forgotten that the other day when we met at The White Dragon Temple Li K'uei did recognize him as his fellow villager."

Then Sung Chiang sent a man to find Chu Kuei and the man ran down the hill as though he flew, and he went straight to the wine shop and he asked Chu Kuei to come. And Sung Chiang said to Chu Kuei, "Today we have the brother Li K'uei and he has gone to his home to fetch hither his old mother. But because his temper is so evil when he drinks we did not wish to send any men to go with him, lest there be some trouble upon the road. Now I know you are of the same village with him and you may go there and hear of him."

Chu Kuei answered, saying, "This lowly brother is a man of I Chou and I have one brother, named Chu Fu, who lives in that place outside the west gate and he has a wine shop. This Li K'uei is a man of the same county of The Village Of A Thousand Feet, and he lives to the east of the shop of a man surnamed Tung. He has an elder brother named Li Ta and he is one who hires himself out in men's houses by the year. This Li K'uei has from his childhood been turbulent and mischievous, and because he beat a man to death he escaped to other places and he has never returned home once. Now if you send me thither to listen it matters nothing to me, but

I only fear there is not one to look after my shop. I have not returned for a long time to my city either, and I have wished to go back and ask after my brother."

And Sung Chiang said, "You need not trouble over this tending of the shop. I will but bid Hou Chien and Shih Yung to tend it for you for the time."

Chu Kuei, having received these commands, wished to take his leave of the chieftains and go down the mountain. He went therefore to his shop and put together his bundle and he gave over the shop to Shih Yung and to Hou Chien and he himself hastened to I Chou.

Now Sung Chiang and Ch'ao Kai were in the lair and every day they feasted and drank wine and made merry and they studied the heavenly books with Wu Yung. Of this no more need be said.

Let it be told how Li K'uei went alone from the mountain lair and he followed the road and came to the regions of I Chou. All along the road he did truly drink no wine and so he stirred up no trouble, and so there is nothing to tell. But when he had come outside the west gate of I Chou region he saw a crowd circled about an official proclamation. Li K'uei went and stood too amid the crowd, and he heard men beside him reading and they said, "The first name is the chief of the robbers, Sung Chiang, and he is a man of Yün Ch'en county. The second name is his accomplice Tai Chung who was the chief gaoler in the gaols at Chiang Chou. The third name is the accomplice Li K'uei, and he is a man of the county of I Chou."

Li K'uei heard this from behind the men and his arms and legs were about to bestir themselves in his anger and he could scarcely stay himself not knowing what he should do, when he saw a man force his way in to the front and he grasped Li K'uei about the waist and yelled, "Elder Brother Chang, what do you here?"

When Li K'uei turned himself about to see he recognized it to be Chu Kuei. Li K'uei asked, saying, "Why have you come hither, too?"

Chu Kuei answered, "Pray come with me and let us talk."

The two went together then outside the west gate and they went into a wine shop there near a village and they went into an empty room at the back, and sat down. Then Chu Kuei pointed at Li K'uei and he said, "And how great daring have you! On that board was written plainly there was a reward of ten thousand pieces of silver for the capture of Sung Chiang, five thousand for Tai Chung, three thousand for Li K'uei. Why did you stop there to see the board? If you had been seen by quick eyes and caught by swift hands and sent to the magistrate, then what would have become of you? Our elder brother Sung Chiang was afraid you would stir up trouble and therefore he was not willing to bid men to come with you. And he was afraid you would do some strange thing here, too, and so he sent me especially to hasten after you and listen about for news of you. I came down the mountain a day later than you, and I reached here a day before you. Why did you reach here only today?"

Li K'uei answered, "Because my elder brother told me I was not to drink wine therefore I walked slowly along the road. How did you know this wine shop? If you are a man of this place then where is your home?"

Chu Kuei said, "This wine shop is indeed the home of my younger brother Chu Fu and I was a man of these parts before, and because I traveled far and wide I lost my capital and took refuge in the mountain lair. Only today have I come back." Then he told his brother to come and meet Li K'uei and Chu Fu poured wine to welcome Li K'uei and Li K'uei said, "Elder Brother commanded me that I was not to drink wine. Today I have come back to my own country and even if I drink two bowls or so, what cursed matter can it be?"

And Chu Fu did not dare to refuse him and so gave him to drink.

That night they drank until the fourth watch and they prepared some food and Li K'uei ate. At the fifth watch when the stars were faint and the moon setting and the sky was brightening and the clouds rosy with dawn they turned toward the village, and Chu Kuei commanded Li K'uei, saying, "Do not go by the small paths. Turn there by the great pine tree and then go on the big road to the east and then go straight to The Village Of A Thousand Feet, and that is the region called East Of The East. There seek your mother in all haste to come back with you soon to the mountain."

But Li K'uei said, "I will go by the small paths only, and truly will I not go by the big road for who can trouble to go so far?"

Then Chu Kuei said, "But there are tigers aplenty on the small paths and there are robbers who lie in wait for the chance to rob those who pass by."

Li K'uei answered, saying, "And what cursed thing do I fear?" So he put on his cap and lifted his sword and hung his knife to his girdle and he took leave of Chu Kuei and of Chu Fu and he went out of the gate toward The Village Of A Thousand Feet. When he had gone some miles the day grew clear and clearer. As he went along the dewy grass a white rabbit darted out and it ran ahead of him and Li K'uei pursued it for a long time and he laughed aloud, saying, "Well, and that beast has led me a long way!"

Even as he was going along he saw ahead of him some fifty-odd great trees. It was autumn at this time, and the leaves just turned to red. Li K'uei came to the edge of the trees and he saw a great fellow come out and this man shouted, "If you have any understanding, you will leave money if you are to pass! Else I will seize your bundle!"

When Li K'uei looked at that man he saw he wore a red turban folded in two points and he wore a padded coat of coarse cloth. In his hands were two axes. He had smeared black ink over his face. When Li K'uei saw all this he gave a great shout, "What cursed man are you? And how dare you stand and cut the road in two?"

Then that man answered, "If you ask my name, it will frighten your heart and gall to pieces! This noble one is called The Black Whirlwind! Put down your bundle and the money to buy your right of way! Then only will I forgive you your life and let you pass!"

But Li K'uei gave a great laugh and he said, "May the cursed joy of your mother be gone! What sort of a thing are you and whence do you come? And how have you taken my name to stay here to do lawlessness?"

And Li K'uei lifted up the sword in his hand and rushed at the man. How could the man withstand him? Even as he was about to run he was thrust in the thigh by Li K'uei's sword and he fell over upon the ground. Then Li K'uei placed one foot on the man's breast and he shouted, saying, "Do you know this noble one who am I?"

That fellow cried out from the ground, "My Father, forgive your son his life!"

And Li K'uei said, "I am truly a good fellow of river and lake, and I am that very Black Whirlwind, Li K'uei, and shall such a thing as you put shame upon my name?"

That fellow said, "Although your son is surnamed Li, yet am I not the true Black Whirlwind. But you, my Father, have such fame far and wide even the very devils do fear you, and for this reason did I secretly take your name, and here did I lawless stand upon this road to divide it. If there passes a lonely traveler and he hears these three words, The Black Whirlwind, he drops his bundle and hastens away. Thus do I gain my booty. But truly I do not dare to harm a man. This lowly one's own small name is Li Kuei, and I live here in the village ahead."

But Li K'uei said, "How cursed and hateful is this lawless thing! Here he is robbing men of their bundles and goods and he spoils my name and he even copies me in using two axes! I will let him taste an axe of mine!"

He snatched an axe out of the man's hand and made to strike him. In haste Li Kuei called out, "Father, if you kill one of me you do kill two!"

At this Li K'uei stayed his hand and asked, "How is it if I kill one of you I kill two of you?"

Li Kuei answered, "I would not of myself have dared to go out and rob, but because I have an old mother at home who is ninety years old and she has no one to nourish her, for this reason did I take your great noble name and use it to frighten people, and rob lonely travelers of their goods so that I could care for my old mother. But truly I have never hurt any man. If you, my Father, kill me, your son, now then will the old mother in my home starve to death."

Now Li K'uei although he was a very king of devils who could kill a man without turning an eye, when he heard these words said, he thought to himself, "I did come home especially to find my mother, and here am I about to kill a man who cares for his own mother! Heaven and Earth would not forgive me." When he had thus thought he said aloud, "I will forgive your life, thing that you are!"

And he let the man rise, and Li Kuei, with the axe in his hand, bent his head to the ground and made obeisance. Then Li K'uei commanded him, "There is only I who am the true Black Whirlwind. From now and always you are not to spoil my fair name."

Li Kuei answered, "Today your son has received again his life, and I will but go back to my home and change my way. Never will I again use your name, my Father, and rob here."

And Li K'uei said, "You have a filial heart. I will give you ten ounces of silver for capital in a trade. Go and change your ways."

Then Li K'uei took out a piece of silver and he gave it to Li Kuei who thanked him and went his way. And Li K'uei laughed to himself and said, "This thing fell into my hand! Since he is a filial man surely he will change his ways. If I had killed him truly Heaven and Earth would not have forgiven me—I will go on my way, also."

So he took up his sword and step by step he went along the lonely mountain road. When he had walked until about mid-morning he found himself both hungry and thirsty, but all about him were the lonely mountain paths and he saw never a wine shop nor an inn. But when he had come to this point he saw in the far distance in a valley two thatched roofs. As soon as he saw them he hastened thither to those houses, and he saw a woman come out from the back and in the coil of her hair and above her ears were thrust many wild flowers and her face was painted white and red. Then Li K'uei put down his sword and said, "Goodwife, I am a traveler passing by and I am both hungry and athirst, and I can find no wine shop nor inn. I will give you some silver and pray let me have some rice and wine to eat."

That woman, seeing what manner of man Li K'uei appeared, did not dare to refuse. She could but answer, "There is no place where wine can be bought, but if you want rice I can prepare some for you."

Li K'uei said, "Well enough, too. Only make a plenty, for I have a mighty hunger in my belly."

And the woman asked, "If I cook a measure of rice, will that be too little?"

Li K'uei answered, "Cook me three measures!"

So the woman burned the grass in the kitchen oven and she went and washed the rice in a little mountain stream, and she brought it in to make his meal. Li K'uei went around behind the village for his own convenience, and there he saw a fellow limping along and returning from the other side of the mountain, and Li K'uei went behind the house to listen. The woman was about to go out on the mountain to seek vegetables and she opened the back door and saw the limping fellow and she asked, "Elder Brother, how have you injured your leg?"

That fellow answered, saying, "Elder Sister, very near was I never to see you again. Did you not say my luck was cursed? I went out and hoped a lone traveler might pass and truly did I wait half a month and I had not a first customer. Only today did I happen upon one, and whom do you guess it was? It was that true Black Whirlwind! Hateful it was to come upon that cursed donkey and how could I withstand him? I had a thrust of his sword and I fell upon the ground. He would have killed me, but I cheated him and I called out, 'If you kill me you kill two.' Then he asked me the reason and I answered falsely, 'I have an old mother ninety years old in my home and there is none to care for her, and surely she will starve.' That cursed donkey believed me and he forgave me my life, and he gave me a piece of silver to be capital for a trade and he told me to change my ways and care for my mother. I feared he might change his mind and come after me and so I left that wood and went into a lonely spot and there I slept awhile. Then I came behind the mountain and so home again."

The woman said, "Do not speak loudly! Even now a great black fellow came here and he told me to make his meal; is it not truly he? Now he is sitting here before the door. Go you and peep through the crack and see if it is he, and then find a drug and put it in his meat and so let him eat of it and fall unconscious to the ground. Then you and I can kill him and gain the gold and silver he has on his person and then we can move into the city and live and do a business. Will that not be better than to stay here and rob?"

Now when Li K'uei heard this he said, "This hateful thing! And I gave him a piece of silver! And I forgave him his life! Yet he is going to injure me. Truly Heaven and Earth will not forgive such an one as this." And he went slowly around to the back.

Now Li Kuei was just coming out of the door and Li K'uei seized him in the breast and held him. The woman in greatest haste went away by the front door. Then Li K'uei, thus holding Li Kuei, threw him down upon the ground and he took his girdle knife from his person and soon he had cut off Li Kuei's head. He took the knife and leaped to the front door to find that woman, but truly it could not be seen whither she had gone. He went again into the house and into the rooms to see. But there he saw only two bamboo baskets that held old clothes, and beneath these were some scattered pieces of silver, and several silver head ornaments such as women wear. Li K'uei took all these. Then he went again to Li Kuei's body and took back that piece of silver and he wrapped all into his bundle.

Then when he went to look in the cauldron there were the three measures of rice already cooked, only there were no vegetables to eat with it. Nevertheless Li K'uei took the rice and ate of it for a while and he thought to himself and laughed, "How great a fool! There is all this good meat before me and I do not know it!"

Then he took out his girdle knife and went to Li Kuei and cut off two pieces of flesh from his leg. He washed the flesh in water, then he lit the fuel in the oven, and cooked it. As he cooked, he ate, and when he had eaten himself full, he threw Li Kuei's dead body under the house. Then he set fire to the house, and taking up his sword he went toward the small path on the mountain.

When he had come swiftly to the east of Tung's shop, the sun was level with the land in the west, and he hastened straight to his home. He pushed the door open and went inside, and he heard his mother asking from the bed, "Who is it who comes in?"

When Li K'uei looked, he saw his mother's two eyes were blind, and she sat upon her bed chanting Buddhist prayers. He said, "Mother, The Iron Ox has come home."

And the mother answered, "My son, you have been long gone. Where have you been living all these years? Your elder brother is hired out in the houses of others and he can get but food to eat, and as for caring for his mother he cannot at all. I have longed for you always and I have wept my tears dry, and because of my weeping my two eyes are blinded. How has it been with you truly all this time?"

Then Li K'uei thought to himself, "If I tell her I have been a robber in the mountain lair, my mother indeed will not be willing to go forth with me. I can but tell some lie and have an end to it." So he answered, "The Iron Ox now is an official, and I have come all this way especially to fetch you, my mother."

His mother said, "If it is so, then how well it is! But how can you fetch me away?"

Li K'uei answered, "The Iron Ox will take you upon his back, Mother, to the road ahead, and then we will find a cart and go on our way."

But his mother said, "Wait, my son, until your elder brother comes and talk it over with him."

Then Li K'uei said, "And for what do we wait? I will but go on with you and there is an end on it."

Even as they were about to start they saw the elder son Li Ta coming and carrying a pot of rice, and he entered into the door. When Li K'uei saw him he made obeisance and said, "Elder Brother, I have not seen you for many years."

Li Ta cursed him, saying, "And what have such as you come back for? You are come to make trouble for people again!"

But his mother said, "The Iron Ox is an official now, and he has come home especially to fetch me."

Then Li Ta replied, "Ah, my mother, do not listen to him pass his wind! He has killed a man and for this did I wear a rack and upon my hands a chain, and I bore thousand thousand bitternesses. Now I hear he has joined with the robbers and they all have gone and robbed the state gaol, and they have made trouble in Chiang Chou, and he is a robber in the robbers' lair. The other day a proclamation came from Chiang Chou that he was to be seized in his home village, and they would even have taken me and kept me in the gaol until he was found except a certain rich man stood for me before the magistrate and he said, 'His brother went away more than ten years ago and no one knows whither, and he has not once come home. Is it not that someone has said falsely he was a man of these parts?' And he used silver for me high and low and for this I did not suffer from the court and so I have been forgiven the penalty of beating if my brother were not found. Even now there are proclamations everywhere that there is a reward of three thousand pieces of silver if he be caught.—And still, you thing, you do not die but you come home and speak wildly like a fool!"

Li K'uei said, "Elder Brother, do not be in a rage! We will go together up the mountain and be happy there, and how good that will be!"

Then Li Ta was very wroth and he would have leaped forward to beat Li K'uei except he knew he could not withstand him, and so he threw down the pot of rice and went straightway out. And Li K'uei said to his mother, "Now he is gone this time and it is surely to seek men to come and seize me, and I shall never be able to get away. Better it is to go the earlier. But my brother has never seen such great pieces of silver as this one I have. I will leave the great fifty-ounce piece here and put it upon the bed, and when my elder brother returns and sees it, he will not dare to come after me."

Then Li K'uei untied his girdle bag and fetched out a great piece of silver and he put it upon the bed, and he cried, "Mother, let me carry you away on my back, then."

His mother answered, "And where will you carry me on your back?"

And Li K'uei said, "You are not to ask me. Only come with me and be happy. I will carry you and you need not trouble."

Then Li K'uei lifted his mother on his back and took up his sword and he went out of the door and turned upon a small side path.

Let it now be told of Li Ta. He hastened to the home of a rich man and made his report and he led out some ten-odd villagers and they went as though winged to the house. When they looked about they did not see the old mother; only they saw left upon the bed a great piece of silver. Li Ta, seeing this great piece of silver, thought to himself in his heart, "The Iron Ox has left this silver and he has carried our mother away and hidden her. Truly there must be some who have come with him from the robbers' lair. If I hasten after them they will kill me. I think he has carried our mother away and they will surely go to the lair and there seek for happiness."

None of them could see Li K'uei and they did not know what to do. Then Li Ta said to the villagers, "I do not know by what path The Iron Ox has gone, carrying our mother on his back. Here there are many small and tangled paths, and how can we go after him?"

Then the villagers, seeing that Li Ta had no plan, delayed for a while, and then each returned also to his home. Of this no more need be said.

Let it here be told only how Li K'uei feared lest Li Ta lead men out to pursue him. Carrying his mother on his back he turned toward the wilds of the mountain into the small lonely paths where no men were. After a while had passed, he saw that the sky was dark with night, and he carried his mother into a valley. Now his old mother's two eyes were dim and she did not know if it were morning or night. But Li K'uei knew this valley, and it was called the I Valley. On the other side only were there any homes. And the mother and son, taking advantage of the light of the new moon, went slowly step by step up the valley, and the mother said as she was on her son's back, "My son, if you could fetch a mouthful of water for me to drink it would be well."

Li K'uei answered, "Old Mother, pray wait until we cross the valley and we will borrow a space in some house to rest in, and we will make some food to eat."

But the mother said, "I ate some dry rice at noon and my mouth is so athirst I cannot bear it."

And Li K'uei said, "And my throat is fiery with thirst, too, and almost the smoke comes out of it. Yet wait, I pray, until I carry you over the valley and there I will seek water for you to drink."

But the mother said again, "My son, truly am I about to die with thirst. Save me, then!"

And again Li K'uei said, "I am suffering more than I can bear, too."

Now Li K'uei saw that step by step he had come to the edge of pine trees and to a place where there was a great green stone. There he put his mother down and he thrust his sword into the earth beside her and he commanded her, saying, "Be patient and sit awhile and I will go and seek water for you to drink."

Now Li K'uei had heard the gurgling sound of water and he sought a path thither and when he had climbed over several foothills he came to the side of a brook and he dipped up water in his hands and he drank several mouthfuls. And to himself he thought, "How can I fetch this water to give my mother to drink?"

He stood up and looked east and he looked west. In the far distance upon the point of the mountain he saw a temple. He said, "Ha, it is well!"

And grasping vines and branches he climbed up the mountain side and went to the front of the temple. When he pushed the gate open and looked in he saw it was a temple to The Dragon God Of Sze Chou. In front of the god was a stone urn for incense. Li K'uei put his hand out to seize this. Now this urn was fastened upon a stone altar beneath and Li K'uei pulled at it awhile, but how could he pull it up? Then his anger rose and he jerked the altar and urn and all and he pulled them up and carried them to the stone terrace in front of the terrace and threw them down and knocked off the urn from the altar. He took the urn then and went again to the brook and he soaked it clean in the brook and he pulled some wild grass and washed the urn clean. Then he dipped up half the urn full of water and, bearing it in both hands, he went along his old path, and stumbling along he came again to the valley.

But when he had come to the stone by the pine trees he did not see his mother. There was only the sword thrust into the ground. Then Li K'uei called, "Mother, drink some water!"

But there was no sound anywhere. When he had called and there was no answer, Li K'uei's heart was filled with fear and he put down the urn and staring about he looked in all four directions. He did not see his mother, but when he had gone not more than thirty-odd paces he saw a pool of blood upon the grass. When he saw this his flesh began to tremble. Following the flow of the blood he went to seek, and he sought to the mouth of a great cave. There he saw two tiger cubs gnawing upon a human leg. Li K'uei could not check his shivering and he said, "I returned from the mountain lair especially to seek out my old mother, and I carried her on my back through a thousand pains and bitternesses, and I did but bring her here for you to eat! As for that leg which that cursed tiger has dragged hither, if it is not my mother's then whose is it?"

When the fire of his anger rose in his heart he ceased his shivering and his red and yellow whiskers stood erect. He lifted up the sword in his hand and he stabbed at those two tiger cubs. Now the two cubs were terrified and with their teeth bared and their claws outspread they charged to attack Li K'uei, but Li K'uei lifted his hand and stabbed one to death. Then the other one turned and hastened into the cave, and Li K'uei pursued it into the cave and stabbed it to death also.

Now when Li K'uei had rushed into the tigers' den, as he stood crouching there and staring about him, he saw the mother tiger standing looking into the den, her teeth bared and her claws outspread. And Li K'uei cried, "Truly it was you, you wicked wild beast, who ate my mother!"

And he put down his sword and he took his dagger out from his person. Now that mother tiger reached the mouth of the cave and she thrust her tail into the den and whirled it about, and was about to sit down upon her haunches in the den. But Li K'uei could see very clearly there in the den and he reached his dagger to the point below the tigress's tail and with all his strength he thrust forward, and he thrust it straight into the beast's anus. Yet he used his strength too heavily and he had thrust the very handle of the dagger through to the tigress's belly and the tigress gave a great growl and with the dagger in her vitals she rushed out of the cave and leaped to a point on the mountain beyond. Then Li K'uei took his sword and he hastened out of the cave. The tigress suffering the pain, leaped down the mountain. Li K'uei was just about to hasten after her when he saw a great wind come out of the trees beside him, and the leaves fell from the trees like rain, and to himself he thought, "Clouds come with the dragon, wind with the tiger."

Now the place where this wind rose was beneath the light of the new moon. There came forth a deep growl and all of a sudden there leaped out a slant-eyed, white-browed tiger. That great beast charged at Li K'uei with its whole strength. But Li K'uei was not fearful nor agitated. He took advantage of the force of the beast's attack and he lifted his sword in his hand and thrust it straight into the tiger's throat.

As for the tiger, he did not attack with his hind feet nor strike with his tail, for he tried to save himself his pain, and moreover, Li K'uei had pierced his windpipe. The tiger retreated not more than five or seven paces when Li K'uei heard a sound as though the half of a great mountain fell. Straightway then did the tiger die there beside the rock.

In this short time did Li K'uei kill the two tigers and their cubs. Then he went once more into the den with his knife and looked about, lest there be yet another tiger. But there was none. And Li K'uei was weary by now also, and he went to The Temple To The Dragon God, and he slept there until dawn.

On the morning of the next day Li K'uei went to collect his mother's two legs and such of her bones as had not been devoured, and he took a cloth and wrapped them up. He went behind The Temple To The Dragon God and he dug a hole and buried them, and there he did weep mightily for a while. Yet he was hungry and thirsty too, and at last he tied up his bundle again and took up his sword and seeking a path he slowly crossed the valley.

Suddenly he saw five or seven hunters setting a trap and preparing their repeating arrows. When they saw Li K'uei coming near covered with blood they cried, "You traveler, you must be the earth god of the mountain else how dare you come alone through such a mountain as this?"

Li K'uei, seeing they asked him, thus thought within himself, "There is a reward offered for me in the city of three thousand pieces of silver to that one who seizes me. How dare I speak the truth? I had better lie then." Therefore he answered, "I am but a traveler. Last night I came across the valley with my mother, and because my mother wanted water to drink I went up the valley to look for it and while I was gone my old mother was dragged away by a tiger and eaten. Then I went myself into the tigers' den and first I killed the two small ones and then I killed the two large tigers. And I slept until dawn in the temple and only then did I come down the mountain."

Then did the hunters cry out together, "We cannot believe it! How could you, who are but one man, kill four tigers? Even in the old times Li Ch'uen Hsiao and Chi Lu killed but one apiece. The two small tigers are no great feat but the two large ones are no slight usual matter. We have been beaten by the magistrate we do not know how many times on account of these two large tigers. Truly for three months while there has been this tigers' den on this mountain not a man has dared to go. We do not believe what you say, for surely you do deceive us."

Li K'uei answered, "But I am not a man of these parts, and why then should I deceive you? If you do not believe me I will go up the valley with you and find those dead tigers and give them to you. Let us go up then and bring them down."

Then all the hunters said, "If there is truly this thing, we can but thank you very deeply, for how great a good it is in truth!" And the hunters blew their shrill whistle and in a short time there were gathered together thirty to fifty men and they all had barbed hooks and staves and they followed after Li K'uei.

When they had come up the valley again it was full dawn and they all went to the crest of the mountain. In the distance they saw the den and truly there were two tiger cubs there killed. One was in the den and one was outside. One great female tiger lay dead on the slope of the mountain, and the great male tiger lay dead before the temple. When the hunters saw these four tigers had been killed they were all mightily rejoiced and they took ropes and bound them up. Then they carried them down the valley and they would have Li K'uei go with them to seek the reward. And they reported to the guards of the city, and the guards and the captain of the guards all came to meet them, and they led them to a certain rich man's house, in his village which was called the village of the old lord Ch'ao.

Now this man was one who had a position in the county seat, and suddenly he had a little money and now he stayed in the village doing naught but making a brew of trouble and grasping all good for himself and making himself proud and pompous, and he boasted of mingling with certain small great men in order to frighten the common people. He loved to pass judgment on this one and on that one, and of who was a loyal statesman and who a filial son; but only his mouth spoke well and his heart was false.

Now this old lord Ch'ao himself came to receive the hunters and when they had met he would invite Li K'uei to come and be seated in the guest hall and he asked how it came about that the tigers were killed. Then Li K'uei explained how his mother had been athirst and how he had come to leave her and how it all happened as it did. Everyone was dazed and the old lord Ch'ao began to ask again, "Sir Brave, what is your surname and what your name?"

And Li K'uei answered, "I am surnamed Chang but I have no name. I am only called Chang The Brave."

And the old lord Ch'ao said, "And truly are you brave. If you had not known bravery, how could you have killed four tigers?"

Then he commanded wine and a feast to be prepared for their entertainment, and of this no more need be said.

Let it be told further. When it was known in the village that four tigers had been killed on the mountain and that they had been carried into the old lord Ch'ao's house then the noise of it went forth into hamlet and street and market and shop and there was uproar in the village both before and behind and even into the distant lonely houses. Grown man and little maid all came in numberless crowds to see the tigers, and they stared at the old lord Ch'ao feasting the hunters for these were in the hall drinking wine.

Now there was among the crowd the woman of that Li Kuei and she had hidden in her parents' home in the village ahead and she had followed the crowd to come and see the tiger. She recognized Li K'uei's face and in great haste she returned to her home and said to her father and mother, "This great black fellow who killed the tigers is the very one who killed my old man and burned my house. He is called The Black Whirlwind of the robbers' lair at Liang Shan P'o."

When her father and mother heard this they came in greatest haste to report it to the police guard, and the guard heard it and he said, "If he is truly The Black Whirlwind then is he Li K'uei of the village behind I Chou who has killed a man and who escaped to Chiang Chou. There again he did evil and a proclamation was sent here saying that the Emperor now offers three thousand pieces of silver to the one who captures him. And he has come hither!"

He sent someone then secretly to the old lord Ch'ao to ask him to come and talk. So the old lord excused himself to Li K'uei, saying, "I have a private business," and he went in all haste to the guard's house, and the guard said, "This strong man who killed the tigers is that one from the village behind the city and he is The Black Whirlwind Li K'uei. Now it is the imperial command that he is to be captured."

Then the old lord Ch'ao said, "You must find out whether it is true or not. If it is not he, he will be angered and evil will come of it. If it is truly he, then it is no trouble. If he is to be captured, it will be easy. But I do only fear it is not he and then it will be hard."

The guards answered, "But we have here Li Kuei's old wife who knows him, for he went to Li Kuei's house to seek for food to eat and he killed Li Kuei."

Then the old lord Ch'ao said, "If it is truly thus, then we will now do naught but set wine before him and let him drink, and we will ask him, 'Now that you have killed these tigers today do you want to go to the city court and ask for the reward or do you wish but for a little money here from the village?' If he is not willing to go to the city court to seek for the reward then truly is he The Black Whirlwind, and I will set men all about him to entice him to be drunken and we will bind him then and we will go and make report of it in the city, and have a captain of a hundred soldiers come and fetch him, and so can we not lose him."

Then they all cried, "You have spoken well."

So the guard made all ready and the old lord returned to entrap Li K'uei, and he had wine brought to pour out for him and he said, "Forgive me that I left you alone. I pray you now unfasten your dagger from your girdle and put your sword aside and sit at your ease a little while."

And Li K'uei said, "Well—well—but my dagger is thrust into the tigress's belly and I have but the sheath here. When you open the tigress I pray you return me the dagger."

The old lord Ch'ao said, "Let your heart rest. Whatever I have here in plenty it is good weapons and I think to present the brave one with one of these to wear."

So Li K'uei unfastened the empty sheath from his girdle and he took off his girdle and bundle and he gave them all to the villagers, and he set aside the sword. Then the old lord Ch'ao called out, "Bring hither a large plate of meat and a great jug of wine!"

Then the tiger killers, the guard, the hunters and all the others drank each in his turn and they pressed great bowls of wine upon Li K'uei and urged him to drink and again the old lord Ch'ao asked Li K'uei, saying, "I do not know whether the brave one wishes to take these tigers to the city court to seek reward or whether you will but ask for some money here."

Li K'uei answered, "I am but a traveler from hither to yon and I am somewhat pressed and I chanced to kill this den of tigers. I need not go and seek a reward at the court. If there is a little to be given here it will do me. If there is none, I will go my way also."

Then the old lord Ch'ao said, "How can I deceive the brave one? In a little while we shall have collected something from the village for you. We will then send the tigers ourselves to the court."

But Li K'uei said, "If you have a cloth coat, I will borrow one first so that I may change my upper garment."

The old lord Ch'ao said, "We have—we have—"

And he took out then and there a sky-blue short quilted coat of fine cloth and he gave it to Li K'uei that he might change the bloody garment upon his upper body. Just then drums were heard to beat and flutes to blow at the door and many came bringing wine to bestow upon Li K'uei, some with cold wine and some with hot.

Now Li K'uei did not know this was a plot and he opened up his heart and drank and was merry and he entirely forgot Sung Chiang's command. In less than four hours he was completely drunken and he could not so much as stand up.

Then they supported him into the inner hall and laid him down to sleep upon a bench. And they found two strands of rope and tied him to the bench, and they bade the guard to go as though he flew to make report at the city court, and they took with them Li Kuei's wife to be the first plaintiff and they added the written accusation also.

By this time the city was aroused and when the magistrate heard it he was terrified. In greatest haste he went into the Hall Of Judgment and he asked, "Where is The Black Whirlwind held? This man is a rebel and he must not be allowed to escape."

Then the plaintiff and the hunters answered, "He is now bound in the home of the old lord Ch'ao, because no one could come near him and we dared not bring him hither lest there be some mishap upon the way."

Then the magistrate straightway commanded a captain of the court, Li Yün, to come to the hall and he commanded him, saying, "Beneath the mountain of I Ning in the home of the Rich Man Ch'ao, The Black Whirlwind Li K'uei is bound. You may take a good number of men and bring him here secretly. Do not make a turmoil in the villages and countryside, and so let him escape."

Captain Li received this command and he came out of the hall. He counted out thirty soldiers who were guards and each took his weapons and they hastened then to the village by I Ning.

Now this city was but a small place and how could it be passed through secretly? By this time the streets were all aroused and everywhere people were saying, "They have captured that one who disturbed the country far and wide—The Black Whirlwind! Now they have sent Captain Li to bring him hither."

Now Chu Kuei was in the home of Chu Fu in the east village and he was outside when he heard this news. In greatest haste he went inside and said to his brother Chu Fu, "This black thing has made trouble again, and how shall I save him now? Sung Chiang, lest some such trouble arise, did especially send me here to listen for news of him. Now he is captured, and if I do not save him, how shall I return to the lair and see again my elder brother? And what is the best way now?"

Chu Fu said, "Elder Brother, pray do not be

in haste. This Captain Li has had the skill of a whole lifetime and even though there were thirty or fifty persons they could not come near him. Though you and I had the same heart and purpose, how could we come near him to withstand him? We must use guile to overcome him and not strength. Now Li Yün has commonly loved me very well and he used always to teach me how to wield weapons. But I have a way to manage him only I cannot rest here safely afterwards. Tonight I will cook twenty or thirty pounds of meat and prepare ten-odd bottles of wine. I will cut the meat into great pieces and I will mix a drug into it. Then at the fifth watch I will take some of my apprentices and we will take it half way upon the road to a lonely place and there wait for him. When he comes by guarding Li K'uei we will pretend it is wine to congratulate him and so will we drug them all. How is this for a way to free Li K'uei?"

Chu Kuei said, "It is a very excellent plan. But it must not be delayed. Let us prepare and go the earlier."

Chu Fu said, "The only thing is that Li Yün cannot drink wine, and even though we drug him he will surely wake early. And there is yet another thing. If later he knows it is I then surely shall I not be able to rest here in safety any more."

Chu Kuei answered, "Brother, and though you stay you cannot make much money at wine selling. It would be better to take your whole house and go with me up the mountain and there we will all be joined together. We weigh out our silver and gold upon scales and when we change our garments it is from the skin out. Will this not be happy for us all? Then call forth two apprentices tonight and find a cart and send out your wife and your best possessions and bid them wait for us at The Crossing Of Ten Roads and we will all go up the mountain. I have a package of drug here with me in my bundle. If Li Yün cannot drink wine then we will scatter the more into his meat and so compel him to eat and he too will fall down drugged. Then we will save Li K'uei and take him with us up the mountain. What is there about it that cannot be done?"

Chu Fu said, "Elder Brother, you have spoken truly. I will tell one to go and find a cart and I will tie up three or five bundles and take them upon the cart. I will throw away the coarser things in the house and I will tell the one I have wed and the children to get up into the cart and command two apprentices to go with the cart and just go on ahead."

Let it be told further. Chu Kuei and Chu Fu cooked the meat that night and cut it into great pieces and mixed the drug into it and together with the wine it made two loads. They took some twenty or thirty empty bowls. There were also many vegetable dishes into which they mixed the drug also, lest there be haply some who did not eat meat who would be entrapped also. Of the two loads of wine and meat the two apprentices each took a load and the two brothers carried comfit boxes. About the fourth watch they went to the lonely cross roads and sat there to wait for the dawn. In the distance they heard a gong beating. Chu Kuei went to the mouth of the road to wait.

As for those soldiers, they had drunk half a night's wine and at about the fourth watch they forced Li K'uei along, his hands bound behind his back and Captain Li sat upon his horse behind. As Chu Fu and Chu Kuei saw them thus approaching, Chu Fu went forward to stay them and he called out, "Teacher, we came especially to meet you in this great happy event so that we may dip into a bucket of wine together." And he poured out a great cup of wine and he besought Li Yün to drink.

Then Chu Kuei came supporting a plate of meat upon his palm and the apprentices so carried the vegetables also. When Li Yün saw this he leaped from his horse in great haste and he came forward and said, "Good Brother, why have you troubled yourself to meet me thus?"

Chu Fu replied, "It is but to show a little of the reverence I have for you in my heart."

So Li Yün received the wine and put it to his mouth but he did not drink it. Then Chu Fu kneeled down and said, "This lowly brother knows that his teacher does not drink wine. But today you must drink half a cup of this wine of gladness."

Li Yün could not refuse then and so he drank a few mouthfuls. Then Chu Fu said, "If the teacher will not drink wine then let him eat meat."

But Li Yün said, "I ate myself full in the night and I can eat no more now."

Then Chu Fu said, "The teacher has gone a long way and his belly must be hungry. Even though the meats be not fit to eat, yet eat a little anyhow and it will spare this lowly one shame."

And he chose two good pieces and presented them. Li Yün, seeing how earnest he was, could but force himself to eat the two pieces. Then Chu Fu brought wine and presented it to the old lord Ch'ao and to the guard to drink and to all the hunters and to the others. Thus besought, they each drank three bowls. Then Chu Fu bade the soldiers and the villagers all to come and drink wine. And such as these, what did they care whether the wine was hot or cold or whether it was good or not? When the meat and wine reached their mouths they did but eat it down and they ate it all clean, and as swiftly as the wind scatters fallen leaves or as flowing water carries away petals from dead flowers. They all crowded forward and seized what they could.

Li K'uei opened wide his eyes and stared at the two brothers, for he saw already what the plot was and he said wilfully, "Ask me to eat some, too!"

Then Chu Kuei shouted, saying, "You are but a fool! Can there be wine and meats for you to eat? Shut your mouth quickly, you who are to be killed!"

And Li Yün looked about on the soldiers and he shouted, "Go on quickly!"

Then were they seen one staring at the other and they could not walk. Their jaws trembled and their feet pricked and grew numb and they all fell down. Then Li Yün cried out in great agitation, "I am ruined!"

And even as he was about to rush forward, without knowing it he himself felt his head grow heavy and his feet grow light and he fell also and his body turned weak and he lay upon the ground.

Then did Chu Kuei and Chu Fu each seize a sword and with a shout, crying, "Children, go quickly!" the two took up the swords and pursued such of the villagers as had not eaten of the wine and meats and all who looked on. The ones who went fast escaped but such as went slowly were stabbed and fell upon the ground. And Li K'uei gave a great shout, and he burst apart the hempen rope that bound him. He seized a sword then and came to kill Li Yün. But Chu Fu made haste to stay him and he said, "Do not behave without law! He is my teacher and he is the best among men. Do you but go ahead."

Then Li K'uei answered, saying, "If I do not kill this old ass, the old lord Ch'ao, then how will I rid myself of my rage?"

And Li K'uei rushed ahead and lifted his sword and he first killed the old lord Ch'ao and Li Kuei's wife. Then he killed the guard also. By now his anger was high in him and he stabbed one after the other and every hunter he stabbed. Then he killed all of the thirty-odd soldiers. Then all those who watched and the villagers did but curse that their parents had given them only two feet apiece at birth and they all fled into the wild small paths. As for Li K'uei, he still searched for someone to kill until Chu Kuei shouted, saying, "It has naught to do with those who look on! Do not seek only to kill men!" and in great haste he stayed Li K'uei. Only then would Li K'uei put down his hand and he took from the bodies of soldiers a couple of garments to wear.

Then the three bearing their swords were about to go by certain small paths. But Chu Fu said, "It is not well. It is as though I had killed my teacher. When he wakes, how can he appear before the magistrate? He will surely pursue us. Do you two go on first and I will wait awhile for him. I do think of his goodness when he taught me and of how faithful he is. I will wait until he pursues us and then I will ask him to come with us and join us. Then this will be my gratitude to him and it will save him the bitterness of his return."

And Chu Kuei said, "Brother, you see very rightly, too. I will go on with the carts. Li K'uei shall stay beside the road and help you to wait for him. If he does not pursue, then do not linger foolishly."

Chu Fu said, "That is of course."

Therefore Chu Kuei went on ahead.

Let it be told now only of Chu Fu and Li K'uei. They sat on beside the road and waited. Before two hours had passed they saw Li Yün bearing a sword coming as though winged and he cried out mightily, saying, "Robbers, you are not to go!"

Li K'uei, seeing him come so fiercely, leaped up and took his sword to fight fearing lest Li Yün injure Chu Fu. Because of this

In the robbers' lair there were two tigers more,
In the Hall was joy, for the new heroes four.

As The Black Whirlwind fought thus with The Blue Eyed Tiger, which was victor and which vanquished? Pray hear it told in the next chapter.

Chapter 43

THE FIVE HUED LEOPARD MEETS TAI CHUNG UPON A BYPATH. YANG HSIUNG MEETS SHIH HSIU UPON A MARKET STREET

IT IS SAID: At that time Li K'uei bearing his sword came to fight Li Yün and they fought there by the highway for five or seven rounds, and it could not be told who was victor and who vanquished. Then Chu Fu took his sword and putting it between the two he divided them and he cried, "Pray fight no more, but hearken to what I have to say!" Then the two stayed their hands and Chu Fu said, "Teacher, I pray you, hear me. I have received unworthily your affection and you did teach me how to use the staff, and it is not that I do not thank you for your grace. But it is that my elder brother Chu Kuei is now a chief in the mountain lair in Liang Shan P'o and he received the command of The Opportune Rain, Sung Chiang, who told him to come and watch over this brother Li, and we did not dream he would be taken by you, and so how could my elder brother go back to meet Sung Chiang? Therefore did we lay this plot, and even now when the brother Li would have taken the opportunity to try to kill you it was I, your younger brother, who would not let him put forth his hand, and so he killed only the soldiers. By this time we should be far on our way but I guessed that you could not return and that you must come to pursue me. And I did think also of the kindness which you have ever given me and so I thought to wait here for you. Teacher, you are one who understands all, and what is there you do not know? Now are there many men killed and The Black Whirlwind is escaped also, and how can you return and face the magistrate? If you go back, in truth you will be put into gaol and there will be no one to think to come and save you. Better it is that you go with us up the mountain and there join with Sung Chiang. I do not know what you, Honored One, do think of this."

Li Yün thought to himself awhile and then he answered, "Good Brother, I do but fear they will not have me there."

But Chu Fu laughed and he said, "Teacher, how is it you do not know the great name of The Opportune Rain, Sung Chiang? He loves above all else to receive those in need and to help all good fellows under Heaven."

When Li Yün heard this he sighed and he said, "You have so injured me that although I have a home I may not return to it; although I have a country I may not remain in it. I am glad only that I have no wife nor child and do not fear the magistrate will seize them. I can but go with you."

Then Li K'uei laughed and cried, "My Elder Brother, why did you not say it sooner?" And he fell down and made obeisance.

Now this Li Yün was without family and without home and so he joined these three and they went after the carts. And Chu Kuei met them half way and he was greatly rejoiced and the four good fellows went with the carts and on their way.

There is naught to tell of the journey. As they saw the robbers' lair coming gradually nearer they met upon the road Ma Ling and Chen T'ien

Shou and they all greeted each other and they said, "The two chieftains Ch'ao and Sung did send us two to come down the mountain to hear news of you. Now we have seen you and we will go ahead and make report."

So the pair went up the mountain first to make report and on the next day the four good fellows bringing Chu Fu's household all met in the great hall. And Chu Kuei went forward leading with him Li Yün to make obeisance before the two chieftains Ch'ao and Sung and to meet with all the good fellows and he said, "This man is a captain of I Suei and his surname is Li and his name is Yün and his nickname is The Blue Eyed Tiger."

After this Chu Kuei led forward his brother to make obeisance to all and he said, "This is my brother Chu Fu and his nickname is The Smiling Faced Tiger."

And they all greeted each other. Then Li K'uei made obeisance to Sung Chiang and was given back his two axes, and he told them the history of the false Li Kuei and everyone laughed loudly. Then he told the story of killing the tigers and how his mother was eaten by them, and when he told it his tears streamed. But Sung Chiang laughed loudly and he said, "And you killed four fierce tigers! And have we added today to our lair two live tigers! Then we ought to congratulate each other."

So all the good fellows were mightily rejoiced, and it was commanded that cows be butchered and horses killed and a feast be made in honor of the newly come chiefs, and Ch'ao Kai told the two of them to go and sit above Pei Sheng. And Wu Yung said, "Now will our lair grow very perfect in greatness and all the brave fellows everywhere will come to us when they hear of it, and it is all because of these two elder brothers Ch'ao Kai and Sung Chiang, and it is the happiness of us all. Although it is thus, yet let us still let Chu Kuei have his wine shop that Shih Yung and Hou Chien may return hither. As for the household of Chu Fu, let a house be set apart for them. Now is our lair a great one and it is not as it has been in the past. Let us therefore open three more wine shops that they may listen and hear what comes of good or ill, and escort all brave fellows up the mountain. If the Emperor sends soldiers out to capture the robbers they may tell us of it and how the soldiers do approach so that we may be early prepared. The land to the west lies in a broad plain; let us therefore bid the brothers T'ung Wei and T'ung Meng to take some ten-odd helpers to go there and open a shop. And let us bid Li Li to take some men and go to the south of the mountain and open a wine shop there. And let us bid Shih Yung take some helpers also and go to the north of the mountain and there open a wine shop. Then let us set up pavilions everywhere in the water from which we may let fly our arrows and let there be boats hidden everywhere by every shore. If there be a war whether urgent or not they can come as though winged to make report. In front of the lair let there be three guard gates built and Tu Ch'ien shall be in command of these, and he is not to be sent forth on any mission at all, nor shall he leave that place from dawn to dark or dark to dawn. Then let T'ao Chung Wang be in command of all enterprises of labor, whether to dig ditches large and small or to mend stream beds or to open canals or to repair the wall of the lair or to mend the large road. He is one used to labor on the land and he is accustomed to such labor. As for Chang Ch'ing, let him be in command of all the treasure and the grain stores and whether these are to be received or dispensed, and let him account for it by hundreds and by thousands written down, and bid Siao Jang prepare all both within and without the lair, both upon and beneath the mountain and the guarding of the three gates of the pass and all the sending and receiving of commands and letters and the ranking of all the chiefs high and low. And let Ching Ta Chien see to all cutting on stone and carving of signs and seals and tables. Then let Hou Chien control cloth and robing and the making of garments of war and the five flags of the directions. Let Li Yün see to the building of all houses in the lair, whether large or small. Let Ma Ling oversee the repairing and building of all ships of battle, both great and small. Let Sung Wan and Pei Sheng go and build themselves a shelter on The Golden Sands and live there as guards. Let Wang The Dwarf Tiger and Chen T'ien Shou go to guard the beach called The Duck's Bill. Let Mu Ch'un and Chu Fu govern the rents of the land on the mountain. Lü Fang and Kao

Shen shall live in two small rooms on either side of the Hall Of Meeting. Let Sung Ch'ing alone see to the feasts."

Thus were all duties set and made fixed and they feasted for three days and of this no more need be told.

Now for a while there was nothing that befell them in the robbers' lair, except that every day the men and the horses were drilled and taught in the feints and postures of war and the chieftains of the water lair taught men how to manage ships and to swim and do all such things as are done upon and in the water and they taught them how to do battle on ships. Of this also no more need be told.

Now upon a certain day Sung Chiang and Ch'ao Kai and Wu Yung were talking idly among the others and suddenly one said, "We who are brothers are all here together this day except that we have not seen Kung Sun Sheng return hither. I thought he did make a vow with us when he went to Chi Chou to seek his mother and teacher that he would return in an hundred days. But many days have passed now and we have no tidings of him. Perhaps he has changed his purpose. Let us ask our brother Tai Chung to go once and see and hear the truth about him and where he is and why he does not come."

And Tai Chung was willing to go and Sung Chiang was very glad and he said, "It is this good brother who will go most quickly. In ten days we may have tidings of him."

On that day Tai Chung bade farewell to them all and he put on the garb of a servant and he left the robbers' lair and wended his way to Chi Chou, having first tied his four magic letters upon his legs so that he could take his magic strides. Upon the road he ate only tea and vegetable dishes and he was three days upon his way when he came to the city of I Suei. There he heard men say, "The other day The Black Whirlwind escaped after he had mortally hurt many a man and he injured the captain Li Yün and we do not know whither he went and he has not been found even to this day."

Tai Chung, hearing this, smiled a chill smile.

On that day even as he was upon his way he saw a man in the far distance turning to come toward him. In his hand the man carried a weapon straight as the handle of a pen and made wholly of iron. The man, seeing how fast Tai Chung went, stayed his feet and cried out, "Mighty Messenger Of The Magic Strides."

Tai Chung, hearing it, turned his face about and when he stared fixedly he saw upon the slope of the mountain beside a narrow path a great tall fellow standing. His head was round and his ears were large, his nose was straight, his mouth was square, his eyebrows were finely marked and his eyes were wide set, his waist was narrow and his shoulders were broad. In haste Tai Chung turned himself about and asked, saying, "Noble Sir, I have never met you before and how is it you know my poor name?"

In haste that fellow replied, "Sir, surely you must be Tai Of The Magic Strides." And he threw aside his weapon and fell down in obeisance upon the ground. Quickly Tai Chung lifted him up again and returning his courtesy he asked, "Noble Sir, what is your high name and your great surname?"

That fellow answered, "Your younger brother is surnamed Yang and named Ling and my ancestors were men of Chang Tê Fu and we have ever been robbers and men of the woods. Far and wide by river and lake men call me The Five Hued Leopard. A few months ago in a wine shop beside the road I saw the teacher Kung Sun Sheng. He drank wine with me there and visited me in the wine shop and he told me all concerning Ch'ao Kai and Sung Chiang and of how they do receive all good fellows from everywhere and how they are thus full of loving kindness toward their friends. He wrote a letter and he told me to come and join with them also. But I did not dare to go thither so boldly. Then the teacher Kung Sun Sheng said again, 'At the mouth of the road to the Li homestead Chu Kuei has a wine shop and there he receives such as do wish to go up the mountain to join the robbers. In the lair there is a chief who can go as though winged and he is called The Magic Messenger. In a day he can go between two and three hundred miles.' "

"Now I saw you, my Elder Brother, walking with no usual steps, and so I called out once to try you who you were for I did not think all of a sudden I might have such heavenly good fortune."

Then Tai Chung said, "I am going on a purpose to find our brother Kung Sun Sheng, for since he went we have heard nothing of him and I am now fulfilling the orders of our two chieftains Ch'ao Kai and Sung Chiang who have sent me to Chi Chou to spy out and listen after news and to seek out Kung Sun Sheng and invite him to return to the lair. I did not dream I might meet you, Noble Sir."

And Yang Ling said, "I, this younger brother, although I am a man of Chang Tê Fu, am yet under the governorship of Chi Chou and I have traveled about in all this region. If you do not despise me I will go with you, my Elder Brother, for the once."

And Tai Chung said, "If I can have you, Noble Sir, for my comrade, then am I fortunate a thousand times. If we do find the teacher Kung Sun Sheng we can go back together to the mountain lair and it will not be too late."

Yang Ling hearing this said, was much rejoiced and he asked that Tai Chung stand to him as his elder brother-friend. And Tai Chung took off his magic letters and the two went slowly on together, and when night came they turned aside to a wayside inn and there rested.

And Yang Ling would have a feast prepared for Tai Chung but Tai Chung said, "When I use my magic I dare not eat meat."

Then they both bought vegetable dishes and each invited the other. When the night was passed they rose early the next day and lit a fire and ate their early meal and they prepared all to set forth again upon their journey. Then Yang Ling asked, "Elder Brother, you use magic to go your way, and how can I keep pace with you? I do but fear I may not go with you."

Tai Chung answered, smiling, "But I can take men with me in my magic. I will put two magic letters upon your legs and I will use my magic and you can go as quickly as I. When we will to go we shall go, and when we will to stop we may stop. If we do not thus, how can you keep pace with me indeed?"

But Yang Ling said again, "I do fear I am a common and an earthy man and I can not compare my body to your godlike person."

Tai Chung replied, "It matters nothing. Any man may use this magic of mine. When it is used then he is the same as I am. Only I do eat no meat and so no trouble comes of the magic."

Then he fetched two magic symbols and tied them upon Yang Ling's legs and Tai Chung wore two also. When he had said the magic rhyme he blew upon the pictures and the two went lightly away and whether they went swiftly or slowly was according to Tai Chung's will.

Now the two of them talked as they went of matters far and wide by river and lake, and although they went along slowly yet they did not know how far they went. They went until midmorning and they came to a place about which on all four sides were high mountains through which the highway passed. Now Yang Ling knew this place and he said then to Tai Chung, "Elder Brother, this is called The Stream For Watering Horses, and in that high mountain ahead there are constantly great bands of robbers. I do not know how it is today. But the mountain is beautiful and the stream winds about one ridge after the other—and it is called by that name."

The two had but come to the side of the mountain when they heard the sudden sound of a gong beaten and the thudding of drums rose in confusion from all sides. And there came forth a hundred or two robbers who blocked the road and at their head were two good fellows. Each carried a sword and they cried in a mighty shout, "Let the travelers stay their feet! What cursed men are you two? Whither do you go? Let such as have understanding quickly bring forth money to buy their right of way! Then only will your two lives be spared."

But Yang Ling laughed and he said, "Elder Brother, watch me go and kill that fool!"

And he took his iron weapon and he charged forward. Those two good fellows seeing how fiercely he came, came on also and they looked at him. Suddenly the first one called loudly, saying, "Do not put forth your hand! Is it not Elder Brother Yang Ling?"

Yang Ling stayed his hand and only then did he know who this was. That first great fellow carrying his weapon downward came forward and made obeisance and then he called the other tall fellow to come and make obeisance likewise. Yang Ling asked Tai Chung to come near and said, "Brother, pray come hither and meet these two brothers."

And Tai Chung asked, saying, "But who are these two braves and how is it they know you, Good Brother?"

Then Yang Ling answered, "This good fellow who knows me, your younger brother, is a man of the city of Siang Yang Fu in the province of Hupei. His surname is Teng and his name is Fei. Because his two eyes are so red he is called by men far and wide The Red Eyed Lion and he can use an iron chain as weapon. No one dares come near him. We were once joined together, but we have been apart now these five years and we have not seen each other face to face. Who would have thought that today we would have met here!"

Then Teng Fei asked, saying, "Elder Brother Yang Ling, who is this honorable one? Surely he is no common man."

And Yang Ling said, "This brother of mine is one of the good fellows in the mountain lair at Liang Shan P'o, and he is Tai Chung The Magic Messenger."

Teng Fei, hearing this, said, "Is he not the head gaoler of Chiang Chou who can go near upon three hundred miles in a single day?"

And Tai Chung answered, "This lowly one is he."

Then those two chiefs made haste to give obeisance and they said, "For many a day have we but heard your great name, and we did not think this day to give reverence in your honorable presence."

Tai Chung then asked, saying, "What is the noble surname and high name of this brave fellow?"

Teng Fei replied, "This younger brother of mine is surnamed Meng K'an. His ancestors were men of Chen Ting Chou, and they have ever had great skill in building ships both great and small. Because it was commanded to bring the flowers and stones of the south to the capital city, he was greatly angered with the one in charge who forced him by every means at his labor, and he was so angered he killed the officer. He left his home then and he escaped to the robbers in the woods and hills and now several years have passed. Because he is so tall and large and the skin on his body so fair and unblemished when men see all his good flesh they have made a name for him and it is The Jade Banner Pole, Meng K'an."

Tai Chung, hearing this, was very pleased and as these four good fellows talked Yang Ling asked, saying, "How long have you two elder brothers lived here?"

Teng Fei said, "I will not deceive you, my Elder Brother, and I will say that we have lived here more than a year. But half a year ago we met an elder brother toward the west of here, whose surname was Pei and his name Hsüan, whose ancestors were men of the capital. He was a scribe in his own city and he could write very well in legal matters, and he was a man of honest heart and clever mind, nor would he take the least personal advantage in anything. Men called him The Iron Faced. He could also use weapon and staff and arrow and knife and his wisdom and his ability were complete. But because the Emperor appointed a certain greedy official to come there as magistrate, who sought for a way to arrest him and brand him and send him into exile, he passed by me here. I killed the guards who were with him and so saved him and here he has rested. We have now gathered together some two or three hundred men. This Pei Hsüan is most clever of all in using the double-edged dagger. We reverence him because he is the eldest of us and he is the chief of our lair. Now do we ask you two noble ones to come for a while into our lowly lair."

Then he called the robbers to lead horses thither. Tai Chung and Yang Ling took off the magic letters from their legs and mounted the horses and went toward the lair. They had not gone for long when they came to the front of the lair, and they dismounted. Now Pei Hsüan had already received word of their coming and in great haste he came out of the lair and came down to meet them. Tai Chung and Yang Ling, as they looked at Pei Hsüan, saw that indeed he was a very fine handsome man. His face was fair and his body large and fat and he stood stable and in good proportion, and they were secretly pleased with him. Pei Hsüan invited the two good men to come into the Hall Of Meeting. When they had all performed the rites of courtesy, he wished to invite Tai Chung to take the seat of honor, and beneath him were Yang Ling, Pei Hsüan, Teng Fei, Meng K'an, these five good fellows, and they all invited one another to drink.

As they sat at the feast table they drank and listened to the music of many instruments, and Tai Chung told of Ch'ao Kai and Sung Chiang, how they received all good fellows there and how they did righteously and despised gain, and how all those good fellows were of one mind and one strength and how great were the many miles of the mountain lair, and how strong and beautiful was the city in its midst, and how on all four sides were mighty waters, and how there were so many men and horses there that the imperial soldiers never came against them. All this he said, hoping to influence these three.

Then Pei Hsüan answered, saying, "This younger brother has also a lair and I also have more than three hundred horses and of treasure I have some ten-odd carts full. Carts, food, and fuel I do not count in this. I have also some three to five hundred lesser ones under me. If you, my Brothers, will not despise us as too lowly, then lead us to join that greater lair. Yet we have but a little strength of our own to give there, and I do not know what you think of it."

Tai Chung answered in great joy, "Ch'ao Kai and Sung Chiang have ever the same heart to all, whether high or low, and if now they have such noble ones as you to aid them it will be as though flowers were set upon gold already fair. If you do truly have this purpose then I pray you make ready your goods and wait until this lowly one and Yang Ling return from Chi Chou and have seen the teacher Kung Sun Sheng and brought him with us. Then let us go together, pretending that we are imperial soldiers and go by day and night thither."

Then were all made greatly glad and they drank until they were near drunkenness and they went into the pavilion at the back of the mountain, called The Pavilion Of Unity, and there they drank wine and looked at the view. They exclaimed at the beauty and Tai Chung and Yang Ling said, "How secret and deep are the recesses of the hills, how winding the streams, how fair a hiding place for many!—But how did you two come hither?"

Then Teng Fei said, "At first there were but a few wretched small robbers who lived together. Then we two came and seized this place."

And they all laughed loudly and the five good fellows drank themselves into a mighty drunkenness and as they drank Pei Hsüan who played with the magic dagger before them helped them in their drinking. Tai Chung cried out in praise without ceasing, and that night they slept in the lair.

On the next day Tai Chung would fain go down the mountain with Yang Ling, and the three good fellows could not stay them with the bitterest entreaty. They escorted them down the mountain therefore, and there they parted, and returned to the lair to prepare their goods and make all ready to start upon their journey. Of this no more need be told.

Let it now be told how Tai Chung and Yang Ling left the lair by The Stream For Watering Horses and they went their way by the light of the sun and rested by night. Soon they had come outside the city of Chi Chou where they went to an inn and there slept. Then Yang Ling said, "Elder Brother, I think the teacher Kung Sun Sheng is one who learns Taoism, and surely he must be in a wood upon some mountain side."

Tai Chung said, "You have spoken truly."

Then the two went outside the city and everywhere they went asking for news of the teacher Kung Sun Sheng, but there was not one who knew of him. They stayed for a day and the next morning they rose early and they went to distant villages and hamlets and asked of him and again there was not one who knew of him. Again they returned to the inn and slept and the third day Tai Chung said, "It may be there are those in the city who know him."

On that day therefore he went with Yang Ling into the city of Chi Chou to seek Kung Sun Sheng. They asked all the old dwellers in the city and everyone answered, "We do not know him. It must be he is no man of this city. Perhaps he is living in some famous mountain or temple outside the city."

Now Yang Ling came to a certain large street and in the distance he saw musicians coming and with drums and gongs they escorted someone. As Tai Chung and Yang Ling stood there in the

YANG HSIUNG MEETS SHIH HSIU UPON A MARKET STREET

street to watch, they saw at the head of these two small prison guards, and one of these bore upon his back a great load of gifts and flowers of paper and silk, while the other carried much satin and many hued embroideries. Behind them was carried a green silk umbrella and beneath this sat a head gaoler who was also a headsman. This man was of a fine handsome person, and upon his flesh there were patterns tattooed in blue. His eyebrows were long and spread across his temples and his eyes, turned to Heaven, were shaped and narrow as the eyes of a phœnix. The skin of his face was a pale yellow in hue, and he had a scanty, fine beard. Now this man's ancestors were men of Honan, and his surname was Yang and his name Hsiung and he had come with a paternal cousin to Chi Chou as magistrate. From then until now he had lived in Chi Chou. Later a new magistrate came who knew him, however. Therefore the new magistrate appointed him to the headship of the two gaols and he was also the headsman in all beheadings. Because he was skilled in the use of all weapons and because the color of his face was so yellow, he was called The Sick Kuan So Yang Hsiung.

As Yang Hsiung thus walked along, behind him was a small official of the gaol who grasped a thick, sharp, devilish, beheading knife. Yang Hsiung was, indeed, on his way home from a beheading, and all his friends were thus escorting him homeward, and he was decked in red and flowers of congratulation, and he passed just before the faces of Yang Ling and Tai Chung. All along the way people stopped him and poured out wine for him to drink.

Suddenly seven or eight soldiers were seen to rush out of an alleyway. The one at the head was called Kicked The Sheep To Death Chang Pao. This fellow was one who guarded the city wall of Chi Chou, and these whom he led were constantly the ne'er-do-wells who asked money of this man or that inside and outside the city, and in spite of punishment from the captain they changed no whit. When it was seen that Yang Hsiung was a man foreign to the city who had come from other parts, and there were those who feared him, Chang Pao grew jealous. On that day, perceiving how Yang Hsiung received all the gifts of satin, Chang Pao led out these dare devil men of his who were besides half drunken, and they were all about to rush forward to anger Yang Hsiung. But seeing how many people surrounded Yang Hsiung and poured out wine for him to drink, Chang Pao divided the crowd and charged to his presence and shouted out, "Head Gaoler, I make obeisance!"

Yang Hsiung said, "Elder Brother, come and drink wine."

Chang Pao said, "I will not drink wine. I have come here on purpose to ask you for a hundred-odd pieces of silver to use."

Yang Hsiung said, "Although I know you, we have had no affair of money between us. How is it you do ask me to borrow money?"

Chang Pao said, "Today have you cheated the people of much of their money and goods, and why will you not lend me some of it?"

Yang Hsiung answered, saying, "This was all given to me in honor by other persons. How can it be said I have deceived the people? You come here seeking to make trouble. You are of the soldiery, I am before the magistrate, and we have naught to do with each other."

Chang Pao would not answer, but he commanded his men to charge forward and they first seized the decorations and the satins. Yang Hsiung shouted out, "How lawless are these!" He was just about to move forward to attack those who robbed him, when Chang Pao seized his bosom. Two came behind him at the same instant and seized his hands. Then they all bestirred themselves, and all the small gaolers who had been with Yang Hsiung hid themselves.

Yang Hsiung was thus held fast by Chang Pao and the two soldiers and he could not use his skill. He could but hold back his wrath, for with all his struggle he could not shake them off. In the midst of this turmoil a great tall fellow was seen carrying a load of grass there. When he saw them thus holding Yang Hsiung fast, so that he could not move, when that tall fellow saw this, and how uneven was the path of justice here, he put down his load of grass and dividing the crowd he came forward to exhort, saying, "Why is it you thus hold this gaoler?"

Then did Chang Pao open wide his eyes and he shouted, saying, "You back-beaten, starved and will not die, frozen and will not die beggar, how dare you come into what is none of your business?"

Then was that tall fellow in a great rage and his anger rose up in him. He lifted Chang Pao up by the knot of his hair and in one swing had thrown him to the ground. Then those who had come with Chang Pao seeing what was come about were about to put forth their hands but the tall fellow with blows of his right arm and his left had already knocked them east and west.

Only then was Yang Hsiung free, and only then could he show what his skill was. His hands went back and forth like weavers' shuttles and those several rascals were all laid upon the ground. And Chang Pao, seeing the road did not lie clear before him, crawled up and straightway ran off, but Yang Hsiung filled with wrath strode after him in great steps. Chang Pao went with those who had seized the goods and Yang Hsiung pursued him from the rear and followed him into an alley. But that tall fellow still did not stay his hands. He searched there in the mouth of the alley for men to strike. Tai Chung and Yang Ling, seeing this, secretly cried out, saying, "Truly is he a good fellow! Truly is he one who when the path of justice is not smooth seizes his knife to kill the oppressor!"

Then they went forward and laid hold on him and they exhorted him, saying, "Good Fellow, consider our poor presence and pray cease."

The two of them led him, exhorting as they went, into a side street, and Yang Ling carried his load for him, while Tai Chung led him by the hand and they went thus into an inn. There Yang Ling set down his load and they all went together into a corner, and the tall fellow clasped his hands together and said, "I do thank you, my two Elder Brothers, that you have saved me from some curse."

And Tai Chung said, "We two brother-friends are also men from outer parts. Because we saw your merciful heart, Brave One, we feared that you might use too heavily the strength of your hand and arm and so without meaning it kill someone. So did we, therefore, come out for your sake. Pray, Brave One, drink three cups with us that here we may bind ourselves together in brother-friendship."

That tall fellow said, "I have received richly of your kindness, my Merciful Brothers, and you have this time delivered me and besides this you have given me wine. Truly it should not be so."

Then Yang Ling said, "About the four seas all men are brothers, and how is it you do speak thus? Pray sit down."

And Tai Chung thought to give place to him, but how could that fellow be willing to take the higher seat? So Tai Chung and the others sat down, and the tall fellow sat opposite. A serving man was called and Yang Ling brought forth some silver from his person and gave it to the man, saying, "You need not ask us what we wish. If you have good meats then bring them and we will buy. We will pay for all together at the end."

The serving man took the silver and he spread forth meat, fruits, and all such things as send the wine down well. When the three men had drunk several cups, Tai Chung asked, saying, "Brave One, what is your noble surname and your high name? Where lives your honored house?"

That man answered, saying, "This lowly one is surnamed Shih and named Hsiu. My ancestors live in Chin Ling, the southern capital. From my childhood I have learned the ways of weapons and all my life have I determined that if I saw the path of justice not smooth, I would go forth to help. For this men have called me The One Who Heeds Not His Life. I came here with my uncle to sell horses and sheep. But I did not dream that when we had gone half our journey my uncle would die and our capital thus be lost, so that I could not return to my home and so I came by chance to this city of Chi Chou. Here I have sold fuel grass for a living. Since you have shown me your friendship I must tell you the truth."

Then Tai Chung said, "We two came hither for a certain purpose, and we have seen how far above all others you are. But how can you rise selling grass for a living? Better it will be to go fearlessly out upon river and lake and seek happiness for the latter half of your life."

Shih Hsiu asked, "This lowly one can but wield a few weapons and I have no other skill and how can I rise and how can I be happy?"

Tai Chung answered, "These are no true good times. The Emperor is veiled from all righteous men, and traitors do their secret work. I have a plan that because of an anger in me I shall go and join Sung Chiang at the mountain lair.

There the silver and gold is weighed in great scales and when garments are changed it is throughout from head to foot. There let us wait until the Emperor calls us forth for our country. Sooner or later must we all be officials."

Then Shih Hsiu drew in his breath and he said, "This lowly one has even been about to go, but there was no way whereby I could enter."

Tai Chung replied, "If the brave one is willing to go, then will I send you thither."

Then Shih Hsiu asked, "This lowly one dares not to ask, but in all reverence what is the noble surname of you two?"

And Tai Chung answered, "This lowly one is surnamed Tai and named Chung. My brother is surnamed Yang and named Ling."

Shih Hsiu said, "I have heard it said by river and lake that there is one mighty to save, surnamed Tai. Is it indeed the noble one present?"

Tai Chung said, "This lowly one is he."

He then bade Yang Ling to bring forth from the bundle beside him a ten-ounce piece of silver to give to Shih Hsiu for capital. Shih Hsiu did not dare to receive it, and only when it had been urged upon him with many courtesies, was he willing at last to take it, and only then did he know this was Tai Chung of the robbers' lair.

Now as they were about to speak of things of their hearts and of how he was to be sent to join the lair, they heard someone seeking and asking outside. When the three of them looked to see, it was Yang Hsiung leading some twenty men, all of whom were court runners, and they hastened into the wine shop. Tai Chung and Yang Ling, when they saw how many were there, gave a start of fear, and they took advantage of the uproar to depart secretly. But Shih Hsiu went forward to meet them and said, "Sir Gaoler, whither do you go?"

And Yang Hsiung said, "Elder Brother, where have I not sought you? And here you are, drinking wine! In that moment of carelessness I was bound by that thing and I could not show forth my strength and how richly did I receive of your strength, Noble Sir, to save me! How greatly have I gained! At that moment I was all for pursuing those things and seizing their bundles and I left you. But all these brothers hearing that I was fighting there all came to help me, and they went and robbed back for me all the satins and silks and embroidered flowers and all I lost. Only we could not find you, Noble Sir. Only now did one say, 'Two guests did beg him to go to the wine shop to drink wine,' and only then did I know to come here especially to seek you."

And Shih Hsiu said, "These were just now but travelers by the way and they invited me to come here to drink three bowls of wine, and to talk together a little idle talk, and I did not know you were seeking me so urgently."

Then Yang Hsiung was overjoyed and he asked, saying, "Noble Sir, what is your high surname and your great name? Where is your honored place of residence? And why are you here?"

Shih Hsiu answered, saying, "This lowly one is surnamed Shih and named Hsiu, and my ancestors were men of Chin Ling, and the purpose of my life has been that if the path of justice was not smooth I would go and give my life to help those in distress. For all this do men call me The One Who Heeds Not His Life. I came hither with my uncle to buy and sell horses and sheep, and I did not dream that my uncle would die upon the journey and lose our capital, and I wander about this city of Chi Chou and sell fuel grass for a living."

Yang Hsiung again asked, "And whither have the two guests gone who did but now drink wine with you, Noble Sir?"

Shih Hsiu answered, "The two of them seeing you bring in men thought you came to make some trouble for them, and for this they have gone."

Yang Hsiung said, "If it is so, then bid the serving men bring two jars of wine hither and a great bowl and pour out thrice for every man. We will drink first and then go our way. Tomorrow I will come and again meet with you."

Then did everyone drink wine and they all parted. And Yang Hsiung said, "Shih Hsiu, do not treat me as a stranger. I do believe that surely you have no relatives here. Then what think you if I swear bond to you today as brother-friend?"

Shih Hsiu, hearing this said, was filled with joy, and he said, "I do not dare to ask how many honorable years have been yours."

Yang Hsiung said, "This year I am twenty-nine years old."

Shih Hsiu said, "This younger brother is

twenty-eight years old this year. Pray sit down, Sir Gaoler, and receive the obeisances of a younger brother."

Then Shih Hsiu made four obeisances, and Yang Hsiung was filled with a mighty joy. He called the serving man to prepare wines and meats and fruits, saying, "This day will I drink me into a mighty drunkenness with my brother before I am done."

Now even as they were in the midst of their drinking they saw Yang Hsiung's father-in-law, the old man P'an, and he came bringing five or seven persons and they came seeking straight to the wine shop. Yang Hsiung, seeing them, rose up and said, "Father-in-law, why have you come?"

The old man P'an replied, "I heard you were fighting with some men, and I came especially to find you."

Yang Hsiung said, "Thank this brother, then, for he saved me and he beat that Chang Pao so that he was frightened even to look on my shadow. Now I do acknowledge this one surnamed Shih to be my brother-friend."

The old man P'an cried out, "Good, good! Pray let these several brothers I have brought here drink a bowl of wine and then go."

So Yang Hsiung bade the serving man fetch wine there and each man drank three bowls before he went. Then the old man P'an was asked to sit in the center, Yang Hsiung sat in the upper side seat, Shih Hsiu in the lower side seat. When the three were seated, the serving man came himself to pour wine for them. When the old man P'an saw Shih Hsiu, how tall and large a hero he was, he was truly pleased in his heart and he said, "It is no vain thing that my son-in-law has such an one as you for brother-friend, for who now will dare to deceive him as he comes and goes out of the court? What business and way of life did you follow before this?"

Shih Hsiu replied, "My departed father was a pig butcher."

The old man P'an said, "And do you then understand the killing of these animals?"

Shih Hsiu laughed and said, "From my childhood did I eat the fare of an apprentice, and how then could it be that I do not know how to kill a beast?"

The old man P'an said, "This old man who am I was also once a butcher, but because I am so old I cannot do it any more. I have no one except this son-in-law and he has gone into the court, and so I have laid aside this livelihood."

These three drank until they were about drunken and then they reckoned the money. Shih Hsiu gave his grass for money and Yang Hsiung paid what was left. Then the three followed the road and returned, and Yang Hsiung entered his door and shouted, "Goodwife! Come quickly here and see this brother-in-law of yours."

Then an answer came from behind a curtain, saying, "Sir, what brother have you?"

Yang Hsiung said, "You need not ask. Come out and see first."

The cloth curtain was put aside then and the woman came out. Now this was a very lucky woman, born on the seventh day of the seventh month of the year. Because of this her name was Ch'ao Yün. At first she had been wed to a scribe in the court, a man of Chi Chou, whose name was Wang The Scribe. But he had died two years before, and then she was wed to Yang Hsiung, and they had not been man and wife a year yet. Shih Hsiu, seeing the woman come forth, in great haste went forward to bow and he said, "Sister-in-law, pray be seated."

Then he made obeisance to her. And the woman said, "I am but a slave and young in years. How dare I receive your obeisance?"

Yang Hsiung said, "This is my brother-friend, newly sworn today. You are his sister-in-law, and you may receive a lesser obeisance."

Then did Shih Hsiu lower his person and his jadelike head and he made obeisance four times. The woman returned two, and she invited them to come and be seated within. Then she prepared an empty room and told her brother-in-law to rest there.

But the tale must not be told in tiresome detail. On the next day Yang Hsiung went out and he went before the magistrate for instructions. And he commanded his wife, saying, "See to Shih Hsiu's clothing and hat. Bring the goods he has at the inn."

This Yang Hsiung's wife did.

Let it be told then how Tai Chung and Yang Ling, having seen the court runners in the wine shop coming to find Shih Hsiu, took advantage of the turmoil to go away and they returned to the inn outside the city to rest. The next day they went to seek for Kung Sun Sheng for two days, but there was not one who knew him, nor did they know where he lived. The two took counsel together then that they would return.

On that day they arranged all their goods and they took their departure from Chi Chou, and they went to The Stream For Watering Horses and together with Pei Hsüan, Teng Fei and all their men and horses, pretending they were imperial soldiers, they went by night and day to the robbers' lair.

Tai Chung wished to show forth his glory and he combined all the men and horses and he led them up the mountain. And a feast of welcome was made there in the mountain lair, and of this no more need be said.

Again it is said:

Now the old man P'an, who was Yang Hsiung's father-in-law, talked with Shih Hsiu of how they might open a butcher's shop, and the old man said, "At the back gate of my home there is a little blind alley, and in the back of this there is an empty room in a house. There is a well near there, too, where we can have a chopping place. If you lived there, Elder Brother, you could manage the whole place."

Hearing this, Shih Hsiu was pleased enough, and he asked the old man P'an to find a former helper of his to aid him. And the old man said, "I do but ask you to see to the accounts."

This Shih Hsiu promised, and the assistant was called, and they took bright green and sky-blue paint and they painted the tables and the tubs and the chopping blocks and they had many knives made and sharpened. When the tables were thus prepared they made ready the pig pens and the butchering places, and they chose out some ten-odd fat hogs and chose a lucky day and they opened their meat shop. All their relatives and neighbors came bringing decorations and congratulations and they drank wine together for a day or two. The whole household of Yang Hsiung were all rejoiced that they had secured Shih Hsiu to open such a shop. Of this no more need be told, for from this time on the old man P'an and Shih Hsiu did their business together, and without their knowing it the time passed quickly on.

When more than two months had gone and autumn was finished and winter was upon them Shih Hsiu had new clothes from his skin out to put upon himself.

One morning Shih Hsiu rose early in the fifth watch and he went to another city to sell pigs, and he did not return home for three days. And on his return he saw the shop was not open. When he went within to see, he saw all the tables and chopping blocks taken away and knives and utensils gone.

Now Shih Hsiu was a man of good understanding and when he thought the thing over he comprehended it all very well. To himself he said, "The proverb says, 'There are not a thousand days of good fortune for any man, nor can a flower be red for a hundred days.' My elder brother goes out every day to the courts and pays no heed to home affairs. Surely my sister-in-law, seeing these new clothes I have now, has said evil things behind my back. When I did not return for two days there have been those who opened their mouths and stirred their tongues against me so that they doubted me and would do no more business. I will not wait until they begin to talk to me. I will first bid them farewell and return to my home. From ancient times it has been said, 'Where can a man of constant heart be found?' "

Then Shih Hsiu drove the pigs into the pen and going into his room he changed his garments, and put together his goods and possessions. And he wrote a very careful account and came in from the back of the house.

Now the old man P'an had already prepared a meal of vegetables and he asked Shih Hsiu to seat himself down and eat. Then the old man P'an said, "Brother-in-law, you have traveled far and suffered much and you have taken the trouble to drive the pigs all this distance yourself."

Shih Hsiu replied, "Father, this is no more than I ought to do. Pray first receive this account. If there be a penny written falsely there, then let Heaven strike me and Earth destroy me."

But the old man P'an asked, "Brother-in-law, why do you speak such words as these? There is naught between us."

Shih Hsiu said, "This lowly one has now left his home for five or seven years. Now I do think to return once more, and so have I on a purpose given this account to you, and tonight I wish to bid my elder brother farewell and tomorrow morning I shall go on my way."

The old man P'an heard this and he laughed loudly and said, "Brother-in-law, you are mistaken. Stay yourself now. Listen to what this old man says."

Now what the old man said was but a few words and he did speak but a short time. Because of this,

The avenging hero took in hand his three-foot blade,
The faithless priest, the eight vows broken, lay dead in the ninth shade.

What words then did the old man P'an speak? Pray hear it told in the next chapter.

Chapter 44

YANG HSIUNG IN DRUNKENNESS CURSES HIS WIFE.
SHIH HSIU BY HIS GUILE KILLS P'EI JU HAI

IT IS SAID: Shih Hsiu returned and seeing the shop closed was about to depart and go out, when the old man P'an said, "Brother-in-law, you have not returned for two nights. Today you are come home. You see everything put away. Surely, you think the shop is no longer to be opened, and for this you wish to go away. But even though we had not this good business yet could we keep you at home. I will not deceive you when I say this daughter of mine was first the wife of a scribe surnamed Wang. His life was ended and two years ago he died. We are making a ceremonial of remembrance for him, and it is for this we have ceased business for these two days. Tomorrow we have invited the abbot of The Temple Of Gratitude to come here and chant the rites. Now I do pray you to manage this all for me. I am an old man and my years are many and I cannot sit awake through the night. For this especially do I tell you all this."

To this Shih Hsiu replied, "If it is as you say, Father-in-law, I will press my purpose into my heart awhile and stay a few days more."

And the old man P'an said, "Brother-in-law, from this time you are not to doubt me. Only do each duty as it comes."

When they had then drunk a few cups of wine and eaten some vegetable dishes it need not be told how the things were cleared away. The next morning the servants of the priests were seen bringing the sacred books and hangings. When the decorations were hung the image of the god was set up and all the vessels of worship, the drum, the cymbals, the bell, the gong, incense, flowers, lamps, candles, were placed in order. In the kitchen vegetable dishes were prepared.

By this time Yang Hsiung had but just returned and he commanded Shih Hsiu, saying, "Good Brother, I must tonight sleep on guard in the gaol, and I cannot come hither. I have to ask you to help me in everything."

Then Shih Hsiu answered, "Elder Brother, only let your heart be at rest and go on. Assuredly will your younger brother do all for you."

And Yang Hsiung went, therefore, and Shih Hsiu stood there by the door to see to all. Now at this hour dawn was but clearly come, and a young priest was seen to draw aside the curtain and enter, and he made a deep priestly bow to Shih Hsiu.

Shih Hsiu bowed in return and he said, "Teacher, seat yourself for a while."

And a serving man followed the priest who bore two boxes and came near. Then Shih Hsiu called, "Father-in-law! There is a teacher here."

The old man P'an heard this and he came out from an inner room, and the priest asked him,

"Foster-father, why is it you have not come for so long to our humble temple?"

The old man answered, "I have newly opened this shop and I have no time to go out."

Then the priest said, "On this day of remembrance for the one dead I have no good gifts to bring. I have but a little of these noodles and a few packages of honey dates."

The old man said, "Ho-yah, and what is this? Why has the teacher so wasted his substance?"

And he bade Shih Hsiu to receive the gifts, and Shih Hsiu took them away, and he commanded tea to be poured inside and brought out and there he asked the priest to drink tea.

Then the woman was seen to come down the stairs from the upper floor. She did not dare to wear the deepest mourning; she wore some pale-hued garment and she had smoothed a little red upon her face. Then she asked, "Brother-in-law, who sent the gifts here?"

And Shih Hsiu answered, "A priest who called your father-in-law foster-father brought them."

Then that woman laughed and said, "It was my priest-brother, that most lofty one, P'ei Ju Hai—a good and honorable priest! He was once the manager of a shop for silken threads and he renounced the world in The Temple Of Gratitude. His abbot was one of my own household and so in reverence he calls my father foster-father. He is older than I by two years and so I call him brother priest. His priestly name is Hai Kung. Brother-in-law, when night comes, do you listen to him when he prays to the gods and sings and hear how fine a good voice he has!"

Then Shih Hsiu answered, "If indeed it is thus—" but in his heart he had already perceived a tenth of the affair.

So the woman came down the stair and she went to see the priest and Shih Hsiu forked his hands behind his back and went out behind her, and he hid behind the curtain and peeped out, and he saw the woman go outside. The priest rose and came forward and he put his two palms together and made a deep priestly bow. Then the woman asked, "And why should you do this? Why have you wasted your money, Brother Priest?"

The priest replied, "Good Sister, so small a thing as this need not hang upon the teeth in words."

But that woman said again, "Brother Priest, and why do you speak like this? How can we receive and use the gifts of holy priests?"

The priest said, "We have now built our Hall Of Land And Water and I have long desired to come hither and invite you, my Good Sister, to go there and take your pleasure as you please. I did but fear your lord might be displeased."

That woman said, "But I think my lord would not thus restrain me. When my mother died she was doomed to lie in a bloody pool in hell, because she died in childbirth, and I long hoped to have the chants sung for her that may free her from it. I made my vow and I shall come soon to the temple to ask you to fulfill it for me."

The priest said, "This is an affair of my own house, and why do you use all this courtesy to speak of it? Whatever you wish to command me, I will but go and do it."

So that woman said, "Brother Priest, then read a few more chants for my mother and it will be well for her."

Now a slave was seen to come from within bearing tea, and the woman took up a bowl of the tea and with her sleeve she wiped the brim of it and with both hands she presented it to the priest. With both hands he received it, and his two longing eyes stared into the woman's eyes, and the woman's two eyes, smiling and bright, did fasten themselves upon the priest's eyes, and their lust spread to the heavens. But they did not know that Shih Hsiu had already seen them from behind the curtains. Now he had seen two parts of the evil, and he said to himself, "Even among the virtuous there is lack of virtue; even among the charitable there is dearth of charity. I have seen that woman some several times and she does ever speak as though at play with me. But I have treated her as my own sister-in-law, although she is of no virtue. Yet whatever you two do, do not come against Shih Hsiu's hand lest I strike a stroke for Yang Hsiung. I cannot be sure!"

As Shih Hsiu thus thought to himself, he had guessed three parts of what was amiss and he jerked aside the curtain and rushed out. That thievish priest in greatest haste put down his tea bowl and said, "Sir, pray seat yourself."

And the adulteress interrupted and said, "This brother-in-law is the brother-friend of my lord."

Then the priest asked Shih Hsiu in an even, polite voice, "Sir, where is your noble village, your honored home? What is your high name, your revered surname?"

Shih Hsiu replied, "I? My surname is Shih and my name is Hsiu and I am a man of Chin Ling. Because I want to do good and work for others, I am also called The One Who Heeds Not His Life. I am but a rude fellow. If I offend you, Priest, you are not to blame me."

The priest answered in haste, "I would not dare—I would not dare—I must go and call the other priests hither."

Still in haste he made ready to go away. The adulteress called, "Brother Priest, return soon!"

But the priest in haste made no answer. So the adulteress escorted the priest outside the gate and then she went alone into the house. And Shih Hsiu sat there outside the door and pondered to himself, and now in his heart he had guessed four parts of what was wrong.

After a long time he saw the priest's serving man come and light candles and incense. In a short time the thievish priest returned leading all the priests and they all came there, and the old man asked Shih Hsiu to greet them and welcome them with tea. When the tea was drunk the drums and cymbals began to beat and their voices rose in a chorus of chant. Then was this thievish priest seen to take the leadership with a young priest of his own age and they began to ring the bell and they burned the written prayers to invite the presence of the god. And sacrifices were set forth also for all the protecting gods of all the universe, and the accepted fulfillment of the vow from the hostess for her ancestor, so that the dead man, The Scribe Wang, might be sent the earlier and the more speedily to the highest Heaven.

Then that adulteress was seen, dressed in garments of dull hue and with no ornament in her hair, coming to this hall where the chanting was. She held a censer in her hand and holding it she chanted and worshiped the god. Then the thievish priest showed forth more than ever his arrogant behavior and he rang the bell and chanted loudly. All the priests seeing the woman sitting shoulder to shoulder with the priest, swaying back and forth, and how vile a thing it was to see, were all in a confusion. When the vow had been sealed between the woman who was hostess and the priest who performed the cermony of remembrance for her, all the priests were invited to go within and eat of the vegetable feast.

Now the thievish priest let all the other priests go first, and he turned his head about and looking at the adulteress he laughed. The adulteress covered her mouth with her hand and laughed also. Then these two let their glances fly, and by their glances they sent their love back and forth, and Shih Hsiu saw it all. Now was he more than five parts angered in his heart.

When they had all seated themselves at the vegetable feast they drank first several cups of a vegetable wine and then the feast was brought on, and an extra fee was given to each priest. After awhile the old man P'an begged pardon of all and he went out to his rest, and later when the priests had finished their eating they all rose also and went out to walk about. When they had made a few turns they came back to the room of chanting.

Now Shih Hsiu was ill at ease, for now indeed did he comprehend six parts, and so he said to the others, "Ah, I have a pain in my belly!" And he went alone and laid himself down behind the partition in the main room of the house.

But the adulteress had already loosed some of her lust and how could she heed whether any saw her or not? She went hither and thither. The priests beat the drum and the cymbals, and again they began their chanting. Fruits and cakes were brought out. The thievish priest adjured them to chant with all their hearts and bow their heads and pray the King Of Heaven to come down and they scattered water and called for the spirit of the dead and they made obeisance before the three great chief images. Thus they did until the third watch. Then were they all weary.

But the wicked priest showed forth all the more of his energy. In a loud voice he chanted on.

Now the adulteress stood for a long time behind the cloth curtain, and the fire of her lusts burned more fiercely than ever, and without her knowing it her heart was stirred, and she called a slave to ask the teacher Hai Kung to come and speak with her. Then the thievish priest, chanting as he walked, came to the side of the adulteress. And the adulteress laid hold on his long sleeve and she said, "Brother Priest, come hither tomorrow to get your fee, and pray speak then to my father concerning my mother's soul and do not forget it."

The wicked priest answered, "I who am your elder brother will remember. If a vow is to be made before the gods, it should be made now." And again that wicked priest spoke and he said, "Yet how fierce this brother-in-law of your house is!"

But the adulteress shook her head and said, "And why should any heed be paid to such as that! He is not of our own bones and flesh."

So the wicked priest said, "If it is so, then can I let my heart rest."

Thus speaking he put his hand forth out of his sleeve and pinched the hand of the adulteress and the adulteress in pretended modesty drew the curtain between them. The wicked priest gave a laugh and went out alone to the room of chanting to bid the dead man's souls depart once more. Neither of them knew that Shih Hsiu was behind the partition, in a false sleep, and that he saw it. By now he knew seven parts of it all.

That night in the fifth watch the chanting was finished, and the paper money was burned and the god taken home. All the priests gave thanks and returned. That adulteress went upstairs and to sleep. But Shih Hsiu, pondering to himself, was angered and he said, "As fine a brave man as my elder brother is, and how hateful a thing it is that he has chanced upon this adulteress for wife!"

Yet he had to suppress his whole belly filled with wrath and he could but go also to his room and sleep.

On the next day Yang Hsiung came home and no one told him a word, and after he had eaten he went out again. Then was that wicked priest seen to come once more, and he had changed to a fine clean robe and he entered the home of the old man P'an. The adulteress, hearing the priest was come, came down stairs in great haste and went out to meet him. She invited him to come and sit within and she called out that tea was to be brought. And she thanked him, saying, "We did weary you much, my Brother Priest, with the chanting in the night. Nor have I given you the money yet for the chanting."

The wicked priest answered, "It need not so much as pass your teeth, so small a thing as this. What I said last night concerning the rites for your mother's soul I have come especially humbly to explain to you, learned and virtuous sister. If you do indeed wish to make the vow and have the rites, then you need only to write what you wish and our priests will chant."

Then the adulteress said, "Good—good!"

In great haste, then, she called the slave to invite her father to come and discuss the matter. And the old man P'an came out and he thanked the priest also and he said, "So old a man as I cannot do without my sleep, and I do ask your pardon that in the night I could not watch with you. Nor did I think that Shih Hsiu would need to take to his bed because of pain in his belly, so there was left no one to look after your entertainment. But pray forgive me—forgive me!"

The wicked priest replied, "Foster-father, you ought to take a little ease."

Then the adulteress said to the old man, "I do desire to take a vow to release my mother's soul from its bloody pool. Our brother priest says that tomorrow the temple is to perform such ceremonials, and we can put our share in them also. We will ask this brother priest to go first and begin the chants and tomorrow you and I will go to the temple after we have eaten and there set our seal to the directions for the vow. Then will this duty which is before us be accomplished."

And the old man P'an said, "Well enough, too. Only I do fear that tomorrow business will be too good, and there will be no one to mind the counter."

But the adulteress said, "There is our brother-in-law Shih at home to see to it, and so what have you to fear?"

Then the old man P'an said, "My child, whatever comes out of your mouth before a god is a vow. You must go tomorrow."

So the adulteress brought out some silver to be fee for the chanting of the day before and she gave it to the wicked priest, saying, "Again I must trouble my brother priest not to reproach me that I gave too little silver. Tomorrow I will assuredly come to the temple and ask you for some of your vegetable noodles."

And the wicked priest said, "I will take care

to wait for you to come and burn incense." And he received the silver and, rising, he thanked her, saying, "I do greatly thank you for this silver I have received. I will take it and divide it among all the priests. Tomorrow I will do nothing but wait for you, learned and virtuous sister!"

The woman then escorted the priest outside the gate. Shih Hsiu had been sleeping in the chopping room of the shop but now he was up to kill the pigs and do business. On this day Yang Hsiung did not return until night, and the woman waited until he had eaten his night meal and had washed his hands and feet. Then she asked the old man P'an to speak to Yang Hsiung and he said, "When my wife died this daughter of mine made a vow for her at The Temple Of Gratitude. Tomorrow I will go with my daughter to that place to fulfill the vow and then we will return. I tell you that you may know of it."

But Yang Hsiung asked, "Goodwife, why did you not tell me of it yourself, and what would it have mattered?"

That woman replied, "I was afraid if I told you you might be angry with me, and for this I did not dare to tell you."

There was no more said that night and each went to his rest.

On the next day at the fifth watch Yang Hsiung arose and he went to the court and signed his name as having come and he made himself busy for the magistrate. And Shih Hsiu arose also and he went about his business in the shop. Then was the adulteress seen to rise. She combed her hair and bound her feet freshly and she washed her neck and scented her garments. And her slave Ying Er arose and sought for the box of incense and hurried the morning meal.

The old man P'an rose also and he bought paper money and candles and called for sedan chairs. But Shih Hsiu did naught the whole morning but mind the shop and he did not come to pay any heed to all this. After they had eaten the morning meal, the slave Ying Er made herself clean also and at the mid-morning hour, in the fourth watch, the old man P'an changed all his garments and he came and said to Shih Hsiu, "I must trouble you, Brother-in-law, to watch the gate. I and my daughter go to fulfill a vow and then we will return."

Shih Hsiu laughed and said, "And of course I will watch the gate! Do you, old Father-in-law, look well after my sister-in-law, and take care to burn very good incense! And return soon!"

By now he had guessed eight parts of the evil to come.

Let it now be told of the old man P'an and the slave Ying Er running beside the chairs. They came to The Temple Of Gratitude, and there the wicked priest was already at the temple gate waiting. When he saw the chairs were come, he was secretly glad but he said not a word. He went forward to meet them and the old man P'an said, "Truly have we again put you to trouble, Sir Priest."

And the adulteress came down out of her chair and she also thanked him, saying, "Again have we put brother priest to great trouble."

But the wicked priest answered, "I do not presume—I do not presume—I have been already with the others in the Hall of Ceremonial. We have been up since the fifth watch chanting and they chant even until now without rest. We have but been waiting until you came, Good Sister, to fulfill your vow. This deed will bring you great merit," and he led the woman and the old man into the Hall of Ceremonial.

There lamps and candles and incense and embroideries were already set forth and there were some ten-odd priests chanting. The adulteress made an obeisance to each priest and she knocked her head before each of the three chief gods. Then the wicked priest led them before a certain god of shades, and there they knocked their heads on the ground and announced their repentance, and when the paper of announcement had been read before the god by a priest the paper was burned to ashes. Then the priests were invited to go and eat a vegetable meal, and a young acolyte was sent to go with the priests.

That wicked priest, however, asked that his good sister and his foster-father go into his own lowly room to eat, and he led the adulteress into a distant inner room where all had been prepared long before, and he called to another priest to bring tea thither. Then two serving priests were seen bringing tea. The cups were of the finest white ware and the saucers were scarlet, and the tea was of the very finest leaf. When they had drunk they put their bowls down, and the priest asked his good sister to go and sit within and he led her still further into a little corner of a room. There was a black, low table highly polished, above which were hung a few sayings and pictures of famous men. Upon the table burned an urn of good incense. The old man P'an and his daughter sat down on one bench. The wicked priest sat opposite, and the slave stood to one side.

And that adulteress said, "Brother Priest, how fine a place is this for one who has renounced the world! Ordered, silent, clean, happy!"

But the wicked priest answered, "My Sister, do not laugh at me. How can this compare to your palace?"

The old man P'an said, "Truly have we put you to a whole day's trouble. Let us go back."

But how could the wicked priest be willing for this? He said then, "It is not easy to persuade you hither, my Foster-father, nor are you a stranger. Moreover, the priests' feast we eat today was given to us by this good sister, and why do you not eat of it before you go? Brother," and he called to a priest, "bring the food hither quickly!"

Before he had finished speaking the tray of dishes was brought in. They were all such as were kept for occasions, unusual fruits and special dishes and every sort of vegetable dainty, and they filled a table. Then the adulteress said, "Brother Priest, why do you have a feast? The order is turned about and we instead of helping are making trouble for you."

But the wicked priest replied, "This does express only in the very least my poor friendship. Brother Priest, bring wine hither and fill the cups!" And again he said, "Foster-father, for long have you not come. Taste this wine."

When the old man had drunk of it he said, "Good wine—indeed how strong and heavy a taste it has!"

The wicked priest said, "One day there was one from the home of one of our patrons who taught us how to make it. We have already used three to five hundred pounds of rice to make this wine. Tomorrow I will send several bottles to your honored son-in-law to drink."

The old man said, "And for what reason is this?"

Again the wicked priest exhorted him, saying, "But I have no other way in which I can thank my sister, this goodwife. At least, drink a cup of wine, I pray!"

Then the two acolytes did one after the other pour out wine and they even persuaded the little slave to drink several cups of wine. At last the adulteress said, "Stay the wine. We can drink no more."

But the wicked priest said, "It is hard to persuade the goodwife to come here. Pray drink one more cup!"

And the old man P'an called the chair bearers to come and to each was given a cup of wine, but the wicked priest said, "Foster-father, you need not be anxious. I have already given directions for everything. We have already asked the serving priests to invite them to feast outside. They have a place elsewhere to eat noodles and to drink wine. Let your heart rest, my Foster-father. Pray loose your heart and drink a few more cups."

Now the wicked priest had of special purpose prepared for the woman this good strong wine. As for the old man P'an, being so pressed, he did drink a few cups more than he usually took, and these he could not withstand, so that he became drunken. Then the priest said to the acolytes, "Support my foster-father to the bed and let him sleep awhile."

Thus he bade the two of them to support the old man, and they put him into a quiet cool room to sleep alone. Then the priest exhorted the woman, saying, "Goodwife, open your heart and drink another cup."

Now in the first place the woman's heart was already turned to the priest, and in the second place, the wine had entered the seat of her lusts and she felt a sort of dreamy confusion rise in her. She muttered vaguely, "Brother Priest, why do you only keep begging me to drink wine?"

Then the wicked priest told her in a low small voice, "I have no other purpose, Goodwife, except that I do respect and love you."

But the adulteress said, "As for the wine, I can have no more of it."

The wicked priest said, "Pray let the goodwife go into my room and see the tooth of a god I have there."

Then the adulteress said, "I came really to see the tooth of that god."

So the wicked priest led that adulteress, and, leading, he led her into an upper room. It was indeed that wicked priest's own sleeping room. The bed was spread very neatly and cleanly. When the adulteress saw this she was already more than half pleased and she said, "How nice a room have you, indeed—so clean and fresh!"

At this the wicked priest laughed and he said, "It does but lack a goodwife."

Then the adulteress laughed also and she said, "And are there none for you to go and find?"

The wicked priest said, "But where can I find such a lay-sister as this?"

The adulteress said, "Let me see the tooth of the god first."

And the wicked priest said, "Bid the little slave to go downstairs and I will bring it out."

Then the adulteress said to the slave Ying Er, "Go downstairs, I pray you, and see if the old father is awake or not."

So the little slave went down the stairs alone, and she went to see the old man P'an and the wicked priest closed the door of the stair. Then the adulteress laughed and said, "Brother Priest, what are you doing that you shut me in here?"

Now was the lusty heart of the priest all aflame and he went to the woman and embraced her and he said, "I do love and long for you with all my heart—I have planned for this with all my heart for two years! It has been hard indeed to get you here this day. So good a chance I pray you fulfill my hopes, then!"

But the adulteress said, "But my old man is no good man to anger. If you have deceived me hither for this and if he knows of it indeed he will not forgive you."

Then the wicked priest knelt down and he said, "But I do implore you to have pity on me."

Then that adulteress stretched out her hand to him and she said, "You cursed priest, how you do know how to wheedle a woman! I will just use all my strength on that cheek of yours."

But the wicked priest giggled and he said, "I will bear your blows, Goodwife! I do but fear you will wound your hand!"

Now the lusts of the adulteress were stirred also and so she embraced the priest also and she lifted him up, saying, "And could I ever truly strike you!"

Then the wicked priest embraced the adulteress and leading her to the bed, he unfastened her girdle and so fulfilled the desire of his heart. After a long time only were they finished with each other. Then the wicked priest held the adulteress once more and he said, "If you have such a heart of love for me, even though I die for it, I will fear no revenge. Fortunate it is that today you have fulfilled my hopes so that I have this short time of mutual love. Yet I cannot be happy like this a whole night long, and longing must fill me until I shall die of it."

Then the adulteress said, "Pray do not be in such haste. I have already thought of a plan. My husband every month must sleep twenty nights in the gaol. I will bribe the little slave and bid her to wait every day at the back gate. If that night he is surely not to be at home, then I will have her bring out a censer of incense and burn it for a sign. Then you may come and it will matter nothing. But I only fear you will sleep past the fifth watch in the morning and you will not wake. Where can we find a priest who calls for the morning chants that we may bribe him to come to our back door and there beat his drum loudly as though to call to prayer? Then could you go out easily. If you bribe one like this he could on the one hand watch and on the other hand see that you did not lose your chance to get away at dawn."

The wicked priest listened to this and he was very pleased and he said, "Praise be indeed! Do you only carry this plan out, for I have an unshaven priest here named Hu The Taoist. I will command him to come and stand on guard and there will be an end of it."

Then the adulteress said, "I do not dare to linger here too long, lest someone suspects me. It will be better if I return quickly now. But do not delay in carrying out our troth."

Then that adulteress rose in haste and ordered her hair and painted and powdered her face afresh and she opened the door to the stair and went down and she called to the slave to wake the old man P'an and in great haste she came out of the priest's room. The chair bearers had eaten their noodles and wine and were already waiting at the door of the temple. The wicked priest escorted the adulteress straight outside the gate of the temple. There the adulteress took her farewell and went into her chair and she returned home with the old man P'an and the slave. Of this there is no more to be said.

Let it be told further. This wicked priest went himself to find the Taoist priest. There had once been such a man in their temple who was named Hu The Taoist and he had now retired to a solitary cell at the back of the temple and there he lived alone. Everyone called him Hu The Monk. Each morning he rose in the fifth watch and struck the wooden drum until dawn exhorting people to the Buddhist prayers. At dawn he went about to people's houses begging for food. The wicked priest called him to come to his room and there he had prepared three cups of good wine to entertain him. He brought out silver also and gave it to him. Then Hu The Monk rose and said, "This lowly one, your pupil, has no merit before you. How dare I then receive this bounty from you? I have always received of your grace."

The wicked priest answered, "I have but seen that you are an honest man, and sooner or later I shall bring out some silver and buy you a certificate of priesthood that you may shave your head and become true priest. This silver here you are to take now and buy clothes to wear."

Now this wicked priest had often told his acolytes to take some of the good noon meal and give to the monk, and at times of special feasts he had commanded them to lead him with them to read the special chants so that he might receive of the money given for the rites and Hu The Monk was very grateful for this favor. To himself now he thought, "Today he has given me more silver, and it must be he has some place to use me. Why should I wait until he opens his mouth?" So aloud he said, "Teacher, if there is any work you have for me to do, I will go at once to do it."

Then the wicked priest said, "Hu The Monk, if you speak thus out of so good a heart, I will not deceive you. The daughter of the old man P'an wants to have intercourse with me. We have made a covenant that if a table is put for incense at the back door, it is to call me there. But it is hard for me to run back and forth thither; if you go there first and see if the table is there or not, then I can go. Also must I trouble you to rise at the fifth watch, and when you go forth to call men to their prayers, then come there to the back gate. If you see no one is there, then beat your drum heartily and call aloud that dawn is come, and in a loud voice call upon the Buddha. Then can I come out easily."

Hu The Monk replied, "And what hardship is there in this?" And so at that time he gave his promise. On the next day he went to the gate of the old man P'an and begged for priest's food. There he saw the slave Ying Er come forth and say, "You monk, why do you not come and beg for your food at the front gate? No, here you are at the back gate."

Then the monk began to murmur his prayers and the adulteress within heard him and she came out to the back gate and asked, saying, "You monk, are you not the one who comes and calls at the fifth watch before dawn?"

The monk answered, saying, "This humble priest is indeed that one who comes and calls at the fifth watch and exhorts men to shorten their sleep and also to burn incense at evening. Thus are the gods pleased."

The adulteress heard this and she was glad and she told the little slave to go upstairs and find a string of cash to give him. As soon as he saw the girl had turned to go away, he said to the adulteress, "I am one who does trust to the Teacher Hai and he sent me hither especially to see first how the road lay."

And the adulteress answered, "I know this already. Tonight you may come and see. If there is an incense table outside, you may go back and tell him of it."

Hu The Monk nodded his head and Ying Er brought the copper cash and gave them to him. Then the adulteress went upstairs and she told what was in her heart to Ying Er.

As for a lowly slave, if she can reap a little benefit from it, how can she refuse her mistress?

Let it now be told further. This day was exactly the day when Yang Hsiung had to go and sleep at the gaol and before night came he brought out his bedding and went to the gaol to rest. Ying Er could scarcely wait for the night to fall. She went early to set forth the incense table and at twilight she moved it outside the back gate. The woman hid herself beside the door and waited. At the beginning of the night she saw a man wearing a head kerchief come running in. Ying Er gave a start of fright and called out, "Who is it?"

But the man made no answer. Then the adulteress reached out and took the kerchief from his head, and there shone forth a shaven head and she scolded him in love, saying, "You cursed priest! What a clever trick is this!"

Then the two of them embracing each other went upstairs and Ying Er went and brought back the incense table, and she closed the back gate and she also went to her sleep.

Those two throughout that night were together like glue and like paint, like sugar and like honey, melted together like oil and oil, as fish are to the water. And in their joy they had their intercourse some five or seven times. But even as they had fallen into good sleep they heard the clatter of the wooden drum and a loud voice exhorting to prayer and the wicked priest and the adulteress woke together. And the wicked priest drawing on his clothes rose and said, "I must go. Tonight we will hope to meet again."

The adulteress said, "From now on if there is the incense table outside you cannot but keep your covenant and come. If there is no table at the back gate you must not come by any means."

And the wicked priest came down from the bed and the adulteress put on his head kerchief for him. Ying Er opened the back gate for him, and with a rush he was gone. From the beginning at this time whenever Yang Hsiung went to the gaol, the wicked priest came to his house. As for the old monk, when it was not night, yet he was asleep. And this slave, Ying Er, slept with the woman and grew like her. Only Shih Hsiu was told nothing.

Now the lusts of the adulteress rose in her and what cared she for aught else? The wicked priest had by now learned also the taste of a woman and it was as though all day long she held his souls and his seven spirits and left him dazed. He could but wait until the monk brought his message when he left his temple and came to this place. The adulteress had Ying Er to do for her, and she let her go out and come in. Because of this, the merriment and the byplay and the lewdness increased during more than a month.

Let it be told now of Shih Hsiu. Every day he had tended the shop and at night he closed the door, and he slept there upon the counter and he was continually anxious because of this affair. Every day he could not let his heart rest, although he never saw this wicked priest come. Yet every day he woke at the fifth watch and he leaped up from his bed and pondered upon the matter. He only heard the monk come and beat his drum and call loudly for prayers. Now Shih Hsiu was a clever tricky fellow and he had soon guessed nine parts of the matter. When he was alone he pondered and thought to himself, "But this alley is a blind one. Why should this priest come here day after day and beat his drum for prayers? This makes me suspect something."

Now these were the middle ten days of the twelfth month of the year and it was the fifth watch of the day. Shih Hsiu could not sleep. He heard the clatter of the wooden drum. The priest beat his way into the alley and when he had come to the back gate he called in a loud voice, saying, "Pray for all living things! Pray to every god who saves us from bitterness and from distress!"

Shih Hsiu, listening, thought the call had a strange sound and he jumped down and went to the crack of the door and looked through. Then he saw a man with a kerchief on his head come dashing out of the black shadow and go away with the monk. Afterwards Ying Er closed the door. Now Shih Hsiu had guessed ten parts and he was angry and he thought in his heart, "How noble a man is my elder brother Yang Hsiung and he has got this adulteress! This female has deceived him, and she has gone and committed such a crime as this!"

When dawn was come he hung the carcasses of the pigs up at the front of the shop ready for the early morning trade. When this was done, he went about and collected such moneys as were owing to him. At about the hour of noon he went to the bridge in front of the court where Yang Hsiung worked. He had come just about to the side of the bridge when he met Yang Hsiung and Yang Hsiung asked him, saying, "Brother, from whence have you come and whither do you go?"

Shih Hsiu answered, "I have been out seeking such debts as are owing me, and so I came by to see my elder brother."

Yang Hsiung said, "I have been always busy with the affairs of the magistrate and I have not had time to go and make merry and drink wine with you, my Brother. Pray come hither and sit for a while."

And Yang Hsiung led Shih Hsiu to a wine shop on the bridge and they found a peaceful corner and there the two sat down. He bade the serving man to bring a bottle of good wine and to set forth meats and foods from the sea and such things as are eaten to send down wine. When the two had drunk three cups, Yang Hsiung saw that Shih Hsiu hung his head and thought of something to himself. Now Yang Hsiung was a man of impatient temper and he asked, saying, "Brother, you have something sad in your heart. Has there been some rumor at home that has wounded you?"

Shih Hsiu replied, "There has been nothing said at home. But I do look upon you, my Elder Brother, as my own flesh and bones. There is something—dare I tell it?"

Then Yang Hsiung asked, "Brother, why do you hold me to be a stranger this day? Whatever you have to say, say on, and it is nothing."

So Shih Hsiu said, "Elder Brother, every day that you come away in truth you do not know what goes on behind your back. This sister-in-law of mine is not a good woman. I have seen it many times with my own eyes, but all this time I have not dared to tell you. Today I saw it very clearly and I could bear it no longer. Therefore did I come to seek my elder brother. If I speak straightly, do not blame me."

Then Yang Hsiung said, "Assuredly I have no eyes in my back. Speak out who it is."

And Shih Hsiu said again, "Some time ago when there were rites in our house we asked that wicked priest Hai to come, and my sister-in-law spoke with him through eyes and brows. I saw it all. On the third day she went to the temple to fulfill the vow she made for her mother dead in childbirth. The two of them, the old man and she, came back drunk with wine. These several days I have heard a monk come into the alley to beat his wooden drum and call for prayers, yet he did beat very strangely. Today at the fifth watch, therefore, I rose and peeped through the crack of the door and I saw that indeed it was that wicked bald-headed priest, a kerchief wrapped about his head. He came out from our house and went away. Such an adulteress as this —and why should you want her?"

When Yang Hsiung heard this he was in a mighty wrath and he said, "How dare this worthless one behave thus?"

And Shih Hsiu said again, "Elder Brother, pray cease your wrath. Do not mention the matter tonight, but act as you do every day. Tomorrow say you must go again to the gaol and after the third watch come and knock at the gate. That thing will assuredly first run through the back gate, and I will seize him in a grasp and bring him and then you shall do with him as you please."

And Yang Hsiung said, "Brother, you have seen well."

Again Shih Hsiu directed, saying, "Elder Brother, you are not to speak foolishly tonight."

Yang Hsiung answered, "I will make a covenant with you for tomorrow and there is an end of it."

The two then drank several cups more of wine and paid their money for it and went down the stairs together and when they had gone out of the wine shop each was about to go his own way.

Then suddenly four or five guards were seen to call Yang Hsiung and they said, "Where have we not looked for you! The magistrate sits in his inner garden and he asks for you to come and tilt staves with us. Quickly come—quickly come!"

Then Yang Hsiung told Shih Hsiu, saying, "My magistrate calls for me and I can but go quickly. Brother, do you go home first."

Then Shih Hsiu went home at that very time and put his shop into order and he went into the butchery to rest himself.

Let it be told now that when Yang Hsiung was thus summoned by the magistrate he went into the inner garden and tilted a few times with the staves. Seeing it, the magistrate was much pleased and he called for wine to be brought out and one after the other ten large cups were poured out for reward for Yang Hsiung. And Yang Hsiung drank them and he said farewell.

But again others invited Yang Hsiung to go

and drink wine and that night he drank himself into a mighty drunkenness and he was supported home. The adulteress seeing her husband drunken thanked those who brought him and alone with Ying Er they supported him upstairs. They lit a bright light. Yang Hsiung sat upon the bed and the slave bent to take off his stockings and shoes. The adulteress took off his head kerchief for him and untied the under cloth. Yang Hsiung, seeing her thus come to untie it, suddenly remembered what he had been told and to himself he thought, "Whatever a man says when he is drunken is what he would not say when he is sober." And pointing at the adulteress he began to curse, saying, "You trollop! You deceiving female! Whatever comes, I shall kill you."

The adulteress gave a start of fright and did not dare to make answer, but she helped Yang Hsiung to sleep. Yang Hsiung as soon as his head lay on the pillow began to curse bitterly, saying, "You trash—you adulteress! You—you—you—bold enough to creep into a tiger's mouth and make it water—you—you—my hand will not let you go lightly—"

How did that adulteress so much as dare to breathe? She waited until Yang Hsiung was asleep and so slowly it came to the fifth watch of the night. Then Yang Hsiung woke from his drunkenness and sought for water to drink, and the adulteress rose and dipped a bowl of water and gave it to Yang Hsiung to drink. The flickering lamp upon the table still gave forth a dim light and Yang Hsiung drank the water and then he asked, saying, "Goodwife, do you not take off your clothes to sleep in the night?"

That adulteress answered, "You had drunk yourself rotten drunk. I was afraid you would vomit, and how could I dare to take off my clothes? I could but throw myself behind your feet for the night."

Yang Hsiung asked, "Did I say anything?"

The adulteress answered, "Your temper in wine has always been good. As soon as you are drunken you sleep. But tonight I cannot let my heart rest."

Again Yang Hsiung asked, "I have not made merry with Shih Hsiu for all these days nor drunk a few cups with him. Prepare something for him here at home and invite him."

But the adulteress did not answer. She sat on the footstool of the bed and her eyes filled with tears and she sighed. Again Yang Hsiung asked, saying, "Goodwife, when I came home drunken in the night, surely I did not trouble you? What makes you weep?"

The adulteress covered her tear-filled eyes with her hand and did not answer. Yang Hsiung asked several times but the woman covered her face and pretended to weep. At last Yang Hsiung pulled her up from the footstool on to the bed and he was determined to ask her what troubled her. Then the woman wept on and said as she wept, "My father and mother gave me first in marriage to Wang The Scribe and they hoped that it was the once for my life, as a bamboo thrust into a pool once strikes the bottom. Who would have thought that he would leave me half way? Then because you were so noble a lord, they thought they had given me again to a good fellow. Who would have thought you would pay no heed to me?"

Yang Hsiung said, "Here is a strange thing again! Who dares to deceive you? And so I pay you no heed?"

The adulteress answered, "I thought at first I would not tell you because I was afraid you would suffer by him. When I thought to tell you I was afraid you would keep your anger in you."

Yang Hsiung heard this and said, "Speak out what it is."

The adulteress said, "I will tell you, if you will not kill yourself with anger. But since you have left this Shih Hsiu in our house,—at first he was well enough, but afterwards he began to let his claws out. When he saw you did not come back he continually looked at me and said, 'Elder Brother again does not come today. How lonely it is for you to sleep solitary!' But I paid no heed to him. It has not been just the one day, either—But this is nothing. Yesterday morning when I was in the kitchen washing my neck this thing came out from behind me and seeing no one was there he put his hand out from the back and felt of my bosom and he said, 'Sister-in-law, have you conceived?' I beat his hand away and was just about to scream out but I was afraid the neighbors would know of it and make a joke of it to shame you. I could but wish you had come home. Yet when you came you were drunk as rotten clay and again I did not dare to tell you. I hate him enough to eat him alive, and yet you come and ask how your brother Shih Hsiu is!"

Then did the fire rise in Yang Hsiung's heart when he heard this and he cursed, saying, "If I would paint a tiger, I could but paint his skin and not his bones. When I see a man I do but know his face and not his heart. And this thing came before me and said many things to injure you! He said it without any proof at all. I can see very clearly he was frightened and so he first came and told this tale. How tricky a fellow!" And in great fury he said, "Nor is he my own brother—drive him out and let there be an end to it!"

When dawn came Yang Hsiung came down stairs and said to the old man P'an, "Take these pigs that are already killed and salt them down. From today on do no more business." And in an instant he had torn apart all the tables and counters where meat was sold.

Now at dawn Shih Hsiu had just brought the meat out and opened the door of the shop to do trade. There he saw the counter and the tables all overturned, and he was a very clever man and so how could he not understand this? He laughed and said, "Let it be so, then. Because of what Yang Hsiung must have said after his wine the tale is out, and the adulteress has thought of a way to compel her husband to this. Surely she has said I have behaved without courtesy and she has told her husband to close the shop. If I quarrel with her over it Yang Hsiung will be troubled by it. I will withdraw a step and I will think of some other way."

Then Shih Hsiu went into the butchery and put together his possessions but Yang Hsiung, fearing the shame of Shih Hsiu, went away first. Then Shih Hsiu took up his bundle and hung his sharp dagger and went to take his farewell of the old man P'an and he said, "This lowly one has troubled you in many ways and for a long time here in your house. Today Elder Brother has closed the shop and I will go my way again. The accounts are all clear and not a penny has come or gone wrongly. If there has been the least dishonesty may Heaven strike me and Earth destroy me."

Now the old man P'an had been commanded by his son-in-law and he did not dare to have Shih Hsiu stay and so he could but let him have his way and go. Shih Hsiu then sought out an inn near by and there he rented a room and took up his abode. But he thought to himself, saying, "Yang Hsiung and I have sworn a brother-vow. If I do not clear up this affair his life will be vainly lost. Although he has this once listened to the woman and blames me in his heart, yet I cannot separate from him. I must make him understand this matter. I will go now and hear of him and see when it is he goes to the gaol. On that day if I rise but the once at the fourth watch, I can make the whole thing plain to him."

He lived there in the inn for two days and he went to Yang Hsiung's door to see and hear. On that very night he saw a serving man take bedding and go to the gaol and Shih Hsiu said to himself, "Tonight assuredly he goes to the gaol. I will take some pains and see to the matter, and so end it all."

On that night he went back to the inn and slept until the fourth watch when he rose. He hung at his girdle his protecting sharp dagger and carefully he opened the door of the inn and went straight to the alley that ran by the back gate of Yang Hsiung's home. There while he hid in the dark shadows and peered out it was exactly the time of the fifth watch. Then he saw that monk carrying his wooden fish-head drum coming to the alleyway and looking here and there as he came. Shih Hsiu leaped back into hiding and he slipped around behind the monk. With one hand he laid hold on the monk and with his other hand he held his knife against the monk's neck and in a low voice he said fiercely, "Do not struggle! If you call out I will kill you! Tell me the truth! Why does the priest Hai tell you to come here?"

That monk answered, "Good Fellow, forgive me and I will tell you."

Then Shih Hsiu said, "Speak quickly and I will not kill you."

And the monk said, "The priest Hai has evil intercourse with the daughter of the old man P'an. Every night he comes and he told me to watch at the back gate and there is an incense table for a sign and this is to tell him to come to the house and sleep. At the fifth watch he tells me to come and beat my wooden drum and cry for prayers and so call him out."

Shih Hsiu asked, "And where is he now?"

The monk replied, "He is still there in the house asleep. I will strike the wooden drum now and make a din, and he will come out."

But Shih Hsiu said, "Give me your robes and your wooden drum."

He seized the drum out of the monk's hand and the monk had just taken his robes off when Shih Hsiu plunged his dagger into his throat and he lay killed upon the ground. When the monk was dead Shih Hsiu put on his robes and his long priest's stockings. Then he thrust the dagger into his girdle and beating the drum he came down the alley.

The wicked priest upon the bed heard the thud of the wooden drum and in great haste he rose and throwing on his clothes came downstairs. Ying Er came first to open the door and the wicked priest came behind and darted out. But Shih Hsiu still beat at the wooden drum. Then the priest said in a low voice, "Why do you keep on beating it?"

But Shih Hsiu did not answer him. He let him go to the mouth of the alley and with one grasp he threw him to the ground and holding him fast he shouted out, "Do not lift your voice! If you do I will kill you. Wait until I tear off your clothes and it will be enough."

Then did the wicked priest know it was Shih Hsiu, and how did he dare to struggle or to speak? Shih Hsiu stripped him of his clothes and he had not a stitch on him from head to foot, and secretly Shih Hsiu brought out his dagger and in three or four thrusts he had killed the priest. Then he placed the dagger beside the dead priest's side, and he tied the clothes of the two priests up into a bundle. He returned to the inn and opening the door softly he went in, and closing the door gently he went to sleep. Of this no more need be told.

Let it be said then that a vendor of cakes and rice gruel, Old Wang, rising this day at the fifth watch, carrying his load of cakes and gruel, and his lantern lit and with him a little boy, went out to seek for early trade. He came to the place where the dead body lay and he stumbled over it and fell, and all the old fellow's cakes and gruel were spilled upon the ground. Then the little boy cried out, saying, "Ah, bitter—there is a priest here drunken and fallen down!"

But the old man feeling his way and scrambling up found his two hands covered with blood and he cried out bitterness and did not know whither to turn. Several families of neighbors, hearing it all, opened their doors and came out and brought lights. They saw blood everywhere and there the two dead bodies lay on the ground. Then they laid hold on the old man and would fain go to accuse him before the magistrate.

It seemed this curse had fallen from Heaven and sprung from the Earth, and how then did this old man Wang escape? Pray hear it told in the next chapter.

Chapter 45

YANG HSIUNG GREATLY DISTURBS THE MOUNTAIN CALLED THE JADE SCREEN. SHIH HSIU BURNS THE INN OF THE CHU FAMILY

IT IS SAID: At that time when all the neighbors laid hold on the old man Wang and had made haste to the magistrate's court to accuse him, the magistrate had but just ascended into his Hall Of Judgment. Then did all these people kneel in a row and make accusation, saying, "This old man was carrying a load of cakes and rice congee and he stumbled and he fell in a heap upon the ground. When he looked about him he saw two dead bodies lying there in the congee. One was a priest and one was a Taoist monk. Neither one of these had a stitch upon him. Beside the corpse of the monk there was a dagger."

And the old man made his report, saying, "Every day do I, an old man, sell cakes and congee for my living and I come out at the fifth watch to fetch the early trade. Today I rose a little earlier than usual and I came out with this iron-skulled monkey of a boy. I did not look beneath my feet, and suffering a stumble I fell, and I broke my bowls and saucers all to bits. Magistrate, have pity on me! There, lying in blood, I saw two corpses! I gave a start of fear and called out the neighbors and they laid hold on me and brought me here to court. O my lord, search out and see where the truth lies!"

Then immediately did the magistrate cause to be written down all they had said and he sent forth a proclamation and he appointed the police of that district to take the coroners and runners of the court, and they compelled the neighbors and the old man Wang to go to where the corpses lay. There they examined all, and when they understood clearly what had taken place, they went back and gave report to the magistrate. And they reported that the dead priest was P'ei Ju Hai of The Temple Of Gratitude. The monk at the side was the Taoist who lived by the temple. The priest was without clothing and by him there was a very fierce-looking dagger. It could be seen that the Taoist had been slashed across the throat. It must have been that after the monk had stabbed the priest to death he was frightened and drew the weapon across his own throat.

Then the magistrate ordered that the abbot and priests of the temple be brought thither and questioned as to the reason for the crime. But not one of the priests knew why it had been. There was no way of telling the magistrate and the man who was the scribe in the court then said, "It can be seen very clearly that since this priest was stark naked he must have been doing something unlawful with that monk and they killed each other savagely, nor had it anything to do with the old man Wang. Let the neighbors be commanded, therefore, to bring a guarantor and let the coroner be commanded to put the dead bodies at once into coffins and let them be placed elsewhere, and let a memorandum be made saying that these two killed each other."

And the magistrate replied, "You have spoken well, too." And immediately he appointed such persons, and of this no more need be told.

But the young busybodies in the front alley had made a song out of the affair and they sang thus,

"How mirthful that the temple priest
Has met his fate at last!
Deceiving he a noble man
He hooked away the wife.
Her body to him a joyful sacrifice
She gave in pitying love.

"How, when receiving the goddess,
Just when they met in love,
Could it be he lay
In a bloody hell
There for all men to see!
But naught is lust
And lust is naught.
He forgot 'tis told in The Book Of Souls
That though the smaller part
Was satisfied,
The greater lay dead on the street.

"If the smaller part had he saved,
Then saved now would all be
And lived together for ever and aye
Nor died in such cruelty.

"We would say the priest died thus,
As one of old died for his mother,
Save that never did we see
A priest die for a woman."

Then there were other busybodies in the inner alleys who, hearing such a song in the front, also made a song to sing in competition and sang,

"The broken vow of chastity
Has called him to his death.
Such fruit to such a seed was naught but sure and just.
Too strange it was that he should lie
Naked as he was born
So that not a single thread or shred
Upon him hung forlorn.
He threw his dagger down and straightway was a god,
The priest today is dead,
Last night his lesser part died,
The monk slashed his throat also.
What friendship this, we trow!
Struggling together, jealous to death,
He would not forgive the lover."

These two songs were soon ringing through one alley after another. The woman, hearing it, was utterly confounded and she did not dare to speak and she could but cry bitterness secretly in her heart. Yang Hsiung in the gaol was told by certain persons that a priest and monk had been killed, and he soon understood somewhat of what had happened. To himself he thought, "This deed assuredly was done by Shih Hsiu. In a moment's time the other day I blamed him wrongly. Today I am at leisure and therefore I will go and seek him and ask him what the truth is."

But even as he had passed by the bridge in front he heard someone calling behind his back, saying, "Elder Brother, whither do you go?"

Yang Hsiung, turning his head, saw it was Shih Hsiu, and so he answered, "Brother, I had indeed no place to seek you."

And Shih Hsiu said, "Elder Brother, pray come here to where I live for I have something to talk of with you."

And he led Yang Hsiung then to a small room in the inn and he said, "Elder Brother, I did not lie, did I?"

Yang Hsiung replied, "Brother, do not blame me. It was that in a moment's foolishness, after drinking wine, I let my speech free, and the woman guessed my purpose and she spoke of many faults of yours. Now have I come especially to bear any punishment you put upon me."

Then Shih Hsiu said, "Elder Brother, although I am but a lowly and an unlearned man, yet though Heaven fall I will bear it up and though the Earth slide askew I will straighten it. How then could I be willing to do such deeds as that? Because I feared you would suffer from their wickedness one day, I came to seek you. Here are proofs for you to see."

Then he brought out the garments of the priest and of the monk and he said again, "Here is what I tore from them."

Yang Hsiung saw these and the fire began to rise in his heart and he cried, "Brother, do not blame me! Tonight I will return and slice into pieces that cheap trollop and so free the wrath from my heart!"

But Shih Hsiu laughed and said, "Here you are again! You are one who works in the magistrate's court and how is it you do not know the law? You did not see the real evidence and so how can you kill a person? If I have spoken falsely then will you not have killed one by mistake?"

Yang Hsiung asked, "But how can I let such a thing as this pass?"

Shih Hsiu replied, "Elder Brother, do you only as I say. I will tell you how to be a good fellow."

And Yang Hsiung asked again, "Good Brother, how will you tell me to be a good fellow?"

And Shih Hsiu answered, "Outside the east gate there is a mountain called The Jade Screen and it is a lonely spot. Do you tomorrow say, 'I have not for long burned incense. Today I will go with my goodwife to worship.' Thus do you deceive the woman into coming out. Take her and the slave Ying Er together upon the mountain and I will be there waiting for you. There face to face we will make clear her accusations against me. Then, Elder Brother, give her then and there a writing of divorcement. Will this not be the best way?"

Yang Hsiung said, "Brother, why need you speak of it? Well I know your body is pure. It is all the lies of that woman."

But Shih Hsiu said, "I do not mean that. I want you also, my Elder Brother, to know all the truth of this coming and going with the priest."

And Yang Hsiung said, "If this is the clear insight of my brother, indeed there is no mistake in it. I will decide to come with that trollop tomorrow. But do not delay and do not go away."

Then Shih Hsiu answered, "If I do not come, then is all I have said false."

Then Yang Hsiung took his farewell of Shih Hsiu and he left the inn and he went back to the court to attend to his business. When night came he went home and he said nothing of what had occurred nor did he speak at all. He was as he was every day. On the next day at dawn he said to the woman, "Last night I dreamed the god reproached me and he said that for many days I had not come to worship. In the old days I used to go to the temple outside the east gate and I promised the god I would come again and burn incense there and I have not fulfilled my vow. Today I have nothing to do and I will go and fulfill it and I will go together with you."

The woman said, "Do you go alone and fulfill it. What is the use of wanting me to go?"

But Yang Hsiung said, "But this vow was made in the days of our betrothal and it is necessary that we go together."

Then the woman said, "If it must be thus, then let us eat a little vegetable food early and heat some water and bathe ourselves."

And Yang Hsiung said, "I will go and buy incense and paper money and hire the chairs. Do you bathe yourself first and comb your hair and place the flowers in it and then await me. Bid Ying Er to come also."

Then again did Yang Hsiung go to the inn to meet Shih Hsiu and he told him, "As soon as we have eaten I will come. Brother, do not delay."

And Shih Hsiu said, "Elder Brother, when you bring her to the mountain bid the chair bearers to let the chair down half way up the mountain. Then do the three of you walk up. I will wait for you in a lonely spot on top. Do not bring any idlers up."

So Yang Hsiung promised Shih Hsiu and he bought the paper and the candles and he returned and ate his early meal. Now the woman did not know of the affair and she made her person very beautiful and she took with her Ying Er. The chairs were already waiting outside the gate and Yang Hsiung said, "Father-in-law, do you watch the house. I and the goodwife, when we have burned our incense, will return."

And the old man P'an replied, "Burn plenty of incense, go early and come back soon."

Then the woman mounted her chair and Ying Er walked beside her and Yang Hsiung walked behind. When they had come out of the east gate Yang Hsiung commanded the chair bearers in a low voice, saying, "Take her up the mountain of The Jade Screen for me and I will give you more money for it."

In less than four hours they had already come to the mountain. Now this mountain was about seven miles outside the east gate and it was covered with many graves. If one looked toward the top there were tall grasses and trees and there was no temple large or small nor any house there where men dwelt. And Yang Hsiung had the woman carried half way up the mountain. Then he bade the chair bearers put the chair down and he opened the latch of the door of the sedan and lifted up the curtain and he told the woman to come out. And the woman asked, saying, "Why have we come hither to this mountain?"

But Yang Hsiung only said, "You must walk on up. The chair bearers will wait for us here. They are not to come." And to the bearers he said, "Wait together here for a little while, and I will give you all extra money."

And the chair bearers answered, "This will be no trouble to us. We will wait here and there is an end on it."

Then Yang Hsiung leading the woman and Ying Er, the three of them, climbed up two or three ridges. There they saw Shih Hsiu sitting above them, and the woman said, "How is it you did not bring the paper and the incense?"

Yang Hsiung said, "I have already sent men up with them." Thus he led the woman and he led her to an ancient grave. And Shih Hsiu had placed his bundle, his staff, and his knife all there by the foot of a tree and he said, "Sister-in-law, I make my obeisance to you."

In haste the woman answered, saying, "Brother-in-law, how is it you also are here?" And while she spoke thus she was secretly afraid in her heart.

Shih Hsiu said, "I have been waiting for you here and for a long time."

Then Yang Hsiung said to the woman, "The other day you told me that my brother-in-law had many times made light of you and that he took his hand and felt of your bosom and asked you if you conceived or not. Today here in this spot where no man is you two shall come to understand each other."

Then that woman said, "Ai-yah! Why should we speak of what is passed?"

But Shih Hsiu opened wide his eyes and he said, "Sister-in-law, how is it you speak thus?"

And that woman said, "Brother-in-law, why do you when you have naught else to do, go seeking trouble out?"

But Shih Hsiu cried, "Sister-in-law—ha!" and he opened his bundle and he brought out the garments of the priest and of the monk and he scattered them upon the ground and he said, "Do you know these or not?"

Then the woman looked and the red flew into

her face and she had not a word to say in return. And Shih Hsiu seized his dagger from his girdle and he gave it to Yang Hsiung, saying, "Only ask Ying Er of this matter."

Then Yang Hsiung seized the slave by the hair and she knelt before him and he shouted, "You little trollop, speak quickly and truthfully. How was it that the adultery came about with the priest in his room? How was it that the incense table was made a sign? How was it the monk was told to come and beat his wooden drum? Speak all the truth to me! Then will I forgive you this life of yours. If you deceive me I will chop you into pieces and mince you."

Then Ying Er cried out, saying, "Sir, this has nothing to do with me. Do not kill me! I will tell you how it was we came to be drinking wine in the priest's room—how it was we went upstairs to look at the god's tooth—how it was I was told to come downstairs to watch by the old man P'an until he woke from his drunken sleep—how it was on the third day the monk came to the back gate to beg for alms and I brought out some copper pence to give him—how it was that the lady went to make her troth with the priest that on the days when you went to the gaol—Sir, she would have me place an incense table outside the gate to be a secret sign! The monk was to come and see this and go back and tell the priest. And then I will tell you how the priest dressed himself to look like a common man and came with his head wrapped in a kerchief and dressed to look like a common man and—and I will tell how the lady took the head kerchief off and there his shaven head shone out—and how at the fifth watch when the wooden drum sounded I had to open the gate and let him out and how the lady gave me a pair of bracelets and a suit of new clothes to make me do her bidding, and the priest came back and forth I do not know how many tens of times before he was killed. But he had given me some more ornaments for my hair and he told me to tell you, Sir, that Shih Hsiu was seeking to do wrong to the lady. But this, Sir, I did not dare to tell you. This is the very truth, Sir, and there is not a lie in it."

When Ying Er had finished speaking Shih Hsiu said, "Do you know all now, Elder Brother? These words are surely none that I have told her to speak. Now I pray you, my Elder Brother, to ask my sister-in-law closely how all this came about."

Then Yang Hsiung dragged the woman over to him and he shouted out, "You worthless trollop, your slave has confessed all! Do not then deny the least thing. Speak nothing but the truth, and I will forgive you your worthless life!"

That woman said, "It is my fault indeed. But think of what I used to be as your wife and forgive me this one time!"

But Shih Hsiu said, "Elder Brother, do not be careless now. Indeed you must ask my sister-in-law closely how this all came about from the very beginning."

Then Yang Hsiung roared forth, "Trollop, speak quickly!"

So that woman could but tell how the priest had begun even some two years before to have this desire and how it was he came to call her father his foster-father, and how on that night when they did the good deed of the ceremonial how he came first to present gifts. "And when I gave him his tea," she said, "I will tell you how he did but look at me and smile,—and how when my brother-in-law Shih came he went quickly away,—and how when I went out to worship he would stand so near me. In the middle of the night he came by the curtain and took hold of my hand and he told me to fulfill my vows and—and he began to call me lady and he deceived me into going upstairs to see the god's tooth and—and he begged me to think of some way quickly whereby he might meet for a long time with me and he taught me a plan to make trouble between you and Shih Hsiu so that you would drive him forth. And he would have me give Ying Er to him, too, and he said, 'If you will not, I will come no more.' "

Thus she told it all bit by bit. Then Shih Hsiu said, "And how was it you came to tell my elder brother that I sought to betray you?"

And that woman answered, "The other day when he was drunken he cursed me and seeing how aptly he did curse me I guessed that my brother-in-law must have seen the evil and told him. And the priest had taught me what to say a night or two before. Therefore that morning did I think of a way to use these words to deceive my husband. But truly my brother-in-law did not do thus."

Then Shih Hsiu said, "Now today is the whole thing spoken out clearly. Now let it be done according to my elder brother's heart."

And Yang Hsiung said, "Brother, take the ornaments out of this trollop's hair for me and strip her clothes from her and then will I attend her myself."

And Shih Hsiu took the ornaments from the woman's hair and he took her clothes from her body and Yang Hsiung tied together the two strings of her skirts and he bound the woman to a tree. Then Shih Hsiu took Ying Er's ornaments from her also and he took a sword and he said, "Elder Brother, why should we leave this little trollop? If we do not dig the weeds up by the root they will sprout again."

Then Yang Hsiung answered, saying, "Of a certainty. Brother, give me the sword and I will put out my own hand to it."

Ying Er, seeing how evil was the outlook for her, was about to scream, but Yang Hsiung's hand lifted once with the sword and with one stroke she was cut in two pieces. Then the woman on the tree screamed out, "Brother-in-law, beseech him for me!"

But Shih Hsiu said, "Sister-in-law, it is not I who do this."

Yang Hsiung then went to the woman and he first dug out her tongue with one stroke so that the woman could cry out no more. Then pointing at her he cursed her, saying, "You cheap and thieving trollop! Because I was not careful and for the moment listened to your lies and was nearly deceived by you, almost I broke the vow of friendship with my brother and afterwards you would surely have killed me. I do marvel how it is your heart and vitals are so evil as this! I will look at them and see what they are."

With one blow he cut her open from her breast to her lower belly and he hooked out her heart and her liver and all her vitals and hung these upon the pine tree. Then did Yang Hsiung cut this woman into her seven parts, and all her gold hair ornaments and bracelets and rings he tied into a bundle and he said, "Brother, pray come hither to me. I wish to talk with you concerning a plan for the future. Now the adulterer and the adulteress herself are both dead, but whither shall we go, you and I, to seek for safety?"

Shih Hsiu answered, "I have a place of surety and I do but ask you, Elder Brother, to go thither at once."

Yang Hsiung asked, "And whither shall we go?"

And Shih Hsiu answered, "Elder Brother, you have killed a person. I, your younger brother, have also killed a person. If we do not go and join the robbers at the great lair, then whither can we go?"

But Yang Hsiung said, "Yet stay—you and I, we do not know a single man there. How then can they be willing to receive us?"

Shih Hsiu answered, "Elder Brother, these words of yours are mistaken. The Opportune Rain, Sung Chiang, is there now and he receives all good fellows who come to him under Heaven. Who does not know this? And why should we fear, you and I, who have such good skill in the use of weapons?"

Then Yang Hsiung said, "But whatever we do, we must think first of the hardships, and then it will be easier and so will we spare ourselves later troubles. I ought not to be one employed in the courts. If I go there he will suspect me, and he will not be willing to receive me."

But Shih Hsiu laughed and said, "Was he not himself a court scribe? I will tell you something to rest your heart the more. Long before the day when you took me for your brother-friend, of those two men who drank tea with me in the inn, one was Tai Chung of the mountain lair who walks with the magic strides. The other one was The Five Hued Leopard Yang Ling. He gave me a ten-ounce piece of silver that I have still in my bundle. Therefore may we go and seek them."

Then Yang Hsiung said, "If there is such a path for us as this, I will return and get some money for our journey and we will set forth straightway."

But Shih Hsiu cried, "Elder Brother, and how foolish you are! If when you enter the city the matter has come out and you are seized how can you escape? Here we have these hair ornaments and bracelets and all these things in our bundle, and I also have some silver. Even though one other man went with us it would be more than enough. Why should you go and seek for more and thus disturb things and make difficult our escape? This matter must come out in a very short time and we must not delay. We can but go around behind the mountain."

Then Shih Hsiu put the bundle on his back and he took up his staff and Yang Hsiung thrust his girdle knife into his girdle and took up his sword. Even as he was about to leave this old grave he saw a man come out from behind the pine tree and he cried out, saying, "In such a clear and peaceful world as this, under such a wide sky and upon so great an earth when you have cut a person to pieces need you go and join the robbers in the great lair? I have listened for a long time."

And when Yang Hsiung and Shih Hsiu looked to see, that man bent his head down in obeisance. Then did Yang Hsiung know this man that his surname was Shih and his name Ch'ien, and his ancestors were men of Kao T'an Chou of Shantung, and he was idling there. He was one who could leap from the ground to the roof of a house, he could walk upon walls and jump over fences to steal horses. But he was caught and was even now under accusation at the court but Yang Hsiung had saved him. By men he was nicknamed Flea On A Drum. Then Yang Hsiung inquired of Shih Ch'ien, saying, "Why are you here?"

And Shih Ch'ien answered, "Pray let the head gaoler hear me humbly speak. For a long time there has been no way for me to go, and I have been digging in these ancient graves to seek for a few treasures. Because I saw you, my Elder Brother, doing something here, I did not dare come forth lest I offend. But I heard it said that you would go and join them at the robbers' lair. Now this lowly one is here and I can only steal a few poor fowls or dogs, and how long can I continue thus? If I can go with you, my two Brothers, up that mountain, will it not be well? But I do not know what your will is and if you will have me go with you or not."

Then Shih Hsiu said, "If you are a good fellow among good fellows, why, then, they seek for such strong men as you, and one more such as you will be nothing! If you speak thus, why, then, let us go on together."

And Shih Ch'ien said, "Then, lowly as I am, I know a small path by which we may go."

At that time therefore did he lead Yang Hsiung and Shih Hsiu and the three of them went by a small path down the mountain at the back, and they went toward the robbers' lair.

Let it be told further now of those two chair bearers who were half way up the mountain. They waited until the red sun was level with the western horizon and still they did not see the three persons come down, nor being so commanded, neither did they dare go up, nor if they waited longer could they go down because of the darkness. Therefore they let their feet carry them as they would and they wandered up the mountain side.

There they saw a circle of crows in a great flock upon an ancient grave. When the two chair bearers went up to see, there the crows were snatching at the woman's inwards and they were there cawing and quarreling. When the chair bearers saw this they gave a start of fear and in great haste they rushed home and made report of it to the old man P'an, and then they all went together to make accusation at the city court in Chi Chou. Immediately the magistrate sent an officer who took with him five runners of the coroner and they went to The Jade Screen Mountain. When they had examined into the murder they went back to the magistrate and they made humble report, saying, "We saw a woman, named P'an Ch'ao Yün, who was cut to pieces beside a pine tree. There was also her serving maid, Ying Er, who was killed beneath the ancient grave. There by the grave also was a pile of clothing belonging to women and to priests."

The magistrate heard this and he remembered the affair of the priest and the monk that befell the other day and he examined the old man P'an very carefully. Then the old man told in detail the story of his drunkenness in the priest's rooms and the story of how Shih Hsiu had been driven forth. And the magistrate said, "The eye can see that the woman had something to do with the priest, and the monk and the maid were their tools. I think that Shih Hsiu, seeing the path of justice was not smooth, killed the monk and the priest. This Yang Hsiung assuredly killed the woman and the maid today. Surely it must have been thus. If we do but find Yang Hsiung and Shih Hsiu, those two, we can know for a certainty."

Immediately then he sent forth official letters to order the arrest of Yang Hsiung and Shih Hsiu. As for the others, the chair bearers and such, he freed them to return when he called for them. The old man P'an then went to buy coffins and he had the dead bodies buried. Of this no more need be said.

Let it be told again. Now Yang Hsiung and Shih Hsiu and Shih Ch'ien left the region of Chi Chou and on the way they slept by night and rose early in the morning, and in less than a day they had come to the region of Yün Chou and they passed The Hollow Of Fragrant Wood. There they soon saw a high mountain. Now without their knowing it the sky had darkened gradually to night. Ahead of them there was an inn beside a small brook, and the three men went to the threshold and even as the servant of the inn was about to close the door, he saw these three men hastening forward. He asked them, saying, "Have you not come far today, Sir Guests, that you reach here so late?"

And Shih Ch'ien answered, "We have today walked more than thirty miles and therefore we come so late."

Then the man allowed the three men to come into rest and he asked them, saying, "Sir Guests, you have not lighted a fire for food yet?"

And Shih Ch'ien said, "We will see to this ourselves."

And the serving man said, "Today we have had no guests and there are the two cauldrons clean on the oven. Use them and it matters nothing."

Then Shih Ch'ien asked him, "Is there wine and is there meat to sell in your inn?"

And the man replied, "Today early we had some meat but it was all bought by the villagers near by us. There is left only a jar of wine here, and beyond this there are no meats."

Then Shih Ch'ien said, "Let it be so, then. We will first borrow five measures of rice for food and then we will plan further."

So the man brought out the rice and gave it to Shih Ch'ien and he washed it and made a cauldron of food. Now Shih Hsiu was in the room settling their possessions. And Yang Hsiung brought out a woman's hair ornament and he gave it to the serving man to pay for the jar of wine to drink saying that tomorrow they would pay the whole account. The man received the ornament and he went within and brought out the jar of wine and he opened it, and with it he brought out a dish of salted vegetables and put it upon the table. Shih Ch'ien first fetched a bucket of boiling water there and he invited Yang Hsiung and Shih Hsiu to wash their hands and feet. Then pouring out wine he asked the man to come and drink with them. He put down four large bowls and filled them with wine and they drank

Now Shih Hsiu looking about under the eaves of the inn saw that there were thrust there some ten-odd very good swords and he asked the serving man, "How is it that your inn has such weapons of war as these?"

And the serving man answered, saying, "They are all such as the host has left here."

Again Shih Hsiu asked, "And what manner of man is the host of your inn?"

And the serving man answered, "Sir Guest, you are a traveler by river and lake, and how is it you do not know the name of this place? That high mountain in front is called The Mountain Of The Lonely Dragon. In front of it is a very high and steep cliff and it is called The Cliff Of The Lonely Dragon. Upon it is the house of the host of this inn. This region about here has some ten miles within it and it is called the region of the Chu family, and the head of this family is named Chu Ch'ai Feng. He has three sons and they are called the braves of the Chu family. Behind and before their village there are some five to seven hundred families all of whom are their tenants. To each family are given two swords. This inn is called the inn of the Chu family and there are always some ten-odd of this family who live here in the inn, and that is why they have left their swords here."

Then Shih Hsiu asked, "But what is the use of weapons left in an inn?"

Then the man answered, "This place is not far from the robbers' lair and they are only afraid lest those robbers come hither to rob and therefore they leave these weapons here ready to use."

And Shih Hsiu said, "I will give you some silver if you will give me a spear in return. How will that be?'

But that serving man answered, "This I cannot do. On every handle is name and number and I cannot bear the beating of my master, for this master of mine does not punish lightly."

Then Shih Hsiu laughed and said, "I was but joking with you, and you are afraid. Pray drink your wine."

But the serving man said, "This lowly one can drink no more. I will go first to my bed. Do you yourselves drink on at your will, Sir Guests, and take a few more cups."

The man went away and Yang Hsiung and Shih Hsiu then each drank another round of wine. Then they heard Shih Ch'ien say, "Elder Brothers, will you have meat to eat?"

But Yang Hsiung said, "The serving man said there was no meat to sell. Where can you fetch it from?"

Shih Ch'ien tittered a little laugh and he went to the oven and he brought forth a huge old cock. Yang Hsiung asked, saying, "And whence came this fowl?"

Shih Ch'ien answered, "I did just now go to the back of the inn to piss and I saw this fowl in a cage and I remembered we had nothing to eat with our wine and I took it secretly to the side of the brook and killed it. Then I carried a bucket of boiling water to the back and there I picked it clean and I cooked it tender and I fetched it hither for my two elder brothers to eat."

But Yang Hsiung said, "Such as you, and your thieving hands and feet!"

And Shih Hsiu laughed and said, "He has not changed his old trade!"

The three laughed together for a time and they took the fowl and tore it apart with their fingers and ate it, and they fetched the rest of the rice and ate it also.

Now the serving man did sleep but lightly and for a little while and he could not let his heart rest and he crawled up again. He took his lamp and went to the front and to the back to see if aught was amiss. Then he saw on the table in the kitchen there were the feathers and bones of a fowl. When he went to the oven and looked there was half a cauldron of rice chicken soup. In great haste he went back to look into the cage and the cock was not to be seen. Quickly he came out and asked, "Sir Guests, how little of proper behavior do you understand! Why have you killed the cock that crows for the dawn in our inn?"

Shih Ch'ien said, "You have seen a ghost! Eh—eh! Why, I bought this fowl upon the road to eat and when did I ever see your cock?"

The serving man asked, "Where then has the cock of our inn gone?"

Shih Ch'ien replied, "Doubtless a wild cat has stolen it, or a weasel has got it, or a hawk has seized it, and how do I know?"

The serving man said again, "But my fowl was but just now in its cage and if you did not steal it then who did?"

Then Shih Hsiu said, "Do not quarrel. I will give you the money for this fowl and there will be an end of it."

But the serving man said, "Mine was a cock who crew every dawn and the inn cannot do without him. Even though you give me ten ounces of silver it is not enough. You must return my fowl."

Then in great wrath Shih Hsiu asked, "And whom do you think you are deceiving? And if I, a lord, will not even pay for it, what can you do?"

The serving man laughed and said, "Sir Guests, do not seek here for wild fire to eat. This inn of mine is not like other inns. I will seize you and take you to the village and they will hold you as robbers from the great lair."

Now when Shih Hsiu heard this he cursed mightily and he said, "Even though we were good fellows from the great lair how could you seize us and ask your host for a reward?"

And Yang Hsiung was angry also and he said, "In good will we would have paid you money. Now that I will not give it, how will you seize me?"

Then the man cried out, "Thieves—thieves!"

Then out of the inn were seen to come out, stark naked, three or five great fellows and they rushed forward to Yang Hsiung and Shih Hsiu. But Shih Hsiu put up his fist and knocked them down with a blow each. The serving man was about to cry out again when Shih Ch'ien gave him a blow that made his face swell and he could not cry out.

Then these several big fellows all went out by the back door, and Yang Hsiung said, "Brothers, these fellows are surely going to call for others to come. Let us eat quickly and go." Then the three ate until they were satisfied and they divided their bundles and tied them on their backs and put their hempen shoes upon their feet and they hung their knives to their girdles and each man went to the weapon rack and chose out a good sword apiece. And Shih Hsiu said, "Let it be as it will now. We cannot let the matter pass."

Then he went to the front of the oven and found a handful of grass and he lit it from the mouth of the oven and he went within and set fire to the house on all four sides. The thatched roofs were fanned into blaze by the wind and the fire began to crackle and roar and in a moment the fire was as great as the heavens. Then the three let their paces free and turning to the highway they went their way.

Now when the three had walked some four hours they saw countless torches flaming before and behind and suddenly there were some hundred or two men who rushed out shouting as they came. But Shih Hsiu said, "Pray do not be confused. We will choose a small path and go by it."

But Yang Hsiung said, "Stay—we will kill them one by one as they come, and if they come by twos, we will kill them by twos. We will wait until dawn before we go on."

Before he had finished speaking they were surrounded on all four sides. Now Yang Hsiung was before, Shih Hsiu behind, and Shih Ch'ien in the middle and the three of them held up their swords and went forward to fight with the villagers. Now those villagers at first did not know what skill these three men had, and lifting their staves and weapons they came charging forward. But Yang Hsiung raised his sword high in his hands, and soon he had stabbed some seven or eight. Then those in front ran away and even as the ones behind were about to run also, Shih Hsiu charged after them and he also stabbed some six or seven of them. Then the other villagers hearing it said that some ten-odd men were killed, all feared for their own lives and they thought to themselves that this was no good thing for them to be about and they all retreated. But as they retreated a step the three men pursued a step and when they were going along thus the shouting again rose and out of the dried grass were thrust two hooked spears and Shih Ch'ien was caught by one of these and dragged into the grass. In great haste Shih Hsiu turned himself to save Shih Ch'ien when again behind his back two more barbed spears were thrust out. Fortunately Yang Hsiung's eyes were quick and he drove them aside with his sword and he stabbed into the grass. There was a cry and those in the grass ran away also.

But the two seeing Shih Ch'ien was caught, feared to penetrate too far into the enemy stronghold nor did they desire to fight further with them since they could do no more for Shih Ch'ien now. They could but look about on all sides for a path to choose. In the distance they saw the confused glare of the torches and there were no trees or woods upon the small paths. They chose a path at random therefore and they went straight to the east. And the villagers from the four directions could not pursue them. They could but rescue those who had been wounded and they led Shih Ch'ien away with his hands tied behind his back and thus they took him bound to the village.

Let it now be told of Yang Hsiung and Shih Hsiu. They walked until dawn and they saw a wine shop in a village and Shih Hsiu said, "Elder Brother, ahead of us is a wine shop. Let us therefore buy a bowl of rice and some wine and then we can ask what road to take."

Then the two went to the inn and putting aside their swords they sat down and they called to the serving man to bring forth wine and to cook rice for them to eat. Then the serving man spread forth the meats and he heated the wine hot and brought it. Even as they were about to eat they saw a tall fellow come by from the outside and his face was broad and his jaw square. His eyes were wide and his ears large. His appearance was rude and without intelligence. He wore a silk robe the brown color of tea and he wore a turban with a sign of the swastika upon it. About his waist was a girdle of white silk and below on his feet he wore a pair of oiled leather boots. And he cried out, saying, "The lord bids you carry the loads into the village and give them to him!"

In great haste the innkeeper answered, "We have already tied up the loads and in a little while we will send them."

That man, having so commanded, turned himself about and again he said, "Bring them quickly!"

Even as he was about to go out the gate he passed by Yang Hsiung and Shih Hsiu. And Yang Hsiung knew him and he called out, "Ha, you fellow! Why are you here? And you do not look at me!"

That man turned his head and, looking, he knew Yang Hsiung. Then he cried out, "Most Gracious, why have you come hither?" And still staring at Yang Hsiung he made obeisance.

Because Yang Hsiung came upon this man,
The three villages stood empty and still,
A curse fell—and tigers leaped from the hill.

Who in truth was this man whom Yang Hsiung and Shih Hsiu saw? Pray hear it told in the next chapter.

Chapter 46

THE EAGLE WHO SMITES THE HEAVENS TWICE WRITES A LETTER OF BROTHERHOOD. SUNG CHIANG GOES FOR THE FIRST TIME TO ATTACK THE VILLAGE OF THE CHU FAMILY

IT IS SAID: At the time when Yang Hsiung lifted up that man and Shih Hsiu saw him then Shih Hsiu asked, saying, "Who is this brother?"

Yang Hsiung answered, "This brother is surnamed Tu and his name is Hsing, and his ancestors were men of Chung Shan Fu. Because his face is so coarse and wild men all call him The Devil Faced. Last year he came to Chi Chou to do business and in a fit of anger he killed his fellow traveler and so he was taken to court and put into the gaol at Chi Chou. I, seeing that he understood boxing and the use of all weapons, made every effort to save him, and I did not think to meet him again here today."

Tu Hsing then asked, saying, "Most Gracious, what official matter brings you hither?"

Yang Hsiung put his mouth to his ear and said, "I killed a person in Chi Chou and now we are turning to the mountain lair to join them there. Last night we sought shelter in the inn of the Chu family, and because a fellow traveler of ours, Shih Ch'ien, stole a fowl of the inn and ate it, in a moment of time a quarrel arose with the keeper of the inn. His temper rose and in the end we burned the inn. We three then escaped by night nor did we trouble ourselves that behind us would come pursuers. We two brothers stabbed several of them, but we did not think that out of the wild grass there should be thrust forth two barbed spears and that they would hook Shih Ch'ien away. We two ran hither, then, and were about to ask the way, and we did not think to meet you, Good Brother!"

Then Tu Hsing said, "Most Gracious, do not be in such haste. I will bid them free Shih Ch'ien for you."

And Yang Hsiung said, "Good Brother, stay a little and drink a cup with us."

The three then sat down and they drank wine, and Tu Hsing said, "Ever since I left Chi Chou I have received greatly of your kindness and I came hither and thanks to a certain great lord here he let me stay as a bailiff in his house. Every day I send out money or I bargain with this one and that and all such matters he places upon me and greatly does he trust me. Because of this I do not now wish to return to my home."

And Yang Hsiung asked, "Who is this great lord?"

Then Tu Hsing answered, "Before The Ridge Of The Lonely Dragon are three ridges and upon each ridge is a village. The one in the middle is the village of the Chu family, the one on the west is the village of the Hu family, the one on the east is the village of the Li family. The three villages and these three families have altogether some ten thousand or so of men and horses. But the village of the Chu family is the best. The head of this village is named Chu Ch'ao Feng. He has three sons, who are the braves of the Chu family. The eldest is called Chu The Dragon, the next is called Chu The Tiger, and the third son is called Chu The Tiger Cub. They have a teacher who is called Luan T'ing Yü, The Iron Staff. Among ten thousand there is not one to match him. In the village there are 5 to 7 hundred of fierce, able tenants. In the village to the west belonging to the Hu family the head is the old lord Hu. He has a son called Hu Ch'en, and he is also exceedingly fearsome. He has besides a daughter most heroic of all, and her name is The Ten Foot Green Snake The Goodwife Hu. She uses double knives that are like sun and moon in her hands. On horseback in battle she is a terror to see. In the village to the east is my lord. His surname is Li and his name is Yün and he can wield a staff of pure iron. On his shoulders he wears five flying knives, and even at a hundred paces away these knives are dreadful. Now the people of these three villages have made a vow that they will live and die together and that they will have one heart and one mind. Whichever village has a calamity the others will help it. Fearing lest the good fellows of the mountain lair will come to ask them for goods they are prepared to withstand them. Now I will take you two honored ones to the village and when you have seen the lord Li, I will ask for a letter to be sent to save Shih Ch'ien."

Again Yang Hsiung asked, "That lord Li of yours—is he not the one who far and wide is called The Eagle Who Smites The Heavens?"

And Tu Hsing answered, "It is indeed he."

Then Shih Hsiu said, "By river and lake I have heard it said there is upon The Ridge Of The Lonely Dragon a Li called The Eagle Who Smites The Heavens who is indeed a good fellow. And so he is here then! I have long heard that indeed he is an astounding and very fine fellow. Let us go therefore the once."

Then Yang Hsiung bade the serving man to bring the wine account. But how could Tu Hsing be willing to let him pay for the wine? He would do this himself.

The three then left the village wine shop and Yang Hsiung and Shih Hsiu were led to the village. Now when Yang Hsiung looked about he saw it was a very fine large village. All around the outside flowed a stream and beside it was a whitewashed wall, and there were many great elms so large that two men could not reach around them. Outside the village gate was a drawbridge. They crossed over this and entering the village gate went into the great hall. On both sides of the hall were more than twenty racks for weapons and they were filled with glittering weapons. And Tu Hsing said, "Wait here for a little while my two Honorable Brothers, and wait until I go and announce your coming and ask my lord to come out and meet you."

Tu Hsing was not long gone before he returned and they saw Li Yün the lord come from inside, and Tu Hsing led Yang Hsiung and Shih Hsiu in to make obeisance. In great haste the lord Li made response and he invited them to come in and sit down. But Yang Hsiung and Shih Hsiu were thrice courteous before they would sit down. Then Li Yün commanded that wine should be brought out to entertain them. Again did Yang Hsiung and Shih Hsiu make obeisance and say, "We do pray the great lord will send a letter to the village of the Chu family and save the life of Shih Ch'ien. Then living or dead we will not dare to forget your mercy."

So Li Yün commanded that the tutor should be sent for who wrote a letter and he wrote the lord's own name to it and he set his seal upon it also. Then the lord commanded that one be sent with the letter and a swift horse prepared that he might go to the village of Chu to seek for the man. So the messenger took his lord's letter and mounted the horse and was gone. Then Yang Hsiung and Shih Hsiu made obeisance in thanks and the lord Li replied, "Let the hearts of the two braves be at rest. As soon as my letter reaches there he will be released."

Again Yang Hsiung and Shih Hsiu thanked him and the lord Li said, "Pray come into the inner hall and we will drink some wine and wait."

The three then went with him within, and an early meal was prepared for them to eat, and when they had eaten and while they were drinking their tea, the lord Li asked concerning some methods of using weapons. Seeing that Yang Hsiung and Shih Hsiu answered very well he was pleased in his heart. About mid-morning the messenger returned and the lord Li called him into the inner hall and asked him, saying, "Where is the man you went to seek?"

The messenger answered, "I saw Chu Ch'ao Feng myself and I gave him the letter and he had the heart to let him go free. But the three Chu braves came out and they grew angry and they would not write an answering letter nor would they let the man go free and they are determined to send him into the city to court."

The lord Li gave a start of fear at this and he said, "They are under a covenant with me and our vow is made with each other already. If my letter reached him, he ought to have answered it. How has it come about thus? Surely it is that you have spoken wrongly that it has come about thus. Tu Hsing, do you go and see Chu Ch'ao Feng yourself and tell him in detail how all this came about."

Then Tu Hsing said, "This lowly one is willing to go. Only I do ask my lord to write a letter himself. Only thus will they be willing to free him when I reach there."

The lord Li said, "You have spoken well."

Then he brought out a sheet of flowered letter paper and the lord Li himself wrote a letter. Upon the envelope he set a seal of his name and rank and this he gave to Tu Hsing and Tu Hsing went to the back and chose a swift horse and he put on it saddle and bridle. Then he took a whip and going out of the gate he mounted the horse and whipped him several times and so hastened to the village of the Chu family.

And lord Li said to Yang Hsiung and Shih Hsiu again, "Let your hearts be at rest, Honored Sirs. This letter written with my own pen will surely free him in a very short time."

Then deeply did Yang Hsiung and Shih Hsiu bow their thanks and there in the inner hall they drank wine and waited. Seeing that the sky darkened with night and they did not see Tu Hsing return doubt arose in lord Li's heart and he sent men out to meet him. Then these villagers made report, saying, "The bailiff Tu Hsing has returned."

Then Li Yün asked, saying, "How many men have come back?"

The villagers said, "Only the bailiff himself has come running back alone."

Then Li Yün shook his head and said, "Here is a strange thing. Usually they do not treat me so meanly as this. Why is it they are thus today?" And he came out of the outer hall and Yang Hsiung and Shih Hsiu came with him. There they saw Tu Hsing come down from his horse and he came to the gate of the village. When they saw his appearance he was so angered the skin of his face was empurpled and his teeth were bared. For a time he could not speak and at last Li Yün asked him, saying, "Pray speak out all the cause for this. How has this come about?"

But Tu Hsing had to let his anger go down before he could speak, and he said, "This lowly one took my lord's letter and I went to the third gate and there I met the three brothers, Chu The Dragon, Chu The Tiger, and Chu The Tiger Cub. There they sat. I made three greetings. But Chu The Tiger Cub shouted out, 'For what have you come hither again?' Then I bowed and said humbly, 'My lord has a letter here.' Then that Chu The Tiger Cub changed the look of his face and he began to curse, saying, 'That lord of yours —how is it he knows so little of propriety? This morning a worthless evil fellow came hither bringing a letter and he sought for that robber from the robbers' lair, Shih Ch'ien. Now even as I am about to send him into the city court how is it you are come again?' This lowly one then replied, 'This Shih Ch'ien is not one of the horde at the robbers' lair. He is only a traveler from Chi Chou and he was coming to see the lord of our humble village. In carelessness he burned your inn, but our lord will have it built again as it was before. Ten thousand times do I hope you will consider our poor pride and raise your hand high in mercy and let him go free. Forgive—forgive!' Then the three Chus all began to cry out, 'We will not give him back—we will not give him back—' Again did I say, 'My lord, pray look for yourselves at this letter that my lord has written with his own pen for you.' But those three Chus, although they took the letter, they did not open it to read it; they tore it into many pieces and they shouted to a villager to thrust me out of the gate by my neck. And Chu The Tiger and Chu The Tiger Cub said too, 'Do not rouse the anger of your superiors! Or we will—' I do not dare to tell you plainly what they said for those three beasts are without any sense of propriety, and they said, 'And we will take that Li of yours, that Li Yün of yours, and we will treat him like a robber of the robbers' lair and send him to court, too!' Then they shouted to the villagers to seize me but I made my horse fly and so I came away. But on the road I was like to die of my anger—those accursed—for naught have we sworn all these years of brotherhood—to be so without any righteousness or mercy today—"

Li Yün heard to the end and the uncontrollable anger of his heart rose as it were thirty thousand feet into the air nor could he smother it down and in a great voice he called to the villagers, "Saddle me my horse immediately!"

Then Yang Hsiung and Shih Hsiu exhorted him, saying, "Great lord, cease your anger. Do not because of ones so lowly as we are spoil the harmony of this place."

But how could Li Yün be willing to hear them? He went into his room and he put on a yellow robe of war and girdled it with a clasp and he put on his front and back shield with the faces of beasts upon them. Over this he wore a full robe of red and on his back he hung his bow and his flying arrows. He took his staff of iron and steel and wore his helmet winged like a phœnix, and he went outside the village. There he counted out three hundred fierce brave villagers and they also put on their garments of war. With his weapon in his hand he mounted his horse, and with him also he took some twenty horsemen. And Yang Hsiung and Shih Hsiu also tied up their garments securely and grasping their swords they went with Li Yün beside his horse and they all hastened to the village of Chu, and as the sun was about to sink behind the mountains they had already come to the front of The Ridge Of The Lonely Dragon and there they lined up their men and horses.

Now this village of Chu was better built than the village of Li and they claimed the whole ridge as their land. Around it was a broad stream and the village was set on the very top of the ridge. It was encircled by three walls about twenty feet high and all made of great piled rocks. There were two gates, one back, one front, and a drawbridge to each. Within the walls were built small houses and in all of them were swords, spears, and weapons of all sorts. On the towers of the walls were placed drums and brass gongs of war.

And Li Yün sat upon his horse at the front of the village and he shouted in a mighty voice and he said, "You three of the house of Chu! How dare you curse me and speak evil of me?"

Then was the gate of the village seen to open and out charged some fifty or sixty horses. The front horse was as red as coals and upon it sat the third son of Chu, The Tiger Cub! But Li Yün pointed at him and cursed mightily, saying, "Such as you! There is still the smell of milk on your lips—you have your new born hair still on your head—your father swore the vow of brotherhood with me to live and die together so that whatever we did we would be of the same mind and heart and protect our villages. If there were trouble in your house and he came to ask me for men in the morning I would send men that same morning. If you wanted anything I would not once deny you. Now I have but a common fellow for whom I have written twice to ask him of you and why did you tear up my letter and spoil my name? What sort of reason is this?"

Then Chu The Tiger Cub answered, "My house did swear such a vow that we would stay together in heart and mind to fight against the robbers of the great lair and we swore that we would sweep the lair clean. How is it you have joined with these rebels? Is it your wish to be a rebel?"

Li Yün shouted out, "And whom do you say is in the great lair? Such as you—you take a common man for a robber and what crime is this!"

The Tiger Cub replied, "This robber Shih Ch'ien has already confessed what he is. Do not talk here so foolishly and wildly. You cannot cover it up! If you are going, then go—or we will seize you also and we will send you as a robber as well!"

Then indeed was Li Yün mightily angry and he beat his horse and with his weapons in his hands he charged upon The Tiger Cub. The Tiger Cub gave his horse free rein also that he might go and fight against Li Yün and there before The Ridge Of The Lonely Dragon these two fought back and forth and from side to side for some seventeen or eighteen rounds. But The Tiger Cub could not overcome Li Yün. He turned his horse and was about to retreat. But Li Yün urged his horse on in pursuit. The Tiger Cub held his weapon upright on his horse. With his left hand he reached for his bow, with his right he took at the same time his arrow and he fitted the arrow to the bow, and he stretched full his bow, he took true aim and turning, he let fly the arrow. In great haste Li Yün dodged to one side, but the arrow was already in his arm. He fell off his horse upon the ground. Then Chu The Tiger Cub turned his horse again to seize Li Yün. Yang Hsiung and Shih Hsiu, seeing this, gave a great shout and they took their two swords and they dashed forward toward The Tiger Cub's horse to kill him. The Tiger Cub could not withstand them and in great haste he turned his horse to go. But Yang Hsiung had already thrust his sword in the horse's thigh and in great pain the horse reared itself upright and nearly threw its rider upon the ground.

Then those men who had come out with The Tiger Cub all rushed forward, their arrows fixed to aim. Seeing this Yang Hsiung and Shih Hsiu thought to themselves, "We have no armor nor shields and there is naught for us to do but to retreat and pursue no more."

Now Tu Hsing had long ago lifted Li Yün up from the ground and mounting their horses they had already gone away. So Yang Hsiung and Shih Hsiu went with the villagers and so departed also. The soldiers and horsemen and villagers of the village of the Chu family pursued them for a mile or so and then seeing that it grew dark with night, they went home also.

Tu Hsing supported Li Yün and they went back to the front of the village and there dismounted and they went back into the inner hall and sat down. Then the women of the house came out to see him and when the arrow had been pulled out they tended him and they took off his garments of war and they spread ointment upon the wound.

That same night they all took counsel together in the inner hall. And Yang Hsiung and Shih Hsiu said to the bailiff Tu Hsing, "This great lord has been cursed by those lawless fellows and even struck with an arrow and Shih Ch'ien still cannot come forth free. It is all because of us that the great lord has become so entangled. We two brothers can but go on to the mountain lair and there see Ch'ao Kai and Sung Chiang and implore their aid, and so also implore all the chieftains that they may come and take revenge for the great lord, and at the same time save Shih Ch'ien."

Thus saying they went to take their farewell of Li Yün and to thank him and Li Yün said, "It was not that I did not use my heart in it, but truly it was that I could not help it. I pray you, Sir Braves, that you will not blame me therefore."

Then he bade Tu Hsing to take out gold and silver and give it to them. But how could Yang Hsiung and Shih Hsiu be willing to receive it? Yet Li Yün said, "Nevertheless, pray accept it, Sirs."

Only then were the two willing to receive the gift. Then they bade Li Yün farewell and Tu Hsing escorted them outside the village gate and pointed out the highway and then he bade them farewell and went back to the village alone. Of this no more need be told.

Let it be told further. Yang Hsiung and Shih Hsiu followed the road toward the robbers' lair and soon they saw in the far distance a newly erected wine shop and the flag hung high before it. The two went into the inn and bought some wine to drink and then they asked the direction of the road. Now this wine shop was one newly built by the robbers for the purpose of spying out the land, and Shih Yung was the keeper of it. As the two drank therefore they asked the serving man what road to take to the mountain lair. Shih Yung, seeing that these two were no common fellows, then came forward himself to talk with them and he said, "From whence have two such honored guests come? And why is it you ask the road up the mountain?"

Yang Hsiung replied, "We have come from Chi Chou."

Then Shih Yung suddenly bethought himself and he asked, "It must be this honorable one is Shih Hsiu?"

Yang Hsiung replied, "I am only Yang Hsiung. This brother is Shih Hsiu. But how is it that you, Elder Brother, know the name of Shih Hsiu?"

In great haste Shih Yung replied, "This lowly one does not know him. But when our brother

Tai Chung went to Chi Chou and returned he said he had known the brother Shih Hsiu. Long have I heard your name and we are rejoiced to have you come up the mountain."

When these three had all made obeisance, Yang Hsiung and Shih Hsiu told Shih Yung all that had happened. Immediately Shih Yung commanded the serving man to bring wine that they might all drink, and he opened the windows of the pavilion in the water and let fly a singing arrow. Then out of the reeds opposite there came soon robbers rowing a boat. Shih Yung then invited the other two to get into the boat and he escorted them to The Duck's Bill Beach. Now Shih Yung had already sent men up the mountain to announce who was coming and they soon saw Tai Chung and Yang Ling coming down the mountain to meet them. When each one of them had made obeisance and had performed the rites of courtesy, they went together into the great lair.

All the chiefs now knew it that this day there were good fellows coming up the mountain and they all came to meet together, and they sat down in the hall of the great lair. And Tai Chung and Yang Ling led Yang Hsiung and Shih Hsiu into the hall to make obeisance before Ch'ao Kai and Sung Chiang and all the chieftains. When they had met each other Ch'ao Kai asked closely into the history of these two. Then Yang Hsiung and Shih Hsiu told what skill they had in weapons, and all were very pleased and gave them seats in their ranks. Then Yang Hsiung slowly said, "There was one who came with us to join this great lair who is called Shih Ch'ien, who did what he should not and in the inn he stole the fowl that crew for the dawn and in a moment there was a quarrel sprung up. Shih Hsiu set fire to the place and burned up the inn and its goods and Shih Ch'ien was captured by them. Li Yün twice wrote a letter to free him but unluckily the three sons of the house of Chu would not let the man go. They swore they would seize all the good fellows in the mountain lair and in every sort of way they insulted and cursed us. Truly indeed those hateful things are without any propriety whatever."

Now if he had not spoken these words to Ch'ao Kai ten thousand things would never have happened, for he had scarce finished speaking when Ch'ao Kai fell into a great rage and he shouted, "Children, kill me these two men and show me their heads when you have done it!"

In great haste Sung Chiang said, "Elder Brother, cease your anger. These two braves, not fearing the distance, came from far away and they came hither to help us. Why then would you kill them?"

Ch'ao Kai said, "We good fellows of the mountain, ever since we killed Wang Lün, have always held first loyalty and propriety. We have always treated the common people with mercy and with righteousness. Whenever we go down the mountain we have never once lost our pure passion. All our brothers here on the mountain, whether newly come or here of old, have the demeanor of noblemen. But these two things have taken our fair name to go and steal fowls to eat and they have made us share their shame! Today then we will first kill these twain and we will hang their heads there by the burned inn for a sign to all men. I will myself take fighting men and horses and lay waste that village, so that our pure passion may not be lost. Children, quickly kill these and bring their heads to me!"

But Sung Chiang exhorted him, saying, "It is not so. Elder Brother, have you not heard what these two good brothers have just now said? That Flea On A Drum Shih Ch'ien has ever been a thief like this, and so because of this he roused the anger of the Chu family. How then is it that these two good brothers have put us to shame? I have often heard men say also that those men in the village of the Chu family would fain war against us here in the lair. Elder Brother, cease your wrath at once therefore. Now our men and horses in the lair are countless in number, but we lack money and food. If we do not go and seek them out for a battle, then those things will come and seek trouble with us, as though one blew aside the hair on a beast's skin to seek for hidden disease. For thus well enough it is for us to seize this chance to go and fight them. If we can capture this village we will have food enough for three or five years. It is not that we have made a quarrel to injure them, but indeed they are without any law at all. But you are chief of the lair and you cannot go hither and thither on these small frays. But I, lowly and unskilled as I am, will myself take men and horses and I will ask some of my good brothers to go down the mountain with me to attack the village of the Chu family. If we do not lay waste that village I will never come up the mountain again. In the first place, I do this so that we will not lose our pure passion of purpose. In the second place, only thus can we wipe away the shame of being cursed by such small men as these. In the third place, we shall gain a great deal of food to give to the lair to use. In the fourth place, we must invite Li Yün to come up the mountain and join us."

Then Counsellor Wu Yung said, "Our brother Sung Chiang speaks very fitly. How can we brothers in the lair kill those of our own number, as though hand should kill foot?"

Then Tai Chung said, "I would cut off my own head rather than have these two brothers beheaded, for then would the brave men of all other places fear to come hither any more."

Thus did all the chiefs exhort, and only then did Ch'ao Kai consent to change his command, and Yang Hsiung and Shih Hsiu then made their apologies. But Sung Chiang comforted them, saying, "Good Brothers, do not think amiss. This is the rule of our lair, and we cannot but act thus. If even I committed some fault even I also would lose my head, and I would not dare beg repeal because of my place. Now the command has been made that The Iron Faced, P'ei Hsüan, shall be chief of police among the fighting men, and there are laws fixed for reward and for punishment. Good Brothers, you can but pardon us, therefore."

Then Yang Hsiung and Shih Hsiu having made obeisances and given apologies, Ch'ao Kai called out, "Go and sit below Yang Ling!"

Then all the lesser robbers were bade to come and make their congratulations to the new chiefs. Cows and horses were butchered and a feast of welcome made. Two houses were set apart and there Yang Hsiung and Shih Hsiu were told to settle themselves, and each person was given two lesser robbers as serving men.

That night after they had feasted and scattered they met again to feast on the second day. When they were all gathered together they took counsel together and Sung Chiang told The Iron Faced P'ei Hsüan to count off certain men to go down the mountain, and he invited other chieftains also to go with him to attack the village of Chu, for he was determined to lay waste that whole village. When they had decided about the affair, besides Ch'ao Kai who stayed always to guard the lair, there stayed behind Wu Yung, Liu T'ang and the three Juan brothers, Lü Fang and Kao Shen to protect the great lair. All those who had certain tasks assigned to their care such as guarding the shores and guarding the gates, tending the wine shops, and all such as these did not go forth. Moreover, the newly appointed boat master Meng K'an was changed for the old master Ma Ling, and a proclamation was written that all chieftains who went down the mountain to attack the village of Chu were to be divided into two companies. The first company was to be Sung Chiang, Hua Yung, Li Chün, Mu Hung, Li K'uei, Yang Hsiung, Shih Hsiu, Huang Hsin, Ou P'eng and Yang Ling, and they led with them three thousand robbers and three hundred horsemen and they put on their armor and took their weapons and went down the mountain and on their way.

The second company was Ling Ch'ung, Ch'ing Ming, Tai Chung, Chang Heng, Chang Shun, Ma Ling, Teng Fei, Wang The Dwarf Tiger and Pei Sheng, and they also led forth three thousand robbers and three hundred horsemen and they followed behind the others. Then were appointed to the two lesser lairs of The Golden Sands and The Duck's Bill Beach Sung Wan and Chen T'ien Shou. They were to remain there and bring food for men and feed for the horses. And Ch'ao Kai escorted the warriors for a distance and then he returned alone to the lair.

Let it be told now how Sung Chiang and the other chieftains all hastened as fast as they could to the village of the Chu family. Of the journey there is nothing to be told for they soon came to the front of The Lonely Dragon Ridge and there was about a third of a mile and a little more to go. The fighting men in front set their ten tents in the form of a square and Sung Chiang's tent stood in the middle. There he took counsel with Hua Yung and he said, "I have heard it said that the small paths into the village of the Chu family are many and confused and it is not possible to take fighting men thither. Let us therefore first send two men in to spy out and hear how the paths wind themselves for we must know clearly what road goes to and what road goes from the village before we can send fighting men in to do battle with them there."

Then Li K'uei said, "Elder Brother, I have been idle for how long and I have not killed a single man all that time. I will go first for once."

But Sung Chiang replied, "Brother, you may not go. When we break the ranks of the enemy and charge in, then will we use you at the front. But this is an affair of spying and we cannot use you."

Li K'uei laughed and said, "But for such an accursed village as this why should you trouble yourself so much, my Elder Brother? Let me just take two or three hundred of our children and we will kill our way in! We will slaughter every person in this accursed village. Why should we want men to go first and spy out?"

But Sung Chiang shouted out, saying, "Do not speak as a fool! Go aside, you! When I call you then only are you to come!"

Li K'uei went away then and to himself he muttered, "What is the use of making such an ado over killing a few flies!"

Then Sung Chiang called Shih Hsiu to come and he said, "Brother, you have already been there. Do you set out early in the morning therefore with Yang Ling."

Shih Hsiu said then, "Now has my elder brother come hither with many men and horses, and will not the village be well prepared for it? How shall we best disguise ourselves to go in?"

Then Yang Ling said, "I will disguise myself as an exorcist priest and in my robes I will hide a dagger and in my hands I will take my sounding wheel and as I go I will turn it around and around. When you hear the sound of it then do not leave my side."

And Shih Hsiu said, "I was once a seller of fuel in Chi Chou. I will therefore but carry in a load of fuel to sell and it will be well enough. I will hide a weapon at my side also, and if something unforeseen comes sudenly to pass I can use my carrying pole as weapon also."

Yang Ling replied, "Good, good. Now we have planned this together and tonight we will make all ready and we will rise at the fifth watch and set forth."

When the next morning was come Shih Hsiu went first carrying his load of fuel and he had gone scarcely seven miles when he saw the paths were many and crossed each other often and on all four sides there were circling, intersecting paths. There were many trees also and it was hard to know what direction to take. Then he put down his load and did not go forward, for he heard beside him begin slowly the sound of the exorcist's wheel. When Shih Hsiu looked he saw Yang Ling, on his head a large broken hat, on his person an old robe of a Taoist priest and in his hand he whirled the sounding wheel. Thus he came all the way whirling it. Shih Hsiu, seeing there was not a person near, called out to Yang Ling, "These roads are very tangled, and I do not know which road it was that I came the other day with Li Yün. The night was dark too, and they all knew the way and came and went quickly and I could not see how they went."

Yang Ling said, "But let us pay no heed to whether the paths go straight or crooked. Let us but follow the big road."

Again Shih Hsiu took up his load and he went ahead on the big road. At last ahead of him he saw a village full of people and there were many meat shops and wine shops. Shih Hsiu, bearing the fuel, went to the door of a wine shop and there put down his load. Then he saw that every shop had knives and weapons thrust into the earth before the door. Every man wore also a yellow sleeveless jacket, and on the jackets were printed a large character Chu and every man who came and went was so garbed. Shih Hsiu saw this and he looked at an old man and called greeting and made obeisance and said, "Elder One, pray tell me what the customs of this place are and why do they thrust all their knives and weapons before their doors?"

That old man replied, "And from whither are you a traveler that you do not know that you can but go quickly on your way?"

Shih Hsiu said, "I am a traveler from Shantung come out to sell dates and I have lost my capital and I cannot return to my native place. For this I have carried fuel hither to sell. But I do not know the customs here nor do I know how the land lies."

Then the old man said, "You can but go speedily on your way and hide somewhere else. There is soon to be a great war here."

But Shih Hsiu asked, "But in such a good and pleasant village as this how can they wish to war such a great war?"

The old man replied, "Sir Guest, I do not know whether you be true or not but I will tell you this. We here are called the village of the Chu family and on the ridge there is the house of our chieftain Chu Ch'ao Feng. Now we have offended the good fellows of the robbers' lair and they have brought soldiers and horsemen to the mouth of the village and they have come to attack and to kill us. But they do fear the entangled paths to our village and so they dare not to come on. They all wait outside and we have already sent out a command from the village that every man of every house who is young and strong shall be prepared for battle. When the command comes they are to rush to our aid."

Shih Hsiu asked, "But how many men have you here in this village, Elder One?"

The old man said, "Only in this one village we have some ten or twenty thousand men. To the east and west are two more villages who will support us. The east village belongs to the lord Li Yün and the west belongs to the lord Hu. He has a daughter who is third daughter of the house of Hu and her nickname is The Ten Foot Green Snake and she is altogether terrible."

Again Shih Hsiu asked, "Then why should such parts as these fear the robbers' lair?"

Again that old man replied, "But even if we ourselves came for the first time and did not know the road they would take us too."

And Shih Hsiu asked, "Elder One, how do you mean when you first came you would be taken?"

The old man replied, "Of these paths in our village men of old have said, 'How good a village is this of the Chu family, to which all the roads circle and entwine! It is easy to go in but one cannot escape from it.' "

When Shih Hsiu heard this he began to weep, and he fell down and made obeisance and he cried to the old man, "I am but one who travels far and wide and who have lost my capital and I can never return to my home. If I sell my load and go out and I come upon the war and cannot escape will it not be bitter for me then? My Father, have pity on me and I will give you this load of fuel! Only point me out the path!"

Then that old man said, "And why should I take your fuel for nothing? I will buy it of you. Come in, then. Pray drink some wine and eat some rice."

Then Shih Hsiu thanked him and taking up his load he went with that old man and so into the house, and the old man poured out two bowls of white wine and he filled a bowl with gruel made from the polishings of rice and he bade Shih Hsiu eat it. Then again Shih Hsiu made obeisance and he thanked him, saying, "Father, do you but tell me now the path out."

And the old man said, "Go out from the village and you will see a white poplar tree. There you may turn. Pay no heed to whether the road be narrow or wide, but wherever the road turns by a white poplar that is the way. If there is not such a tree, then the road is dead. If there is any other tree, it is not the road either. If you go astray, however you turn you cannot get out. Moreover in the earth of these paths there are hidden pointed bamboos and pointed iron prongs. If you go astray you may also fall into a trap and a barb will fly at you and you will be caught. Whither do you think to go?"

And Shih Hsiu made obeisance and he gave thanks and he asked then, "Father, what is your noble surname?"

That old man said, "Of those surnamed Chu the village has the most. There is only I and I have a double surname and it is Chung Li and I have lived here long."

And Shih Hsiu said, "I have eaten enough of both food and wine and on another day I will repay you richly."

Now in the midst of this talk they heard a confusion and a quarreling outside and Shih Hsiu heard them say, "We have caught a spy!"

At this Shih Hsiu gave a start of fear and when he went out with the old man to see what was amiss, there he saw some seventy or eighty fighting men leading a man with his hands bound behind him. When Shih Hsiu looked at this man it was no other than Yang Ling, stripped naked and with thongs binding him. When Shih Hsiu had seen this he could but cry bitterness to himself secretly and in a low voice he asked the old man falsely, saying, "Who is this man they have seized? And why is he thus bound?"

The old man replied, "Did you not hear them say he is a spy from Sung Chiang's side?"

Again Shih Hsiu asked, saying, "How is it he was taken?"

And the old man replied, "They said this thing had the greatest sort of daring. He came here alone as a spy and he wore as disguise the robe of a Taoist exorcist and so he came into the village. But he did not know the paths and so he came only by the big road and he came winding right and left and so he fell into the blind paths. Nor did he know the trick of the white poplar trees that they are signs. Men seeing that he had gone astray began to suspect him as to where he had come from, and they sent report to the guards of the head of the village that they should come and seize him. Then this thing took out his dagger and whenever he moved his hand he wounded some four or five men. But he could not withstand so many men as are here and when they all charged upon him they captured him. There were some who knew him as a robber before and he was called The Five Hued Leopard Yang Ling—"

But before he finished speaking they heard a shout in front, "The third lord of the Chu family comes to examine the people in the streets!"

Now Shih Hsiu was standing and he was peeping out of a crack in the corner of the wall and he saw twenty pair of pointed staves on which waved tassels of horsehair dyed red, and there were four or five men who followed behind on horseback, and they all carried bows and quivers full of arrows. There were three or five pairs of pure white horses and they encircled a young warrior in their midst. He rode upon a snow-white horse, and he wore armor from head to foot, and his bow and his quiver of arrows hung upon his person. In his hand was a silver weapon.

Now Shih Hsiu knew him very well but he asked the old man falsely, saying, "Who is this lord who passes by?"

And that old man replied, "This man is no other than the third son of the head of the village, who is Chu Ch'ao Feng, and his name is Chu The Tiger Cub. He is already betrothed to the maid in the western village of Hu, she who is called The Ten Foot Green Snake. There are three brothers but he is the most terrible of all."

Then Shih Hsiu made obeisance and he gave thanks, saying, "Father, pray point me out the path by which I must go out."

That old man said, "Today it is late and if there is a battle ahead you will have lost your life for nothing."

Then Shih Hsiu said, "My father, save this life of mine!"

And that old man said, "Pray rest a night here in my home. Tomorrow we will listen and if there is no trouble then you shall go out."

So Shih Hsiu made obeisance of thanks again and he stayed at the old man's house. Then he saw suddenly four or five horsemen coming to make report and they went to every house, and they gave the command, saying, "Oh you people, tonight you are to see the red lamps as signals. With united heart and united strength go forth to seize the robbers of the robbers' lair! Then will we take them to the magistrate and ask for our reward!" Thus shouting they went past and on their way. Then Shih Hsiu asked, saying, "Who are these men?"

That old man replied, "The official is the police of this village, and tonight they have all covenanted together that they will seize Sung Chiang."

Shih Hsiu, hearing what was said, pondered for a time in his heart and then he asked the old man for a torch and bade him a good and peaceful night. Then he went into his own thatched room and lay down.

Let it then be told of Sung Chiang and his men and horsemen who waited encamped about the village. They did not see Yang Ling and Shih Hsiu come back to make report, and therefore again they sent Ou P'eng to go to the mouth of the village. He came back and made report, saying, "I hear the people inside stirring and talking together and they say they have caught a spy. But seeing how tangled the road paths were and how hard to tell one from the other, I did not dare to go deeply in."

Sung Chiang listened to the end of his speech and his anger rose in him and he said, "How can we wait until they come back and make report before our fighting men can go in? We have already lost a spy to them and surely our two brothers are held there. This night our fighting men can but press in, killing as we go for we must save our two brothers. But I do not know what all the chieftains think of this."

Then Li K'uei was seen to say, "I will kill my way in first and see how things are."

Sung Chiang heard this and at once he sent forth a command to tell the fighting men to put on armor and weapons and Li K'uei and Yang Hsiung were to go in first as vanguard. Li Chün and others were to bring up the rear. Mu Hung at the left and Huang Hsin at the right, and Sung Chiang, Hua Yung, Ou P'eng and others were chiefs in the midst of the ranks.

Then waving their flags and shouting their war cries, beating their drums and gongs with their great knives and their broadaxes they went charging toward the village, killing as they went until they might reach The Ridge Of The Lonely Dragon.

Now this was the time of twilight and Sung Chiang urged the front men on to attack the village. The vanguard Li K'uei stripped stark naked and grasping two long-handled battle axes, went leaping ahead like a flame. When he came to the village and looked about the drawbridge was already high drawn and there was not a flicker of light to be seen at the gate of the village. Li K'uei then was about to go down into the water of the moat and so cross over, but Yang Hsiung laid hold on him and said, "This you may not do. They have closed the village gate and assuredly there is a plot here. Wait until our Elder Brother comes and we will plan a way."

But how could Li K'uei be patient? Clapping his broadaxes together he roared curses at the other shore and he said, "That cursed old thief of a lord Chu! Come out, you! Your elder The Black Whirlwind is here!"

But there came no answer from the village. Then Sung Chiang and all the chiefs and horsemen and fighting men arrived, and Yang Hsiung went to meet them and he said, "We see neither men nor horses at the village nor is there a sound of anyone stirring."

Then Sung Chiang reined in his horse and he looked about him. There could be seen no weapon nor blade, neither man nor horse about the village. He began to have doubts in his heart and suddenly he bethought himself, "This is my mistake! Those heavenly books commanded me very clearly forbidding me, saying, 'Do not be impatient before battle.' But I did not at that time foresee this. I thought only to save my two brothers, and for this have I led my men out even in the night. I did not dream I would have already come so deeply into danger. If we go straight to the front of the village and see no enemy there, then assuredly there is a plot."

Then quickly he shouted out, "Retreat, all!"

But Li K'uei cried out, saying, "Elder Brothers, the fighting men and the horses have already come to this point, do not retreat! I will go with you two and we will first kill our way across. All of you come after me."

But before he had finished speaking it was already known in the village. There was heard the sound of a single signal rocket that flew across the heavens. Straightway upon The Ridge Of The Lonely Dragon there flamed a hundred thousand torches and they were all flaring. Beneath the gate house on the village wall the arrows came out like a shower of rain. In great haste Sung Chiang went back by the road they had come. Then the chieftains and the men bringing up the rear, Li Chün and his horses and men, first set up a shout, saying, "The road by which we came is all closed and assuredly there are men in ambush!"

Then Sung Chiang sent out men and horsemen to seek in all four directions for a road by which to go. Li K'uei, brandishing his two axes, ran hither and thither seeking for someone to kill. But there was not an enemy to be seen. Only upon the crest of The Ridge Of The Lonely Dragon a rocket again was set free. Before the report of it was ended there rose a roar of voices from all four sides that made the very earth shake and it so frightened Sung Chiang that his eyes were fixed and his mouth ajar. He did not know what to do.

Though one had all the books that tell of the feints of war, how still could he escape the nets spread upon earth and sky? Truly,

They have trapped the tiger and they hold the dragon fast,
The greatest hero under heaven is captured at last.

How then did Sung Chiang and the chieftains escape? Pray hear it told in the next chapter.

Chapter 47

THE TEN FOOT GREEN SNAKE ALONE CAPTURES WANG THE DWARF TIGER. SUNG CHIANG ATTACKS THE VILLAGE OF CHU FOR THE SECOND TIME

IT IS SAID: At that time when Sung Chiang, mounted on his horse, looked about him there were men hidden on all four sides, and he could but direct the robbers to fight their way through by the main road. But he heard them all suddenly stayed and they began to cry out bitterness. Then Sung Chiang asked, saying, "Why do you call bitterness?"

And the fighting men replied, "Ahead of us the roads are all entwined together and we have already walked about them but we have only circled our way back here again!"

Then Sung Chiang said, "Bid all the horses and men go toward the torches where there are men and houses and there seek for a road to go!"

Again they were not gone long when the fighting men in front once more cried out, saying, "We can only walk straight toward the torches, and there are pointed bamboos set up to barb us and there are iron thongs here to catch us and they are scattered everywhere like green horns! They fill the mouth of every path!"

Then Sung Chiang said, "Is this not that Heaven wills me to die?"

Even as they were in the midst of this terror they heard a noise and confusion among the men to the left, where were the men led by Mu Hung and a report was brought, saying, "Shih Hsiu has come!"

When Sung Chiang looked he saw Shih Hsiu had in his hand a knife and he came rushing before the horse and he said, "Elder Brother, do not be in haste! I know now where the road is!"

Then a secret command was sent out to tell all the scattered fighting men that wherever they saw a white poplar tree there they were to turn, and they were to pay no heed to whether the road was wide or narrow. And Sung Chiang urged on men and horses and wherever they saw a white poplar tree there they turned.

Now when they had gone some two miles it was seen that the men and horses were suddenly increased in number, and Sung Chiang began to have a suspicion and he called Shih Hsiu and asked, saying, "Brother, how is it that there are more men in front?"

And Shih Hsiu said, "They have a lighted lantern for a sign."

Hua Yung on horseback saw this also and he pointed it out to Sung Chiang and he said, "Elder Brother, look there in the shadows of the trees—do you see the candle-lit lantern there? When they see our men go east they move the lantern east. If we go toward the west they move the lantern to the west. We do think that thing we can see is their sign!"

Then Sung Chiang asked, "And what can we do with that lantern?"

Hua Yung replied, "What is there difficult in it?" And he took up his bow and fitted an arrow to it and urging his horse he galloped to the lantern. Then staring straight into the shadow of the lantern he let his arrow fly, and without moving to either side the arrow struck the lantern exactly and it fell. As for the ambushed men, suddenly not seeing the red light they all ran in confusion. Then Sung Chiang told Shih Hsiu to lead the way and they charged out and away from the village.

But suddenly a mighty shout was heard from the hill ahead and there a line of torches was seen, some held straight and some awry. Then Sung Chiang commanded, "Men in the front, stay! Let Shih Hsiu lead the way and spy out ahead!"

In a short time Shih Hsiu returned and made report, saying, "The second division of men has arrived from the mountain lair. They have come to our aid and they have killed and scattered all these ambushed fighting men."

When Sung Chiang had heard this he pressed

forward and ordered his men to draw together to the center and they forced their way and rushed out of the mouth of the village, and so were the men and horses of the village of Chu all scattered and routed. Then the others went on and they met Ling Ch'ung and Ch'ing Ming and their horses and men. And there outside the mouth of the village they all halted their men.

It was now about the time of dawn and they chose out a certain hill and there prepared to encamp the men and to count the number of men and horses. Now among the men the Chief Huang Hsin was not found. Then was Sung Chiang in great fright and he asked for the reason of this, and there was a fighting man who had gone with Huang Hsin the night before who saw him and he came and said, "Our chief Huang heard the elder brother's command and he went ahead to spy out the way. But he was not prepared for two barbed hooks that came out of the reeds and dragged him in and he was captured alive by some five or seven men. Nor could we save him."

When Sung Chiang heard this he fell into a mighty fury and he was fain to kill all those who had gone with Huang Hsin because they had not come long ago and reported the matter, except that Ling Ch'ung and Hua Yung exhorted him. Then Sung Chiang and all the others grieved and they said each to the other, "Nor did we lay waste the village—and we have lost two of our brothers! What then can we do?"

At last Yang Hsiung said, "There are here three villages joined together. But that thing The Tiger Cub did wound the lord Li, who lives in the eastern village. Now he is in his village seeking to cure himself. Elder Brother, why do you not go and take counsel with him?"

And Sung Chiang replied, "I had truly forgot him, and yet he must know very well how the roads go hereabouts." So he commanded that two bolts of satin, a pair of sheep, and two jars of wine should be fetched and a good horse chosen complete with saddle and bridle and he would himself go thither and ask for meeting, and Ling Ch'ung and Ch'ing Ming he commanded to guard the encampment meanwhile.

Then Sung Chiang took with him Yang Hsiung, Hua Yung and Shih Hsiu and they mounted their horses and they led forth with them three hundred horsemen, and they turned toward the village of Li. When they had come to the front of the village they saw the gates were already closed fast and the bridge was drawn high from the moat. Upon the wall were placed many men and horses and in the tower above the gate, drums and gongs were already beating. Then Sung Chiang called from horseback, saying, "I am the nobleman Sung Chiang from the great lair of Liang Shan P'o and I have come hither only to see the great lord! No other purpose have I than this! Do not oppose me!"

Then from the tower Tu Hsing saw Yang Hsiung and Shih Hsiu were there and in great haste he opened the village and he came in a small boat across the moat and gave greeting to Sung Chiang. In great haste also did Sung Chiang come down from his horse and he returned the courtesy. Then Yang Hsiung and Shih Hsiu said humbly to Sung Chiang, "This honorable brother was he who led us to meet the lord Li, and he is called The Devil Faced Tu Hsing."

And Sung Chiang said, "Then you are the head of the village. I seek to trouble you to say to the great lord Li that I, Sung Chiang of the mountain lair, have long heard of his great name, but we have had no chance of meeting. Today because the village of Chu seeks to fight against us we passed by this place and I have come especially to present this flowered satin, this famous steed, these sheep, this wine, poor gifts all, yet I do pray that he will see me the once. Beyond this I have no other purpose."

Tu Hsing received these words and he then crossed the moat again and went straight into the hall. There Li Yün sat in bed nursing his wound, his quilt wrapped about him, and Tu Hsing told him the words with which Sung Chiang had implored him and Li Yün answered, "He is a rebel of the robbers' lair and why should I meet with him, for even though I have naught to do with him yet would it seem that I did. You may reply to him saying that I am ill upon my bed in my room and I cannot move, and I cannot meet with him. On some other day I will exchange greetings. These gifts he has sent I dare not receive."

Then Tu Hsing went across the moat again and he said humbly to Sung Chiang, "My lord thrice sends his greetings and obeisances and he

THE TEN FOOT GREEN SNAKE AND WANG

thought to come out himself to meet the noble one, but because he is heavily wounded he lies ill upon his bed and he cannot meet with you. Some other day he will come especially to greet you. These great gifts recently presented he does not indeed dare to receive."

Then Sung Chiang said, "I know now what your lord's meaning is. Yet because I fought against the Chu village and was vanquished I came hither hoping to see him, and now because he fears the blame of the Chu village he will not come out to meet me."

But Tu Hsing replied, "Indeed it is not thus. He is truly ill. Although I am a man of Chung Shan I have been here for many years, and well do I know all the affairs of this region. In the midst is the village of the Chu family. Here at the east are we, the village of the Li family, at the west is the village of the family of Hu. These three villages have vowed to live and to die together and whenever there is trouble they will come ever to aid each other. This time they have offended my lord and of course he will not go to aid them, although it may be the village to the west will come to their aid. But there is no one to fear in that village except a woman warrior who is called The Ten Foot Green Snake and she uses two knives that glitter like the sun and moon, and how terrible is she in her skill! She is betrothed to the third son of the Chu family to be his wife. Soon he will wed her. If fighting men wish to attack the Chu village then do not prepare against us here in the east; only take heed for the west. There are two gates to the Chu village at both front and back; one is in the front of The Lonely Dragon Ridge and one is behind The Lonely Dragon Ridge. If you attack the front gate you surely cannot accomplish your purpose. You must attack front and back at the same time and only then can you prevail. When you have broken in the front gate the paths are entwined and hard to separate one from the other and everywhere the paths cross each other in circles, whether narrow or wide. But wherever there is a white poplar tree there you may turn and that is the true road. If there is not this tree then it is a blind alley."

Shih Hsiu said, "But they have now cut down all the white poplar trees, and what then can we take for a sign?"

And Tu Hsing replied, "Even though the trees are cut down how can they dig out the roots? There must be roots there by the road. You can only send men in by day to fight. You must not go in the black night."

Sung Chiang listened to the end and he thanked Tu Hsing. Then all the men and horses went back to their encampment. There Ling Ch'ung was waiting and he met them and they all went into the great central tent and sat down, and Sung Chiang told to all the chiefs the whole tale of how Li Yün would not see him and all that Tu Hsing had said. Then Li K'uei interrupted, saying, "And see how kind a meaning we had to send gifts to him, and that thing would not even come out to meet our elder brother! I will myself take three hundred men out and break open his accursed village! And I will drag him out by the hair to do obeisance to you, Elder Brother!"

But Sung Chiang said, "Brother, you do not understand. He is a man both rich and of high position and he fears the magistrate. Why should he meet us easily?"

Li K'uei laughed and said, "He is like a little child who is afraid to see a stranger!"

Then everybody began to laugh and Sung Chiang said, "While you are speaking thus, yet our two brothers are still locked within the village yonder, and I do not know whether they are alive or dead. Do you, my Brothers, press forward with all your strength and go again with me to attack the village of Chu."

Then every man rose and said, "Elder Brother, if you send out the command, who dares not to obey it? But we do not know who is commanded to go first."

Then The Black Whirlwind Li K'uei cried out, saying, "You are afraid of children,—I will go first!"

But Sung Chiang said, "It will not do to make you the vanguard. Today we cannot use you."

At this Li K'uei dropped his head and he nursed anger secretly in his breast. But Sung Chiang appointed Ma Ling and Teng Fei, Ou P'eng and Wang The Dwarf Tiger, these four, to go with himself to be the vanguard. And he appointed Tai Chung, Ch'ing Ming, Yang Hsiung, Shih Hsiu, Li Chün, Chang Heng, Chang Shun and Pei Sheng to prepare to go through water.

And he appointed Ling Ch'ung, Hua Yung, Mu Hung and Li K'uei to divide into two lines to be the aids. When all these men were thus appointed in order they all took food and then they put on their armor and mounted their horses.

Let it be told further. Sung Chiang would go himself to be the vanguard and the first to fight in the first battle and before him he had one bear a red banner to mark his leadership, and he led with him four chiefs and a hundred and fifty horsemen and a thousand fighting men on foot and they hastened to the village of Chu. When they had come to the front of The Lonely Dragon Ridge, Sung Chiang drew back his horse, and when he looked toward the village there were hung on either side of it white banners and upon the white banners were embroidered very plainly fourteen letters which said,

"Fill the pool of the robbers' lair that Ch'ao
Kai may be seized,
Stamp till the mountain's crest is smooth to
fetch away Sung Chiang."

Then was Sung Chiang's heart filled with wrath as he sat there upon his horse and he made a vow, saying, "If I do not overcome this village of Chu then may I never return to the great lair!"

Now all the chiefs heard this vow and they all saw the letters and they also were all filled with wrath. Then Sung Chiang, hearing that the men and horsemen from the rear were all come, divided off the second division of chiefs and men to attack the front gate, and he himself led the men and horsemen in the first division to go to the back of The Lonely Dragon Ridge. When he went to see what the village was there he saw the wall was as strong as though it were made of iron or copper and it was built exceedingly fast and strong without any crevice or crack in it. And even as he was looking at it, he saw from the west a crowd of fighting men and horsemen come charging forward shouting as they came.

Then Sung Chiang left Ma Ling and Teng Fei to guard the back gate of the village and he himself led Ou P'eng and Wang The Dwarf Tiger and a half of the men and horsemen and he went forward to meet these others from the west who came by the ridge. There were perhaps twenty or thirty horsemen among these and they encircled a female warrior. It was that very Ten Foot Green Snake of the village of Hu and she rode upon an ash-grey horse. In her hands she held two swords that glittered like sun and moon and she led some three or five hundred villagers and they came to the aid of the village of Chu. And Sung Chiang said, "We have just now heard there was such a female warrior in the village of Hu and that she was altogether terrible. I think this must surely be she. Who among you dares to oppose her?"

Before he had finished speaking this Wang The Dwarf Tiger, who was a lusty fellow with women, heard him say it was a female warrior and he hoped to seize her with one round of battle. So he gave a yell and he pressed his horse to the front and held his weapon in his hand and he came out to fight against her. The soldiers on both sides shouted. The woman whipped up her horse and whirled her two swords and she came to fight Wang The Dwarf Tiger.

Now this woman had used her swords until she had a very perfect skill and Wang The Dwarf Tiger was above all in the use of his single weapon. They fought some ten-odd rounds and then Sung Chiang as he watched from his horse saw that Wang The Dwarf Tiger could not withstand her longer. Now when Wang The Dwarf Tiger first saw The Green Snake he longed exceedingly to make her his own, and who would have thought when he had fought more than ten rounds that his hands began to tremble and his feet to shiver and so his parries and thrusts became uncertain? If it had not been that these two were to fight to the very death, Wang The Dwarf Tiger would have given himself up as vanquished.

Now that Green Snake was a very tricky female and in her heart she thought, "How mannerless is this thing!"

And with her two swords she thrust from above and beneath and how could Wang The Dwarf Tiger withstand her? He turned his horse about to make his escape, but The Green Snake urged on her horse and she pursued him and she put aside the sword from her right hand and stretched forth her fair woman's arm and she lifted Wang The Dwarf Tiger up from his saddle by his hair, and all the villagers crowded about and dragged him this way and that and so away.

Now when Ou P'eng saw that Wang The Dwarf Tiger was thus captured he lifted up his weapon and dashed forward to help him. The Green Snake gave rein to her horse and took up her two swords again and she came to meet Ou P'eng. Then the two fought. Now Ou P'eng's very ancestors had been warriors and he used the iron spear with exceeding skill. Yet as Sung Chiang watched the combat he cried secretly to himself, "How is it that in spite of all Ou P'eng's skill he cannot overcome the woman at all!"

Now Teng Fei from afar saw that Wang The Dwarf Tiger had been taken and that Ou P'eng could not vanquish this woman warrior either and he made his horse gallop forward and swung high his weapon and iron chain and shouting mightily he charged forward. Now the men of the village of Chu had long been watching this battle and they feared lest The Green Snake might suddenly fall and be killed or be captured and in great haste they let down the drawbridge and opened the village gate. Chu The Dragon himself led out more than three hundred men and urging on his horse and carrying his weapon aloft he pressed on to seize Sung Chiang. Then Ma Ling saw this and let his horse free and he came on brandishing his two knives and so he came to meet Chu The Dragon and kill him as he came.

Now Teng Fei feared lest Sung Chiang come to some mishap and he would not leave either right or left, although the battle raged on either side and the war cries rose from everywhere.

Then Sung Chiang when he perceived that Ma Ling could not overcome Chu The Dragon and Ou P'eng could not vanquish The Green Snake was greatly agitated. But suddenly he saw a crowd of horsemen and men come from the side. When Sung Chiang saw these he was greatly pleased for the company was led by The Fire In The Thunder Clap Ch'ing Ming who had heard the battle raging behind the village and he came quickly to their aid. In a loud voice Sung Chiang called out, "Ch'ing, my Brother, do you help Ma Ling!"

Now Ch'ing Ming was a man of swift temper and when he heard that the villagers had taken his scholar Huang Hsin he had indeed no way to vent his black anger. He beat his horse and galloped as though he were flying, brandishing his spiked mace, and he dashed forward to fight with Chu The Dragon. The Dragon also turned his weapon aside to fight with Ch'ing Ming. As for Ma Ling, he led certain men with him to go after Wang The Dwarf Tiger.

Now when The Green Snake saw Ma Ling pursue the prisoner she deserted Ou P'eng and came to meet Ma Ling to do battle with him. Each of them could use the double swords and each opposed the other from horseback. Truly did the swords glitter like the wind-blowing jade snowflakes that fell in fairy petals to the ground. Watching them Sung Chiang felt his eyes grow confused.

On his other side Ch'ing Ming and The Dragon fought more than ten rounds and how could The Dragon overcome Ch'ing Ming? Inside the gate of the village the instructor in war, surnamed Luan, brought his iron hammer and he mounted his horse with the weapon in his hand and he came charging out to do battle. Then did Ou P'eng come to meet him also to do battle, but Luan T'ing Yü did not come to oppose him, and as he brought his weapon he galloped to one side. Ou P'eng pursued him and suddenly Luan T'ing Yü's iron hammer flew out and beat him a blow, and Ou P'eng turned over and fell under his horse. Then Teng Fei gave a great cry, "Children, to the rescue!", and swinging his iron chain he charged forward and Sung Chiang commanded his men to rescue Ou P'eng with all haste.

Now of a certainty Chu The Dragon could not withstand Ch'ing Ming and he whipped his horse and retreated. Luan T'ing Yü also left Teng Fei and he came to oppose Ch'ing Ming. The two fought some ten or twenty rounds and it could not be told who was the victor and who the vanquished. Then Luan T'ing Yü made a false feint and he galloped out into the open field. Ch'ing Ming, bearing his weapon aloft, pursued him straightway. Then Luang T'ing Yü ran his horse into the midst of the long wild grass, but Ch'ing Ming did not know this was a plot and he still followed in pursuit.

Now the villagers of Chu had already placed men there in ambush and when they saw Ch'ing Ming's horse coming they drew hard on a rope on the ground and the horse stumbled on it and fell and Ch'ing Ming with it. Then the villagers gave a great shout and they captured Ch'ing Ming also. Teng Fei, seeing Ch'ing Ming fallen from his horse, went in great haste to save him but he saw the trap rope again come up and he could but turn himself and retreat. Then the men on both sides yelled forth, "We have him!" and the barbed hooks came out on every side and dragged him alive from his horse.

Now Sung Chiang seeing all this could but cry out bitterness and he helped Ou P'eng up on his horse again, and Ma Ling left The Green Snake and in haste came rushing to protect Sung Chiang and they went toward the south. Behind them Luan T'ing Yü, Chu The Dragon, and The Green Snake divided and came in hot pursuit. Then they saw there was no way open ahead of them and even as they were about to give themselves up to be bound they saw in the due south a fine fellow galloping as though his horse were winged. Behind him following him were some five hundred men and horsemen. When Sung Chiang looked at them, he saw it was He Whom No Obstacle Can Stay Mu Hung. Toward the southeast were also more than three hundred men and two good fellows leading them, hastening forward as though they flew. One was Yang Hsiung, and the other was Shih Hsiu. To the northeast was yet another good fellow and in a loud voice he shouted out that the two were not to be captured. When Sung Chiang looked, he saw it was Hua Yung. There were these three ranks of men and horsemen coming and they all came near together. Then Sung Chiang's heart was mightily rejoiced for that they all were come together with a great shout to do battle with Chu The Dragon and Luan T'ing Yü.

Now those who were watching from the village saw these and they feared lest The Dragon and Luan T'ing Yü come to some mishap and they bade Chu The Tiger guard the village gates. Then Chu The Tiger Cub, riding a prancing spirited war horse and bearing a long spear and himself leading five hundred men and horsemen, came out from behind the village to give battle and so they all plunged together into battle.

At the front of the village Li Chün, Chang Heng and Chang Shun crossed over through the water of the moat under the shower of arrows coming in all directions from the village and they could do nothing. As for Tai Chung and Pei Sheng, they could but stand on the opposite shore and shout. Sung Chiang, seeing the sky darkening with night, impatiently called to Ma Ling to protect Ou P'eng and lead him out of the mouth of the village. Then he bade the robbers beat their gongs and gather together all the good fellows and as they fought to retreat. He himself beat his horse and went everywhere searching among his men, for he feared lest his brothers might lose their way.

Even as Sung Chiang went thus he saw The Green Snake coming near on her winged horse and he had no time to withstand her and whipping his horse he escaped to the east. Behind him in hot pursuit came The Green Snake and their horses' hoofs sounded like bowls rolling on the ground. She pursued him into the very village and even as she was about to capture him and put forth her hand to seize him someone called in a loud voice, saying, "Where is that accursed hag driving my elder brother?"

When Sung Chiang looked to see it was no other than The Black Whirlwind Li K'uei whirling his two battle axes and leading some seventy or eighty robbers and with great strides he made haste hither. Then did The Green Snake rein in her horse and she went toward the wood, and Sung Chiang reined his horse in also to look about him and there he saw at the edge of the wood some ten-odd men on horseback charging forward and at their head was a brave and it was that very one The Leopard Headed, Ling Ch'ung. From his horse he gave a great shout, saying, "Ha, you hag, where do you go?"

Whirling her swords The Green Snake gave rein to her horse and dashed at Ling Ch'ung. Ling Ch'ung lifted his spear and the two fought less than ten rounds when suddenly Ling Ch'ung pretended to make a feint and he let The Green Snake come at him with her two swords. Then he stayed them fast with his spear held crosswise. The two swords glanced aside and Ling Ch'ung seized the opportunity and stretched out his apelike arm silently and he bent his wolf-like back and laying hold on The Green Snake he dragged her over upon his own horse. Sung Chiang, seeing, gave him a shout of praise, but paying no heed Ling Ch'ung bade the soldiers bind the woman. Then urging his horse he galloped before Sung Chiang and he asked, "You have not been wounded or annoyed, Elder Brother?"

Sung Chiang replied, "I am not wounded." Then he bade Li K'uei go quickly to the village and there meet all the good fellows and ask them to come to the mouth of the village and take counsel together for now the sky had darkened to night and the battle could be waged no longer. So The Black Whirlwind led out such men and horsemen as he commanded and Ling Ch'ung protected Sung Chiang and guarded The Green Snake who was now bound upon her horse, and he followed the road out to the mouth of the village. Now even until this night the robber chiefs had made no gain in the battle and in great haste they all came out of the village precincts. The men and horsemen of the village of Chu also went back to their own village and the village was filled with the countless dead.

And Chu The Dragon commanded that such as had been captured should all be put into prisoner carts, and when Sung Chiang was captured also they would take them all to the court in the eastern capital. The village of Hu also sent Wang The Dwarf Tiger to the village of Chu.

Now let it be told concerning Sung Chiang as he called together his great horde of fighting men and horsemen. When they came to the mouth of the village they put down camp there, and Sung Chiang called first for The Green Snake to be brought to him. Then he commanded twenty very honest robbers and four lesser chiefs to ride four swift horses and he had The Green Snake's two hands tied fast and he put her upon a horse also and he commanded, "This very night send her up the mountain to the lair for me, and give her into the keeping of my old father and then come back and make report of it to me. When I return to the lair myself, I will of a certainty have a way to arrange the matter."

All the chiefs then thought Sung Chiang wanted this woman for himself and they took great care in escorting her thither. A cart was called for Ou P'eng that he might ride up the mountain and care for his wounds. Thus were all the commands of Sung Chiang received and they went that selfsame night. As for Sung Chiang, he sat in his tent and grieved the night through nor did he sleep at all, but he sat and waited for the dawn. On the next day he saw a spy come and the spy made report, saying, "Our counselor Wu Yung comes hither leading the three chieftains who are the three Juan brothers, and Lü Fang and Kao Shen also and they are bringing five hundred fighting men and horsemen here."

Sung Chiang heard this and he went out to meet the counselor Wu Yung and they went in and sat down in the central tent. Now Wu Yung had brought with him food and wine and he poured out a cup of wine to honor Sung Chiang and he gave out food and wine to all the fighting men and their captains. Then he said, "Our chieftain Ch'ao Kai has already heard how you, our Elder Brother Sung Chiang, were defeated in the first attack and so he sent me, Wu Yung, and these five chieftains to aid you in the battle. But we cannot know how it will be with us today whether we shall be victorious or vanquished."

Sung Chiang answered, "It is difficult to tell of it all in a word. Those accursed villagers of the Chu village have put up white banners on either side of the gate, and on these is written

'Fill the pool of the robbers' lair that Ch'ao
Kai may be seized,
Stamp till the mountain's crest is smooth to
fetch away Sung Chiang.'

How without propriety are these men! We sent in a vanguard to attack them, but because we did not know how the land lay, we lost Yang Ling and Huang Hsin. Then by night we attacked again and that Ten Foot Green Snake captured Wang The Dwarf Tiger and Luan T'ing Yü with his iron mace felled Ou P'eng. Then a hidden trap of rope caused Ch'ing Ming and Teng Fei to fall from their horses. Thus have we been vanquished! If it had not been that the chief Ling Ch'ung opportunely caught The Green Snake alive then would our whole spirit of battle have been dispelled. At such a pass as this to which we have come, what shall we do? If I cannot lay waste this village and save these brothers of mine I will to die here by my own hand, for I have no honor left to go back and see my elder brother, Ch'ao Kai."

Then Wu Yung the counselor laughed and he said, "But this village ought to be destroyed by Heaven itself! Well indeed it is that there is now this opportunity. I think that soon or late, by night or day, this village can be destroyed."

Sung Chiang listened to the end of this and he was wholly delighted, and in great haste he asked, saying, "How is it that this village can be destroyed? From whence will this chance come?"

Wu Yung laughed and without haste or speed he held up his two fingers and he told how the chance would come. Truly was it,

Out of space a hand will come from where the clouds lie
To rescue those now held in this cage of earth and sky.

Now what was this chance of which Wu Yung the counselor spoke? Pray hear it told in the next chapter.

Chapter 48

THE TWO BROTHERS HSIEH ESCAPE FROM THE GAOL. THE TWO BROTHERS SHENG RUSH INTO THE GAOL MIGHTY TO SAVE

IT IS SAID: When Wu Yung the counselor was thus speaking to Sung Chiang he said, "There is a friend of Shih Yung's who has come to the lair to join with us and he is the best of friends with Luan T'ing Yü of the Chu village. He is moreover the beloved friend of Yang Ling and Teng Fei. He knows also that our elder brother has not succeeded in capturing the village and he has come to join us especially so he can show us a way and he brought this plan as a gift to us upon arrival. They are coming soon. Within five days the plan will be completed. Is this not well, therefore?"

Sung Chiang heard this with great joy and he said, "Most wonderful!" And only thus was his heart lightened so that he could smile again.

Now this which is to be told was happening at the same time that Sung Chiang was attacking the Chu village. Upon the sea shore in the province of Shantung there was a provincial city which was called Teng Chou. Outside the city of Teng Chou there was a mountain and upon that mountain wolves and tigers and leopards came out to attack people. For this did the magistrate of Teng Chou call together all hunters and as they listened he gave them a mandate that they must go and catch the beasts upon this mountain by a certain date. He commanded also that the guards of the region behind and before the mountain should also be given a proclamation to go out and capture the tigers. If outside of this set day the tigers were not brought to the court then would the hunters be heavily punished and racks be set upon their necks and their crime would not be forgiven them.

Now let it be told that at the foot of the mountain there was a certain family of hunters and there were two brothers. The elder was called Hsieh Chen and the younger one Hsieh Pao. These two brothers were both men who used forked iron spears for weapons, and they knew every feint and posture wherewith to frighten an enemy. Among the hunters of the city of Teng Chou they were allowed to be the first and best. The nickname whereby Hsieh Chen was called was The Double Headed Snake, and Hsieh Pao was called The Double Tailed Scorpion. Their parents were dead and they had never taken to themselves wives. The elder brother was more than seven feet tall and his skin was purplish black in hue. His waist was narrow and his shoulders were broad. But the younger brother was even more fierce to look upon. He was also more than seven feet tall, and his face was round and his flesh black. Upon his two legs were tattooed the pictures of two wild and savage devils. When his anger rose in him he could jerk a tree up by the roots and rock the very mountain on its foundations; he could leap against the sky and fall back upon the earth.

These two brothers received the command of

the set day in the presence of the magistrate and they returned to their home and they put into order their traps and poisoned barbs and their repeating arrows and their iron forked spears. They put on leopard skin garments and took up their forked spears and they went straightway and in haste to The Mountain Of Teng Chou and they set their traps. Then they climbed into the trees and waited for a whole day, but nothing happened. They took up their traps, therefore, and went down the mountain.

The next day they returned bringing dried foods with them and again they went up the mountain and waited. Seeing the day at last darken to night the two brothers set their traps and climbed into trees. There they waited until the fifth watch and again there came nothing. Then they moved the traps to another place and went to the west of the mountain and there they stayed until it was full dawn, when they could again wait no longer. These two surnamed Hsieh then said, "The magistrate allowed us three days in which to give him this great tiger and if it is later we will be punished and now what shall we do?"

On the third day the pair hid until the fourth watch and without knowing it they grew full of their sleep and leaning back to back they slumbered for a while. But scarcely had their eyes closed when suddenly they heard the sound of the trap. They leaped up and took their forked spears and as they looked in all four directions they saw a great tiger whose body was pierced by a poisoned arrow, and it was rolling there on the ground. Then the two, holding their spears, came up to the tiger. But the tiger when it saw men come near ran off with the arrow.

The two men pursued it and in less than the sixth of a mile the poison had worked through the tiger's whole body and the beast could no longer endure it. It gave a groan and went rolling down the mountain side, and Hsieh Pao said, "Well enough now! I know this mountain belongs to the old lord Mao and this is the land behind his garden. I will go down with you to his home and seek for the tiger."

Then did the two brothers holding their spears go straight down the mountain and they went to the village of the old lord Mao and there they knocked on the gate. Now it was but barely dawn and the two entered into the village when the gate was opened and the villagers went to take the news to the lord of the village. After a long time the old lord Mao came out and Hsieh Pao and Hsieh Chen put down their spears and called out greeting and they said, "Uncle, we have not seen you for a long time and today we have troubled you by coming especially to ask after you."

The old lord Mao replied, "Good Sons, how is it you have come so early as this? What have you to say to me?"

Then Hsieh Chen said, "We would not dare to come and disturb our uncle's sleep if there were nothing amiss. But now the magistrate has sent a command to us, your sons, that we are to capture the tiger and we have waited three days together. This morning at the fifth watch we pierced it with an arrow and we did not dream that it would roll down the back of the mountain and fall into our uncle's garden. Ten thousand times do we beg for the right of way there that we may fetch the beast."

The old lord Mao said, "It is no trouble. If it has fallen in my garden then pray seat yourselves for a little while, Honored Sirs, for I am sure you are hungered. Eat first some food therefore and then go and seek the tiger."

Then he bade the villagers go and prepare some food for the brothers and when he had invited them to eat and to drink Hsieh Chen and Hsieh Pao rose and thanked him and said, "We greatly thank our uncle for his deep kindness and we pray that you will trouble yourself to lead us thither, so that we may seek for the tiger."

But the old lord Mao replied, "If it is behind our village then why do you fear anything? Pray seat yourselves and drink tea and then it will not be too late to go and seek it."

Hsieh Chen and Hsieh Pao did not dare to refuse him and they could but seat themselves again and the villagers brought tea for the two to drink and at last the old lord Mao said, "Now I will go with you to seek for the tiger."

And Hsieh Chen and Hsieh Pao said, "Deeply do we thank our uncle."

Then the old lord Mao led the two and they went behind the village and only then did he call to a villager to come and open the gate with the key. Yet although the man tried in a hundred ways he could not open it. The old lord said, "This is because no one has come for a long time to open it. It must be the iron of the lock is rusted and so we cannot open it. Go and find an iron hammer and bring it hither and knock it open."

Then the villager brought forth an iron hammer from his person and beat open the lock and when everyone went into the garden to see and even up the mountain side they could find nothing. The old lord said, "Good Sons, you two must have seen wrongly, and you did not look clearly. Perhaps the tiger did not drop into my garden."

But Hsieh Chen said, "How could we two have seen wrongly? We were born here in these parts and here we have grown up and how is it we do not know?"

The old lord Mao said, "Then well it would be if you would yourselves seek for the tiger, and if you can find it then carry it away."

So Hsieh Pao said, "Elder Brother, do you come and see. Here is the place where the grass has been rolled flat and there are marks of blood upon it. How can it be said that it was never here? It must be that the villagers in our uncle's village have carried it away."

Then the old lord said, "Do not speak such words! How could the villagers of my village know there was a tiger here and how could they carry it away? You must have seen it if this had happened. We have only now broken open the lock and how can you speak such words as these?"

But Hsieh Chen said, "Uncle, you must return to me this tiger of mine so that I can take it to the magistrate."

The old lord replied, "How mannerless are you two! In my kindness I invited you to eat and to drink and you turn about and say that I took your tiger!"

Hsieh Pao said, "And what have we done that you say we have turned about? Your household is also among the guards and the magistrate has given you this command for a set day also. But you have no skill to catch the beast and it is you who turn about and take the beast we have already killed and you will go and look for the reward and make us two suffer punishment!"

The old lord Mao said, "And what has it to do with me if you suffer punishment?"

Then Hsieh Pao and Hsieh Chen made their eyes wide and they said, "And do you dare to let us search?"

At this the old lord Mao cried, "And can my house be like yours? It has its inner parts and its outer parts. Look, all of you, at these two beggarly heads, how mannerless they are!"

But Hsieh Pao rushed into the front of the hall. Nevertheless he could not find the tiger, and the wrath rose in his heart and he began to fight there in front of the hall. Hsieh Chen also broke the screen and rushed into the hall. Then the old lord Mao cried out, "Hsieh Chen and Hsieh Pao are robbing us in broad daylight!"

But the two brothers broke the chairs and smashed the tables in the hall, and when they saw the whole village prepare to oppose them they strode out of the village gate and they shook their fingers at the village and they cursed, saying, "You deny that you have taken our tiger—then let us go to court over it!"

Now even as they were in the midst of their cursing they saw two or three horses turning toward the village leading a group of men and Hsieh Chen knew that it was the son of the old lord Mao, whose name was Mao Chung I, and he said to him, meeting him, "The villagers of your village have taken our tiger and your father will not bring it out and return it to us, and more than that he would accuse us two brothers."

Mao Chung I replied, "These villagers understand nothing. My father has certainly been deceived by them. Do not be angered, therefore. Come with me into my home and I will find the tiger and return it to you and there will be an end of it."

Then Hsieh Chen and Hsieh Pao thanked Mao Chung I and he commanded the gate to be opened and he bade the two to go in, and leading them within the gates he called out that the gates were to be closed. Then giving a shout he put forth his hand and out from the verandas came some twenty or thirty villagers and the men who were with him were seen to be runners of the court. The two brothers had no time to prepare to fight for all these men rushed together against them and bound them. Then Mao Chung I said, "Last night we ourselves killed a tiger with an arrow and how is it you have come openly to accuse us that our tiger is yours? You have taken this chance to come and rob my house and to break to pieces the furniture here and what crime should be fixed upon you? We will take you to the court and thus will these parts be rid of dangerous men."

Now Mao Chung I had already taken the tiger into the city at the fifth watch of the night and he led back with him court runners who were come to seize Hsieh Chen and Hsieh Pao. He did not dream that these two would not see what was come about and so suffer from him, and he would hear no argument from them. And the old lord Mao brought the two spears and he brought also a bundle of goods wrapped together which was to be their false booty and he had fetched all the broken furniture. Then he stripped Hsieh Chen and Hsieh Pao of all their clothing and he bound their hands behind their backs and took them into the city.

Now there was one in the court whose business it was to write down all accusations and his surname was Wang and his name Cheng and he was the son-in-law of the old lord Mao and he had already gone into the presence of the magistrate and told the tale. Therefore now he forced the two brothers into the court and he would not allow them to defend themselves. He bound them and had them beaten and he forced them to confess that they had claimed a tiger belonging to another and then had taken their spears and gone in to rob, for Hsieh Chen and Hsieh Pao could no longer endure the beating and they could but do as he wished. Then the magistrate commanded, "Bring out two heavy racks weighing twenty-five catties apiece and place them on these two men and lock them into the great gaol."

Then the old lord Mao and Mao Chung I returned to the village and there they took counsel together, saying, "These two men cannot be let free again. Better it is we fasten their crime on them more heavily and so bring them to their death and then we shall be spared future trouble."

Then the father and son went themselves again to the court and they commanded the scribe Wang Cheng, saying, "Dig the grass up by the very roots and settle the whole affair to the end and we will ourselves force the thing through with bribes."

Now let it be told that Hsieh Chen and Hsieh Pao were locked into the gaol with the worst criminals and they were taken into the court and into the center of the court and there they saw the gaoler. Now the chief gaoler was surnamed Pao and his name was Chi, and because he had already received silver from the old lord Mao and had heard the words of Wang Cheng that he was to take the lives of these two, he came and sat in the center of the court. The lesser gaolers then said to the two brothers, "Come quickly and kneel before the gaoler."

Then Pao Chi shouted out, "Who are you two then? Are you The Double Headed Snake and The Double Tailed Scorpion?"

Hsieh Chen answered, "Although others call us by these names, lowly as we are, we have never hurt a good man."

But the gaoler shouted, saying, "You two beasts, now you are in my hands! I shall make The Double Headed Snake into a one headed snake, and The Double Tailed Scorpion into a single-tailed scorpion. Take them for me into the great gaol!"

Then the lesser gaoler led the two into the gaol and seeing no one about the lesser gaoler said, "Do you you two know me? I am the brother of your elder brother's wife."

But Hsieh Chen said, "We are but two brothers and we have no other elder brother."

Then the lesser gaoler said, "You two must be the brothers of the captain surnamed Sheng."

And Hsieh Chen answered, "Captain Sheng is the son of our uncle and our aunt. But you I have never seen before. It must be, Sir, that you are Yo Ho?"

Then the gaoler said, "I am that very one. My surname is Yo and my name is Ho, and my ancestors were men of Mao Chou. But my father brought the family hither and he gave an elder sister to Captain Sheng for wife. I make my living here in this court and I am one of the lesser gaolers. Men think that I sing very well and so they all call me The Iron Whistle, Yo Ho, and my brother-in-law sees how well I do in military things and so he also has taught me several ways of wielding weapons."

Now this Yo Ho was indeed a knowing and an able man and he could learn every sort of way of weapon as soon as he tried. In telling him of any duty, as soon as he perceived the head of it he knew what the tail was also. In speaking with him of weapons and of ways of waging war, he spoke as he would of honey and of sugar which he loved and when he saw that Hsieh Chen and Hsieh Pao were good fellows he had the heart to save them. Yet one strand does not make a thread nor can one clap with one hand, and he could but tell them this one thing. He said, "I can tell you two something. This Pao Chi has received money now from the old lord Mao and he is assuredly determined to kill you both. What then will you do?"

Hsieh Chen answered, "If you had not spoken of Captain Sheng, there would have been an end to it. But since you have spoken of him then we can but ask you to take a letter."

Yo Ho asked, "And to whom do you bid me take a letter?"

Hsieh Chen answered, "I have an elder female relative and she is a relative on my father's side and she is the wife of the younger brother of Captain Sheng and now she lives about three miles outside the east gate of the city. She is the daughter of my paternal aunt, and her name is The Female Tiger, The Goodwife Ku, and she opens a wine shop there and it is a beef butchery also, and a gambling place as well. That cousin of mine is so able that even twenty or thirty men cannot come near her. Skilled as her husband Sheng is, yet she can vanquish him in a battle. Now this cousin of ours is very fond of us two brothers. The paternal aunt of Sheng Sing and Sheng Li was indeed my mother, and therefore they are also my cousin-brothers. Therefore I ask you to give them a letter secretly, and I will tell them my trouble so they may know it. Then indeed will my cousin come herself to save me."

Yo Ho heard this to the end and he bade them, "Good Cousins, let your hearts be at rest."

Then he went out first and found some meat and some wheaten cakes and hid them in his garments and came back to the gaol and opened the door and he gave them to Hsieh Chen and Hsieh Pao. After this he pretended to have some business and he locked the gate of the gaol and commanded some other small gaoler to see to the door. Then he hastened straightway outside the east gate of the city and went toward a place called The Three Mile Arch, and there he soon saw a wine shop. In front of the door hung pieces of cow's flesh and sheep's flesh. At the back there were a crowd of people gambling. And Yo Ho saw a woman behind the counter in the shop and he knew in his heart it was The Goodwife Ku. He went before her then and he called out a greeting and he said, "Is the name of this house Sheng?"

In great haste the woman answered, saying, "It is, truly. Sir, will you buy wine or meat? If you wish to gamble then pray seat yourself at the back of the shop."

Yo Ho replied, "This lowly one is the brother of Captain Sheng's wife and I am named Yo Ho."

Then the woman laughed and said, "Then it is Uncle Yo Ho and it is not strange, for your face is like my sister-in-law's. Pray come in and take some tea!"

So Yo Ho went in and he sat down in the guest's seat and then The Goodwife Ku began to ask him, saying, "I have heard that you, my Uncle, have a place in the magistrate's court. But in this house of mine we are very poor and we have little time and so we never meet. What wind has blown you hither this day?"

Yo Ho answered, saying, "This humble one if I had not business would not dare to come here and trouble you. Today we have had suddenly two prisoners sent down from the court. Although I have never met them before, yet have I long heard their great names. One is The Double Headed Snake Hsieh Chen, and the other is The Double Tailed Scorpion Hsieh Pao."

The Goodwife Ku said, "These two are my brother-cousins and I do not know what sin they have committed that they should be put into gaol."

And Yo Ho said, "The two of them killed a tiger and a rich man of our town, the old lord Mao, laid false claim to it, and he took the two of them by force as robbers and he accuses them of having stolen money from him and so he brought them to the court. Moreover the old lord has given money to all, high and low, and soon the head gaoler Pao Chi will take their lives. This humble one, seeing the path of justice is not smooth, yet finds it hard to save them by my lone strength. I can but remember first that we are relatives, and second that we so ought to help each other, and so I told them and they said, 'There is only our sister-cousin who can save us.' But if you do not soon use all your heart and strength they cannot be saved."

The Goodwife Ku listened to the end and she began to cry over and over, "Ah, bitter—bitter—bitter—" and she commanded her clerk to go quickly and bid her husband come home, for she had something to say to him.

The Clerk had not been long gone when he found Sheng Sing and fetched him home and he met Yo Ho. Now this Sheng Sing's ancestors were originally men of Ch'ung Chou and he was the descendant of military heroes, and because the army was moved to Teng Chou he had come hither to live, and now the two brothers called this place their home. Sheng Sing was a man of tall and strong body and he had learned all his brother's skill. He could use in many ways the spear jointed like a bamboo, and therefore the people compared the two brothers to a famous warrior of T'ang, Yü Ts'e Kung, and they called Sheng Sing The Lesser Yü Ts'e. The Goodwife Ku told him all that had happened and Sheng Sing answered, "If it is thus, then let us tell our uncle to return first. The two are already in gaol, and we can but hope that you, our uncle, will take care of them and protect them. We two will talk together and plan a very good plot and we will go and tell you."

Yo Ho said, "If there is any way in which you can use me, humble as I am, I can put forth my strength in anything."

Then the goodwife gave him wine to drink and when he had drunk she brought a packet of small silver and she gave it to Yo Ho, saying, "When you go into the gaol then give this among all and among the lesser gaolers, and ask them to care well for the two prisoners."

Yo Ho thanked them and he received the silver and went back to the gaol and spent the money for the gaolers, and of this no more need be told.

Let it be told now of The Goodwife Ku and of Sheng Sing. They took counsel together and the goodwife said, "What way have you to save my two brother-cousins?"

And Sheng Sing said, "That thing the old lord Mao has both money and power. He fears that if your two brothers are freed they will surely seek for revenge and therefore he is determined to kill the pair of them. Thus it is they will certainly die by his hand. If we do not go and save them out of the gaol there is no other way to save them."

The Goodwife Ku answered, "I will go with you this very night."

But Sheng Sing laughed and said, "How stupid and careless you are! We must make a very good plot. And after they are escaped there must be a place where they can go. If we do not get my elder brother's aid and the aid of two other men, we cannot do it alone."

Then The Goodwife Ku asked, "And who are these two men?"

Sheng Sing replied, "They are two good gamblers, uncle and nephew, and the one is Chou Yuen and the other Chou Jun. They are robbers now on The Mountain Of Ascending Clouds, and there they have gathered together many brave men. They are very good friends with me. If those two will help us, then the matter can be finished."

The goodwife said, "The mountain is not far from here. Go then tonight and find these two and bring them hither to take counsel with us."

And Sheng Sing replied, "I will go now. Do you prepare wines and meats and good dishes. I will go and surely will I ask them to come here."

Then the goodwife bade her clerks kill a pig and she prepared dishes of vegetables and jars of wines and plates of fruits, and she set the table. When twilight drew on she saw Sheng Sing returning and leading with him the two goodly men. The one in front was surnamed Chou and his name was Yuen, and he was originally a man of Lai Chou. But from his childhood he had loved gambling above all else and he was idle and had no trade, although in heart he was loyal and kind and helpful to others and he had moreover great skill in wielding weapons. In temper he was high and proud and he would not forgive anyone. By river and lake he was named Dragon Out Of The Wood.

The second good fellow was surnamed Chou and named Jun and he was the other's nephew, but his age was about the same, and there was little difference in years between them. He was tall and large in body and he had the same unusual look, except at the back of his head there was a large wen. He was a man of fierce temper and he was daily angry with someone and in his fits of anger he turned and twisted his head with great force. One day he knocked his head thus against a pine tree and snapped the trunk in two. Those who saw it were all frightened into a daze and therefore they called him The One Horned Dragon.

When The Goodwife Ku saw them she asked them to come and sit in the inner hall and she told them the whole story. After that they took counsel together concerning a plan for breaking into the gaol and Chou Yuen said, "Although I have eighty or ninety men in that place of mine I only have some twenty who are truly loyal. When we have broken into the gaol like this then can we no longer stay here. But I have a place whither we may go, and I have long had the heart to go there anyway. Only I do not know whether you two, husband and wife, are willing to go?"

The Goodwife Ku replied, "To whatever place you choose we will go, if you will but save my two brother-cousins."

Chou Yuen said, "Now in these days is the robbers' lair on Liang Shan P'o in the height of its prosperity and the chieftain Sung Chiang is very willing to receive all who have skill. There are three of my friends there under his hand now. One is The Five Hued Leopard Yang Ling, one is The Red Eyed Lion Teng Fei, and the last is The Stone Warrior Shih Yung. They are all there and they have joined the robbers this long time. When we have saved your two brothers we must all go together to that lair and join them. What think you of this?"

And The Goodwife Ku said, "Nothing could be better. If there is one who will not go I will take up my spear and stab him through."

Then Chou Jun said, "There is yet another matter. If we have saved the men perhaps there will be fighting men and horsemen who will pursue us out of the city of Teng Chou. Then what shall we do?"

Sheng Sing answered, "My own blood-brother is now the instructor of the horsemen and fighting men in the city and he is the greatest of all in that city. Several times have the robbers drawn near to the city and each time it has been he who has driven them back vanquished and his name has spread far and wide. Tomorrow I will go myself and ask him to come hither. He will give his promise and there will be an end of it."

Chou Jun said, "I do but fear he will not be willing to become a robber."

But Sheng Sing said, "I have myself a good plan."

That night they drank wine for half the night and they rested until dawn. They left the two braves in the house and they sent out a clerk or two to go out and secure a cart or so and go quickly to the city and to the prison and there ask for the military instructor and his lady and they were to say, "Our goodwife is very ill in her house and she begs that you come to her house to see her."

And the goodwife again commanded the clerks, saying, "Do you only say I am very ill and very near my death and I have a few very important words that I must tell them and they must assuredly come and quickly. We can meet but this once more."

The clerks went pushing the cart before them and Sheng Sing waited at the door for them to meet his brother. When they had eaten their meal they saw in the distance the cart coming and there on the cart was the lady and behind her was the instructor Sheng, riding on his horse, and some ten-odd soldiers were with them and they came toward The Three Mile Arch. Sheng Sing went and told the goodwife that she might know it and he said, "My elder brother and his lady have come."

The goodwife commanded him, saying, "Do as I have said."

So Sheng Sing went out to meet his brother and he invited the lady to come down out of her cart and go with him into the house to see the goodwife who was ill. The instructor Sheng came down from his horse and he entered the door, and truly he was a fine tall fellow, his skin as yellow as the yolk of an egg, and he had a beard all around his jaws. His body was more than eight feet tall and his surname was Sheng and his name was Li, and he could draw a very stiff bow. He rode a fierce spirited horse and he wielded a long spear. Around his wrist was hung by the handle an iron club shining as a tiger's eye and jointed like a bamboo. When the men on the shores of the sea saw him they needed not to look at him even, but when they caught the very wind of his coming they were so frightened they fell flat to the ground.

Thus did this man come down from his horse and when he went into the door he asked, "Brother, what illness has my sister-in-law?"

Sheng Sing answered, saying, "She has a very strange illness. Pray go in to talk, my Elder Brother."

Then Sheng Li went in and Sheng Sing commanded the clerks to take the soldiers who had come to the inn opposite to drink wine, and he told one clerk to lead aside the horse. Then he invited Sheng Li within and to seat himself, and he poured wine and Sheng Sing said, "Pray go with your lady, my Elder Brother, into the room and see the one who is ill."

Sheng Li and his lady then went into the room and there was no one ill there. Then Sheng Li asked, saying, "Where is the room where my sister-in-law lies ill?"

Then they saw the goodwife come past from the outside, and Chou Yuen and Chou Jun came behind her, and Sheng Li asked, "Sister-in-law, what illness have you?"

The Goodwife Ku said, "Sir, I make you an obeisance. I have the illness called save-my-brothers."

Sheng Li said, "Here is a very strange thing. Save what brothers?"

The Goodwife Ku said, "Sir, do not pretend you are a deaf and dumb person. You are in the midst of the city and can you not have known those two are my brothers? And are they not yours also, therefore?"

But Sheng Li said, "I do not indeed know the cause for this. What two brothers are they?"

The Goodwife Ku said, "Sir, you are above me. Yet I can but speak frankly now for the business is urgent. These two, Hsieh Chen and Hsieh Pao, have been wilfully injured by the old lord Mao and by Wang The Scribe, and sooner or later they will be killed. Now I have taken counsel with these two good fellows and we have planned a certain way. We will go into the city and save them out of the gaol and rescue those two brothers and then we will all go and join the robbers on Liang Shan P'o, for we fear that tomorrow by now the thing will have become known and that you will be implicated. For this, therefore, did I feign an illness, and invite you and your lady hither. We must plan a lasting and convenient way. If you will not go, Uncle, we can but go ourselves to the robbers' lair. In these days what justice is there upon the Earth and under Heaven? If we escape then there will be no trouble. If we stay we shall be seized by the law. The proverb has it, 'What is nearest the fire is first burned.' Uncle, even though you go to court for us and suffer for us in the gaol there will be no one to bring food to you there and to save you. Uncle, what then is your mind?"

Sheng Li answered, "But I am a military official of Teng Chou, and how dare I do such a thing as this?"

The goodwife said, "If you will not do this today, Uncle, then it must be between you and me today as to which one of us dies."

Then from her side she drew forth two knives, and Chou Yuen and Chou Jun each took forth a short knife also, but Sheng Li cried out, saying, "Sister-in-law, pray stay! Do not be so impatient. Wait until I have thought awhile and seen what is best. Let us take time and consult together."

Now the lady Yo was so frightened that she was in a daze and had not been able to speak for a long time. Then did the goodwife say again, "If you will not go, Uncle, then pray send the lady on ahead for a way, and we will go ourselves and put forth our hands to do what must be done."

Sheng Li said, "Although this must be done, yet must you wait until I return home and prepare my goods and my clothing and see what the opportunity is. Only then can we proceed."

The goodwife said, "Your uncle has already told us what the circumstances are. We will on the one hand go and rescue them out of the gaol, and do you on the other hand go and see to your goods."

Then Sheng Li sighed and said, "If all of you are going to do thus, then how can I refuse? If I do not, then must I suffer for you at the court afterward. Let be—let be, then! We will join together and plan and then go forth."

Then Chou Yuen was told to return to his lair and make ready his treasure and horses, and he was to bring the twenty-odd faithful men he had and come to the shop and from there they would start and Chou Yuen went, therefore. Then Sheng Sing was told to come into the city and ask Yo Ho for news and take the opportunity to fix the time of the plot and tell the matter secretly to Hsieh Chen and Hsieh Pao. The next day Chou Yuen of the lair of The Mountain Of Ascending Clouds having gathered together his silver and gold went with his men to the place assigned. In Sheng Sing's house there were also some seven or eight loyal clerks, and the ten-odd soldiers whom Sheng Li had brought with him. In all there were more than forty men and Sheng Sing killed two pigs and a sheep and everyone ate himself full.

Then The Goodwife Ku put her sword next her flesh and she dressed herself as one who takes food to a prisoner in the gaol and Sheng Sing went with Sheng Li and Chou Yuen and Chou Jun and each took his men with him and they divided their numbers to avoid suspicion.

Let it be told now that the head gaoler in the Teng Chou gaol, Pao Chi, having received the silver of the old lord Mao, set about taking the lives of Hsieh Chen and Hsieh Pao. On that day Yo Ho took his cruel club and he stood at the door of the gaol called The Lion's Mouth. There he suddenly heard the outer bell ring. And Yo Ho asked, "Who is it?"

The Goodwife Ku answered, saying, "It is a woman who brings food."

Now Yo Ho had already guessed who it was and he came to open the gate and he let the goodwife come in and he closed the gate again, and the woman was even about to pass along when at that moment Pao Chi sat in the center of the gaol hall. When he saw her he shouted out, saying, "Who is this woman? How dares she bring food like this into the gaol? From ancient times until now even the wind is shut out of this gaol."

But Yo Ho replied, "This is the elder sister of Hsieh Chen and Hsieh Pao and she comes herself to bring them food."

Then the head gaoler Pao shouted out, "Do not allow her to go in! You take it in yourself, and there is an end of it!"

So Yo Ho asked for the food and he went and he opened the door of the gaol and gave it to the pair. And Hsieh Chen and Hsieh Pao asked him, saying, "Uncle, what of the matter of which you spoke to us last night?"

Then Yo Ho answered, "Your sister has come and she does but wait until those within and without are near, then she will begin."

Then Yo Ho freed them from their fetters and even as he did so a lesser gaoler came to make report to the head gaoler, saying, "Captain Sheng knocks at the gate and wishes to come in."

The head gaoler said, "But he is a captain of the soldiers, and what has he to do here in my gaol? Do not open the gate."

Now The Goodwife Ku had walked slowly along until she had come before the hall where the head gaoler sat when suddenly again a cry came from outside, saying, "Captain Sheng is in a mighty wrath and he is beating the gate!"

At this the head gaoler in great anger came out from the hall. Then the goodwife gave a great cry, "Where are my brothers?"

And she took out the glittering shining knives from her person. Then did the head gaoler see the outlook was very bad for him and he went out from the hall. Now Hsieh Chen and Hsieh Pao, holding high their racks, were just dashing out a hole in the wall of the gaol and they met the head gaoler full on, and the head gaoler had no time to stay them for Hsieh Pao lifted up his rack and brought it down and he split into fragments the skull of the head gaoler.

Then did the goodwife come forward with her knives and she had soon stabbed to death two or three of the lesser gaolers and as they killed thus they all yelled and fought their way out of the gaol. Sheng Sing and Sheng Li, the two of them, held the gate to the gaol, and when they saw the four coming out they all ran together past the magistrate's court. Chou Yuen and Chou Jun had already come out from the court and they bore the head of Wang The Scribe with them, and they all cried out together.

Then the ones who walked went ahead. Captain Sheng, riding his horse and with his bow stretched taut to the arrow, rode alone at the last. All the people on the street closed their doors and none dared to come out. Those who worked in the court recognized the Captain Sheng and who of them dared to come forth to oppose him?

Every one of the others surrounded Captain Sheng and they went outside the city and toward the Village Of The Three Mile Arch. There, supporting and leading the lady Yo, they placed her in the cart. The Goodwife Ku mounted a horse, and thus helping each other they went on, and Hsieh Chen and Hsieh Pao said to the others, "Why do we not revenge ourselves before we go upon that hateful old thief, the old lord Mao?"

And Sheng Li replied, "You have spoken well."

Then he took aside his brother Sheng Sing and his uncle Yo Ho and they guarded the carts and went ahead, and he said to them, "We will follow you."

Shen Sing and Yo Ho then went on with the cart guarding it, and Sheng Li led Hsieh Chen and Hsieh Pao, Chou Yuen and Chou Jun and all the clerks and they all hastened to the village of the old lord Mao. Now it happened to be the very day on which the son of the old lord made a feast for his father to congratulate him upon his birthday and they were there eating and drinking and they were not prepared and this horde of good fellows, yelling as they came, dashed in killing their way in. Of all that house they left not one. They killed the old lord and his son and their wives and their children and there was not one left. Then they went into the inner rooms and they gathered together some ten-odd bundles of gold and treasure and of jewels. In the back of the garden they led forth some seven or eight good horses and they placed their booty upon four of these. And Hsieh Chen and Hsieh Pao chose out some goodly garments and put them on, and after this they took a torch and set fire to the whole house.

Then each man mounted his horse and they led forth the others and they had gone not more than ten miles when they had caught up with the cart and the other men and the horses and they went along the road together. And as they passed by they took from farmers some three or five more good horses and that very night this whole horde went toward the mountain to the robbers' lair. In a day or two they had come to Shih Yung's wine shop and Chou Yuen met with him and he asked after Yang Ling and Teng Fei, and Shih Yung said, "Sung Chiang went to attack the village of Chu and these two went with him Twice did they do battle, and I have heard it said by one who reported that Yang Ling and Teng Fei are both imprisoned there, and I do not know how it is with them. We have heard that there are three brave young lords in the village of Chu, and there is also their instructor The Iron Staff Luan T'ing Yü. Because of these the attackers twice could not break open that village."

Now Sheng Li when he had heard this laughed loudly and he said, "All of us have come to join you, although indeed we have not a particle of glory. But we will take this opportunity to show forth what we can do and we will go and break open the village of Chu. How will this be for an entrance to the lair?"

Then Shih Yung was greatly pleased and he said, "I would hear this good plan you have."

So Sheng Li said, "Luan T'ing Yü and I were taught by the same master in ways of battle. The ways of war which I know he knows also, and the ways he has learned I have learned as well. Today we will pretend we are soldiers sent from Teng Chou to guard Yün Chou and we come to inquire after them in passing. Surely they will come out to meet us and thus we will get into the village. Then if we attack from within and without surely we can conquer the village. How is this for a plan?"

But before he could finish speaking of his plot to Shih Yung there was seen to come a lesser fighting man who came to make report, saying, "Wu Yung has come down the mountain and he is going forward to the village of Chu to come to the rescue."

Shih Yung heard this and he told the fighting man quickly to ask Wu Yung to come hither and see them. Before he had finished speaking there came fighting men and horsemen to the front of the shop and they were Lü Fang, Kao Shen, and the three brothers Juan. After them came the counselor Wu Yung and he had with him five hundred men and horses. Shih Yung met them and brought them into the wine shop and they all met those who had come, and those told why they had come thither and the plan they had made. Wu Yung heard it and he said with great pleasure, "If all these good fellows are willing to help the lair then pray do not go up the mountain, but come with all speed, I pray you, to the village of Chu and carry out this plan and thus complete this glory. How seems this to you?"

And Sheng Li and all the others were all pleased and they all promised. Then Wu Yung said, "I will bid the men and the horses go first, and then let all the good fellows go behind."

Now after Wu Yung had counseled thus he went first to Sung Chiang's camp and there seeing Sung Chiang's brows knitted together and his face sad, Wu Yung poured wine for Sung Chiang to drive away his sadness and then he told him everything of all the friends whom Shih Yung, Yang Ling and Teng Fei had. There was the instructor of the military at Teng Chou, Sheng Li, who was taught by the same master as the instructor in ways of war in the village of Chu, and he came this day with eight men and they all went to the lair to join with them. These had thought of an especial plot of how to come to the rescue, and everything was now planned that they should fight within the village and the others without and so they would aid each other, and they were even now coming to see him.

When Sung Chiang had finished hearing this, he was overjoyed and he threw his despondency beyond the clouds of the ninth heaven and in all haste he commanded a feast to be prepared in the lair to entertain them all as soon as they came.

Let it then be told of Sheng Li and how he told his men to follow the horses and men and go thither to encamp with the others. He only took with him Hsieh Chen, Hsieh Pao, Chou Yuen, Chou Jun, Sheng Sing, The Goodwife Ku and Yo Ho, eight in all, and they all came to pay respects to Sung Chiang. After they had performed the rites of courtesy Sung Chiang had wine prepared and a feast made ready for them to eat, and of this no more need be told.

Wu Yung then gave forth a secret command to everyone and he told them that they should do thus on the third day and thus on the fifth day. When he had finished commanding them Sheng Li and the others having their plans made, all went with their men and carts toward the village of Chu, there to do what they had to do.

But it must be told again of what the counselor Wu Yung said. He said, "Pray let the chief Tai Chung return at once to the lair and quickly bring these four chiefs hither to me, for I have ways to use them."

If he had not bade Tai Chung to go that very night and seek those four men then would not have

To the watery lair had been added more wings still,
Though the villages were never more so strong as the hill.

What four men therefore did Wu Yung seek? Pray hear it told in the next chapter.

Chapter 49

WU YUNG USES A DOUBLE-LINKED PLOT. SUNG CHIANG THRICE ATTACKS THE VILLAGE OF CHU

IT IS SAID: At that time did the chieftain Wu Yung ask Tai Chung, saying, "Good Brother, return for me to the mountain lair and seek out The Iron Faced P'ei Hsüan, The Magic Scribe Siao Jang, The Strong Armed Gorilla Hou Chien and The Jade Armed Warrior Ching Ta Chien, and tell these men to bring all they ought to have with them. Let them come down the mountain by night, for I have ways to use them."

Tai Chung went therefore. Now there were seen to come soldiers from the outside of the camp and they came to make report, saying, "Hu Ch'en of the western village of the Hu family is leading out sheep and carrying jars of wine and he is coming especially to beg to see you."

Sung Chiang commanded that he should be asked to come thither. Then Hu Ch'en came there to the central tent and he made two obeisances and he said humbly, "My little sister was too unmannerly in that short time and she is too young and she does not understand how people should behave and in her carelessness she has offended you. Now she is captured, and I come to implore the great captain to forgive her, for this sister of mine is already promised to one in the village of the Chu family. She should not have in that short space of time showed forth all her skill of war so that now she has fallen to be your prisoner. If we receive your forgiveness, O Great Chief, so that you will forgive and release her, however much you want of us, we ought to give to you according to your demand."

Sung Chiang answered, "I pray you sit down and let us talk. Such as those in the village of Chu—how mannerless are they! They are continually oppressing us who live in the lair, and for this we have brought hither our fighting men to take our revenge. But this had naught to do with you of the Hu village. Nevertheless, your sister has captured my Wang The Dwarf Tiger, and for this did we take her in exchange. If you will bring Wang The Dwarf Tiger back and give him to me, I will return your sister to you."

Hu Ch'en answered, saying, "I did not foresee that the Chu village would already have taken this good fellow."

Then the counselor Wu Yung said, "Where is this Wang The Dwarf Tiger of ours now?"

Hu Ch'en replied, "He is now held and fettered in the village of Chu. How dare this lowly one go there to seek him?"

Then Sung Chiang said, "If you do not go and seek out Wang The Dwarf Tiger and return him to me, then how can you have back your sister?"

But Wu Yung said, "Brother Chief, do not speak like this.—Sir, pray listen to but one word from me. From now on if there is any trouble at the village of Chu you shall not send out men from your village to aid them. If anyone from the village of Chu takes refuge with you, you are to seize him and hold him. When you so seize a man then will I return your sister to your village. But here is a pity and it is that she is not now in this camp. We sent her the other day to the mountain lair to be cared for by the father of Sung Chiang. Pray rest your heart and return. Surely have I a way for this."

And Hu Ch'en promised, saying, "From this time forth will I indeed go no more to their aid. If any man comes from that village to mine surely will I bring him here into your presence fettered."

And Sung Chiang said, "If you do this in truth it will be more to me than if you gave me silver and gold."

So Hu Ch'en made obeisance and gave his thanks and went away.

Now Sheng Li changed the letters on his banner to those saying he came as captain from Teng Chou, and he led a company of men and horses and they all came before the back gate of the village of the Chu family and the men on the wall there seeing from the banner that they were come from Teng Chou took the report into the village. Luan T'ing Yü, hearing it was Captain Sheng of Teng Chou, came to see him, and he said to the three Chu brothers, "This Captain Sheng is my brother, and we learned our military skill together. I do not know why he has come hither today."

Then leading out twenty and more men and horses, he opened the village gate and he caused the drawbridge to be put down and he went out to meet Sheng Li. And Sheng Li and all his men came down from their horses and after they had all performed the rites of courtesy Luan T'ing Yü asked, saying, "Good Brother, you are guard in Teng Chou and why have you come hither?"

Sheng Li answered, saying, "The one above me has sent forth a command and he has appointed me to be changed with the one in Ying Chou to oppose the robbers in Liang Shan P'o. I pass here on my way, and I heard you, my Brother, were here in this village of the Chu family, and so I have come on purpose to ask after you. I did think first to come by the front gate, but I saw many men and horses there before the village, and I could not force my way through, and so I sought out a way to come here by small paths so that I might come in to make my obeisances before my brother."

Luan T'ing Yü said, "We have these last days been fighting daily with the robbers and we have also captured several of their chiefs and we have them here in the village. If we can but capture the head of them all, Sung Chiang, then we will take them all together to the magistrate. Heaven has sent us the fortune that you, my Brother, have come hither to aid us. Truly it is as though upon gold were flowers carved, as if upon the drought-smitten fields, rains poured down."

But Sheng Li laughed and said, "No skill have I, but pray see how I shall help you to seize these and so complete your glory."

Then Luan T'ing Yü was overjoyed and he led all these into the village and then he drew up again the drawbridge and closed the village gate. And Sheng Li and all the men with him arranged themselves and their horses. They changed their clothing and they all went to the great hall and there met with Chu Ch'ao Feng, and they met there also Chu The Dragon, Chu The Tiger and Chu The Tiger Cub. The whole family of these was there in the hall to meet with them and Luan T'ing Yü led Sheng Li and the others forward into the hall and when the rites of courtesy had been performed, Luan T'ing Yü said to Chu Ch'ao Feng, "This good brother of mine, Sheng Li, who is nicknamed after a warrior of old, Yü Ts'e, has been the instructor of soldiers at Teng Chou and now the general has sent him hither to protect this region of Yün Chou."

Then Chu Ch'ao Feng said, "This old man who am I, I am also one of those beneath your rule."

But Sheng Li said, "And what is there to talk about in so small and lowly an official place as mine? At all times do I hope for your guidance that you will point out to me that which I ought to do."

Then the three Chu sons invited each guest to take his seat, and Sheng Li then asked, saying, "These several days you have been fighting and you must be weary."

Chu The Dragon answered, saying, "Nor could it be seen who was victor and who vanquished. But you, Honored Brothers, who have come riding so far on your horses, it has not been easy to come so far without fatigue."

Then Sheng Li commanded that his two sisters-in-law be led back to make greeting to the ladies of the Chu house, and after this he called for Sheng Sing and Hsieh Chen and Hsieh Pao to come forward and make themselves known, and he said, "These three are my brothers," and pointing to Yo Ho he said, "This is one who was sent to me from Yün Chou to bid me come thither." Pointing to Chou Yuen and Chou Jun he said, "These are two military officials sent hither from Teng Chou."

Now the old Chu and the three sons of Chu, although they were clever, when they saw he had his women with him and much goods and many fighting men and horses and when they heard he was a brother-friend of their teacher Luan T'ing Yü, how could they doubt Sheng Li? They did but see to killing cows and horses and they prepared a feast to welcome them all. After a day or two were passed, and the third day was come, a fighting man of the village made report, saying, "Sung Chiang is again leading men and horsemen and he is charging upon the village."

Then Chu The Tiger Cub said, "I will mount my horse and go myself and capture this robber," and he went out of the village and he let down the drawbridge and he led out more than a hundred horsemen and there were some five hundred men and more. And there came forward two leaders from among them and they had bows and arrows thrust into their girdles, and whipping up their horses, they held their weapons aloft. Now one was Hua Yung, and when Chu The Tiger Cub saw him he urged his horse on and holding his weapon he came forward to fight. Hua Yung also pressed his horse on to meet Chu The Tiger Cub, and the two there in front of The Ridge Of The Lonely Dragon fought some tens of rounds and it could not be told who was victor and who vanquished. Then Hua Yung made a false feint and he turned his horse about. Even as The Tiger Cub was about to give his horse free rein in pursuit, there was one behind him who knew Hua Yung who said, "Sir, do not pursue him. Perhaps you will fall into his plot for this man is greatly skilled with the bow and arrows."

When The Tiger Cub heard this, he drew back his horse and pursued no more. He led back his men and horsemen and went toward the village and there he drew up again the drawbridge. When he looked again at Hua Yung, he also had led away his fighting men and horsemen and gone back.

Then Chu The Tiger Cub went to the hall and there he dismounted and he went into the inner hall to drink wine and Sheng Li asked him, saying, "Little General, what robber did you capture today?"

And Chu The Tiger Cub replied, "Among those robbers who is that Hua Yung, who is terrible with his weapon? I fought with him more than fifty rounds and then he turned away. Even as I was about to pursue him my fighting men said, 'That thing is skilled with the bow and arrow,' and for this we took each our men and led them home again."

Sheng Li said, "Tomorrow if you wish, although I have no skill, I will take from him several of his men."

On that day as they feasted they told Yo Ho to sing them a song, that all might be merry, and when night came they parted.

Again they rested another night. At the fifth watch of the fourth day there came suddenly a fighting man of the village who made report, saying, "Sung Chiang and his fighting men and horses have come again to the front of the village."

Then the three, Chu The Dragon, Chu The Tiger and Chu The Tiger Cub, all put on their garb of war and they went outside the gate of the village and there in the far distance they could hear the beating of gongs and the beating of drums and the sound of shouting and they could see banners waving. Shouting their war cry they went forward. Opposite the fighting men were already ranked. On this side the old lord Chu sat above the village gate and on the left was Luan T'ing Yü, and on the right was Captain Sheng. The three Chu sons and all the men and horsemen that Sheng Li had brought with him were beside the gate. Soon Sung Chiang's men were seen. There was The Leopard Headed Ling Ch'ung, who cursed in a loud voice as he came. At this the anger rose in Chu The Dragon and he shouted out that the drawbridge was to be lowered, and seizing his weapon he mounted his horse. Leading a hundred or two horsemen he gave a mighty shout and he hastened straight to Ling Ch'ung. Then the gongs began to beat beneath the village gate, and on both sides the bows were drawn and the repeating arrows flew back and forth.

Then Ling Ch'ung, whirling his weapon like a snake, came forward to do battle with Chu The Dragon and they fought in succession some thirty and more rounds and it could not be told who was victor and who vanquished. Each side then beat their gongs and each man retired. Then was Chu The Tiger in a mighty rage and he took up his knife and he mounted his horse and he galloped to the front of the village. There in a great voice he called for Sung Chiang to come forth and do battle. Before he had finished speaking Sung Chiang from among his ranks sent forth one of his captains riding on horseback. This was He Whom No Obstacle Can Stay, Mu Hung, and he came out to do battle with Chu The Tiger. The two fought together more than thirty rounds, and again there was neither victor nor vanquished.

Then Chu The Tiger Cub, seeing this, grew mighty in anger, and taking his weapon he flew upon his horse and he led out some two hundred and more horsemen and they charged to the front of the village. From among Sung Chiang's ranks there came one, who was Yang Hsiung, and he came out upon his horse and with his weapon, and he came flying out to do battle with The Tiger Cub. Sheng Li, seeing them fighting there, could be patient no longer and then he called Sheng Sing, "Bring out my jointed iron staff and bring my garments of war and my headdress and lead my own horse hither."

Now this horse was a black horse and it could run three hundred miles in a day. It was saddled and they placed three girths about its belly. On Sheng Li's wrist he hung his jointed staff, sharp as a tiger's eyes, and with his weapon he rode forth. Then did the gong beat in the village of Chu and Sheng Li rode his horse forth to the front of the village. And these came forth from the ranks of Sung Chiang, Ling Ch'ung, Mu Hung and Yang Hsiung, and they came forward and reining in their horses stood before the ranks of men. Sheng Li had already galloped forward on his horse and he said, "See how, worthless as I am, I shall capture all these!"

Now Sheng Li brought his horse to a stand and he asked, shouting, "If there be a good warrior among your ranks of robbers, let him come forth to do battle with me!"

Then was there a sound of horse bells from

among Sung Chiang's ranks and a horse and rider galloped forth. When they looked to see who it was, they saw it was The One Who Heeds Not His Life Shih Hsiu, and he came forward to fight with Sheng Li. The two horses came together and each man raised his weapon. They fought some fifty-odd rounds, when Sheng Li feigned and he allowed Shih Hsiu to charge at him with his weapon and then he dodged aside and with little effort he lifted Shih Hsiu up from his horse, and holding him fast under his arm he carried him to the front of the village and there cast him down. Then he shouted out, "Take him and bind him!"

The three Chu sons then rushed forward into the ranks of Sung Chiang's men and stirred them up and scattered them all. Then they called their soldiers and went back beneath the gate tower. There they saw Sheng Li and all the others with their hands clasped in the obeisance of respect. Sheng Li then asked, "In all how many robbers have been captured?"

Then old Chu Ch'ao Feng replied, "First we captured a Shih Ch'ien. Then we captured a spy Yang Ling. Again we captured a Huang Hsin. In the village of Hu they captured a Wang The Dwarf Tiger. Upon the battle field we captured two, Ch'ing Ming and Teng Fei. Today we have captured this Shih Hsiu. This is the very one who burned down my inn. Altogether we have seven."

Sheng Li said, "Let us not injure one of them. Quickly make seven prisoner carts and place them therein, and give them some wine and some rice to nourish their bodies. Do not let them starve nor injure them for it will not look well. Then when we have captured Sung Chiang, we will take them all together to the eastern capital, and so will your name be spread wide over the earth, and they will tell of the Chu village."

And Chu Ch'ao Feng thanked him, saying, "Great fortune was it for us that you, Sir Captain, came to help us. In my opinion this robbers' lair ought to be destroyed."

Then he invited Sheng Li to come to the inner hall and drink wine. Shih Hsiu of course was put into the prisoner's cart.

You, Noble Sirs, who read, listen to me. The skill of Shih Hsiu in fighting was no less than Sheng Li's, but in order that the men of the village might be wholly deceived Shih Hsiu was captured on purpose, so that the men of Chu might the more believe in Sheng Li. Then secretly did Sheng Li bid these three, Chou Yuen, Chou Jun, and Yo Ho go to the inner hall of the village where the prisoners were and see where every door and window was. When Yang Ling and Teng Fei saw them they were secretly pleased. Yo Ho, spying on all sides, saw there was no one there, and he told a little of the news to them and The Goodwife Ku and the lady Yo were within and they also had seen where the windows and doors were.

On the fifth day Sheng Li and the others were all in the village idling here and there, and in the early part of the morning after they had eaten their early meal they saw a village fighting man come to make report, saying, "Today Sung Chiang has divided his men into four ranks and he comes to attack the village."

Sheng Li said, "And even though he divided into ten what of it! Do not let the men be impatient. Let them only be early prepared. Let barbed hooks be made ready and nooses of ropes, so that we may capture the robbers alive. The dead we will not count."

Then the men in the village put on their garments of war and Chu Ch'ao Feng led out these men himself and when he went up into the gate tower to look about him, he saw to the east some men and horses. The chief in front of them was the Leopard Headed Ling Ch'ung. Behind him were Li Chün and Juan The Second. There were in all more than five hundred men and horses. Then from the west were seen to come also some five hundred men and horses, and the chief who led them was Hua Yung, and those behind him were Chang Heng and Chang Shun. When he looked from the south tower he saw also five hundred men and horses and there were three chiefs in front who were Mu Hung, Yang Hsiung, and The Black Whirlwind Li K'uei and there were men and horsemen on all four sides.

Now did all the drums of war begin to sound and there was a mighty sound of shouting. Luan T'ing Yü, hearing it, said, "Today, when these come to do battle with us we must not consider them lightly. I will take a company of men and go out the back gate and I will do battle with these to the north and west."

And Chu The Dragon said, "I will go out the front gate and I will do battle with those to the east."

And Chu The Tiger said, "I will also go out the back gate and I will kill those to the west and the south."

And Chu The Tiger Cub said, "I will myself go out the front gate and I will capture Sung Chiang. He is the greatest chieftain among the robbers."

Then was Chu Ch'ao Feng greatly pleased and he gave wine to them all and each mounted his horse, and each man led with him some three hundred horsemen and all the others stayed about the village and shouted their war cries.

Now at this time Chou Yuen and Chou Jun each secretly bearing a great axe watched to the left of the gaol where the prisoners were, and Hsieh Chen and Hsieh Pao, with hidden weapons, did not leave the back gate. The Goodwife Ku first set apart some soldiers to guard the lady Yo, and then she herself took her pair of knives and walked back and forth before the great hall waiting until she heard from without the signal for battle.

Let it be told now that thrice did the drums of battle sound in the village of Chu, and a rocket was sent up. Then the front and back gates were both opened and the drawbridge was let down and they all went charging forth to battle. The four companies of soldiers went forward and they divided into four directions. Behind them Sheng Li led forth ten-odd fighting men and stood by the drawbridge and Sheng Sing within the gate took the banner he had brought with him and raised it on the tower above the gate. Yo Ho then taking up his weapon came forth singing and Chou Yuen and Chou Jun, hearing Yo Ho sing, shouted several times and whirling their axes killed some tens of the men who guarded the gaol and they opened the prisoners' carts and freed the seven great tigers. Each of them seized a weapon from the rack and they raised one shout together. Then The Goodwife Ku took out her pair of knives and leaped into the hall and with a blow apiece she killed every woman there.

Now Chu Ch'ao Feng, seeing the outlook was evil, was about to leap into a well when with one thrust of his knife he was overturned by Shih Hsiu, and his head was cut off. Then those ten-odd good fellows divided and killed the men in the village. Hsieh Chen and Hsieh Pao at the back gate went to the haystacks and set them afire and the black smoke filled the very heavens. Then the four companies of robbers, seeing the fire in the village, pushed forward with every strength. Chu The Tiger, seeing the fire blaze forth, first hastened back. Sheng Li was guarding the drawbridge and with a mighty shout he said, "You, there—whither do you go?" And he stood across the bridge.

Then did Chu The Tiger understand and he turned his horse's head and again hastened toward Sung Chiang. Here Lü Fang and Kao Shen on their horses raised their barbed spears and soon Chu The Tiger and his horse were stabbed and lying upon the ground and all the robbers rushed forward and chopped them into bits like dust. The village fighting men in front then scattered and ran away and Sheng Li and Sheng Hsin went out to meet Sung Chiang and bring him to the village.

Now on the road to the east Chu The Dragon could not overcome Ling Ch'ung and on his flying horse he galloped to the back of the village. When he had come beside the drawbridge he saw Hsieh Chen and Hsieh Pao throwing down the dead bodies of the villagers they had killed from the tower above the gate. In great haste Chu The Dragon turned his horse to the north, and suddenly he came upon The Black Whirlwind who leaped from a great distance whirling his two battle axes. He soon cut off the legs of the enemy's horse and Chu The Dragon had no time to return his blows and he tumbled on to the ground. There with one blow of his axe Li K'uei split his head apart.

Chu The Tiger Cub, hearing the report from the village, did not dare to return. He went for refuge to the village of Hu, and there Hu Ch'en told the villagers to capture him, and they took ropes and tied him and took him to Sung Chiang. But on the way they met Li K'uei and with one blow of his axe he cut off The Tiger Cub's head, and the villagers all scattered and went away. Then Li K'uei whirling his axes went to attack Hu Ch'en. Hu Ch'en, seeing the outlook was evil for him, turned his horse and went off alone into the wilderness, and left his home and escaped for his life, and went toward Yien An Fu. Later in another dynasty he became a general.

Let it be told further that Li K'uei thus killed whomever he saw without any stay and thus he charged into the village of the Hu family. There he killed clean the whole house of the lord Hu, nor did he leave one alive. Then he commanded the villagers to bring such horses as were there and he commanded all the treasure to be brought and there were loads for some forty or fifty horses. After this he set fire to the village and then he went to Sung Chiang and presented all to him.

Now let it be said that Sung Chiang was there sitting in the central hall of the Chu village and all the chieftains came to pay their allegiance to him and in all there were some four or five hundred men. Of good horses there had been seized more than five hundred and the cows and sheep that had been seized were beyond number. Sung Chiang seeing all this was greatly rejoiced and he said, "I do but grieve that we killed that good fellow, Luan T'ing Yü."

Even as he was thus grieving he heard one making report and saying, "The Black Whirlwind has burned the village of Hu and he is bringing the heads he has cut off as a pledge."

Then Sung Chiang said, "But the other day the village of Hu had already paid its allegiance to us. Who bade him go and kill these? Why has he burned their village?"

Then The Black Whirlwind was seen coming, covered with blood from head to foot, his axes thrust into his girdle, and he came straight into Sung Chiang's presence and made loud greeting and he said, "It was I, your younger brother, who killed Chu The Dragon. Chu The Tiger did I also smite. That Hu Ch'en has run away. The whole house of the old lord Hu I have killed clean. I, your younger brother, have come to ask your praise."

But Sung Chiang shouted out, "You were seen to kill Chu The Dragon, but these others, did you truly kill them?"

And The Black Whirlwind answered, "I killed as I went and without any let. I hastened to the village of Hu and there I came upon the brother of The Green Snake bringing The Tiger Cub out of the village. I killed him with one blow of my axe. It is only a pity that that Hu Ch'en has run away. I have killed his village clean and there is not one left."

Then Sung Chiang shouted, saying, "Such as you! Who told you to go there? Surely you knew that the other day the village of Hu gave us their allegiance. Why have you not listened to my words? Why did you go of your own accord and kill them and so wilfully disobey my commands?"

Li K'uei replied, "You have forgotten but I have surely not forgotten. Those things but the other day told that woman to chase you, Elder Brother, and kill you. And now you want to be friends with them! Nor did you take the woman for your wife! Then why do you look on them as brothers-in-law and fathers-in-law?"

But Sung Chiang shouted out, "You Iron Ox! Do not speak like a fool! Why should I want that woman? I have assuredly a place for her. You black thing, how many have you taken alive?"

Li K'uei answered, "And to what cursed living man would I pay heed? If I saw one I killed him!"

Then Sung Chiang said, "You have disobeyed my commands. You deserve to be beheaded. But I will measure to your crime the righteousness of having killed Chu The Dragon and Chu The Tiger Cub. The next time you disobey my commands surely will I not forgive you."

At this The Black Whirlwind laughed and said, "Although I have not any glory for it, yet have I made myself happy with all this killing!"

Then was the counselor Wu Yung seen coming near leading a company of horsemen and they all came to the village, and they poured out wine to do honor to Sung Chiang. And Sung Chiang took counsel with Wu Yung as to how they might lay waste the village of Chu. But, hearing this, Shih Hsiu made bold to remind them that there was the old man who had pointed out the road to him and other good men in the village who might not be injured. When Sung Chiang heard this he bade Shih Hsiu go and ask the old man to come hither and when Shih Hsiu had not been long gone he led the old man back to the village, and the old man made obeisance to Sung Chiang and to Wu Yung. Then Sung Chiang took out a packet of smooth silver and with it he rewarded the old man and bade him remain forever a dweller in this village and he said, "If it had not been for the mercy you have shown us, Old Man, we would have laid waste this village nor would we have left one house. But because your house has been good to us for this will we forgive the whole village."

The old man could but kneel and give thanks. Again did Sung Chiang say, "Day after day have I disturbed you who dwell here as common people. Today we have broken into the village of Chu and we have injured your village. But we will give to every house a measure of rice to show forth our friendliness."

Then did he bid the old man be the chief one to divide the rice and he had the rice left after the measures were given put onto carts, and he gave gold and silver and treasure to all the fighting men and their captains. The rest, the cows, sheep, mules and horses and such things he sent to the robbers' lair to be used. In seizing the village of Chu he had joy, and when all the fighting men and horses and goods were prepared he set forth. He had also many new chieftains, Sheng Li, Sheng Sing, Hsieh Chen, Hsieh Pao, Chou Yuen, Chou Jun, Yo Ho, The Goodwife Ku, and the seven good fellows they had saved.

And Sheng Li and his company brought with them their own horses and such goods as they had brought with them, and with his family and the lady Yo they all went with the others up to the mountain lair. At this time of departure did the villagers and the peasants of that countryside, supporting their old and leading their little ones, come forth and burn incense and paper money and they lit lanterns and candles all along the sides of the road and they knelt and made obeisance and gave thanks.

Sung Chiang and the others all mounted their horses, and the horsemen and fighting men were divided into three companies, and through that night they returned to the lair.

The story now is divided. Let it be told that The Eagle Who Smites The Heavens Li Yün was only now healed of his arrow wound, and he had closed the gate of the village nor did he come forth. But secretly he continually sent forth men to spy out what was happening at the village of Chu, and he heard how it had been broken into by Sung Chiang, and he was half frightened and half pleased. Then was a villager seen coming to make report and he said, "The magistrate of Yün Chou brings hither some thirty or fifty strong men, and he asks concerning the village of Chu."

In great haste Li Yün told Tu Hsing to open the village gate and to let down the drawbridge and go forth to meet them and bring them to the village. Li Yün wrapped his wounded hand in a length of white silk and he came forth to greet them and to ask them to come into the guest hall of the village. The magistrate came down from his horse and he came to the hall and sat down in the central seat. Beside him sat his scribe. On the other hand beneath him sat the chief of those who make arrests. Beyond these there were several guards. Outside the hall were many wardens and keepers from the gaol. When Li Yün had made obeisance he stood before the magistrate and the magistrate asked him, saying, "How did these murders come about in the village of Chu?"

And Li Yün made answer, saying, "Because this humble one was wounded with an arrow by Chu The Tiger Cub, so that my left arm was injured, I closed the gate and dared not go forth, and I do not know the truth."

But the magistrate said, "You speak like a fool! The Chu village has sent me a report accusing you that you have joined yourself to the robbers and directed their horsemen to the village. The other day you received as gifts riding horses, sheep, wine and silks and satins and treasures, silver and gold. How can you deny this?"

Li Yün said humbly, "This humble one is a man who knows the law, and how would I dare receive their gifts?"

The magistrate said, "Scarcely can I believe what you say. I shall take you to the court and there you may face your accusers plainly." And he shouted to the guards and to the runners from the gaol that this man was to be seized and taken to the court where he might face his accuser. Then did the guards and the gaolers from both sides lay hold on Li Yün and bind him, and they surrounded the magistrate as he mounted his horse. Again the magistrate asked, "Which is Tu Hsing, the bailiff?"

And Tu Hsing answered, "This humble one is he."

Then the magistrate said, "There is your name on the accusation.—Take him also and let him be bound."

Then did the company come out of the village and thus did they take Li Yün and Tu Hsing, and they departed from the village of Li and they went with all speed, nor did they let their feet so much as leave the ground.

But when they had gone not more than some ten miles they saw Sung Chiang leap out of the wood and with him Ling Ch'ung, Hua Yung, Yang Hsiung and Shih Hsiu, and their fighting men and horsemen, and they stood in the road. And Ling Ch'ung shouted mightily and he said, "The good fellows of the mountain lair are gathered together here!"

That magistrate and his men did not dare to oppose the robbers. They threw down Li Yün and Tu Hsing and ran for their lives. Sung Chiang shouted, "After them with all speed!"

So the robbers all pursued for a while and then they came back, saying, "If we could catch them we would already have killed this accursed old magistrate, but we do not know where they are."

Then they took off the bonds from Li Yün and Tu Hsing and they opened their fetters and led two horses up and gave them to the two men to ride upon. And Sung Chiang said, "Pray, Noble Sirs, come to our lair and hide yourselves for a while."

Li Yün replied, "This indeed we cannot do. If you have killed the magistrate it has nothing to do with me."

But Sung Chiang laughed and said, "Then why was the magistrate thus disputing with you? If we had gone, surely it would have had something to do with you. If you, Sir, will not become a robber, then at least come and live for a few days in the mountain lair, and when we have heard there is no danger then come down again and it will not be too late."

And he would not let Li Yün and Tu Hsing decide, but he took them willy-nilly, and how could they set themselves against so great a company? They could but go on. Then did the three companies of men and horsemen go winding along the road back to the mountain lair.

Now the chieftains in the lair, Ch'ao Kai and the others, beating drums and blowing pipes, came down the mountain to meet them, and they poured forth the wine of greeting, and then they all went up to the lair and gathered in the Hall Of Meeting, and there they sat in the shape of a fan. Li Yün and Tu Hsing were presented to all the chieftains, and when they had performed the rites of courtesy Li Yün said respectfully to Sung Chiang, "We two humble ones have already been thus brought to your great lair and we have met all these chieftains. It matters nothing to us if we stand here to serve you, but we do not know how it is with our homes and families. Allow us, therefore, to go down the mountain."

At this the counselor Wu Yung laughed and he said, "My lord, you are mistaken. We have already sent messengers to bring your noble family to the mountain. As for your honored village, a torch has already set fire to it so that it is now laid waste. Whither then, my lord, will you return?"

But Li Yün would not believe Wu Yung. Suddenly he saw a procession of carts and people coming up the mountain. When Li Yün looked, he saw they were the villagers from his own village and the young and old of his own house. Then in great haste he went to ask of them and his wife answered, "You were seized by the magistrate and brought hither, and afterwards there came two officers and they brought with them four guards and more than three hundred local soldiers and they came and confiscated all our goods and they put us all into carts. They took all our boxes and baskets and cows and sheep and horses and donkeys and mules and all such. Then they set fire to our courts and burned the village."

Now when Li Yün heard this he could but cry bitterness, but Ch'ao Kai and Sung Chiang came down from the hall and they knelt before him and they acknowledged their guilt and said, "We, your brothers, have long heard, Sir, of your great name, and because of this have we worked this guile. Ten thousand times ten thousand do we ask for the noble one's forgiveness."

When Li Yün heard such words as these he

could but let it be as they wished. And then Sung Chiang said, "Pray let the honored one's family retire to the two rooms on either side of the inner hall."

Now Li Yün again saw all these chiefs at the front and the back of the hall and he saw that they also had wives and children and parents with them and so he said to his wife, "We can but do as they say."

Then Sung Chiang invited him to come into the hall and he talked with him for a while of small matters, and all were greatly pleased. And Sung Chiang seeking to make merriment said, "Great lord, look at me now, and see how I shall bid that magistrate and his two aides come and talk with you."

Now the magistrate who had gone to Li Yün's house was Siao Jang in disguise and the other two were Tai Chung and Yang Ling. He who was the scribe was P'ei Hsüan, and he who was the chief guard was Hou Chien. Then he called for the four guards and these were Li Chün, Chang Shun, Ma Ling and Pei Sheng. Li Yün looked at them all, and he was so astonished that his mouth hung ajar and he had not a word to say. Then Sung Chiang shouted to the lesser chieftains quickly to kill cows and horses and so make an apology to the lord, and to make a welcome to the twelve new chieftains who came up the mountain. These ten were Li Yün, Sheng Li, Sheng Sing, Hsieh Chen, Hsieh Pao, Chou Yuen, Chou Jun, Tu Hsing, Yo Ho, and Shih Ch'ien. Of females there were The Ten Foot Green Snake who was the third daughter of the house of Hu, The Goodwife Ku, the lady Yo and Li Yün's lady. For these a separate feast was prepared in the inner hall. For the lesser chiefs and the fighting men and all underlings there were of course rewards of food and all else.

Now in the great hall were there the mighty sound of pipes and of drums and all the good fellows drank their wine nor did they separate until the night. The newly come chieftains were each given a place to stay. On the next day again there was feasting and all the chiefs were invited to come and feast and Sung Chiang called Wang The Dwarf Tiger to come and he said, "When I was upon the other mountain I promised to find you a wife, and ever since then the matter has hung in my heart, nor have I forgotten it until now. Today my father has a daughter, and he seeks a son-in-law who will join his house."

Then Sung Chiang himself went and asked his father to come out and he led The Ten Foot Green Snake to the feasting place. Then Sung Chiang himself made apologies to her, saying, "This brother of mine, surnamed Wang, although in skill of war he is lesser than you, my Sister, yet did I promise him long ago to find him a wife, but from that time to this I have not done it. Today, Good Sister, acknowledge my father as your own, and let all these chieftains be go-betweens, for today is a fortunate, good day for weddings. Therefore, Good Sister, wed Wang Ying this day."

Then The Ten Foot Green Snake, seeing how kind a man Sung Chiang was, could not refuse him, and the two of them could but make obeisance and give thanks. And Ch'ao Kai and the others were greatly rejoiced; and they all acknowledged that Sung Chiang was a very righteous and kind man. On that day they feasted and drank wine and gave congratulations.

But even as they were in the midst of their feasting they saw one come to the foot of the mountain who made report, saying, "There is a man from Yün Ch'en in the wine shop of Chu Kuei. He wishes to come and meet the chieftains."

And Ch'ao Kai and Sung Chiang heard the man's report and they were rejoiced and said, "If this man of mercy comes to join us here on the mountain, then will the wishes of our whole life be fulfilled."

Truly is it,

If it be same to any man to thank or take revenge, then he is mean in heart,
If black be white to him and wrong be right to him, then his is no great part.

Who then was this man who came from the city of Yün Ch'en? Pray hear it told in the next chapter.

Chapter 50

THE WINGED TIGER
USES HIS RACK
TO STRIKE A MAID.
THE BEAUTIFUL BEARDED
IN A CARELESS INSTANT
LOSES THE
MAGISTRATE'S SON

IT IS SAID: Thus Sung Chiang was minded to give The Green Snake to Wang The Dwarf Tiger for wife, and all acclaimed Sung Chiang as a good and noble man, and on that day again a feast was made for congratulations. Now even as they feasted there came a man from Chu Kuei's wine shop, and he came up the mountain to make report that in front of the wood upon the road there was a great company of travelers passing, and the robbers had gone out to stay them. Among them was a man who called himself a captain of the guards from Yün Ch'en whose name was Lei Heng, and the chieftain Chu Kuei held him and now feasted him in the wine shop. It was a small robber who first made this report.

Then Ch'ao Kai and Sung Chiang, hearing it, were greatly rejoiced and they went down at once with the counselor Wu Yung to make Lei Heng welcome, and Chu Kuei had already sent the boat to The Golden Sands with him. When Sung Chiang saw him he made haste to kneel and give obeisance and he said, "Long have we been separated but always has my heart remembered you. Why do you pass by us here today?"

In great haste Lei Heng returned obeisance and he said, "I, your younger brother, was sent by my own city to go on business to an eastern city of Shantung, and now as I return I have passed by on your road and the lesser robbers stayed us and asked for money to buy our right of way. Then did I, your younger brother, mention my lowly name, and for this did our brother Chu stay me."

And Sung Chiang said, "Heaven has given me this fortune. Pray come into the lair, so that all the chieftains may see you and that we may have wine and feasting to welcome you."

So Lei Heng stayed five days and every day he talked with Sung Chiang of many things and Ch'ao Kai asked for news of Chu T'ung and Lei Heng answered, saying, "Chu T'ung in these days is now the governor of the gaols in the city, and the new magistrate likes him very much."

Then Sung Chiang began to speak in roundabout ways of Lei Heng's coming to join them on the mountain, but Lei Heng refused, saying that his mother was now very old and he could not join them, but after his mother was dead he would come. After this he made his obeisances of farewell and prepared to go down the mountain, nor could Sung Chiang and the others stay him by any urging. And all the chieftains brought out gold and silver and gave it to him. Of Sung Chiang and Ch'ao Kai it need not be told for Lei Heng received thus a great bundle of gold and silver and he went down the mountain, and all the chieftains escorted him to the mouth of the road and there they parted. Then the boat took him across to the great road, and so Lei Heng returned alone to Yün Ch'en. Of this no more need be said.

Let it be told further that Ch'ao Kai and Sung Chiang returned to the great lair and they went into the Hall Of Meeting. There they asked the counselor Wu Yung to decide what the duty of each should be in the lair, and Wu Yung took counsel with Sung Chiang and decided all things, and on that certain day all the chieftains met together to hear the announcement. Now the chieftains of the outer parts where the wine shops stood were first decided upon. And Sung Chiang said, "Sheng Sing and The Goodwife Ku were from the beginning persons who kept a wine shop. Let these two then take the place of T'ung Wei and T'ung Meng, and let these two be used elsewhere. Then let Shih Ch'ien go and help Shih Yung and Yo Ho go and help Chu Kuei and Chen T'ien Shou go and help Li Li, so that in the four wine shops in the south, the east, the west, the north, in each shop there shall be two chieftains to welcome the good fellows from every direction. And The Ten Foot Green Snake and Wang The Dwarf Tiger and such soldiers as they have of their own shall live in the part of the lair that is at the back, and they shall have charge of the horses. The encampment on The Golden Sands shall be under the charge of T'ung Wei and T'ung Meng. The Duck's Bill encampment shall be under Chou Yuen and Chou Jun, uncle and nephew. The great road to the front of the mountain Huang Hsin and Yien Shun shall guard, and they shall take horsemen to help them. Hsieh Chen and Hsieh Pao shall guard the first pass to the lair. Tu Ch'ien and Sung Wan shall guard the second pass. Liu T'ang and Mu Hung shall guard the third pass to the lair. The three Juan brothers shall guard all the encampments of the fighting men on water. Meng K'an shall do as he has done, and make boats of war. Tu Hsing and Chiang Ching shall all guard the moneys, the silver and gold, of the mountain. T'ao Chung Wang and Hsüeh Yung shall guard the walls and the terraces. Hou Chien alone shall be in charge of the making of clothing and garments of war and banners. Chu Fu and Sung Ch'ing shall be in charge of all feasts. Mu Ch'un and Li Yün shall be in charge of the building of houses and ramparts of wood. Siao Jang and Ching Ta Chien shall be in charge of all letters and announcements of visitors. P'ei Hsüan alone shall be in charge of the rules of the fighting men, and he shall reward those who are worthy and punish those who deserve it. The others, Lü Fang, Kao Shen, Sheng Li, Ou P'eng, Ma Ling, Teng Fei, Yang Ling and Pei Sheng shall divide into a company of eight and guard the great lair. Ch'ao Kai, Sung Chiang and Wu Yung shall dwell on the top of the mountain in the center. Hua Yung and Ch'ing Ming shall live to the left of the mountain peak. Ling Ch'ung and Tai Chung shall live to the right. Li Chün and Li K'uei shall live at the front. Chang Heng and Chang Shun shall live at the back of the mountain. Yang Hsiung and Shih Hsiu shall guard the two verandas at the two sides of the Hall of Meeting."

Thus were all the chieftains assigned. Each day one was appointed to prepare a feast and in truth the outlook of this lair was very clear and peaceful.

Let it be told further now of Lei Heng. He left the robbers' lair and he put his bundle on his back and took up his sword and he followed the road back to the city of Yün Ch'en. When he had reached his home he went to see his mother, and he changed his soiled garments. Then he took the letter he had brought back with him and he went at once toward the court.

When he had made his obeisance to the magistrate and had given his report he returned all his signs and official's pledges to the magistrate, and then he returned to his own house to rest. Every day, however, he went to the court to sign his name there and there he received the magistrate's commands.

Now one day he went to the east of the court and there he heard someone calling from behind his back, "Captain, when did you return?"

When Lei Heng turned about to see, it was a man of the town who worked here and there, one called Li The Second. And Lei Heng answered, saying, "I did but return home the day before yesterday."

And Li The Second said, "The Captain was gone for a long time. You do not know that there has been a courtesan who came hither from the eastern capital to stay for a few days. Her face and her skill in music are equally above all others, and her name is Pei Hsiu Ying. She came to make her obeisances to the Captain, but it was at the very time when you were away. Now she is in a brothel and she sings every sort of tune. Every day she practices with all skill, whether in dancing or acting or whether in playing the lute or whether in singing songs. She entices mountains and oceans full of people to go and see her. Why do you not go there, Captain, and take a look at her? Truly she is a very fine painted female."

Now Lei Heng heard this and he bethought himself that he was idle enough in heart that day and so he went with the man Li The Second to that place to look about. There he saw outside the door many scrolls of horizontal strips of silk with gold letters on them, and there were banners on supports as tall as a man's body. When he went inside he went to the left to the room called The Sky-Blue Dragon, and as he looked upon the hall there, it was the very moment when a merry play was being acted. Suddenly Li The Second turned and leaving Lei Heng there in the crowd he went away and he went outside and went to a gambling place.

Now when the play was over there was seen an old man whose head was bound in a kerchief down to his eyebrows, and he wore a robe of openwork, tea-colored silk. Around his waist was tied a black girdle and he carried a fan. He came to the front of the hall to speak and he spoke thus, "This old man is a man of the eastern capital, and I am named Pei Yü Ch'iao. Now I am old and I live only by my daughter Hsiu Ying's singing and dancing and playing the lute. Everywhere do we go to serve such as you who will look upon us."

Then did a drum sound forth and Pei Hsiu Ying mounted the dais and she bowed to all four sides and she took up the stick with which she beat the drum and she beat the drum as though beans were being scattered, and she struck the castanets, and sang a rhyme of four lines and seven words in each line, and so she sang,

"Nestlings twitter, the old birds come back,
Lambkins thrive, but the old sheep lack,
Birth until death, man sad must be,
Not like the wild ducks, flying free."

When Lei Heng heard this he cried out it was well done. Then Pei Hsiu Ying said, "Today upon Hsiu Ying's program it is said very clearly the name of the book from which I shall recite. It is a fair tale of love, and the name of it is 'The Pursuit of Su Ching by the Twain,' by Yu Chang."

When she had said these opening words she began to sing again and when she had sung again she spoke and the people listening shouted out without ceasing in praise of her. Now when she had sung to the end of the book Pei Yü Ch'iao cried out aside, "Although my daughter is not one by whom I have gained horses and gold, yet does she move the wise and able. These who have heard have already cried out well done. My daughter, come down now! This time it has been like a play of old."

Then Pei Hsiu Ying took up a plate and pointed with it and she said, "I rise at a rich man's door, I stay where my fortune is good, I pass in peace, I go to prosperous places. If my hand comes before you, let it not pass you empty."

And Pei Yü Ch'iao said, "My daughter, pray go around. These who have heard you are eager to reward you."

So Pei Hsiu Ying took the plate and she went first before Lei Heng. Now Lei Heng when he went to feel in his girdle did not dream that he was without a penny, and he said, "Today I have forgotten—I did not bring money with me. Tomorrow I will give it to you all together."

But Pei Hsiu Ying laughed and said, "If the first brewing of vinegar is not strong, the second has no taste. Sir, you have sat in the best place—then be an example and give the most!"

Now was Lei Heng's whole face red and he said, "For this little once I did not bring money with me. Truly it is not that I would not give it to you."

But Pei Hsiu Ying asked, "Sir, if you came to hear me sing, why did you not remember to bring money with you?"

And Lei Heng answered, "Though I should give you three or five ounces of silver, I would consider it nothing, but it is a very ill-fortune that today I forgot to bring any here."

Then Pei Hsiu Ying said, "Sir, today you have nothing at all, and how is it you talk of three or five ounces of silver? It is as though you made my mouth water to quench my thirst; it is as though you gave me the picture of a loaf and bade me be fed."

Then Pei Yü Ch'iao cried out, saying, "My daughter, blame yourself that you have no eyes. You do not look to see whether he is a city man or a country man, but you only ask something of him. Go to one of the wise and clever men who know what should be done and ask him to give you a sum to start with!"

At this Lei Heng said, "And how am I not one who understands what should be done?"

Pei Yü Ch'iao replied, "If you know what a son and brother ought to do then may a dog's head sprout horns!" And hearing this the whole crowd shouted out with him.

Now Lei Heng was in a mighty anger and he began to curse, saying, "How dare you shame me, you bumptious small fellow!"

But Pei Yü Ch'iao replied, "And though I do curse you, you cowherd from a hamlet, what does it matter so greatly?"

Now there were those who knew Lei Heng who shouted out to the old man, "You cannot behave thus. This is a captain in our city!"

Pei Yü Ch'iao said, "And I only fear he is a donkey in your city!"

Now how could Lei Heng endure further? He leaped from his seat and he laid hold upon Pei Yü Ch'iao and with one foot and one fist he split the old man's lip and knocked out his teeth. The crowd, seeing how fiercely Lei Heng struck, came to separate them, and they exhorted Lei Heng to go home, and everybody who had come there to find amusement scattered with a burst of noise.

Now this Pei Hsiu Ying formerly had had intercourse with the newly come magistrate and so today she had come especially to Yün Ch'en to open her business. This courtesan seeing her father thus beaten by Lei Heng and how heavily he was hurt called for a chair and went straight to the magistrate's court and there she made report of how Lei Heng had beaten her father and scattered all the crowds who had come to listen to her, and how he had deceived her.

When the magistrate heard this he was full of wrath and he cried, "Quickly write down the accusation!"

Now was this indeed listening to the female's words, and it is called listening to the bell by the pillow, for if a woman may not speak to a man in the day yet at night by the pillow the bell rings continuously. But Pei Yü Ch'iao wrote down the accusation and the magistrate looked also at the old man's wound and confirmed the proof.

Now there were many in this court who were friendly with Lei Heng and there were those who went to plead for him with the magistrate that he would let the matter pass. But how could they withstand that woman, pressing the magistrate unceasingly, crying and moaning for her will, so that he could but let her have it? She stood there and waited until the magistrate should send someone to seize Lei Heng and bring him there and beat him then and there in the hall.

So when the accusation had been presented a rack was brought and put on Lei Heng and he was led forth and marched up and down the streets as a warning to others. Then that woman wanted to show forth her powers and again she went before the magistrate and she said, "Lei Heng must be shown in that very place where I sang."

Therefore on the second day when the woman went again to sing at the brothel the magistrate gave the command that Lei Heng should be taken and shown there bound. Now all those who led Lei Heng forth were men like unto himself, and how could they be willing to bind him? After this woman had thought to herself for a time thus, "I have already used my name against him, and however much bitterness I make him eat now he will blame me still the same."

Therefore she came out of the door of the brothel and she went to a teashop and there she called an underling of the court to her and she said to him, "You all have friendship with him, and you have let him be free and unbound. Though the magistrate has commanded you to bind him with ropes, yet you have remembered your friendship. Soon I shall tell the magistrate and then see if I cannot make you suffer!"

And the runner replied, "Lady, you should not be angry. We will go and bind him then and there will be an end of it."

And Pei Hsiu Ying said, "If it be so, then I will reward you with silver."

So the runner could but come and say to Lei Heng, "Brother, we cannot help it. Let us bind you anyhow for a little while."

So he bound Lei Heng and took him on the streets where there were many people. Now it was even at this moment that Lei Heng's mother came to bring food to him, and when she saw her son there bound she began to weep and she began to curse the runner, saying, "You are a comrade of my son in the court—and do you hold bribes so dear as this, then! Ah, who can swear that he will never be in trouble?"

Then the runner answered, saying, "My Old Mother, hear me speak. We wished to act according to friendship, but unhappily the accuser stands near and will have me bind him, nor did I have any way to escape from it. If I did not, she would go and tell of it to the magistrate and so would she make us suffer. Because of this we could not consider his face."

The old woman said, "And whoever heard of

an accuser who himself stood to see whether the accused was bound and taken on the streets or not?"

Again did the runner say in a whisper, "Old Mother, but she is on good terms with the magistrate and one word from her will condemn us! For this has it been hard on all sides."

But the old woman herself went and untied the ropes and she continued to curse, saying, "This trollop! And how can she use the magistrate's power to oppress people like this! I shall untie these ropes myself and see what she will do then!"

Now Pei Hsiu Ying heard these words from the teashop and she came forth and she said, "You old servant woman! What was it you just said?"

But by this time what good feeling could there be in the old woman's heart? She pointed at the courtesan and she cursed, saying, "You low bitch that have been ridden by a thousand and by ten thousand dogs! And what are you doing that you dare curse me?"

Now when Pei Hsiu Ying heard this her eyebrows, shaped like willow leaves, flew upwards, and her starry eyes grew round and she fell to mighty cursing and she said, "You old biting insect! You old beggar woman! You good for nothing! How dare you curse me?"

And the old woman cried, "And if I have cursed you what will you do? You are not the magistrate of the city!"

Then was Pei Hsiu Ying so full of anger she rushed forward and she slapped the old woman in the face until she staggered. Even as she righted herself again Pei Hsiu Ying rushed forward again and she beat the old woman again and again on the ears.

Now Lei Heng's heart was already oppressed with anger and when he saw his mother thus suffering such blows he could not bear it and his anger rushed up out of his heart. He pushed up his rack and brought it down upon the crown of Pei Hsiu Ying's head and he hit her full and he split her skull. She fell with a thud. When all the crowd looked at her, they saw the white stuff of her brains pouring out and her eyeballs gushing forth, and she could not move. Then did all know she was dead.

Now when they all saw Pei Hsiu Ying thus killed they guarded Lei Heng and they all went to the court to make confession. There they saw the magistrate and they told him all. At once the magistrate sent men to take Lei Heng back to the corpse and with him those officials whose duty it was to examine into sudden deaths and the local police and the neighbors were all called together. When the dead body had been closely examined again they were all brought to the court and Lei Heng confessed to everything nor was there any difficulty. His mother gave a guarantor and went home to await call.

Again Lei Heng's rack was put on him and again he was put in the gaol. Now the head gaoler at this time was Chu T'ung, The Beautiful Bearded. When he saw Lei Heng brought thither, he had no plan of help for him and he could but prepare food and wine for his pleasure, and he bade the under gaolers to choose a clean room and there he placed Lei Heng. In a short time Lei Heng's mother came into the gaol to bring food and she pled, weeping, with Chu T'ung, saying, "This old body is already more than sixty years old, and my eyes have been fixed steadfastly upon this one son. Ten thousand times do I beg you, Noble Elder Brother, to remember your old brother-friendship for him and take pity on this child of mine. Help him and protect him!"

Then Chu T'ung said, "Old Mother, let your heart rest and return to your home. Nor need you send food after this day. I will myself look after him. If there comes a chance convenient for saving him, I will save him."

And Lei Heng's mother said, "Elder Brother, if you save my child, it will be as though my parents were born again to me for if there comes anything untoward to this son of mine, then is my life ended also."

Chu T'ung replied, "I will bear naught but this in my heart. Old Mother, you need not be anxious."

Then the old woman made obeisance of thanks and went her way.

Now Chu T'ung thought to himself for a whole day nor could he think of any way to save Lei Heng. He could but send men to the magistrate and ask that the crime be lightened, and he used money high and low to make good feeling.

But that magistrate, although he loved Chu T'ung, yet he could but hate Lei Heng because he had killed this courtesan of his, and he would not hear these messages. Nor could he withstand the importunings of that old man Pei Yü Ch'iao, that Lei Heng should be killed for what he had done.

When Lei Heng had been sixty days in the gaol, the time was come for the case, and the crime was fixed and he was to be exiled to Chi Chou. The scribe who had attended the case brought together all the proofs and went with them first. Then Chu T'ung was bade to guard Lei Heng thither.

Chu T'ung led with him some ten-odd lesser gaolers to guard Lei Heng and so they left the city of Yün Ch'en. When they had gone some miles they saw a wine shop and Chu T'ung said, "Let us all stay to drink a bowl of wine and then go on."

So they all went into the wine shop to drink wine. Now Chu T'ung himself took Lei Heng with him to relieve himself somewhere and they came to a place behind the house where no one was and there he took off Lei Heng's rack and he let him escape free, and he commanded him, saying, "Good Brother, go back yourself and go to your home and fetch your old mother and escape by night to some other place. I will go to court for you."

But Lei Heng answered, "If I go it matters little, but surely you will suffer for it."

Then Chu T'ung said, "Brother, you do not know. The magistrate blames you for having killed his courtesan and he has not lightened a word of your punishment. If I take you to Chi Chou they will surely want your life. Though I let you escape, it will not be a crime great enough to cost my life. Moreover I have no parents for whom to be anxious and I can use all I have in my house for this sake of yours. Do not think of me, but only of what is ahead of you. Go quickly!"

So Lei Heng made obeisance and gave thanks and he hastened homewards by a small path to the back of the house and he gathered together such things as he valued and he led out his old mother and that same night he went to the robbers' lair there to join them. Of this no more need be told.

Let it be told now of Chu T'ung. He took the empty rack and he cast it into the grass. Then he came out and he said to all the other gaolers, "Lei Heng has gone! Now what shall we do?"

All the others said, "Quickly, let us go to his home and catch him!"

But Chu T'ung on purpose seemed to meditate for a long time until he thought Lei Heng must be gone a long way and then he led the others back to the court to say that Lei Heng was escaped and he said humbly, "It was this lowly one who was not careful. Lei Heng escaped on the way, and when he did so, we could not catch him. I am now willing to receive meet punishment, for I have nothing to say."

Now the magistrate had loved Chu T'ung and he had the heart to save him out of this trouble, but Pei Yü Ch'iao threatened to carry the matter higher, saying, "Chu T'ung freed Lei Heng on purpose!"

So the magistrate could but make report on to the higher court at Chi Chou of what Lei Heng had done. As for Chu T'ung's house, they could but use money high and low freely. Only then was Chu T'ung sent to Chi Chou, and there in the presence of the higher governor he was questioned as to those things of which he was accused.

Then he was beaten twenty times upon his back and branded upon his face and sent to the gaol in Ch'ang Chou. And Chu T'ung put on his traveling rack and the two guards who were to accompany him on his way brought with them the official papers, and thus they set forth, guarding Chu T'ung.

As for his household, there were assuredly those who sent money and garments upon the way, and first of all they gave the two guards money. Thus they left the city of Yün Ch'en and winding their way along they went toward the city of Ch'ang Chou.

Of the journey there is nothing to be told. When they were come to Ch'ang Chou they went into the midst of the city and toward the court and it was at the hour when the magistrate ascended into his Hall Of Audience and the two guards forced Chu T'ung to the front of the hall and presented their papers and the magistrate looked at them. Then he looked at Chu T'ung and saw he was in face and figure no common man, and his face was as red as a dried date. His beard, moreover, was beautiful, and so long it covered his belly. Seeing all this, the magistrate was eight parts pleased with him, and he commanded, "This prisoner is not to be put into the city gaol. Let him stay here in the court to serve me."

Then was his traveling rack taken off, and answering papers were given and the two guards made their farewells and returned.

Let it now be told of Chu T'ung alone in the court. Every day he stood by the hall and served the magistrate. Now in that court the police and the guards, the gatemen and the runner, the wardens and the gaolers of the gaol, were all given gifts by Chu T'ung and when they saw how courteous he was they all liked him well.

Suddenly one day even as the magistrate was sitting in judgment in his hall, and Chu T'ung stood on the pavilion in front, the magistrate called to Chu T'ung to come forward into the hall and he asked him, saying, "Why did you free Lei Heng and yourself come hither to suffer punishment?"

And Chu T'ung answered humbly, "And how could this lowly one dare to free Lei Heng on purpose? It was because for an instant I was not careful and so he escaped from me."

And the magistrate said, "Then should you not have been punished so heavily as this."

But Chu T'ung replied, "The accuser was determined that I should acknowledge I had freed him purposely, and so was my punishment fixed thus heavily."

Again the magistrate asked, "And why did Lei Heng beat to death that courtesan?"

Then did Chu T'ung tell all of the story of Lei Heng and the magistrate said, "It may be you saw how he respected his mother and because of your brother-friendship you freed him."

But Chu T'ung replied, "How could I dare to deceive thus those who are above me?"

Now in the midst of this questioning there came out from behind the screen one of the young lords, the magistrate's son, and he was but four years old. He was a child of noble bearing and his face was full of beauty and he was the son of the magistrate's first and true wife and the magistrate loved him like gold and like jade. And the little lord saw Chu T'ung and he came over and would be taken into his arms. So Chu T'ung could but take the child and hold him to his bosom. Then the little lord held Chu T'ung fast with both hands in his beard and he cried, "I will have only this bearded one to hold me!"

The magistrate said, "Child, take your hands away quickly. Do not be troublesome."

But again the little lord cried, "I will have this bearded one hold me and play with me!"

At last Chu T'ung said humbly, "This humble one will take the little lord to the front of the court and walk and play there a little while, and then return."

And the magistrate made answer, "If the child must have you hold him, go then and play with him for a while."

So Chu T'ung, holding the little lord, went outside to the front of the court, and he bought some dainty sweets and fruits for him to eat, and he walked around with him once, and then he carried him back into the court. The magistrate saw him and he asked the little lord, saying, "Child, where did you go and whence have you come?"

And the little lord replied, "This bearded one went with me on the street to play and he bought sweets and fruits and asked me to eat them."

Then the magistrate said to Chu T'ung, "And whence have you money to buy things for the child to eat?"

Chu T'ung answered humbly, "It is but to show forth a little of my loyal heart, and why need so small a thing even pass one's teeth?"

And the magistrate commanded, "Bring out wine for Chu T'ung to drink."

Then a slave came bringing on a tray a silver wine jug and a comfit box, and she poured out wine. Three cups of wine were poured forth for Chu T'ung to drink, one after the other, and the magistrate commanded, "Whenever the child wants you to go and play, go as you like and take him out to play."

And Chu T'ung replied, "Most Merciful, how dare I refuse such a command as this?"

From this time on, therefore, every day he came in and went out on the street with the little lord to play. In Chu T'ung's girdle there was plenty of money and he wished only that the magistrate be pleased, and so he took out his money freely for the little lord.

When time had passed for about half a month, it came to the fifteenth day of the seventh month, the day of devils, and there were priests everywhere chanting against evil spells, and according to the custom of every year there were lights put out upon the river in addition to the chanting. On that day in the evening the slaves and the wet nurses cried out, saying, "Captain Chu, the little lord wishes today to go and see the river lights and our master has commanded that you may carry him to see them."

And Chu T'ung answered, "I will carry the little one thither then."

Then the little lord, wearing a gown of thin summer silk, his hair braided into two horns, and with hanging jewels on the braids, came walking from within, and Chu T'ung put him upon his shoulder and they went out to the front of the court, and they went toward The Temple Of The King Of Devils to see the lights upon the river. Now at that time it was the hour of the first watch of evening and Chu T'ung went everywhere through the temple with the little lord on his shoulder, and at last he came to the part of the temple that was upon the river where there was a great pool wherein people placed living things to save their lives for merit. There they watched the lights upon the water, and the little lord crawled upon the balustrade and watched and laughed and played.

Suddenly someone from behind pulled at Chu T'ung's sleeve and whispered, "Elder Brother, walk a few steps with me. I have something to say to you."

When Chu T'ung turned about to see, it was Lei Heng. He gave a start of fright and he said, "Pray come down, little lord, and sit here. I will go and buy sweets for you to eat. Do not move or go away."

The little lord said, "Come back quickly, for I want to go on the bridge and see the lights."

Chu T'ung replied, "I will come soon."

Then he turned himself about to talk with Lei Heng and he said, "Good Brother, why have you come hither?"

But Lei Heng besought Chu T'ung to come to a lonely spot, and he made obeisance to him, saying, "Ever since my elder brother saved my life I have had no place to escape with my old mother. I could but go to the mountain lair, and there I went to Sung Chiang and I have joined myself with them, and I told them of my elder brother's mercy. And Sung Chiang himself also remembers often your mercy in helping him also to escape and our great chieftain and all the chiefs are all filled with gratitude toward you. For this they have especially sent me, your younger brother, and our counselor Wu Yung also, to come hither to seek you."

Chu T'ung asked, "And where is the teacher Wu?"

Then from behind him the counselor Wu said, "Wu Yung is here." And when he had said these words he made obeisance.

In great haste Chu T'ung returned the courtesy and said, "Long have we not met. Sir, has it been well with you all this time?"

The counselor Wu Yung answered, "The chieftains in the lair all asked much after you. Today they have sent Captain Lei and me hither to ask you, Sir, to come up the mountain, and there we will all be together. We have been here for many days, but we did not dare meet you. Tonight we waited for you. Pray then, Elder Brother, prepare at once to come with us and let us go together to the lair, and so fulfill the hopes of Ch'ao Kai and Sung Chiang."

When Chu T'ung had heard this, for a long time he pondered and he could make no answer, but at last he said, "Sir, you are mistaken. Do not mention this matter, lest others hear it and evil come. Brother Lei has committed a crime for which death was the punishment, and out of our friendship I let him go free, and he had no place of escape, and so he must needs go and join you on the mountain and I am exiled here for him. Heaven will pity me, and in a year or a half year or more, I may have the chance to return home and again become a good citizen. How then can I be willing to do such a thing as this? I pray you, therefore, return, and do not stay here and stir up talk."

But Lei Heng said, "Elder Brother, you can be but an underling here to serve others, and this is no fit duty for a true man and true warrior. It is not only that I, your younger brother, am come to urge you up the mountain, but the two chieftains Ch'ao Kai and Sung Chiang have long hoped for your coming. Do not long delay."

Again Chu T'ung made answer, "Brother,

what words of these are yours? Have you not remembered that it was because of your old mother and the poverty of your house that I set you free? Yet today you come to injure me and bid me do evil."

At last Wu Yung said, "If he is not willing to come we can but bid you farewell and return."

And Chu T'ung said, "When you return mention my lowly name before the chieftains in thanks."

Then they went together to the bridge. Now Chu T'ung returned and he did not see the little lord. He began to cry out bitterness, for he did not know where to go and search for him. But Lei Heng laid hold on Chu T'ung and he said, "Elder Brother, do not seek for him. It must be because the two men I brought with me, when they heard Elder Brother would not come with us, have carried the little lord away. Let us go together and seek them."

Chu T'ung cried, "Brother, this is no matter for play. If anything happens to this little lord, then is my life entangled with it."

Lei Heng answered, "Elder Brother, pray come with me."

And Chu T'ung would not let Lei Heng and Wu Yung go away. He laid hold on them and the three of them went away together and they went outside the city. Now Chu T'ung's heart was frightened and he asked, saying, "Where are these men of yours who have carried the little lord away?"

Lei Heng answered, "Elder Brother, pray go to where I am living, and I swear I will return the child to you."

But Chu T'ung said, "If it is too late the magistrate will see it and blame me."

Wu Yung said, "Those two whom we brought with us are but ignorant men and they have assuredly but carried him to where we are staying."

And Chu T'ung asked, "What are the surnames and names of these followers of yours?"

Lei Heng answered, saying, "I do not know that either. I have only heard him called The Black Whirlwind."

Then did Chu T'ung give a start of fright and he said, "Is it not that murderer of Chiang Chou who is Li K'uei?"

Wu Yung said, "It is that man."

Then Chu T'ung stamped his feet and he cried out bitterness and in great haste he pursued Li K'uei. They had gone perhaps some six or seven miles from the city when they saw Li K'uei in front calling out, "Here I am!"

Chu T'ung rushed forward and he asked, saying, "Where have you put the little lord?"

Li K'uei cried out greeting and he said, "I make obeisance, Noble Elder Brother. We have the little lord here."

Chu T'ung said, "Bring him out carefully and return him to me."

Li K'uei pointed to his head and said, "The little lord's jewels that were on his hair are on my hair."

Chu T'ung looked and in haste he asked, "Truly where is the little lord?"

Li K'uei replied, "I put some poison in his mouth and dragged him out of the city. Now he is there sleeping in the wood. You go yourself and seek and see."

Then Chu T'ung went by the light of the moon into the wood to search and there he saw the little lord lying on the ground. But when Chu T'ung went to put out his hands to lift him up he saw that his head was split in half and there he lay—dead!

Then was Chu T'ung's heart filled with a mighty wrath and he leaped out of the wood but the three were already not to be seen. When he looked in all four directions he saw The Black Whirlwind in the far distance whirling his battle axes and shouting forth, "Come—come—!"

Then the anger rose in Chu T'ung's heart and he rushed on without regard for himself. He pulled up his long gown and with great strides he hastened on. But Li K'uei turned himself about and he also went on and behind him Chu T'ung hastened in pursuit.

Now this Li K'uei, whether he climbed mountain or valley, was one accustomed to such walking, and how could Chu T'ung come up with him? He was already panting heavily. Then Li K'uei again called from in front, "Come—come—come!"

And Chu T'ung longed for a mouthful of breath to overturn that other but he could not come up with him.

So the day came gradually to dawn. Li K'uei ran ahead, and if he were pursued quickly went quickly; and if he were pursued slowly, he went slowly; if the pursuer stopped, he stopped. Thus gradually he was pursued into a great village. Chu T'ung, seeing this, said, "Even though that thing has a place to hide, yet am I not finished with him!"

Chu T'ung then did but pursue him into the central hall of the village and he saw on either side within this hall many weapons hung upon racks, and he said, "I do think this is also an official house." So he stayed his feet and he called out in a loud voice, "Is there anyone here in the village?"

Then was a man seen to come from behind the screen. And who was this man? He was that Little Whirlwind, Ch'ai Chin. He asked, saying, "Ha, and who are you?"

Chu T'ung, seeing this man that he walked like a dragon and that his face and appearance were like the very sun, in great haste made obeisance and he answered, saying, "This lowly one is a warden of the gaol in Yün Ch'en, named Chu T'ung. I committed a sin and I was exiled to this place. Last night I led the magistrate's little lord out to see the river lights and The Black Whirlwind killed the little lord. Now he has escaped into your honorable village, and ten thousand times do I pray you will command men to help me and seize him and send him to gaol."

But Ch'ai Chin said, "If you are The Beautiful Bearded, then pray be seated."

Chu T'ung said, "This lowly one does not dare to ask what the high surname of the noble one is."

Ch'ai Chin answered, saying, "This lowly one is called The Little Whirlwind."

Chu T'ung said, "Long have I heard of the great lord Ch'ai." And in great haste he bowed in obeisance and said, "I did not dream that on this day I should have this fortunate opportunity."

And Ch'ai Chin said, "Long have I also heard of The Beautiful Bearded. Pray come and talk in the innermost hall."

So Chu T'ung followed Ch'ai Chin within, and then Chu T'ung asked, "How dared such as The Black Whirlwind come into your honored village to hide?"

Ch'ai Chin answered, "Pray give me leave to answer. I, this lowly one, called The Little Whirlwind, have long loved good fellows from everywhere by river and lake. Because an ancestor of my house had the merit of giving up his royal seat to another, the Emperor gave us imperial pledges of a scroll and an iron symbol. If therefore there be any criminal who comes to hide in my house no one dares to come hither to arrest him. Not long since I had a dearly loved friend and he was a friend of yours, also, Sir, who is now a chieftain in the great lair, whose name is called The Opportune Rain, Sung Chiang, who wrote a false letter and he and Wu Yung and Lei Heng and The Black Whirlwind all gathered together to this village to ask you with every courtesy to go up the mountain with them. Here they gathered for such a purpose. But seeing, Sir, how you refused them and would not go with them they bade Li K'uei purposely to kill the little lord to cut off from you the path of return, so that you could but go up the mountain and there sit in the seat of a chieftain. Wu Yung, Lei Heng, why do you not come out and make your apologies?"

Then were seen Wu Yung and Lei Heng coming out from a small corner room and they faced Chu T'ung and they made obeisance and they said, "Brother Captain, we hope and beseech that you will forgive us our sin, but this was the command of our elder brother Sung Chiang, and he commanded us thus. If you will go to the mountain lair you will understand for yourself."

But Chu T'ung answered, "This—this you have done—true—and true it is you have done it out of a good heart for me, yet you have overreached yourselves in such poisonous ways."

Then Ch'ai Chin exerted himself to exhort both sides and at last Chu T'ung said, "If I am to go, then I go. I only ask to see The Black Whirlwind's face, and I will go."

So Ch'ai Chin said, "Elder Brother Li, come out quickly and make your apologies."

Then Li K'uei also came out from the corner room and he called a loud greeting. But when Chu T'ung saw him out of his heart sprang a flame of fierce fire and it reached thirty thousand feet into the air nor could he hold it down. He gathered himself and he sprang upon Li K'uei and sought to tear his life from him. Ch'ai Chin, Lei Heng and Wu Yung, the three of them, besought him most bitterly and at last Chu T'ung said, "If you will have me go up the mountain, you must grant me one thing and I will go."

And Wu Yung said, "Do not say one thing only. If there were tens of things we would grant them all. We would ask what the thing is."

But it could not be dreamed that what Chu T'ung asked would set into turmoil the city of Kao T'ang Chou, and it stirred up also Liang Shan P'o. Because of this truly was it,

Sprung of kings, and seeking heroes, he in gaol must sit,
He whose halls were free to all, himself fell in a pit.

What then did Chu T'ung say? Pray hear it told in the next chapter.

Chapter 51

LI K'UEI KILLS YING T'IEN HSI. CH'AI CHIN IS MADE PRISONER IN KAO T'ANG CHOU

IT IS SAID: At that time when Chu T'ung was talking to the others, he said, "If you would have me go up the mountain, you must kill first The Black Whirlwind and so free me of this anger in me; then will I go."

Li K'uei heard this and he was filled with a great anger and he cried, "And you would—you would—would you— My elder brothers bade me do what I did, and what has it to do with my hide?"

Then Chu T'ung grew the more filled with fury at this and again he would have fought with Li K'uei except that the three again held him and exhorted him, and he said, "If this Black Whirlwind is there too, then though I die I will not go up the mountain."

At last Ch'ai Chin answered, "If it is thus indeed, then it is easy enough, too. I have a way myself. Let our brother Li stay here with me and there will be an end of it. You three therefore go up the mountain and so fulfill the purpose of Ch'ao Kai and Sung Chiang."

Again Chu T'ung spoke, "Since this thing has now already been done, the magistrate will certainly send out a proclamation to the city of Yün Ch'en to seize me and my whole house. What then can be done?"

Then Wu Yung made answer, "Sir, let your heart rest. By now doubtless Sung Chiang has already brought your house to the mountain."

Only then could Chu T'ung let his heart be at rest. And Ch'ai Chin brought out wine to entertain them, and that same night they set forth on their way. And they bade farewell to the lord Ch'ai Chin and they prepared to part from him. And Ch'ai Chin had commanded the villagers to saddle three horses and he escorted them outside the suburb. When they parted Wu Yung again commanded Li K'uei, saying, "Do you be careful now that you are living for a while in the village of this great lord. By no means are you to act wildly and stir up anger of men. Wait half a year or three months until this other's heart is free of anger, and then you may come back again to the mountain. Then doubtless will we also come and ask the lord Ch'ai to come and join with us also."

And the three mounted their horses and went their way.

It will not be told now of Ch'ai Chin and Li K'uei returning to the village. Let us rather tell of Chu T'ung following Wu Yung and Lei Heng and going to the robbers' lair at Liang Shan P'o to join the robbers. When they had gone a stage of their journey they came out of the region of Ch'ang Chou and the villagers riding their horses returned. Then the three followed the road to the robbers' lair and of the journey there is naught to tell. They soon came to Chu Kuei's wine shop and first someone was sent up the mountain to make report and Ch'ao Kai and Sung Chiang leading the chieftains great and small, beating drums and blowing pipes, came to The Golden Sands to meet them. When all had met each one turned his horse toward the great lair in the mountain and there they dismounted, and they went all of them to the Hall Of Meeting and they told of what had passed.

And Chu T'ung said, "This younger brother has today received the command to come up the mountain. But the magistrate of Ch'ang Chou will assuredly send a proclamation to Yien Chou to seek me and my house. What then shall be done?"

Then Sung Chiang gave a great laugh and said, "I do bid my brother to let his heart rest. The honorable lady and the young lords have already come here for many days."

Chu T'ung then asked, saying, "And where are they now?"

Sung Chiang said, "I have already been caring for them in my old father's house. Pray go thither yourself, my Brother Captain, and see them."

Then Chu T'ung was much rejoiced, and Sung Chiang commanded one to lead Chu T'ung to where the old father lived, and there he saw his whole house young and old and even all his best and finest goods. And his wife said, "A few days ago one came with a letter saying you were already on the mountain and had joined with them here. For this I put our things together and came hither by night."

After this Chu T'ung came out and gave thanks to all the chiefs and Sung Chiang then asked Chu T'ung and Lei Heng to go and live with the soldiers on the topmost peak of the mountain.

And he prepared a feast and on that day he invited this new chieftain, and of this there is no more to be told.

Let it be told now of the magistrate at Ch'ang Chou. When, as it grew late, he did not see Chu T'ung carrying the little lord back, he sent men out in all four directions to seek for him and they sought through half the night. On the next day one found the child killed in the wood and he brought back the report so that the magistrate knew of it. When he heard of it he gave a start of terror and in great anger he himself went to the wood to see, and when he saw he wept without ceasing and he prepared a coffin for the child and then burned it.

On the next day he went into the hall and he sent forth proclamations in all directions that everywhere Chu T'ung himself was to be sought for arrest. From Yün Ch'en word was sent to him that Chu T'ung's whole house had already escaped, and it was not known whither they had gone. But still the command of arrest was sent to every city and a reward was offered to any who might find him. Of this no more need be said.

Let it be told now only of Li K'uei in the village of Ch'ai Chin. He lived there for more than a month. Suddenly on a certain day he saw a man coming and bringing a letter, and hastening with all speed to the village. The lord Ch'ai went to meet him and, taking the letter, read it. Then he gave a start of terror and he said, "If it is thus I can but go at once."

And Li K'uei asked, saying, "What important business has the lord?"

Ch'ai Chin replied, "I have an uncle named Ch'ai Huan Ch'en and he lives in Kao T'ang Chou, and now Ying T'ien Hsi, that thing, who is the brother of the wife of the magistrate there, wants to confiscate his flower garden, and so his anger has risen so that he is ill of it and lies upon his bed, and his life cannot be long assured. It must be that he has dying words to give me, and so for this has he sent especially to call me to him. My uncle has neither son nor daughter, and so I must go at once myself."

Then Li K'uei said, "If the lord is going, then I will go at once with you also."

And Ch'ai Chin said, "Elder Brother, if you wish to go, then come with me."

So Ch'ai Chin in great haste prepared his goods and he chose some ten-odd fine horses and he took with him several villagers. On the next day at the fifth watch of early morning, Ch'ai Chin and Li K'uei and the ones who were to accompany them all mounted their horses, and they left the village and went toward the city of Kao T'ang Chou. In less than a day they had arrived there. They entered the city and went straight to the uncle's house and there dismounted and Ch'ai Chin left Li K'uei and those who had come with him in the outer room, and he himself went into the bedroom to see his uncle who lay reclining upon a long couch. Then Ch'ai Chin let his voice out in great weeping. But his uncle's second wife came out and exhorted Ch'ai Chin, saying, "Sir, you have suffered by wind and weather riding hither on this journey. Now that you have just come here do not thus weep and exhaust yourself."

When Ch'ai Chin had made his obeisances to her he asked about the affair of the garden. The lady replied, "The magistrate here is newly come and his name is Kao Lien. He is not only magistrate but he is in charge of the soldiers and horsemen also of the city, and he is a cousin of the Commander Kao in the eastern capital. And he takes advantage of his cousin's power and here he does every sort of evil thing. He brought with him a wife's brother called Ying T'ien Hsi. Men all call him the prime minister, although he is but a youth, for he trusts to his brother-in-law's power and he does as he wishes here of every sort of evil. There are those too who fawn for his favor, and they have told him that behind our house there is a flower garden and there is a pool with a well-built pavilion in it. So that thing came bringing with him some twenty or thirty wicked rascals and they came into our home and looked about, and they would have driven us out, for they wished to come and live here. But Huan Ch'en, my lord, your uncle, said to him, 'Our house is of royal descent, gold root, jade leaves, and above the gate of our old home there is an iron pledge with red letters, given us by an Emperor of old. No one dares to molest us. How dare you rob me of my home therefore? And whither will you drive out my household?' But that thing would not listen to us speaking thus, and he was determined to have us get out of the house. So Huan Ch'en went and laid hands on him, but that thing pushed him and beat him. For this has he suffered with this wrath in him. From the time he lay down he has not risen once. Food he will not eat, and even medicine makes him no better. Looking at him we see that he is not far from Heaven, and very near his grave in the earth. But today you, my lord, have come hither to act for us. Even though the unexpected comes, high as the mountains, deep as the depths of the waters, yet will we not grieve."

And Ch'ai Chin answered, saying, "My aunt, let your heart rest. I do but hope to find a good physician to come and heal my uncle. If there comes this evil then surely will I send one back to bring from above my gate the pledge given us by imperial favor and though I go before the magistrate, or even before the Emperor himself, I shall not be afraid."

The wife replied, "What Huan Ch'en does is of no use. What you say is the best."

Then Ch'ai Chin, having seen his uncle for a while, came out again to Li K'uei and he told those he had brought with him of the affair. Now when Li K'uei heard it he leaped up and he said, "How without any righteousness is such an one as this fellow! I have these great axes here, and I will make him eat a few blows of them! Then we can talk!"

But Ch'ai Chin answered, "Elder Brother Li, I pray you still your wrath. Why should we begin to battle with him now without occasion? Although he does the best he can to injure others, yet in my home have I already a pledge from the imperial home to protect us. Here we cannot contend with him. But there are surely higher than he in the capital city. We are in the right, and we will go to law with him."

But Li K'uei cried, "Oh, law, law—if everybody acted according to law then there would be no more trouble on the earth! As for me, I strike first and then talk! If that thing goes before the magistrate to accuse us I will kill even the accursed magistrate with him!"

At this Ch'ai Chin laughed and he said, "I can see how Chu T'ung wanted to quarrel with you, for you two could not so much as look upon each other's faces. But this is one of the royal cities of the Emperor, and how can you act as freely as you did in your mountain lair?"

But Li K'uei replied, "And what if it is a royal city? In Chiang Chou and Wu Wei Chün was there only I who killed men?"

Then Ch'ai Chin said, "Wait until I have seen through this all clearly. When I can use you, my Elder Brother, then will I come and seek you. But so long as there is naught to do, pray do you stay within the house."

Now in the midst of his speaking there came out a maid from the house to ask in great haste that Ch'ai Chin come in to see his uncle, and Ch'ai Chin hastened to the chamber. There he saw his uncle's eyes filled with tears, and he said to Ch'ai Chin, "Good Nephew, your ambitions are high indeed. But it is true you must not let our ancestors come to shame, for today am I killed by anger with Ying T'ien Hsi. Consider therefore that we are one blood and one bone, and do you yourself fetch the royal pledge and when the Emperor comes forth stand in his way and cry to him for justice, and so revenge me. Then though I lie in the ninth Hades yet will I be grateful to you. But take heed of your body. I will speak no more."

And when he had finished speaking he let his soul go free. Then Ch'ai Chin wept for a long time, until the wife of his uncle, fearing he might weep himself into a faint, exhorted him, saying, "Sir, there are many days in which you may weep. Pray let us take counsel of what must be done now that he is dead."

Ch'ai Chin said, "The pledge is in my house, and I did not bring it here. But this very night I will send men out to fetch it, for we must take it to the very capital and accuse before the Emperor himself. Let us now prepare the inner and outer coffins for this honored body of my uncle and let us put on our mourning robes, and then we can take counsel further."

So Ch'ai Chin gave command that according to his uncle's requirements the inner and outer coffins should be measured and made, and according to rite and ritual should the tablets be prepared to place before it. And the whole house then put on whole mourning and great and small lifted up their voices in mourning and wailing.

Now Li K'uei, outside, hearing the weeping rise from within began to wring his hands and to rub his palms together, but when he asked the others who were with him about it, not one would tell him. But he saw priests were asked to come within and chant their rites.

On the third day Ying T'ien Hsi was seen coming riding a swift horse and he led a crowd of some twenty or thirty idlers with him. In their hands they bore bows that flew bullets of iron or stone or returning arrows, and they had blow pipes, kickballs, and chains on bamboo poles, and musical instruments. They went outside the city and amused themselves awhile, and they were half or seven parts drunken, and half they pretended to be wholly drunken and half they pretended to be crazed and they came straight then to the front of Ch'ai Huan Ch'en's house. There they reined in their horses and called for the one within who controlled the house to come out and speak with them.

Then Ch'ai Chin, hearing them call, came out in haste to make answer, clad as he was in full mourning, and that Ying T'ien Hsi asked, sitting on his horse, saying, "And who are you in his house?"

Ch'ai Chin made answer, saying, "This lowly one is his nephew by own blood."

And Ying T'ien Hsi said, "The other day I commanded saying that they must move out of this house. Why have they not heeded my words?"

Ch'ai Chin replied, "My uncle was ill and he did not dare to move himself and he died. Wait until the days of mourning are fulfilled and we will move out."

But Ying T'ien Hsi said, "You pass your wind! I will give you only three days and you must be out of the house. If you have not moved within the three days, then will I put a rack upon such as you and stand you up for men to see. And first I will beat you a hundred blows of the bamboo."

Then Ch'ai Chin made answer, "Do not thus oppress me. My house is royal also, sons and grandsons are we of the Dragon. We have the pledge of the Emperor of former times, and who dares not to pay it respect?"

But Ying T'ien Hsi shouted out, "Bring it out and let me see it!"

And Ch'ai Chin answered, "It is now in our home in Ch'ang Chou. There is one already gone to fetch it hither."

In great wrath Ying T'ien Hsi said, "How like a fool does this one speak! Even though it be a royal pledge I do not fear it. You to right and left, beat this one for me!"

Even as the others were about to put forth their hands, Li K'uei, who had been standing behind the door looking through the crack, when he heard Ch'ai Chin go out to answer the shout, now pushed open the door and with a mighty roar he charged to the side of the horse. In a trice he had dragged Ying T'ien Hsi from his horse and with a blow of his fist had knocked him over.

When those twenty or thirty men came forward to attack him he had already knocked over five or six of them with his lifted fists and the rest fled in a mob. Again he jerked up Ying T'ien Hsi and with fists and feet going together, how could Ch'ai Chin stay him now? When he looked at Ying T'ien Hsi, he saw he was already dead upon the ground.

Then Ch'ai Chin could but cry bitterness and he bade Li K'uei come into the inner hall to take counsel with him, and Ch'ai Chin said, "It can be seen easily enough that immediately there will be men here, and you can no longer stay here. I will assume the responsibility at court for the killing of this Ying T'ien Hsi. Do you go quickly and return to the mountain lair."

But Li K'uei answered, "If I go it will drag you into the matter."

Ch'ai Chin said, "I have the royal pledge with which to protect my person. Do you go then, and let there be no delay."

So Li K'uei lifted up his two axes and he took some money for travel and he went out the back gate and went alone toward the robbers' lair.

In a short time there were seen more than two hundred persons each bearing knives and staves and weapons and they surrounded the house of Ch'ai Huan Ch'en, and Ch'ai Chin, seeing all these persons, came out and said, "I will go with you to the magistrate's courts and there take sides against you."

Now the people first bound Ch'ai Chin, but when they went in to find the black man who had killed their friend they could not find him. They could but take Ch'ai Chin bound to the magistrate's court, and there he knelt before the dais.

Now the magistrate Kao Lien, hearing that his brother-in-law had been killed, was at that time in the Audience Hall gnashing and grinding his teeth, and waiting until the man was brought before him.

Now Ch'ai Chin, having already been driven there, was kneeling before him, and Kao Lien shouted out, "How dared you beat to death Ying T'ien Hsi?"

Then Ch'ai Chin answered with humility, saying, "This lowly one is own nephew to Ch'ai Huan Ch'en, of royal favor. We have the imperial pledge of the Emperor hanging over the gate of our home, and we are now living at Ch'ang Chou. Because my uncle's illness was heavy, I came here especially to see him. I did not dream he would die. But even now his coffin is in his house. And Ying T'ien Hsi brought some twenty or thirty men to our house and would by all means drive us forth out of our house, and he would not let me reason with him, and he bade the others to come and beat me. Then one of my tenants, surnamed Li, thinking to save me, came forward and in a moment had killed him."

Kao Lien shouted out, demanding, "Where is this Li now?"

Ch'ai Chin replied, "He was frightened and has already escaped."

Again Kao Lien asked, "If he was your tenant, how dared he without your command kill a man? Moreover you have helped him to escape, and yet you think to come here and deceive a magistrate. If I do not beat such as you, how can I force you to confess your crime? Gaolers, put forth your hands, and beat this man with all your strength!"

Then Ch'ai Chin cried out, "But my tenant Li, that he might save his lord, killed a man by accident! This has nothing to do with me. I have the pledge of the first Emperor of Sung! How dare you beat me?"

Then Kao Lien asked, "Where is this pledge?"

Ch'ai Chin replied, "A man is already returned to Ch'ang Chou to fetch it."

Then was Kao Lien in great wrath and he shouted out, "This fellow assuredly opposes the government. You to right and left of me, make strong your wrists and beat him well!"

Then did they all put forth their hands and they beat Ch'ai Chin until his skin was broken and his flesh swollen, and the red blood flowed without ceasing, and at last he could but confess then that he had commanded the one surnamed Li to kill Ying T'ien Hsi. Then a rack twenty-five catties in weight, such as is put on those who are condemned to death, was fastened on him and he was thrown into the gaol. And the dead body of Ying T'ien Hsi was examined and then put into a coffin. Of this no more need be told.

Now the sister of Ying T'ien Hsi was determined to have her revenge. So she told her husband Kao Lien to confiscate the entire house of

Ch'ai Huan Ch'en, and put the whole family into gaol. So the house was taken and the house and garden sealed and Ch'ai Chin could but languish in the gaol.

Let it be further told. Li K'uei went back by night to the robbers' lair and he came into the lair and he went before all the chieftains. Now Chu T'ung the instant he saw Li K'uei felt the wrath rise out of his heart and he drew forth a sword and leaped toward Li K'uei. But The Black Whirlwind jerked out his battle axes and fought against Chu T'ung. Then Ch'ao Kai and Sung Chiang and all the other chiefs all rushed forward to make peace, and Sung Chiang made apologies to Chu T'ung thus, "Li K'uei had nothing to do with the killing of that little lord. It was indeed Wu Yung who thought of this plan because you, Elder Brother, would not come up the mountain. But today since you have come to our lair, remember this no more in your heart. Let us have but one heart to help each other to a greater strength. Do not make outsiders laugh at us." And he called, "Li K'uei, my Brother, make apologies to The Beautiful Bearded!"

But Li K'uei widened his strange eyes and he shouted, "However beautiful he be, yet did not I also use to put forth my strength in the lair? He has not the least merit, and why do you tell me I must say I am wrong?"

Then Sung Chiang answered, "Brother, but it was you who killed the lord—although it was the chieftain's command—moreover, in years also he is your elder brother—then pray consider my honor and make an obeisance of apology before him. Then I will come and make an obeisance to you and there will be an end of it."

Thus persuaded, Li K'uei could not withstand Sung Chiang and he said to Chu T'ung, "I am not afraid of you, but because my elder brother presses me, I can do nothing but tell you I am sorry."

And Li K'uei thus pressed by Sung Chiang put aside his two axes and he made two obeisances to Chu T'ung. Only then did the anger subside in Chu T'ung.

Then Ch'ao Kai commanded a feast to be prepared to seal the peace. But Li K'uei began to speak, saying, "The great lord Ch'ai because he went to see his uncle, Ch'ai Huan Ch'en, who was ill in Kao T'ang Chou, was oppressed by the brother of the magistrate, Ying T'ien Hsi, who wanted to seize his garden, and he cursed and beat Ch'ai Chin. Then I went and killed that thing Ying T'ien Hsi."

When Sung Chiang heard this he gave a start of fear and he said, "Now well I know when you came away you involved the lord Ch'ai with the court."

But the counselor Wu Yung said, "Brother, do not be afraid. Wait until Tai Chung comes back and we will understand the affair."

Then Li K'uei asked, saying, "Where has Elder Brother Tai Chung gone?"

And Wu Yung replied, "I feared you might stir up some trouble in the village of the lord Ch'ai and it would not be well, and so for this special purpose did I bid him go and call you back up the mountain. When he reached there and did not see you he would certainly go to Kao T'ang Chou to seek for you."

Now before he finished speaking there was a lesser robber who came to make report, saying, "The chieftain Tai Chung has returned."

Sung Chiang then went to meet him and when they came to the Hall Of Meeting they sat down, and he asked after the affairs of the lord Ch'ai. And Tai Chung answered, saying, "When I went to the village of the lord Ch'ai he had already gone with Li K'uei to Kao T'ang Chou, and I went thither to hear what I could. There I heard all the people of the city talking and saying that because Ying T'ien Hsi wished to seize the house of Ch'ai Huan Ch'en, he was killed by a great black fellow. Now the lord Ch'ai has become involved in this, and he is accused and he is in gaol. All of the persons and the house of Ch'ai Huan Ch'en have already been seized by the magistrate Kao Lien. Sooner or later the lord Ch'ai Chin's life also will be taken."

Then Ch'ao Kai said, "This black fellow again has done something. Wherever he goes trouble comes of it."

But Li K'uei answered, "Ch'ai Huan Ch'en was beaten by him and he died of his anger, and more than that he came to seize his house and more than that he shouted out that he was going to beat the lord Ch'ai. Even though I were a living Buddha I could not have held myself in!"

Then Ch'ao Kai said, "The lord Ch'ai has always been most gracious to us here upon the mountain. Today when he is in difficulties why should we not go down the mountain and save him? I will myself go at once."

But Sung Chiang said, "Elder Brother, you are the chief of the lair, and how can you go forth so lightly as this? This humble one has long had kindness from the lord Ch'ai and I am fain to go down the mountain for my elder brother."

Then the counselor Wu Yung said, "Although the city of Kao T'ang Chou is small in space, yet there are very many people there. Moreover there are many soldiers, and much food for men and horses, and the place cannot be lightly considered. I will ask Ling Ch'ung, Hua Yung, Ch'ing Ming, Li Chün, Lü Fang, Kao Shen, Sheng Li, Ou P'eng, Yang Ling, Teng Fei, Ma Ling, Pei Sheng, these twelve chieftains, to take horsemen and fighting men to the number of five thousand and be the vanguard. After them the first shall be Sung Chiang, Wu Yung, Chu T'ung, Lei Heng, Tai Chung, Li K'uei, Chang Heng, Chang Shun, Yang Hsiung and Shih Hsiu, these ten chiefs. They shall have of horsemen and fighting men to the number of three thousand to support the vanguard."

Then these twenty-two chieftains bade farewell to Ch'ao Kai and the other chieftains and they left the mountain lair and went toward Kao T'ang Chou. And the first army reached the region of Kao T'ang Chou and early were there soldiers who had told Kao Lien of their coming. When Kao Lien heard it he smiled coldly and said, "You robbers in the grass who have your nest in Liang Shan P'o—I was coming to destroy you all but today you come to me to be bound! It is the will of Heaven for me to accomplish it! You to the right and left, quickly receive my commands! Prepare and count out the soldiers and horses and go out of the city to meet them and do combat with them. Bid the men climb the walls and protect the city!"

So spoke the magistrate Kao Lien, and from his horse he directed the soldiers, on foot he directed the people. Having shouted forth this command, those who stood in front of him of generals, examiners of the soldiers, captains, sergeants, instructors, corporals, and all such men in command, each led forth his soldiers and horsemen. When all had been appointed and prepared, these officers prepared to go outside the city and meet the enemy.

Now beneath Kao Lien's command there were three hundred very trusty soldiers and they were named Magic Soldiers Of The Flying God. They were all chosen one by one from Shantung, Hopei, Kiangsi, Hunan, Liang Huai, and Chekiang, north and south, and they were men of strength and skill. These three hundred the magistrate Kao Lien led out himself, and he put on his garments of war and hung upon his back his scabbard and a double-edged sword and went outside the city. All his captains he stationed at regular intervals about the city and the three hundred finest soldiers he put in the center. Then waving their banners and shouting their war cries and beating drums and gongs they did but wait until the enemy soldiers arrived.

Let it be told further. Ling Ch'ung, Hua Yung and Ch'ing Ming, leading the five thousand fighting men and horsemen, came so near to the enemy that either side could see the other's banners and drum. Then each side took out their strong bows and let fly their repeating arrows to stay the enemy where it stood. On both sides bugles were blown, and the sound of the drums and gongs arose.

Hua Yung and Ch'ing Ming, leading each ten captains, came to the front and there they reined in their horses. The chieftain Ling Ch'ung held crosswise his whirling spear and he galloped out upon his horse. Then in a loud fierce voice he shouted, "You thief surnamed Kao, come forth with all speed!"

Then Kao Lien gave free rein to his horse and he led out some thirty captains, and they all came forth and stood under their banners. There he reined in his horse and pointing at Ling Ch'ung he cursed, saying, "You horde of thieves and rebels, who do not know you ought to die, how dare you come straight hither to attack my city?"

Again Ling Ch'ung shouted forth, "You robber who bleeds the people, soon or late shall I kill my way into the capital and I will kill that thievish relative of yours, that traitor of a Kao Ch'iu, and I will cut his flesh into ten thousand pieces! Then only shall I have fulfilled the hope of my heart."

Then was Kao Lien filled with a great wrath, and he turned his head and he cried, "Who among my men will come forth on his horse? Let us first seize this robber!"

Then out of the midst of the soldiers charged the captain of a company, whose surname was Kan and his name Chi, and he came out whipping his horse, his weapon held aloft, and he came out in front of the ranks. Ling Ch'ung saw him and he went in pursuit of him. But before the two had fought five rounds Ling Ch'ung had pierced the breast of Kan Chi with a single thrust, and the man turned over and fell under his horse.

Then Kao Lien, seeing it, was startled with a great fright and he cried, "Who other is there who will come out to seek revenge?"

Again out of the midst of the soldiers there charged the captain of a company, surnamed Wen and named a double name Wen Pao. He held a long spear and he rode a fine yellow horse, on whose head the bells jingled, and there were jangling things upon the bridle also. He soon was out in front of the ranks, and as his horse galloped the dust rolled up into the air and he charged straight upon Ling Ch'ung.

Now Ch'ing Ming saw this and he cried out in a loud voice, "Elder Brother, rest yourself a little! Watch me kill this thief at once as I stand here!"

So Ling Ch'ung reined in his horse and he drew back his weapon and he allowed Ch'ing Ming to do combat with Wen Wen Pao. The two of them fought more than ten rounds, when suddenly Ch'ing Ming used guile and he took a certain posture and allowed the other's weapon to come in toward him. Then lifting his hand he brought down his own weapon and split in two the crown of Wen Wen Pao's head so that he fell dead from his horse. And the horse ran back to his own place. Then the two armies drew nearer and lifted their voices and cried their battle cries.

Now Kao Lien, seeing he had lost two captains one after the other, drew forth from its scabbard his double-edged sword and muttering like a Taoist priest he shouted forth, "Speed!" Then from the midst of his soldiers was seen to arise a dense black cloud. It rose to the heaven and spread there. Suddenly a strange and mighty wind arose, and sand and stones blew upon the earth and the earth shook and black winds and dust and stones blew hard upon the robbers and Ling Ch'ung, Ch'ing Ming, Hua Yung and the other chieftains could not see one another's faces in the darkness. Even the horses were so frightened that they ran every way and leaped hither and thither and everybody turned and retreated.

Then Kao Lien flung out his weapon once and out from his soldiers charged the three hundred Magic Soldiers Of The Flying God. Behind them the city soldiers came to aid them. Thus charging together in a mass they pursued Ling Ch'ung, men and horsemen, until they were scattered in four directions, until they were in fragments, and from all sides came cries of those who called in their terror upon brother or sons or father. Of the five thousand more than a thousand were killed, and they pursued the others for fifteen miles and more before they encamped. Kao Lien, seeing men and horsemen of the enemy were thus pushed back, then called back all his men and they went back into the city and there rested.

Let it be told now that when Sung Chiang and his men and horses came there Ling Ch'ung and the others met them and they told of all that had happened. Then Sung Chiang and Wu Yung hearing it were in great terror and Sung Chiang said to Wu Yung, "What guile has he so fierce as this?"

The counselor Wu Yung answered, "I believe it is magic. If when he calls forth this wind we can turn it back, or if when he sends out fire we can return it, only then can we conquer him."

Now Sung Chiang heard this and he opened his heavenly book to look at it, and upon the third volume there was written a way to send back a wind and turn back fire. Then was Sung Chiang greatly rejoiced and with all his heart he memorized the words and the magic and again he prepared men and horsemen. By the fifth watch they had eaten and with waving banners and throbbing drums and beating gongs they charged toward the city.

There were those who ran to take report into the city. Kao Lien again led out his victorious soldiers and horsemen and his three hundred magic soldiers and the gates of the city were opened, the drawbridge let down across the moat and he led the men out and ranked them ready. Now Sung Chiang, himself bearing a magic sword, galloped his horse to the front of the army. Then, looking, he saw in the midst of Kao Lien's army a flock of black banners. The counselor Wu Yung said, "Those black banners there in the midst of the soldiers are to mark the magic soldiers. Doubtless again he will use his old way. How can we conquer him?"

Then Sung Chiang replied, "Let your heart rest, Sir Counselor. I have a way to break his magic spells and to conquer him. Let no captain and no fighting man be afraid. Only let each man kill his way forward."

Then Kao Lien commanded all his captains high and low that they were not to go forward and do combat one by one with the enemy. He said, "When you hear this gong of mine sound which is named 'That which gathers wild beasts' then rush forward with all your strength and seize Sung Chiang. I will surely reward you all heavily."

Then the soldiers on both sides shouted and Kao Lien hung upon the saddle of his horse the gong upon which were written signs of the dragon and the phœnix, and holding in his hand his magic sword, he went out in front of his ranks. And Sung Chiang, pointing at Kao Lien, cursed, saying, "Last night I did not come and in that carelessness my brothers were vanquished the once. But today surely will I kill you to the last man."

Then Kao Lien shouted out, "You rebel robber! Come down from your horse with all speed and let me bind you, and spare me the stink of fresh blood upon my hand and the soil of fresh blood upon my foot!"

When he had so spoken he held out his sword and again he muttered between his teeth and again he shouted, "Speed!" Out of the black banners already the strange wind had arisen. But Sung Chiang did not wait for the wind before he also began to mutter between his teeth, and he shaped according to a certain fashion the fingers of his left hand, and with his right hand he thrust out his magic sword. Then he shouted, "Speed!"

Then that wind did not blow toward Sung Chiang, but it turned and blew among Kao Lien's magic soldiers, and Sung Chiang commanded his men and horsemen to charge among the enemy. But Kao Lien, seeing the wind returned on him, quickly took up the brass gong and beat upon it with his magic sword. Suddenly out of the midst of the soldiers blew a yellow storm of sand, and then came strange beasts and poisonous reptiles and they poured forth. Then were the men and horses in Sung Chiang's company frightened into a daze and even Sung Chiang threw down his magic sword, and turning the head of his horse, ran away. And all the chieftains surrounding him fled for their lives and soldiers high and low paid no heed to one another, but each took what way he could and ran.

Behind them Kao Lien thrust out his sword and the magic soldiers were in front, the official army was behind, and they all charged in pursuit. Then did Sung Chiang's men and horsemen suffer frightful loss for Kao Lien followed, killing them for some seven miles. Then he beat upon his brass gong and called back his men and they went back once more into the city.

Now Sung Chiang came upon a ridge and there he gathered together his men and horses and there they encamped. Although they had lost both men and horses yet every chieftain was still alive. There they all stayed, men and horses, and Sung Chiang took counsel with Wu Yung and he said, "This time we have attacked the city of Kao T'ang Chou and we have been twice vanquished, and there is no way whereby we can overcome these magic soldiers. What shall we do, then?"

The counselor Wu Yung answered, "If this fellow can really work magic spells then will he surely come secretly upon us tonight. Let us first prepare a plot to foil this. Here we can but gather together a very few men and horses, and let us go back therefore to our former place of encampment."

So Sung Chiang sent forth his command, and there were left but Yang Ling and Pei Sheng. The rest of the men and horsemen returned to the former encampment to rest.

Let it be told now of Yang Ling and Pei Sheng. Leading out their soldiers, they left the encampment and went to one side and hid in the grass and they waited until the first watch of the night. Suddenly they saw a mighty wind arise and heard the sound of great thunder. Yang Ling and Pei Sheng, with some three hundred men seeing this as they hid in the grass, saw Kao Lien walking along leading his three hundred magic men. Blowing their bugles they came running into the encampment. When they saw it was empty they turned around and went away. Yang Ling and Pei Sheng then lifted their voices and shouted. Then Kao Lien fearing to suffer from them divided his men and they retreated, and each of the three hundred ran for himself.

And Yang Ling and Pei Sheng shot arrows wildly after them and they did naught but let their arrows fly. Now one of the arrows flying flew exactly into Kao Lien's left shoulder. Then did all the robbers regardless of the falling rain rush after them. But by this time Kao Lien had already led his men to a great distance and Yang Ling and Pei Sheng, their men being few, did not dare to go on after them.

In a short time when the rain was passed and the clouds dispersed, the heavens were again seen to be full of stars and the constellations stood clear and bright. Under the light of the moon in front of the grass where the robbers had hidden they found some of the magic soldiers, and with spears and swords and arrows they seized some twenty of them and they took them to the place where Sung Chiang was encamped.

And they told of the rains and the wind and the clouds and the thunder. Sung Chiang hearing of this felt a great fear and he said, "But we are less than two miles away from that place, and here there was neither rain nor wind."

Then they all said among themselves, "This must be true magic. If there was that storm but two miles from us, and the rain and clouds but thirty or forty feet above the earth, then the clouds and rain were but lifted up out of the near-by pools."

And Yang Ling said, "Kao Lien when he came toward us had his hair hanging all loose about him and in his hand he held his magic sword and he came charging to the encampment. But I wounded him with one of my arrows and he went back again to the city and because I had so few men with me I did not dare to pursue him thither."

And Sung Chiang rewarded the two, Yang Ling and Pei Sheng, and he beheaded the wounded soldiers who had been captured. Then he divided the chieftains into seven or eight small encampments and with these he surrounded the central camp in order to withstand Kao Lien if again he came on secret attack and he sent men back to the mountain lair to ask for more men and horsemen.

Let it be told now that Kao Lien, wounded with the arrow, went back to the city to take care of his wound, and he commanded the soldiers to guard the city, and to guard it night and day, nor were they to wage war again for the time, until his wound was healed. Then again would they go forth to seize Sung Chiang.

Let it again be told of Sung Chiang. When he saw all the horsemen and men he had lost he was sad in his heart and he took counsel with Wu Yung and he said, "There is only this Kao Lien whom we cannot overcome. If he gathers together men and horsemen from other parts and comes to attack us then what shall we do?"

And the counselor Wu Yung answered, "I do think if we are to break Kao Lien's magic spell it must be only by this means. If we do not go and ask a certain person to come it will be hard indeed also to save the life of the great lord Ch'ai, nor can we ever take the city of Kao T'ang Chou."

Truly if of cloud and wind we are to break the spell
Seek we must some man who knows the Heavens and Earth full well.

Who then was this man of whom the counselor Wu Yung spoke? Pray hear it told in the next chapter.

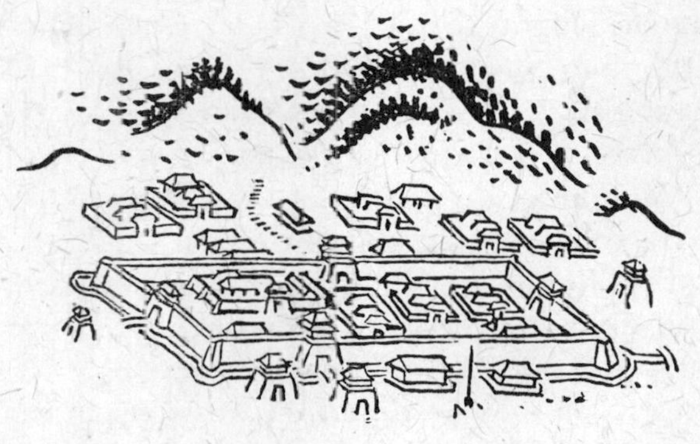

Chapter 52

TAI CHUNG FOR THE SECOND TIME SEEKS KUNG SUN SHENG. LI K'UEI ALONE SPLITS IN HALF LO THE HOLY MAN

IT IS SAID: At that time when Wu Yung said to Sung Chiang, "We must break this spell and we can but send a man at once to Chi Chou to seek for Kung Sun Sheng and only then can we break the spell of Kao Lien," Sung Chiang replied, "Tai Chung has already gone forth once to seek him and he could hear nothing of him, and whither shall we go to find him?"

Then Wu Yung answered, "Before this I have only heard he went to the city of Chi Chou. But about the city there are many lesser towns and villages and hamlets, and in those he surely did not search. I know that Kung Sun Sheng is a man who learns of Taoism, and he must surely be on some famous mountain or beside some great water, or in the cave of some holy hermit. Let us now bid Tai Chung to go and search among the environs of Chi Chou, and surely will he be found."

And Sung Chiang listened to this and at once he sent to invite Tai Chung to come for counsel that he might go to Chi Chou and search for Kung Sun Sheng. And Tai Chung said, "This humble one is willing to go. But it will be well if I have a comrade to go with me."

Wu Yung asked, "But if you use your magic steps, who can keep up with you?"

Tai Chung replied, "If it is a comrade of mine, I will put the magic letters on his legs as well, and so he can also go with speed."

Li K'uei spoke and said, "I will go right early with Tai Chung and be his comrade."

But Tai Chung answered, "If you wish to go with me, you must eat no meat by the way, and you must listen to all my commands."

Li K'uei cried, "And what is hard about this? I will obey you in all and there will be an end of it."

Then Sung Chiang and Wu Yung commanded him, saying, "On the way take all heed that you do not stir up trouble. If you find him then come back soon."

Li K'uei said, "I did beat to death Ying T'ien Hsi and I made the lord Ch'ai go to gaol. How then can I not wish to save him? This time I will not let myself stir up trouble."

Then the two hid weapons in their garments and tied up their bundles and they took farewell of Sung Chiang and all the others and they left the city of Kao T'ang Chou and followed the road to Chi Chou. When they had gone some ten or fifteen miles Li K'uei stayed his feet and he said, "Elder Brother, let us buy a bowl of wine and drink it and then go on, and it will be well enough."

Tai Chung said, "If you want to go with me by means of magic, you can eat no meats with your wine but only vegetable dishes."

Li K'uei laughed and said, "And if I eat a little meat, what great matter is that?"

At this Tai Chung cried, "Here you come again! Nevertheless it is now already near night. Let us go on and seek an inn and there rest. Tomorrow we will start early."

Again the two went some ten miles and more and the color of the sky turned dim and dark. They sought an inn and there rested and they lit a fire to make food and they sent for a measure of wine to drink. Now Li K'uei fetched a bowl of vegetable food and a bowl of vegetable soup and he brought these into the room to Tai Chung to eat. And Tai Chung said, "Why do you also not eat?"

Li K'uei answered, saying, "I do not wish to eat yet."

To himself Tai Chung thought, "This thing is surely deceiving me and he is eating meat secretly!" But he ate the vegetable and the soup and then silently he tiptoed to the back of the house and peeped to see and there he saw Li K'uei with two measures of wine he had bought and a plate of cow's flesh, standing there and gobbling it anyhow. Tai Chung said to himself, "And what did I say? But I will say nothing to him now. Tomorrow I will make a little fun of him and there will be an end of it."

Then he went to his room and to sleep. Li K'uei drank wine for a while and then fearing lest Tai Chung ask of him he went silently to his room and there slept also. When the fifth watch was come, Tai Chung rose and he bade Li K'uei light the fire and prepare some vegetable food and he ate it. Each then lifted his bundle upon his back, and they paid for the room and so they left the inn. They had gone less than two thirds of a mile when Tai Chung said, "Yesterday we did not really use our magic. Today we must make haste. Tie your bundle fast first, and I will make the magic on you. When we have gone near three hundred miles we will stop."

So Tai Chung brought out four magic letters and tied them upon Li K'uei's two legs and he commanded, saying, "You await me in the inn ahead." Then Tai Chung muttered a few words and blew a breath on Li K'uei's legs. Li K'uei let his strides free and he flew forth as though he walked on clouds. Then Tai Chung laughed and said to himself, "I will let him endure a day's hunger." Then Tai Chung tied on his own magic and hastened after him.

Now Li K'uei did not understand this magic and he thought it would be as easy a pleasure as though he walked after his own fashion, and how did he know that the roar of the air in his ears would be like the roar of great winds and rains? The houses and the trees on either side of him seemed to topple backward in a heap; under his feet it seemed as though he were pursued by clouds and mists. Then Li K'uei began to be afraid and again and again he thought to stay his feet, but how could he hold back his two legs? It was as though there were someone pushing him from beneath. His feet did not touch the earth and he could but go on. He saw the wine shops and the meat shops and the inns fly past one after the other, nor could he enter and buy and eat. At last Li K'uei could but roar out to his own legs, "Oh, my fathers! Let us stay a bit!"

And he looked and saw that he had walked until the sun was even with the west. His belly was both thirsty and hungry, and yet his legs but went the more quickly. He was in such terror that his whole body poured forth a stinking sweat, and he panted great bursts of breath. Tai Chung, coming upon him from behind, called forth, "Brother Li, how is it you do not buy some dainties to eat?"

Li K'uei answered, saying, "Elder Brother, save me this once! The Iron Ox is nigh to death from starving!"

Then Tai Chung felt in his bosom and brought forth several wheaten cakes and began to eat them. Li K'uei cried out, saying, "I cannot stop my feet and buy to eat—give me something to stay my hunger!"

Tai Chung said, "Brother, stop and I will give you some to eat."

Li K'uei stretched out his hand but he was still ten feet off and he could not reach the cakes, and he roared out, "Good Elder Brother, pray stop me a little!"

Tai Chung said, "Truly there is something strange today. Even my two legs I cannot stop."

Li K'uei cried, "Ah-yah! These two cursed feet of mine will not obey me for half a minute, even! They do but hurry on down there of their own will! Well, and if my temper comes up in me, I will punish them—I will take my two axes and cut them off!"

And Tai Chung answered, "And if you do not use this way, doubtless we will go on thus until the beginning of next year, and we cannot stop ourselves."

But Li K'uei said, "Good Elder Brother, do not make a joke of me. If I cut off my two legs, what shall I use to walk back?"

Tai Chung said, "Perhaps it is because yesterday you did not obey me, so that today even I leap on and cannot stay myself. Go on then and leap—I will have naught to do with you!"

Then Li K'uei cried out, "Good Father, forgive me and let me stay for a while!"

But Tai Chung replied, "This magic of mine does not allow one to eat meat. The first meat forbidden is the flesh of cows. If one piece of meat has been eaten then must one leap on like this until he is dead before he can stop."

Then Li K'uei said, "If it is so, then is this bitterness indeed! Last night I should not have cheated you, Elder Brother—it is true that I secretly did buy and eat some ten-odd catties of cow's flesh, and now what shall we do?"

Tai Chung replied, "It is not strange then that today even these legs of mine I have not been able to restrain. You Iron Ox, you will injure and kill me, too!"

Now Li K'uei heard this and he began to bellow out his sorrow to the very heavens until Tai Chung laughed and said, "From this day on if you will obey me in one thing I can break this magic spell."

Then Li K'uei cried, "Oh, my Lord, speak quickly what it is! See if I will obey you!"

And Tai Chung asked, "Now will you dare to deceive me again and eat meat?"

And Li K'uei replied, "If I eat meat again from this day on, then may I have a canker on my tongue as big as a bowl! I see that you, Elder Brother, can eat vegetable, but as for The Iron Ox it is very hard. For this did I try for once to deceive you, my Elder Brother. But after this surely will I not dare again."

Then Tai Chung said, "If it is thus, I will forgive you the once."

And he hastened forward a step and struck Li K'uei's legs with his sleeve and he shouted out, "Stay!" Immediately Li K'uei stopped. And Tai Chung said, "I will go first. Do you come slowly after me."

But even as Li K'uei was about to lift up his feet, he could not make them move at all. Though he used all his strength he could not lift them up. They were as though made of iron and fastened there. Then Li K'uei roared out, "Here is bitterness again! Elder Brother, come and save me once more!"

Tai Chung turned his head back and laughed and he said, "Is this vow you make a true one?"

Li K'uei said, "You are as my own father. How dare I disobey your words?"

Again Tai Chung asked, "This time will you truly obey me?" Then he reached out his hands and laid hold on Li K'uei and he shouted out, "Rise!" Then the two went lightly on. And Li K'uei said, "Elder Brother, have pity on The Iron Ox. Let us stop a little early."

They saw then an inn and they entered it to rest. When they came into the room they took the magic letters from their legs and brought out paper money and with it burned the letters of magic. And Tai Chung asked Li K'uei, saying, "How is it with you now?"

Then Li K'uei grasped his feet and he heaved a sigh and said, "Only now are these two legs mine again!"

And Tai Chung told Li K'uei to prepare some vegetable food to eat with their wine and they heated water and washed their feet. Then they mounted on their beds and went to sleep. They slept until the fifth watch and then rose. When they had washed themselves and rinsed their mouths and eaten their meal and paid the bill the two again set forth on their journey. They had gone scarcely a mile when Tai Chung brought out the magic letters and said, "Brother, today I will put two on you and so let you go more slowly."

But Li K'uei said, "My Father, I do not want them tied on me any more."

Then Tai Chung said, "If you obey my words and we are on a great business together how can I then make you suffer? But if you do not obey me then I will hold you here fixed exactly as you were yesterday fixed, and I shall only free you when I have been to Chi Chou and found Kung Sun Sheng and come back."

In great haste then Li K'uei called out, saying, "Tie them—tie them—"

So Tai Chung tied on but two letters on his leg and again he performed his magic spell and holding Li K'uei they went on together. Now Tai Chung's magic was such that if he wished to go he could go and if he wished to stop he could stop, and so from this time on how could Li K'uei dare to disobey his commands? On the road therefore he did but buy vegetable food to eat and thus they went on their way.

But the story must not be too long. The two thus used magic and in less than ten days they came to the environs of Chi Chou to an inn there and they rested. On the next day the two went into the city. Now Tai Chung disguised himself as a master and Li K'uei disguised himself as his servant and they went about the city seeking for a day, but there was not one who knew Kung Sun Sheng. The two then could but return to the inn and rest. On the next day again they went into the city and sought among the small streets and the narrow alleyways and again they sought a day. But there was not the least news of him. Then Li K'uei's heart grew impatient and he began to curse, saying, "This beggarly Taoist, in what cursed place does he hide? If I see him I will grasp him by the topknot and drag him forth to see our elder brother."

Tai Chung looked at him sidewise and he said, "Here you come again! You cannot remember that you ate bitterness."

But Li K'uei smiled in apology and said, "I do not dare—I do not dare. I was only making a little joke—"

But Tai Chung reproached him again, and Li K'uei did not dare to answer anything. Again the two came into the inn and rested. On the next morning they rose early and they went to the villages and hamlets near the city to seek. Whenever Tai Chung saw an old man he made obeisance and asked where the house of Kung Sun Sheng was. But not one knew, although Tai Chung asked in scores of places.

Now on this day about noon the two had walked until they were hungry, and they saw beside the road an inn where vegetable foods were sold, and the two went in to buy some cakes to eat. They saw then that the inn was full of men and there was not an empty place, and Tai Chung and Li K'uei stood there in the road. At last a waiter came and said, "If you want to eat some noodles, Sir Guests, then come and sit at the table with this old man."

Then Tai Chung saw an old man sitting alone at a large table and he made obeisance to him and called a greeting and sat opposite him, and Li K'uei sat beside Tai Chung and they commanded then that four great bowls of noodles were to be prepared. And Tai Chung said, "I will eat one and if you eat three it will not be too little, will it?"

But Li K'uei replied, "It is not enough for me. If six are brought on together I can eat them all."

Hearing this the waiter laughed. After a long time had passed the noodles were still not to be seen coming, but Li K'uei saw many bowls of noodles being carried into an inner room. He was by now half angry. Then he saw the waiter bring a bowl of hot noodles and put it before the old man who sat with them. Nor was this old man at all courteous with them. He took up the bowl of noodles at once and began to eat. Now the noodles were very hot and the old man bent his head over the bowl set on the table and supped them. Li K'uei being very impatient of heart shouted out, "Waiter!" Then he began to curse, saying, "You have made this lord wait half a day!" And he pounded his fist on the table so that the hot noodle soup splashed up all over the old man's face, and the bowl was overturned. Then the old man grew angry and he laid hold of Li K'uei and he shouted out, "What right have you to overturn my noodles?"

Li K'uei clenched his fists and was about to strike the old man, but in great haste Tai Chung held him back and made apologies for him, saying, "Old Sir, do not behave as he does. This humble one will give you a bowl of noodles."

But the old man replied, "Sir Guest, you do not understand. I am an old man who has come a long way and now I must return and hear one preach. If I am delayed, then I shall be late."

Then Tai Chung asked, saying, "Old Sir, whence do you come? And whom will you hear preach and what does he preach?"

The old man answered, saying, "This old man is one under the rule of Chi Chou city in The County Of The Nine Palaces, and of The Mountain Of The Two Holy Men. I came to this city to buy some good incense, and now I return to the mountain to hear The Holy Man Lo preach of the way to live forever and never die."

Now Tai Chung pondered to himself thus, "May it not be that Kung Sun Sheng is also there?" And he asked the old man, saying, "In the old one's honored village can there be one called Kung Sun Sheng?"

The old man replied, "If you asked any other in this inn he would surely not know, for there are many who do not know him. But this old man is neighbor with him. He has but an old mother. For long has this teacher of Taoism wandered everywhere like a cloud. For this he is called Kung Sun The Most Holy, but now he has renounced even his surname and he is called The Most Clear Taoist, and he is no more called Kung Sun Sheng. This is not his own name now, and no one knows it."

Then Tai Chung said, "Truly is it 'Even though our shoes were iron, yet we could not find him.' And now have we come upon him without effort." Again he asked the old man with an obeisance, "How far from here is The County Of The Nine Palaces and The Mountain Of The

Two Holy Men? Is The Most Clear Taoist in his home?"

The old man replied, "The Mountain Of The Two Holy Men is but less than twenty miles from this city. But The Most Clear Taoist is the first disciple of the Immortal Lo, and how will his teacher be willing to let him leave his side?"

Hearing this, Tai Chung was greatly rejoiced and in great haste he hurried the noodles to be brought and they ate together with the old man. When the money had been paid for the noodles they went out of the inn together, and he asked for the direction of the road, and then Tai Chung said, "Do you go first, Old Sir. We must buy some incense and then we will come also."

So the old man said farewell and went on.

Then Tai Chung and Li K'uei returned to the inn and brought their bundles and goods and again tied on their magic letters and left the inn, and the two turned and followed the road to The County Of The Nine Palaces and to The Mountain Of The Two Holy Men, and Tai Chung used his magic again and in an instant these ten-odd miles were behind them. Then the twain entered the court of The City Of The Nine Palaces and asked where the mountain was and there was one who pointed to it, saying, "Leave the city and go east. In less than two miles you will be there."

So the twain left the county seat and turning to the east they went their way. Suddenly before they had gone the two miles and more they were already come to the mountain. There they saw a fuel cutter and Tai Chung bowed to him and said, "I would ask where the home is of the great one The Most Clear Taoist."

Then the fuel cutter pointed, saying, "Go over this valley and you will see a gate and a stone bridge and that is it."

They passed through the valley therefore and they saw some ten-odd straw huts, and about them a low wall. Outside the wall was a small stone bridge. And the twain came to the bridge and they saw a peasant girl carrying a basket of fresh fruit. Then Tai Chung bowed to her and he asked, "Maiden, you have come from the home of The Most Clear Taoist. Is The Most Clear there?"

The village maiden answered, "He is in the back of the house burning his magic potions."

Then Tai Chung was pleased secretly in his heart and he commanded Li K'uei, saying, "Do you go into the tree shrubbery there and hide for a bit and wait until I go in first and see him alone. Then will I come and call you."

Now when Tai Chung went inside to see, there were a row of thatched houses, and over the door was hung a red curtain and Tai Chung coughed once, and he saw an old white-haired woman coming out from within. Then did Tai Chung make obeisance and he said, "I make humble inquiry of you, Aged Lady, for I would beseech the holy man called The Most Clear Taoist to come forth for a minute that I may speak with him."

The old woman asked, saying, "What is your high surname, Noble Sir?"

Tai Chung replied, "This lowly one is surnamed Tai and named Chung and I came hither from Shantung."

Then the old woman said, "My son has gone forth wandering like a cloud and he has not come home yet."

And Tai Chung said, "This humble one is an old friend of former times, and I have a word of greatest importance to say to him. I pray to see his face but once."

The old woman replied, "He is not at home. What have you to say to him? Leave the words with me and it will be no trouble. When he is home he will surely come to see you."

But Tai Chung said, "This humble one will come again." And he bade the old woman farewell. Then he came outside the gate and said to Li K'uei, "This time I can use you. Just now his mother said he is not at home, but do you go and ask for him. If she says he is not there, then do you begin to be angry, only you are not to injure at all his old mother. If I come and bid you stop, then stop; if I do not come, then be angry."

Li K'uei first opened his bundles and brought out his two axes and thrust them into his girdle. When he had come within the door he shouted out once, "Come out!"

In great haste the old woman asked, "Who is it?" When she saw Li K'uei with his two eyes opened wide, she was at first eight parts afraid of him. She asked him, "Elder Brother, what have you to say?"

Li K'uei said, "I am The Black Whirlwind of

the mountain lair. I am come to fulfill my elder brothers' command who bade me come hither to seek Kung Sun Sheng. Tell him to come forth and I will look on you with the eyes of a god. But if he will not come out I will throw a cursed torch and burn your house all to white ashes!" Then again he shouted, "And tell him to come forth quickly!"

The old woman replied, "Good Fellow, do not behave like this. This is not Kung Sun Sheng's home. My son is named The Most Clear Taoist."

Li K'uei said, "Do you but bid him come forth! I myself know what his cursed face is!"

Again the old woman said, "But he is outside wandering like a cloud, nor has he returned."

Then Li K'uei jerked out his two great axes and with one blow he knocked down the side wall of the room. The old woman rushed forward to stop him, but Li K'uei cried, "If you do not tell your son to come out, I will kill you." And he took up his axes and began to strike blows so that the old woman was so frightened she fell upon the ground. Then was Kung Sun Sheng seen to leap out from within and he shouted out, "You cannot act so without reason!"

And Tai Chung was seen coming also and shouting as he came, "Iron Ox, how is it you frightened the old mother so that she is fallen?" In great haste he lifted up the old woman and Li K'uei threw aside his great axes and he called a greeting and said, "Elder Brother, do not blame me. If I did not thus, you would not come out."

Kung Sun Sheng first supported his mother inside and then he came out and made obeisance to Tai Chung and to Li K'uei and he led them into a very clean room and he asked them, "Strange is it indeed that you two noble ones should come hither!"

Tai Chung said, "When you, Elder Brother, first came down the mountain this humble one went once to seek you, but there was no place to hear of you and I could but lead several brothers up the mountain to join us. This time our elder brother Sung Chiang, when he went to Kao T'ang Chou to save the great lord Ch'ai, was twice or thrice vanquished by the magic spells of the magistrate Kao Lien. He has no device whereby to escape this, and he could but bid this humble one and Li K'uei come hither to find you. We have stirred up the whole city of Chi Chou and we had no place more to go and seek you. In the inn where vegetable foods are sold, suddenly we learned from an old man of these parts to come here. Then we heard that The Most Noble was at home making potions, but the old mother steadily refused us. For this I used Li K'uei to force you to come out, although his is in truth too coarse a way. Ten thousand times do I ask forgiveness for his fault. But in that encampment about the city of Kao T'ang Chou it is as though in every day they lived a year. I pray you, then, Elder Brother, come with us at once so that you may prove that from the beginning you have ever been ready to help in a good cause."

Then Kung Sun Sheng replied, "From my youth I have gone to and fro, a poor Taoist, and I have been much with good fellows far and wide, by river and lake. Ever since I parted from the mountain lair and returned to my home, it has not been because of black and disloyal heart that I have not returned, but firstly because of my old mother, who has had no one to care for her, and secondly, because my teacher The Most Holy One surnamed Lo was fain to have me stay beside his holy seat. I have feared lest there would come someone seeking me from the mountain lair, and so purposely I changed my name to Most Clear Taoist, and here am I now a hermit."

But Tai Chung said, "Yet is Sung Chiang now in the greatest danger. Elder Brother, have pity! You can but go and at once."

Again Kung Sun Sheng replied, "Truly there is no one to care for my old mother, and how can my teacher be willing to let me go? Indeed and in truth I cannot go."

Then Tai Chung fell in obeisance and implored him, and Kung Sun Sheng lifted him up and he said, "Wait a little while, and then we will talk together again."

And Kung Sun Sheng left Tai Chung and Li K'uei sitting there in The Pure Room and he had prepared some vegetable foods and wine to entertain them. The three ate for a time and again Tai Chung implored Kung Sun Sheng most earnestly, saying, "If Elder Brother will not go, Sung Chiang will surely be captured by Kao Lien, and from this time on the great chieftains and their noble deeds and purposes will be ended."

At last Kung Sun Sheng replied, "Pray let me go and ask my teacher. If I can secure his permission I will go with you."

And Tai Chung said, "Then let us go now and ask the aged Taoist."

And Kung Sun Sheng said, "Pray calm your heart and spend the night, and we will go tomorrow morning."

But Tai Chung said, "Yet Sung Chiang is waiting there and every day is to him a year. I must trouble you, my Elder Brother, to go at once and ask."

Then Kung Sun Sheng rose and he led Tai Chung and Li K'uei and they left the house and followed the road to The Mountain Of The Two Holy Men. Now this season was the end of autumn and it was the beginning of winter and the days were short and the nights long, and it grew easily late. When they had gone but half way up the mountain the red sun was already long sunk in the west. Among the pines through the shadows there was a single small path. This went straight to the temple of The Most Holy One Lo. There they saw a red tablet and upon it was written in gold letters, "The Abode Of The Mountain Spirits."

Then the three went into the temple into The Hall Of Robing and there they set in order their garments. And they came out from the verandas and then passed through the great hall of gods into a hall called The Hall Of Pines And Herons, and two acolytes seeing Kung Sun Sheng leading persons thither went and made report to The Most Holy One Lo, and he gave his sacred commands saying that the three were to come in.

Now at this time when Kung Sun Sheng led in Tai Chung and Li K'uei into The Hall Of Pines And Herons, it was at the time when The Holy One had finished worshipping the gods and he sat upon his cloud-like couch. And Kung Sun Sheng went forward and made obeisance and asked after his welfare, and then bowing deeply he stood to one side. Now when Tai Chung saw this holy one, in great haste he fell to the ground in obeisance, but Li K'uei only opened his eyes wide and stared. The holy man asked Kung Sun Sheng, saying, "From whence come these twain?"

And Kung Sun Sheng answered, "They are those of whom your pupil has spoken, my brother-friends from Shantung. Today because the magistrate of Kao T'ang Chou, Kao Lien, uses magic, our brother Sung Chiang has sent these two especially to seek me out. But I did not dare to decide for myself and I ask for my teacher's counsel."

The Holy One said, "You have already escaped once out of the flaming pit of evil, and here with me you are learning the secrets of immortality. How then can you go back to such a place as that?"

Now again did Tai Chung make obeisance and he said, "Let us two implore you now to allow Kung Sun Sheng to go down the mountain the once, and when he has broken the magic spells of Kao Lien we will return him thither again."

But the holy man made answer thus: "The two honored ones do not understand. This is not such a matter as those who have renounced the world ought to control. Do you, therefore, descend from the mountain and return and take counsel together."

So Kung Sun Sheng could then but take the two and leave the holy man and that same night they went down the mountain. Then Li K'uei asked, saying, "What did that old holy teacher man say?"

Tai Chung replied, "And how was it only you did not hear?"

Li K'uei said, "I could not understand the cursed talk he talked."

And Tai Chung said, "It was his teacher and he said that he was not to go."

Now when Li K'uei heard this he began to shout, saying, "He made us walk all that long way, and I have eaten all sorts of bitterness, and here having found him, such wind as this is passed! He had better not get this lord's anger up! With one hand will I squeeze to pieces his Taoist hat and with the other I will grab him by the back and throw the old thief down the mountain!"

But Tai Chung restrained him, saying, "So, you want your legs locked again!"

Then Li K'uei laughed hollowly in apology and he said, "I do not dare—I do not dare—I was but talking thus to be merry—"

So the three then returned to the home of

Kung Sun Sheng. That night food was prepared, and Tai Chung and Kung Sun Sheng ate of it, but Li K'uei could but sit and stare and ponder and eat nothing. Kung Sun Sheng said, "Pray sleep the night here in my house. Tomorrow we will go again and implore The Holy One, for if he is willing I will go."

Tai Chung could but bid him a peaceful night and he put together his possessions and with Li K'uei he went in to The Pure Room, and there they slept.

But how could Li K'uei sleep? Slowly he let the time pass until the fifth watch. Then very softly he arose and when he listened to Tai Chung he heard him snoring soundly. To himself he said, thinking of Kung Sun Sheng, "And does this not make the cursed anger rise in me?—And you used to be a man of the lair, and why do you go and ask any cursed old teacher like this? I thought to kill you with a blow of my axe, but then whom would I find to help my elder brother?" Again he thought awhile and said to himself, "If that thing tomorrow will not let him go will it not again hold back my elder brother's affairs? I can bear it no longer. Better to go and kill that old thief of a Taoist teacher so that he will have no place to go and ask, and so he can but go with me."

Then he felt for his two battle axes and softly he opened the door of the room, and by the light of the new moon he felt his way step by step up the mountain. When he had come to the front of the gate, he saw the two halves of the great gate closed, but the wall about was not very high and Li K'uei leaped over, and then he opened the doors. Step by step he felt his way inside and went straight to the place where the holy man lived. He heard someone reading prayers near the window, and he crawled up and pushed his finger through the paper lattice and looked in. There was the holy man sitting alone upon the thing on which he had sat during the day. Before him on the table clouds of smoke arose and two candles were lit and shone brightly. Then Li K'uei said to himself, "And ought not this thief of a Taoist to die?"

So he came creeping to the side of the window and he pushed it once with his hand and the leaves of the door smashed open and Li K'uei charged in. He lifted up his battle axes and smashed them down upon the brow of the holy man, and soon he was smitten there upon the cloud-like couch. Now when Li K'uei looked he saw white blood flowing and he laughed and said, "It can be seen that this thief of a Taoist was a virgin. He has never from his birth wasted forth his birth essence—truly there is not the smallest spot of red blood in him!"

And when Li K'uei again looked more closely he saw that even the Taoist's hat was split in two and even his head was split clean through in two, and Li K'uei said agian, "I could do nothing else to be rid of this man. Now that the thing is done I need not grieve because Kung Sun Sheng does not go." Then he turned and went away and he leaped out through the verandas.

But there he saw an acolyte in a sky-blue robe who held out his arm to stay him and the youth cried out, "You have killed our holy man—whither do you go then?"

Li K'uei said, "You little thief of a Taoist, you shall eat a blow of my axe too!"

He lifted up his arm and the axe fell and the lad's head dropped and rolled beside the stone terrace. Then Li K'uei laughed and said, "Now I can cast this affair from me!" And he followed the road out of the temple, and went down the mountain as though he flew. He came to Kung Sun Sheng's home and he went quickly in and closed the gate, and he went into The Pure Room and listened to Tai Chung and he had not yet awaked. Then Li K'uei softly laid himself down as he was before, and slept until dawn.

Now Kung Sun Sheng had risen and prepared breakfast and he invited the twain to eat. And Tai Chung said, "Again do we ask you, Sir Teacher, to lead us up to the mountain and let us implore the holy man again that you may go with us."

Li K'uei heard this and bit his lip and smiled chilly. But the three then went on the former road up the mountain and they came into the temple into The Hall Of Pines And Herons. There they saw two young acolytes and Kung Sun Sheng asked, saying, "Is The Holy One here?"

The lads answered, saying, "The holy man sits in a trance on the couch of clouds."

Now when Li K'uei heard this he gave a start of fright and he thrust forth his tongue and for a long time could not draw it in again. The three drew aside the curtain and peered in and they saw the holy man sitting upon the couch in the very middle, and Li K'uei thought to himself secretly, "Last night I must have killed the wrong one."

Then the holy man asked, "You three men, why have you come hither again?"

Tai Chung replied, "We have come especially to ask you to have pity on us and save us all out of our trouble."

The holy man said, "Who is this great black fellow?"

Tai Chung answered, saying, "It is a younger brother of mine on my mother's side, and his surname is Li and his name K'uei."

The holy man laughed and said, "At first I would not let Kung Sun Sheng go. But now that I see this one's face, I will bid Kung Sun Sheng go once."

Then Tai Chung made obeisance and gave thanks and he told Li K'uei but Li K'uei thought to himself, "That thing knows I want to kill him and so he makes such cursed talk as this!"

Then the holy man said, "I will bid you all reach Kao T'ang Chou in an instant of time. Will this be well?"

The three gave thanks and Tai Chung thought to himself, "This holy man is wiser in magic than I."

So the holy man then bid an acolyte bring forth three kerchiefs and Tai Chung asked, "I wish to humbly ask my most noble teacher how can we be sent in an instant to Kao T'ang Chou?"

Then the holy man stood up and he said, "Let all of you come with me."

So the three men followed him out of the gate of the temple and they stood on the brink of a cliff and the holy man brought forth a red kerchief and he spread it upon the rock and he commanded, "Most Clear, stand upon this!" Then Kung Sun Sheng stood upon it with both of his feet. The holy man waved his sleeve and shouted, "Rise!" The kerchief became a piece of red cloud and bearing Kung Sun Sheng it rose slowly up until he was some twenty feet above the mountain. Then the holy man shouted, "Stop!" That red cloud did not move. Then he spread out a sky-blue kerchief and he bade Tai Chung stand upon it. He shouted out, "Rise!" The kerchief was turned into a sky-blue cloud and it rose bearing Tai Chung into midair. These two clouds, one red, one sky-blue, were each about as large as a reed mat, and they rose and circled slowly in the heavens and Li K'uei, watching them, was astonished into a daze. Then the holy man spread a white kerchief upon the rock, and he bade Li K'uei stand upon it and Li K'uei laughed and said, "Are you not making a joke of me? If I fall off what a bump I shall have on me!"

But the holy man replied, "Do you not see those two?"

So Li K'uei stood upon the kerchief and the holy man shouted out, "Rise!" That kerchief changed into a white cloud and flew up. But Li K'uei cried out, "Ai-yah! This cloud of mine is not steady—let me down again!"

The holy man beckoned with his right hand, and the red cloud and the sky-blue cloud came evenly down. Tai Chung made obeisance and thanked him and stood at his right. Kung Sun Sheng stood at his left. Li K'uei from above cried out, "But I have need to piss and I have need to pass my filth—if you do not let me come down, then I will send it all down on your heads!"

Then the holy man inquired of him, saying, "I have always been a priest, one who has renounced the world, nor have I ever offended you and why did you come leaping in the night and split me with your axe? If I had not completed myself in virtue, I would have been killed and moreover you did kill an acolyte of mine."

But Li K'uei replied hastily, "It was not I. You have maybe mistaken me for another!"

Then the holy man laughed and said, "Although what you split was only two gourds, yet is your heart too evil. I shall make you eat a little bitterness and suffering before you go." And he beckoned with his hand and shouted out, "Go!"

Then did an evil fierce wind blow Li K'uei up into the clouds. There two guardian gods, their heads tied in yellow kerchiefs, laid hold on Li K'uei and they went away with him. Now there was a roaring like wind and rain in Li K'uei's ears, and beneath him the trees and houses flew past in a blur. Beneath his feet it was as though clouds pushed him and mists pursued him. Truly he did not know how far he had gone. He was so terrified his souls were gone out of him and his hands and feet shook. All of a sudden he heard a clattering sound, and there he was rolling down the roof of the court of the magistrate in Chi Chou!

Now at this time it was the hour when the magistrate, Ma Shi Hung, sat to hear cases. And in front of him were many runners and underlings. Suddenly they saw a great black man come dropping out of the sky. Everyone was terrified but when the Magistrate Ma saw it he cried out, "Lay hold on this thing and bring him hither!"

Immediately ten-odd gaolers caught Li K'uei and forced him before the magistrate. Then the magistrate shouted, "From whence does a witch-man like you come? Why do you drop out of mid-air?"

Now Li K'uei found he had knocked his head and split open his forehead and for a long time he could not speak. The magistrate said, "Of a certainty he is a witch-man." And he sent for someone to bring speedily something to break spells. The gaolers then bound Li K'uei and pushed him out on to the grassy space in front of the hall and a guardsman brought a basin of dog's blood and poured it over Li K'uei's head and another one brought a pail of urine and fæces and poured it over Li K'uei from head to foot. And Li K'uei's mouth and ears were filled with dog's blood and filth and he cried out, "I am not a witch-man! I am a servant of The Holy Man Lo!"

Now all the people of Chi Chou knew this holy man was a veritable living god of those times, and after this none dared to put forth a hand to injure Li K'uei. Therefore again they brought Li K'uei in front of the hall, and there was one who told the magistrate, saying, "This holy man surnamed Lo is a god priest who has completed the rites of virtue, and he is a very living god. Whoever is with him we may not punish."

But the magistrate laughed and said, "I have read a thousand books and I hear always of things both now and past, and never did I see a holy man have such an acolyte as this! He is naught but a witch-man. Gaolers, beat him for me with all your strength!"

Then they could but stretch Li K'uei upon the ground and they beat him until he was half dead. At last the magistrate shouted out, "You there! Confess at once that you are a witch-man! Then we will not beat you."

So Li K'uei could but say that he was a witch-man named Li Er, and a large rack was brought and nailed upon him and he was locked into the great gaol.

Now Li K'uei came into the condemned cell and there he said, "I am one who stands before a god, and why have you put a rack on me? Whatever comes, I shall kill everyone in Chi Chou!"

And the gaolers and wardens and guards all knew that the power of The Holy Man Lo was very great, and who did not give him reverence? Therefore they all came and asked Li K'uei, "Who in truth are you?"

And Li K'uei answered, "I am the most trusted servant of The Holy Man Lo, and I am one of his regular guards, but because I slipped and made a mistake before him, I offended the holy man, and he has exiled me here and bade me to eat bitterness for a time. Yet in two or three days he will come and save me again. If you do not bring me some wine and meat I will make everyone in your houses die!"

The gaolers, hearing Li K'uei speak thus, were all afraid of him and they could but buy wine and meat and invite him to eat. Li K'uei, seeing them afraid, then began to speak the more wildly and the people in the gaol feared him the more. They brought him hot water also to bathe himself, and clean clothes for him to change, and Li K'uei said, "If you are sparing of my wine and meat I will fly away and you shall suffer."

Then the gaolers and the men in the gaol could but turn about and implore him not to go.

We will not speak further of Li K'uei in the gaol at Chi Chou. Let us speak of The Holy Man Lo who to Tai Chung told all that Li K'uei had done, and Tai Chung could but deplore it all very bitterly, and beg him to save Li K'uei. And then the holy man allowed Tai Chung to stay in the temple and he asked of all the affairs in the mountain lair, and Tai Chung told him of Ch'ao Kai and of Sung Chiang and how kind and how merciful they were, and how they did nothing but act for Heaven to do righteousness, and how they had made a vow that never would they hurt righteous governors nor those who die for their country, nor filial sons, nor good grandsons, nor righteous husbands and faithful wives, and he told of many other of their virtues.

The holy man heard all this and he said nothing. Thus they lived five days one after the other. Each day Tai Chung made obeisance and performed the rites of courtesy and he implored the holy man to save Li K'uei. But the holy man answered, "Such a man as he you ought to purge from your numbers. Do not take him back."

Then Tai Chung said humbly, "The Holy One does not know. This Li K'uei is a stupid fellow, and he does not understand manners. Yet he has his small virtues. First he is straightforward, nor will he take a penny of what is not his. Second, he does not fawn upon any other man, and until he dies he will not change his loyalty. Third, he has not any filthy lusts in him, nor is he covetous or against righteousness. His courage is great and his heart is brave to rush to the front of battle. Because of this Sung Chiang truly loves him. If I do not take this man back with me, then it will be hard indeed for me to face Sung Chiang."

At last the holy man laughed and said, "Well I know he is one of the stars in heaven, of the stars of war, but because men on earth have committed sins too many he has been condemned to earth to kill them. How then can I disobey the command of Heaven and injure this man? I am but making him suffer a little for his temper. I will command that he is to be brought back and returned to you."

Then Tai Chung made obeisance and thanked him. The holy man called out, "Where is the attendant guard?" Even as he spoke a wind arose in front of The Hall Of Pines And Herons and out of it appeared a yellow turbaned genie. He bowed low and he said humbly, "What commands has The Holy One?"

The Holy One said, "That man whom I commanded you before to send to Chi Chou to gaol now has compensated for his sin. Go again to the gaol in Chi Chou and bring him hither. Go quickly and return with speed."

The genie promised and went away and in about an hour he threw Li K'uei down out of the air. Then in great haste Tai Chung lifted up Li K'uei and he asked him, saying, "Brother, where have you been these two days?"

Li K'uei looked at The Holy One and he did nothing but knock his head upon the ground and make obeisance and he said, "Grandfather, The Iron Ox will never so dare again."

The holy man replied, "From today on change this temper of yours, and with all your strength help Sung Chiang. Do not let an evil spirit be roused in you."

Again Li K'uei made obeisance and he said, "You are as my own father, and how dare I disobey you?"

Again Tai Chung asked, "Where in truth have you been these last few days?"

Then Li K'uei made answer, "Ever since that day when the wind blew it blew me straight to Chi Chou and I rolled down off the roof of the magistrate's court. Then they in the court there laid hold on me and that cursed magistrate thought I was a witch-man, and he had me knocked down and bound and he bade the gaolers and guards to take dog's blood and urine and filth and wet me from head to foot. And they beat my two legs rotten and they put a rack on me and cast me into the great gaol. There they asked me what god's warrior was I who dropped out of the sky, and I told them I was the attendant of The Holy Man Lo himself, and because I did wrong I was cast out, but after two or three days he would surely come again and seek me. Although I have been beaten with a bamboo, yet I cheated them into giving me some meat and wine, for those things fear the holy man above all else and they gave me a bath and a change of clothes. And as I was eating the meat and the wine I had got them to give me there in the gaol I saw a yellow turbaned genie leap down out of the mid-air. He opened the lock on my rack and shouted to me to shut my eyes and as though I dreamed I was brought straight hither."

Then Kung Sun Sheng said, "The Holy One has more than a thousand of such genii as this yellow turbaned one, and they are all attendants of my teacher, this holy man."

When Li K'uei heard this he cried out, "Holy Father, why did you not say so earlier? Then would I have been spared the doing of such a sin," and he could but kneel and make obeisance.

Tai Chung knelt also and he implored the holy man, saying, "This humble one has already been here many days, and the fighting in Kao T'ang Chou is very urgent. Ten thousand times do I beg for forgiveness and I pray that the teacher Kung Sun Sheng may be freed to come with me, his pupil, to go and save our elder brother Sung Chiang. As soon as Kao Lien has been vanquished, we will bring him back to this mountain."

The holy man said, "At first I would not have him go, but today because you have such a noble purpose I will bid him to go the once with you. I have a few words, however, which you should remember."

Then Kung Sun Sheng went before the holy man and he knelt and listened for his commands.

Truly now the desire of his heart is fulfilled
for saving the world,
Return he will, like a phœnix on the clouds
the wind has whirled.

What did the holy man say to Kung Sun Sheng? Pray hear it told in the next chapter.

Chapter 53

THE DRAGON OF THE CLOUDS USES HIS MAGIC TO VANQUISH KAO LIEN. THE BLACK WHIRLWIND DESCENDS INTO A WELL TO SAVE CH'AI CHIN

IT IS SAID: And The Holy Man Lo said, "Younger Brother, the magic you learned before was the same as Kao Lien's. Now I shall teach you the ways of the five thunders, the heart of Heaven, and the true magic, and according to these ways you may save Sung Chiang and preserve the country and protect the peace of the people, and work righteousness for Heaven. I will myself appoint someone to look after your old mother day and night, and you need not have anxiety for her. You were once a good, albeit wandering star, among the thirty-six fierce stars, and because of this I let you go the once. Now you must preserve carefully all you have learned from me, and do not be moved by fleshly desires and so delay the important paths of your own feet."

Kung Sun Sheng, having kneeled to receive the holy commands and the magic formulas, then went with Tai Chung and Li K'uei and he bade farewell to the holy man and he parted from all the other Taoist comrades and went down the mountain and toward his hime. There he prepared two magic swords, his Taoist chaplet and robe, and other things and he made obeisance of farewell to his old mother and left the mountain and went his way. When he had gone some ten miles and more, Tai Chung said, "This humble one will go first and make announcement to the elder brother. Do you, my Teacher, come on the big road with Li K'uei and then we will meet again."

Kung Sun Sheng replied, "Well enough! Go first, Good Brother, and make announcement, and I will come after you with all speed."

And Tai Chung made command to Li K'uei, saying, "Upon the road take care of the teacher, for if anything happens amiss, you shall suffer for it."

Li K'uei answered, saying, "He is just as learned in magic as The Holy One, and how can I treat him lightly?"

Then Tai Chung tied on his magic letters and used his magic words and went on ahead.

Let it be told further. Kung Sun Sheng and Li K'uei, the two of them, left The Mountain Of The Two Holy Men and went along the great road. At night they sought for inns and there slept. Now Li K'uei feared the magic of The Holy Man Lo and he took every care to attend upon Kung Sun Sheng, and how dared he let forth any anger? The two had gone thus for three days and they came to a certain town which was called Wu Kan and there the people on the street gathered thickly and Kung Sun Sheng said, "We have grown very weary with these days upon the road. Let us buy some wine and some vegetables to eat."

Li K'uei answered, "Good, too!"

They saw there at the side of the road a small wine shop, and the two entered there and sat down and Kung Sun Sheng sat above, and Li K'uei untied his girdle purse and he sat below. He called for the serving man and bade him pour out wine and prepare some vegetable foods for them to eat with it. And Kung Sun Sheng asked, "Have you any cakes here made with vegetable oils?"

The serving man replied, "I have only wine and meat here. I have no such vegetable cakes. But there is a shop at the mouth of this street which sells date cakes."

Then Li K'uei said, "I will go and buy some and bring them hither."

So he felt in his purse and brought out some copper cash and he went straight to the mouth of the street. There he bought a package of date cakes and was about to return when he heard someone say at the side alley, "How good a strength is this!" Li K'uei looked and there was a crowd of people surrounding a tall fellow, who was swinging a ribbed iron hammer of war. All the people watching him cried out in praise. Now Li K'uei looked at the tall fellow. He was more than ten feet tall, his face was pitted with small pox, and he had a great scar on his nose. Li K'uei, looking at the weapon he used, saw that it was more than thirty catties in weight. The man used it swiftly and with seeming carelessness and suddenly he struck a blow down upon one of the great stones of the street paving. The stone was beaten into powder. Everyone cried out then in his praise. Li K'uei could hold himself no longer. He thrust the date cakes into his bosom and came forward to take the hammer. That fellow shouted out, "What cursed man are you? How dare you come to take my hammer?"

Li K'uei cried, "What cursed bit of a thing have you done to make them all cry you so good? Just to look at it soils my eyes! You watch your lord swing it once! Let everybody see me!"

That fellow replied, "I will lend it to you. If you are not strong enough to use it, then will I give you a blow with my fist upon the back of your neck."

Li K'uei took the hammer and it was as though he took a little sling. He swung it for a while and put it lightly down. His face was not red, nor did his heart beat fast, nor did his breath come in gasps. That fellow, seeing this, fell down before him and made obeisance and he said, "I beg for my elder brother's great name."

Li K'uei asked, "Where is your home?"

That man replied, "It is just a little ahead."

He led Li K'uei then to a certain place and there was a lock fastening a door and the man brought out a key and opened it and he asked Li K'uei to come inside and sit down. Li K'uei, looking about this house, saw everywhere the implements of an ironsmith, anvil and hammer and forge and tongs and all such things, and to himself he thought, "This man must be an ironsmith. We could use him truly very well in our lair. Why should I not bid him come and join us?"

Again he said aloud, "Fellow, give me your surname that I may know what it is."

That fellow replied, "This humble one is named T'ang Lung. My father was a military officer in a small city called Yien An, but because he was so mighty an ironsmith he was raised to this place for his skill in making iron weapons. These two years he has been dead and this humble one loves to gamble and I have wandered about on rivers and lakes. Because of this I now beat out iron here for a living and I love with my very flesh and bones the wielding of weapons. Because I have the pits of small pox over my whole body men call me The Gold Spotted Leopard. Dare I ask my elder brother's high surname and great name?"

Li K'uei said, "I am a good fellow of the great lair and I am called The Black Whirlwind, Li K'uei."

When T'ang Lung heard this again he made obeisance and he said, "Long have I heard the brave name of my elder brother, but who could have thought that suddenly we should meet today?"

Li K'uei answered, "When can you ever grow rich here? Better it would be if you went with me to the great lair and joined us and you could be a chieftain too."

Then T'ang Lung said, "If you will not desert me, Elder Brother, and if you will help me along a little, I would willingly serve you." And he made obeisance to Li K'uei as to an elder brother, and Li K'uei took him for a younger brother.

And T'ang Lung said, "I have no family and no comrades. I will go with my elder brother and we will go and drink three bowls of such tasteless wine as there is to be a pledge of our brotherhood. Tonight we will rest for the night and tomorrow we will start early."

But Li K'uei replied, "I have a teacher in the wine shop ahead and he is waiting for me to go and buy date cake and bring it to him and I must not delay. We can but go at once."

T'ang Lung asked, "Why is it so important as all this?"

Li K'uei answered, "You do not know that Elder Brother Sung Chiang is now at Kao T'ang Chou fighting and he is waiting for this teacher of ours to come and save him."

Again T'ang Lung asked, "And who is this teacher?"

Li K'uei replied, "You are not to ask first. Quickly get ready and let us go."

In haste then T'ang Lung tied together a bundle and prepared money for the road and he put on his fur cap and he hung a knife to his girdle and he took up a sword. Such things as were heavy and old and useless he left in his house. And he went with Li K'uei and they went straight to the wine shop and there they saw Kung Sun Sheng. Then Kung Sun Sheng reproached Li K'uei, saying, "Why have you been so long gone? Had you come later I would have already gone back."

Li K'uei did not dare answer. He led forward T'ang Lung and bade him make obeisance before Kung Sun Sheng and he told in detail the story of their brotherhood, and Kung Sun Sheng hearing he was an ironsmith and maker of weapons was glad in his heart also. Li K'uei brought out the package of dates and gave it to the innkeeper and told him to prepare it. Then the three of them drank several bowls of wine, and when they had eaten the date cakes and paid for the wine, Li K'uei and T'ang Lung each took his bundle on his back and with Kung Sun Sheng they left the village, and went toward Kao T'ang Chou. When they were less than two miles away there were already Lü Fang and Kao Shen and a hundred and more soldiers and horses coming to meet them. When each had performed the rites of courtesy and had proffered the wine of salutation and had spoken a little of what had happened since they last parted, Sung Chiang asked them to come into the central camp. All the other chiefs also came to give greeting. Li K'uei led forward T'ang Lung to see Sung Chiang and Wu Yung and all the chieftains and when obeisance had been made a feast of welcome was made in the camp.

On the second day in the central part of the camp Sung Chiang, Wu Yung and Kung Sun Sheng took counsel as to how to vanquish Kao Lien, and Kung Sun Sheng said, "Let the chieftain send forth a command that all the men are to march forward and we will see what the enemy does. This lowly one has a way."

On that day Sung Chiang sent forth the command that every camp was to start out together and they were to go to the moat about the city of Kao T'ang Chou. So they took down camp and the next day at dawn they prepared food and the fighting men all put on their garments of war and put down the drawbridge and Kao Lien led out the three hundred soldiers and all the captains great and small and they went out of the city to meet the enemy. The two armies came nearer and nearer together and banners waving and drums beating they opposed each other. Each side set its men in rank and they began to beat their musical drums and the great reptile skin drums and they waved banners of every color.

Then Sung Chiang's ranks parted and ten horses were seen advancing and the soldiers stood on either side like the wings of an eagle. On the left were five chiefs, Hua Yung, Ch'ing Ming, Chu T'ung, Ou P'eng and Lü Fang. On the right there were five other chieftains, Ling Ch'ung, Sheng Li, Teng Fei, Ma Ling and Kao Shen. In the midst were three generals, Sung Chiang, Wu Yung and Kung Sun Sheng. Their three horses came out in front of the ranks and they saw that drums were beaten and banners waved in the enemy ranks. Where these enemy ranks parted there were also some twenty or thirty chieftains and they came forth surrounding Kao Lien to the front of the ranks and they held their horses then just under the banners on either side and together they shouted, "You robbers from a watery lair, of a certainty you have come to fight with us, and surely now will we do combat and see who will be victor and who vanquished! He who runs will be held no good fellow!"

Then Sung Chiang asked his own men, saying, "Who of you will go forth and kill this thief straightway?"

Then Hua Yung, holding his weapon, urged forward his horse and he went out. Kao Lien saw him and he shouted, "Who will go and seize this robber for me?"

Then out of his ranks came forth a captain who was named Hsüeh Yuen Huei, and he used two double-edged knives and he rode a fierce horse and he flew out into the middle between the two ranks and he came to oppose Hua Yung. The two of them fought there for several rounds. Then Hua Yung turned his horse and suddenly went toward his own side. Hsüeh Yuen Huei let his horse free and pursued him and came after with all his strength. But Hua Yung held back his horse a little and he brought out his bow and arrow and turning his body he let fly an arrow and it struck Hsüeh Yuen Huei so that he fell head downward from his horse. Then the soldiers on both sides shouted out.

Now Kao Lien, on his horse, seeing what had happened was very angry and in haste he felt beside his saddle and brought forth the magic gong and struck at it with his magic dagger. When he had struck it but three times there was seen to rise among his men a whirling cloud of yellow sand and the heavens grew misted and the earth dark nor had the sun any light, and there was a sound of great shouting and there was the howling of wolves and tigers and leopards and all manner of strange animals and poisonous reptiles and they came charging out of the cloud of yellow sand.

But even as the soldiers were about to rise in retreat Kung Sun Sheng from his horse had already brought out an ancient weapon carved in a pine pattern and he pointed it at the enemy and he muttered his magic rune and he shouted out, "Speed!"

Then was a yellow light seen to shoot forth and the mass of fierce beasts and poisonous reptiles all fell down in confusion on the yellow sand between the ranks of fighting men. When all the soldiers looked at them they were but beasts cut out of white paper and the yellow sand was all dispersed!

Sung Chiang saw this and he pointed his whip and all his men great and small rushed forward. Then were seen the enemy's men fallen dead and the horses lying and the banners and the drums in confusion. In great agitation Kao Lien called back his magic soldiers and Sung Chiang and his men and horsemen pursued them to the city. But there the drawbridge was hastily drawn up from the city wall and the gates were barred. From the wall came rolling down logs of wood and a rain of great stones. Then Sung Chiang commanded that gongs be beaten and his men called back. He counted over their numbers and every man answered, and they returned then to the camp and they thanked Kung Sun Sheng for his merit and straightway all soldiers were rewarded.

The next day the fighting men surrounded the city and they fought with all their strength together and Kung Sun Sheng said to Sung Chiang and to Wu Yung, "Yesterday night although we killed a large half of the enemy soldiers, yet we saw those three hundred magic soldiers go back into the city. Today we are attacking the city fiercely and surely those will come upon us secretly in the night. Tonight let us gather together our men and in the depths of the night we will hide in all four directions. We will put up camps falsely as though there were men here. Then we will tell the chiefs that when they hear thunder sound in the sky and see fire rise in the camp they are all to bring their men forward."

This command was then sent forth. On that day the robbers attacked the city fiercely. At an hour after noon the men were all called back into the encampment, and there in the tents they made music and feasted. As the day drew to night all the chiefs divided secretly and they ambushed themselves on all four sides.

Let it be told now of Sung Chiang and Wu Yung and Kung Sun Sheng and of Hua Yung, Ch'ing Ming, Lü Fang and Kao Shen. They went and mounted upon a slope of the hill. Now on this night Kao Lien did truly count out his three hundred magic soldiers. On his shoulder each of the magic soldiers bore an iron gourd and in these were hidden sulphur and brimstone and rockets and such things. Each man held wire brooms also and in each man's mouth that he might keep silence was a bit of wood. About the time of the second watch of the night they beat open the city gate and put down the drawbridge. Kao Lien in front led the magic soldiers on and behind were some thirty horsemen who came galloping along.

So they came near to the encampment of the enemy and Kao Lien made a spell of magic and a great wind arose and blew a yellow cloud toward the sky. Sand and stones began to fly and the dust rose to the very heaven. Each of the magic soldiers brought out flint and tinder and held a flame to the mouth of their gourds and each whistled through the wood he held in his lips. Out of the darkness the light of the flames shone upon their bodies and with their great swords and broad axes they cast themselves upon the earth before Sung Chiang's camp.

Now Kung Sun Sheng stood upon a high point of a mountain making his magic spells also with his magic dagger. Suddenly out of the air upon the plains there sounded a great clap of thunder. The three hundred magic soldiers were so agitated that they would have retreated at once except even at that instant fire rose from the empty camp and the flames flew in all directions so that heaven and earth were red and there was no road to escape from it. Then the robbers who were ambushed all about surrounded the wooden walls of the encampment and the robbers who were hidden in the darkness saw very clearly the three hundred soldiers and not one escaped. They were all killed there in the camp.

In great haste Kao Lien led away the thirty horsemen and rushed back into the city. Behind them there was a group of horsemen pursuing them and it was led by The Leopard Headed Ling Ch'ung. Seeing at last that he was almost upon them, in utmost haste Kao Lien called out that the drawbridge was to be pulled up. By now Kao Lien had but eight or nine horsemen to take with him into the city, for the rest had been taken alive by Ling Ch'ung, and with these men Kao Lien retreated into the middle of the city. There he counted out all the citizens and he sent them on to the city wall. So were Kao Lien's soldiers and horsemen killed every one by Sung Chiang and Ling Ch'ung's men.

On the next day again did Sung Chiang lead out horsemen and men and again he encompassed strongly the city. And Kao Lien thought to himself, "All these years I have learned this magic and I did not think that he would vanquish me today. Now what shall I do?"

He could but send men out to the neighboring cities and ask for aid to save him. In great haste then he wrote two letters and he bade men go to Tung Ch'ang and K'ou Chou, two cities that were not far from there, and he thought, "The magistrates of these two places are both men that I raised up, and I will bid them send men this very night to save me." And he commanded men to go from among those who stood in his own presence and they took the letters. The gate to the west was then opened and they rushed out and they went on the road toward the west.

Now the robber chieftains were about to pursue them when Wu Yung gave a command, saying, "Let them go and we will use a plan to vanquish him yet."

Then Sung Chiang asked, saying, "Counselor, what is your plan?"

Wu Yung answered, "In the city here the soldiers are very few and the captains are few and so he is seeking aid from outside. Let us, therefore, send out two ranks of men disguised as though they had come to help him and we will pretend to fight on the road. Kao Lien, seeing it, will certainly open the city gate and come forth to their aid. Then we will seize this opportunity to take the city and we will lead Kao Lien astray into the small paths and so indeed can we capture him."

Sung Chiang, hearing this, was much rejoiced and he led Tai Chung and returned to the mountain lair. There two ranks of men were chosen out and horses made ready.

Let it be told further that Kao Lien every night in the city piled up the straw in great heaps and he set fire to them so that they blazed to the very heavens and this he did for a sign. Upon the city wall others watched, hoping for those who would come to save them. After several days had passed the soldiers who were guarding the city saw a confusion rise in the ranks of Sung Chiang's men. In great haste they went to report it to Kao Lien and Kao Lien, hearing it, in great haste put on his garments of war and went upon the city wall to watch. There he saw two ranks of horsemen galloping forward and the dust from their feet and the noise of their cries filled the heavens, and the men and horsemen that were encircling the city scattered and hastened away. Kao Lien thought that two armies of soldiers had come to save him and he led out all the soldiers and horsemen that were left in the city and he opened the city gates and dividing they went in all directions.

Let it now be told further. Kao Lien charged straight to the front of Sung Chiang's camp and there he saw Sung Chiang leading Hua Yung, and Ch'ing Ming, and the three on their horses went down a small path. Then Kao Lien led his men and horsemen and pursued them with all haste. Suddenly he heard on the ridge behind him a continuous succession of reports, and he began to doubt in his heart and he called back his men and horsemen. But on both sides the drums began to sound. On the left was Lü Fang, on the right was Kao Shen, and each led five hundred horsemen and they came charging down.

Then Kao Lien in greatest agitation tried to escape, but he had already lost the greater half of his men. As they ran and ran they looked and they saw that upon the city walls were the emblems of the robbers' lair. When they opened their eyes to stare again there were no soldiers anywhere who had come to save them. And Kao Lien could but lead his defeated broken ranks into the small lonely paths of the hills.

They had gone but little more than three miles when from behind the spur of a mountain dashed out a crowd of horsemen and there was Sheng Li blocking the path before them. In a fierce voice he called out, "I have been waiting long for you—come down as you should from your horse and be bound!"

At this Kao Lien led his men and turned back. But suddenly in front of him there was already another company of men and horses blocking his way, and upon the horse leading them was The Beautiful Bearded, Chu T'ung. And the two companies pressed together upon Kao Lien, and on all four sides escape was cut off. Then Kao Lien could but leave his horse and go on foot up the mountain and on all four sides the men on foot went up the mountain. In haste then did Kao Lien mutter a magic rune and he shouted, "Rise!"

And a black cloud came forth and it rolled up into midair and it mounted straight up to the crest of the mountain. Then from beside the slope of the hill Kung Sun Sheng was seen to come out and he saw the cloud and he stretched his dagger out as he sat upon his horse and he also muttered a magic rune and he shouted, "Speed!" Then he pointed up with his dagger and suddenly Kao Lien was seen to come tumbling down head first out of the cloud. Then from the side Lei Heng was seen to run forward, and with one blow he cut Kao Lien in two pieces, and he cut off Kao Lien's head and lifted it up and they all went down the mountain.

Now first they sent a messenger in all haste to tell Sung Chiang but Sung Chiang already knew that Kao Lien had been killed and he gathered all his men into the city. From thence he sent out a command saying, "You are not to harm the people."

Then he caused proclamations to be put up commanding that not the least thing belonging to anyone was to be taken and he commanded also that the first thing to be done was to go into the gaol and fetch out Ch'ai Chin. The gaolers and lesser officials in the gaol had also all run away, and there were but some thirty to fifty prisoners there, and the robbers took the racks from them all and let them all go free. But among these the lord Ch'ai was not to be seen.

Then was Sung Chiang's heart sad and he went seeking into a room of the gaol and there he found all of Ch'ai Chin uncle's family. Again he went into another room and he found Ch'ai Chin's own family brought thither from Ch'ang Chou, for since Kao Lien had fought day after day they had been left there nor had they been brought out and questioned. Only there was nowhere to find the lord Ch'ai.

Then Wu Yung called together all the small officials of the gaol, and he questioned them closely and among them there was a soldier who said, "I am a warden of the gaol and I am named

Ling Jen. The other day I was appointed by the magistrate Kao Lien and my sole duty was to guard this Ch'ai Chin so that there might be no least way in which he could escape and Kao Lien commanded me further that if the worst came I was first to kill Ch'ai Chin. Three days ago the magistrate Kao Lien wanted to have Ch'ai Chin come out to be killed but I saw he was a good man and I had no heart to do the deed. I could but deny him, saying, 'This man is already nearly dead and it is not necessary to kill him.' But after he pressed me hard I answered, saying, 'Ch'ai Chin is already dead.' Then because there has been this fighting day after day the magistrate has had no time, and I, fearing lest he send someone and find Ch'ai Chin, knew I would suffer for it surely. Therefore I led Ch'ai Chin to a place beside a dry well and I opened the lock of his rack and I put him inside that well to hide. But I do not know now whether he is dead or alive."

Sung Chiang heard this and in great haste he sent Ling Jen to lead him thither to the well. They went into the inner gaol where the well was and they looked down and there was a deep darkness, and they did not know how deep it was. They shouted from above but no one answered. They cast a rope in then and it was nearly eighty or ninety feet deep. And Sung Chiang said, "It seems that the lord Ch'ai has disappeared," and the tears fell from his eyes.

But Wu Yung said, "Chieftain, do not weep. Who dares to go down and see? Then we can know whether he be there or not."

Before he had finished speaking out dashed The Black Whirlwind Li K'uei and he shouted in a great voice, "Wait until I go down!"

Then Sung Chiang said, "Good indeed! It was you who brought him to this pass, and today it should be you who saves him."

Li K'uei laughed and said, "I will go down —I will go down and not be afraid, only you must not cut the rope half way!"

At this Wu Yung said, "Such talk is too mischievous."

Then a great split bamboo basket was brought and a rope tied to the four sides of it, and rope was tied to rope until it was long enough, and a woodwork was put across the mouth of the well and the rope was hung upon it. Then Li K'uei stripped himself stark naked and in his hand he took his two axes and he sat in the basket and so he was let down into the well. Upon the rope were tied two brass bells and gradually they let him down to the bottom. Then Li K'uei climbed out of the basket and he felt all about the bottom of the well. Once he felt something and it was a pile of dead men's bones and Li K'uei cried, "My father and mother! What can this cursed thing be?"

But when he went to feel at the other side there was nothing but water and there was no place where he could get out. Then Li K'uei put the two battle axes into the basket and he took his two hands and felt about the bottom and on all four sides he felt the well, which was very wide and broad. Suddenly as he felt about he felt a man crouched together in the water. Li K'uei called out, "Lord Ch'ai!"

But he heard no movement at all. Yet he put forth his hand to feel of him and he perceived there was a little breath coming from his mouth. Then Li K'uei said, "Now thank Heaven and thank Earth—is he dead or can he yet be saved?"

Straightway he climbed into the basket and shook the brass bells and the others pulled him up, but there was only Li K'uei alone there. But he told of what he found at the bottom of the well in great detail and then Sung Chiang commanded him, "Do you go down again and first put the lord Ch'ai into the basket and we will pull him up and then we will let the basket down again for you."

Li K'uei said, "Elder Brother, you do not understand. I have been twice to gaol in Chi Chou and do not make me go again today the third time."

At this Sung Chiang laughed and said, "And why should I put you into trouble? Go down quickly."

So Li K'uei could then but seat himself again in the basket and again he went down into the well. When he had reached the bottom he climbed out of the basket and he lifted the lord and placed him into it. Then he shook the brass bells tied there and those above heard it and soon pulled him up to the top. Then were all rejoiced when they saw the lord Ch'ai, although his head was broken open, and the flesh and skin on his two legs were split, and he opened his eyes a little only to close them again. Then were all those who saw him greatly sorrowful and they called a physician to heal him.

But Li K'uei was still there in the bottom of the well and now he lifted up his voice and set up a great bellowing. And Sung Chiang heard it and in haste he commanded that the basket was to be lowered again so that Li K'uei might be brought up. Now when Li K'uei came to the top he grew very angry and he said, "Nor are you good fellows either and you would not put the basket down to save me!"

Sung Chiang replied, "We were only thinking of and caring for the lord Ch'ai and for this we forgot you and you must not blame us."

Then Sung Chiang called to the others and they placed the lord Ch'ai into the cart and there he lay, and they took the two houses of his family and very much of household goods so that in all there were more than twenty carts of these, and Sung Chiang commanded Li K'uei and Lei Heng to escort them up to the lair. Then he went and put to death in the streets the whole household of Kao Lien, young and old, good and evil, and he gave money as a reward to Ling Jen. Beyond this he took Kao Lien's treasure and grain and household goods all up the mountain, and after this he took all his men and they went away from Kao T'ang Chou, and so they all returned to the lair. Through the lands which they passed they took nothing and harmed no one, and after they had been on the way for several days they reached the lair again.

And Ch'ai Chin rose in spite of his illness and he gave thanks to his two elder brothers, Ch'ao Kai and Sung Chiang, and to all the chieftains. Then Ch'ao Kai commanded that another house be built beside Sung Chiang's house where the lord Ch'ai might live with all his family. And Ch'ao Kai and Sung Chiang and the others were greatly rejoiced because since they were returned from Kao T'ang Chou they had added to their number Ch'ai Chin and T'ang Lung, and they made a feast of welcome for them and of this there is no more to be told.

Let it be told further of those two cities named Tung Ch'ang and K'ao Chou. When they knew that Kao Lien had been killed and that region lost they could but write a report of the matter and send it to the government and there were those two escaped out of the city and they told the truth. When the official Kao Ch'iu heard of it and when he knew that his brother Kao Lien had been killed on the next day at the fifth watch he rose and went to the higher court and there he waited in the hall and he waited until the great bell should ring for the hour. When no long time had passed all the officials came each in his robe of state into the court and they stood there before the Imperial Hall, and when the hour was come they all went into the Imperial Hall. Thrice was the whip waved, and the civil officials to the east and the military officials to the west all stood in place. The Emperor then arrived in his carriage, and he descended and seated himself upon his throne. Then the governor of the hall said, "Let him who has any business come forward. If there be no business the curtain shall be opened that all may depart."

Then did the magistrate Kao Ch'iu come forward and he told how Ch'ao Kai and Sung Chiang of the robbers' lair at Liang Shan P'o had made a great evil in the land, and how they had robbed granaries and how they gathered together many fierce and evil men and how at Chi Chou they had killed imperial soldiers and how they had stirred up trouble for the soldiers of Chiang Chou and now they had killed governors and people of Kao T'ang Chou clean. The treasures and the grain stores they had taken wholly away. And he said, "This thing is like an illness in the belly and in the vitals. If they are not soon killed and put down, then will it increase and then it will be an illness difficult to heal. Here I kneel and supplicate for redress."

Now the Emperor, hearing this, was much afraid and quickly he sent out a command that soldiers should be moved and sent at once to aid Kao and that by all means the robbers' lair should be swept clean and he commanded that all men of that sort should be killed.

But the Commander Kao again made supplications and he said, "To me it seems not necessary that any great forces should be sent against such small men as these. I have one in mind who can perform the thing."

Then the Emperor replied, "Surely if this one be able to do the deed, let him go at once and perform it and speedily return and make report.

Then will I lift him to a high place as reward, and I will change him to a high place."

Then Kao said respectfully, "This man is first son of a first son of a warrior famous at the beginning of the dynasty, a man who had a double surname Hu Yien and his name was Chen. This man is named Hu Yien Shu. He uses two brass clubs and ten thousand men cannot prevail against him. Now he is in command of some ten thousand men and he has skill and strength in the use of every sort of weapon. This man can vanquish the robbers' lair. Let him be given a body of horsemen and infantry swift and skilled, and within the time set he will have taken the lair and brought back his men."

This the Emperor approved and he sent forth his mandate to his ministers of state that with all speed they should appoint one who should take by night the royal command to that one in the city of Ju Ling Chou and there present it and bid him come thither.

On that day when the audience was over Kao The Commander returned and he chose out from his ministers one to take the imperial mandate who should go forth and bid Hu Yien Shu to come with all speed to the Emperor's palace.

Let it now be told of Hu Yien Shu in the city of Ju Ling Chou. He was sitting at his work in the court there when he heard one say that there was a messenger from the Emperor who had come especially to bring the royal command and take him thither, since there was a special duty appointed to him. And Hu Yien Shu left the place where he was and he went to meet the messenger and returned, and he opened the mandate and read the command, and he prepared a feast of welcome for the messenger. Then he put on his garments and his helmet and his armor. His horse was saddled and he mounted and went his way. He took with him some thirty or forty men and they all went with the messenger and so left the city of Ju Ling.

Now they went with all speed to the capital and there is naught to tell of the journey, for they soon came to the borders of the city and they went first to the courts of Kao Ch'iu and they went in to see the Commander. Now on this day the Commander Kao was sitting in his Hall Of Audience and the gateman announced, "Hu Yien Shu of Ju Ling is now outside the gate."

Then was the Commander Kao greatly rejoiced and he commanded that Hu Yien Shu was to be brought in that he might see him. Commander Kao then asked him how he had fared on the journey and gave him money for reward. On the next morning early they went to see the Emperor. When the Emperor saw that Hu Yien Shu was a man not like the common, he let a smile come upon his imperial countenance and he presented him with a horse that was named Black Horse Who Walks In Snow. Now this name was because the horse's body was black as shadows and his four hoofs were white as snow. His body was black as ink and his hoofs to his fetlocks were snow-white, and so was he given this name of Black Horse Who Walks In Snow. Now this horse could go more than three hundred miles in a day and he was given according to the imperial command to Hu Yien Shu to ride. When Hu Yien Shu had thanked the Emperor for his grace, he followed the Commander Kao again to his palace. There they took counsel together of the affairs of the robbers' lair and Hu Yien Shu said, "Humbly do I say to the most gracious, this humble one is to attack the robbers' lair. But my soldiers are poor, although my captains are good; my horses are weak, although the weapons are well enough. Yet I pray you will not despise them. Only I pray that you will appoint two who may go as the vanguard and fight first. Then after they have attacked, I will take a great army and surely the robbers will be vanquished."

When the Commander heard this he was greatly rejoiced and he asked, saying, "Who can be the vanguard then?"

If Hu Yien Shu had not mentioned these two then indeed would the city of Wan Chi have not added more great warriors, nor the robbers' lair overcome the imperial soldiers.

> Ever his name was writ in victory in a palace fair,
> Surname and name were set on high in the robbers' lair.

Who then was it for whom Hu Yien Shu stood guarantor to the Commander Kao? Pray hear it told in the next chapter.

Chapter 54

THE COMMANDER KAO LEADS FORTH THREE RANKS OF SOLDIERS. HU YIEN SHU SETS OUT TWO RANKS OF HORSEMEN

IT IS SAID: The Commander Kao asked Hu Yien Shu, saying, "Who is that one whom you have to lead out the soldiers as a vanguard?" And Hu Yien Shu replied humbly, "This lowly one can guarantee that one, surnamed Han and named T'ao, who was a man of the city of Chen but who is now in the eastern capital. He has passed his second military degree, and he uses as weapon great wooden clubs. Men call him Victor In A Hundred Battles. This man can be a sure vanguard. There is yet another man, and he is also a military official, and his surname is P'eng and his name Ch'i, and he was a man of the city of Ying, but he also is now in the eastern capital. For generations his forefathers have been warriors, and he uses for weapon a three-pronged spear. He is above all others in military skill. Men call him The Eye Of Heaven. This man can be the leader of the second company."

The Commander Kao, hearing this, was greatly pleased and he said, "If these are vanguard and captain, then who can withstand them?"

On that day therefore the Commander Kao in that very place wrote two mandates and he signed them and set his seal on them, and he commanded that messengers be sent forth that very night to go and seek out Han and P'eng, and they set forth as swift as flying flames. In less than ten days they had gone and come back and they went straight to the Commander's palace, and they made obeisance to the Commander and to Hu Yien Shu. That day the Commander Kao led out his whole company and they went to the imperial reviewing grounds to drill and review. When he had reviewed them he went again into his palace, and there he took counsel with the ministers of state and the three warriors and they discussed all the affairs of the army. The Commander Kao asked, saying, "In your three companies, how many men and horsemen have you?"

Hu Yien Shu answered, saying, "In our three companies of soldiers and horsemen, we have indeed five thousand, and if the foot soldiers are counted we have ten thousand."

The Commander Kao said, "Then do you three return to your own city and do you choose out such of your men as are swift and strong, three thousand in number, and of your foot soldiers five thousand, and we will set a day to meet and to set forth and we will seize the robbers' lair."

Hu Yien Shu said humbly, "As for these three companies of horsemen and foot soldiers, they are such as have daily been exercised and drilled, and the men are strong and the horses swift, and you need have no fear. But there is only one thing to fear, and it is that there be needed a few days the more. So shall I have committed no inconvenient fault, I pray you, Most Gracious, to grant me a few days the more."

The Commander Kao replied, "If you speak thus, then go to the imperial armories where weapons and armor are kept and there take what you need and it matters not how much you take of garments of war, armor, helmets, swords and banners. You may go and fetch them all, for you are only to have all that horses and soldiers may need, so that the battle may be fought well. On that day when you assemble your armies, I will appoint those who are to count off your numbers."

So Hu Yien Shu led out his men, and he led them to the armories. First he chose out three thousand suits of armor and of armor for horses he chose five thousand, of brass helmets he chose three thousand, of long spears he chose two thousand, of whirling knives one thousand, and of bows and arrows he took a countless number. Of fire bombs he took five hundred complete sets and he put all upon carts. On that day on which he was to set forth the Commander Kao added three thousand horses, and he rewarded the three warriors with gold and silver and bolts of satin. And the three warriors received the money and they received the official mandates and they parted from the Commander Kao and all the ministers of state. Then the three mounted their horses and they all went toward the city of Ju Ling.

Of the journey there is naught to be said, and so they came to their own city. Then Hu Yien Shu appointed Han T'ao and P'eng Ch'i that they should lead soldiers from the two cities of Chen and Ying and that they were to meet again in Ju Ling. In less than half a month the three companies of horsemen and soldiers were all gathered there. Then Hu Yien Shu gave out the imperial garments of war and the helmets, the knives, banners, hammers, saddles and horses and he himself had made whatever was needed for horses and for weapons and all such things. When he had given these to the three warriors, he led forth all the soldiers, and the Commander Kao bade two officials from his palace to come and tell off the men. When he had rewarded heavily the three warriors, Hu Yien Shu then led forth the three companies of soldiers and horsemen. The one who led the way was Han T'ao, the one in the middle was led by Hu Yien Shu, and the one in the back was led by P'eng Ch'i. Horsemen and soldiers, the three companies of them went forward with great strength and vigor toward the robbers' lair.

It is told further, the spies of the robbers' lair, riding their horses afar, heard of what was about to come, and they hastened to the lair and made report of it. In the Hall Of Meetings there were Ch'ao Kai and Sung Chiang. Above them sat the counselor Wu Yung. Below them sat the prophet Kung Sun Sheng and all the chieftains, and they all drank wine in honor of Ch'ao Kai and they feasted the livelong day. When they heard the report made that Hu Yien Shu, The Double Clubs, of the city of Ju Ling, led forth horsemen and soldiers they all took counsel together of how they might withstand him with guile. Then Wu Yung said, "I have heard it told that this is a descendant of the honored statesman who lived at the beginning of the dynasty and that this man is skilled and used in all military things. He wields two brass clubs, and none can withstand him. We must first send forth against him one who is very strong, and then we must use guile—"

Before he had finished speaking The Black Whirlwind Li K'uei cried, "I will go and catch this man for you!"

But Sung Chiang made answer, saying, "And how can you go? I have a way of my own. Let us ask The Fire In The Thunder Clap Ch'ing Ming to go forth first, and let The Leopard Headed Ling Ch'ung fight second, and let Hua Yung be the third and let The Ten Foot Green Snake Hu be the fourth, and let Sheng Li fight fifth. Let these five lead forth their companies one by one and stand, and let them fight one after the other like the turning of a spinning wheel. I myself will lead you ten brothers, and we will lead forth a mighty host of horses and men. The warriors on the left shall be Chu T'ung, Lei Heng, Mu Hung, Huang Hsin and Lü Fang. The warriors on the right shall be Yang Hsiung, Shih Hsiu, Ou P'eng, Ma Ling and Ko Shen. Upon the water let these be asked to go forth: Li Chün, Chang Heng, Chang Shun, and the three brothers Juan and they shall keep the boats ready and waiting for us. Li K'uei and Yang Ling shall be asked to lead the robbers on foot, divided into two parts, and ambushed ready for our aid."

When Sung Chiang had thus appointed all, the first company was led forth by Ch'ing Ming and he soon had led forth his men and horsemen down the mountain, and he turned toward the plains and there he set his men in rank. Now although the time was winter it was unusually warm. After they had waited for a day they had already seen the state soldiers coming and they saw the one who was first was Han T'ao and he set out his men one by one. That night they did not fight, but the next day at earliest dawn the two armies stood opposed. The painted drums sounded forth three times and Ch'ing Ming came forth and across his horse hung his wolf-toothed club, and he stood opposite the place where the banners of the enemy were parted. The vanguard Han T'ao held his weapon across his saddle and reined in his horse and he cursed Ch'ing Ming mightily and he said, "The soldiers of Heaven are come, and how is it you have not long ago taken refuge! Yet you dare to oppose yourself to me! Is it not to seek your own death? Now will I fill up this watery waste of yours, and I will break to pieces your mountain lair, and I will not kill you, but I will seize you alive and take you to the capital as a robber, and I will cut you into ten thousand pieces!"

Now Ch'ing Ming had always been a man of impatient temper, and yet when he heard this he answered nothing. He beat his horse and lifting high his wolf-toothed club he charged against Han T'ao. Then Han T'ao lifted his own weapon and he gave rein to his horse, and he came forward to withstand Ch'ing Ming. The two fought more than twenty rounds. Now Han T'ao was insufficient in strength and he turned to go but behind him came Hu Yien Shu, leading his soldiers, and he thought to himself, and seeing that Han T'ao could not withstand Ch'ing Ming, he took out his double clubs from among the soldiers and riding that imperial jade-like horse, black as ink and with snowy feet, he charged forth, the horse neighing and he shouting as they came. Ch'ing Ming saw them and he was about to rush forward to do battle when the second in rank, The Leopard Headed Ling Ch'ung said, "Pray stay, my Comrade, and watch me fight three hundred rounds, and then we will know what is the outcome!"

Then Ling Ch'ung lifted high his snake-like weapon and he hastened against Hu Yien Shu and Ch'ing Ming rode his own horse from the left and he went to the rear. Now did Hu Yien Shu himself withstand Ling Ch'ung, and the two were in truth perfectly matched and it was as fair a sight as many flowers, for the club struck forth and the spear came back swiftly and like a pattern made upon silk, and the two fought more than fifty rounds and it could not be told who was victor and who vanquished.

Then the third in rank, Hua Yung, cried out in a loud voice from where the ranks were divided, "Rest a little, my Comrade Ling, and see what I can do!"

Then Ling Ch'ung turned aside his horse to go and Han T'ao seeing that Ling Ch'ung had not the wish to fight further, also returned to the ranks, and Ling Ch'ung led forth his men and he went around to the rear and he allowed Hua Yung to come out on his horse. Then out of Hu Yien Shu's ranks came forth The Eye Of Heaven P'eng Ch'i and he held across the saddle that weapon of his, the three-pronged, two-bladed, four-holed, eight-rattled spear, and he rode his horse of five brightnesses that could travel more than three thousand miles between dawn and dark, and it was mottled with yellow. So P'eng Ch'i came forth from the ranks and he cursed mightily, saying, "You rebel against the Emperor and you robber! How without virtue are you! Let the two of us compete and see who is victor and who vanquished!"

At this Hua Yung was mightily wroth, yet neither did he answer a word. He did but begin to fight against P'eng Ch'i from his horse, and the two fought more than twenty rounds. Then Hu Yien Shu, seeing that P'eng Chi had not strength enough to withstand his enemy, let free his horse and himself he went to withstand Hua Yung. When they had not fought three rounds, The Ten Foot Green Snake cried from her horse loudly, "Comrade Hua, rest awhile and see what I can do!"

Then Hua Yung also led his men to the rear and thus went away. Then P'eng Ch'i came again to withstand The Ten Foot Green Snake. Then Sheng Li, the fifth chief, came forward and he reined in his horse and stood there and he watched The Ten Foot Green Snake in combat with P'eng Ch'i and the two fought until the dust rose like a fog and obscured all, but they fought on in the cloud. One used a long-handled sword; the other used double knives, and the two fought more than twenty rounds. Then The Ten Foot Green Snake parted her two knives and she turned her horse and went away.

Now P'eng Ch'i, thinking to gain a little glory for himself, gave his horse rein in pursuit. The Ten Foot Green Snake now had hung her two knives upon the horse's saddle and she reached in her garments and fetched out a red-wrapped bundle, and within it was a chain and lock. Upon the chain were twenty-four metal hooks. She waited until P'eng Ch'i had come near on his horse. Then she turned herself on her horse and she threw out the lock on the end of the chain. It could be seen P'eng Ch'i was unprepared for the attack and the hooks fastened themselves in his garments and dragged him down from his horse. Then Sheng Li watching from his horse shouted out, "Let all the fighting men come forward together!" and so they seized P'eng Ch'i.

Now Hu Yien Shu, seeing this, was mightily wroth and he ran forward with all his strength to save P'eng Ch'i. The Ten Foot Green Snake turned her horse to come and meet him, and Hu Yien Shu hated The Ten Foot Green Snake so that he would fain have swallowed her down like a sip of water. The two fought together more than ten rounds, but with all his agitation to win, Hu Yien Shu could not conquer The Ten Foot Green Snake. Then he thought in his heart, "This good-for-naught woman is in my hand and I have fought many rounds with her, and what cursed way shall I use with her!"

His heart was full of impatience and he tried guile to lead her forward. He struck down his two clubs. Now The Ten Foot Green Snake's double knives were thrust into her bosom. Then Hu Yien Shu took up the club in his right hand and was about to bring it down upon her skull. But The Ten Foot Green Snake's eye was clear and her hand swift, and she had already put up her knife to fend it off. Then the knife in her right hand flew up, and when the blow came down it struck the blade of her knife with a ringing sound so that the light flashed from it.

Then The Ten Foot Green Snake turned her horse and went back to her own company. Now Hu Yien Shu let free his horse and galloped in pursuit, but Sheng Li saw this and he lifted his weapon and freed his horse also and he came forward to kill, shouting as he came. Behind him came Sung Chiang in the nick of time leading two ranks of good fellows and they stood in order and The Ten Foot Green Snake leading her horsemen went toward the back of the mountain. Sung Chiang when he saw that P'eng Ch'i had been taken alive was truly rejoiced in heart and he came into the front of the ranks to watch Sheng Li and Hu Yien Shu do combat. Sheng Li lifted in his hand that club notched like a bamboo and he came forward to meet Hu Yien Shu. And the two fought with the same sort of weapons and they were matched in skill and strength.

Now Sheng Li wore a helmet of crossed metal bands and there was cloth in the back, and he wore tied about it a scarlet silk cloth, and he wore a black robe embroidered in many-hued flowers, and he wore a metal armor that gleamed like gold. He rode a black horse and he used a club notched like bamboo and marked with tigers' eyes. Truly was he like Yu Chih Lung, that warrior famed of old. Hu Yien Shu wore a helmet that pointed toward heaven, and he wore wrapped about it a kerchief of gold silk, and he wore a black robe spotted with seven stars, and he wore armor painted black, and he rode the horse the Emperor had given him, which was black as ink and his feet snowy. He used two iron clubs, octagonal in diameter, and gleaming as bright as water in the sun. The one in the left hand weighed twelve catties, and the one in the right hand weighed thirteen catties. Truly was he like his ancestor the warrior of old.

The two of them fought there in front of the ranks whirling to the left, wheeling to the right, and they fought for more than thirty rounds and it could not be told which was victor and which was vanquished. Then the captain of the state soldiery, Han T'ao, hearing that P'eng Ch'i had been captured, went back into the ranks and he found all such horsemen as were there and led them all out and all the foot soldiers also and they all rushed out together to kill.

Then Sung Chiang, fearing they might make a charge, pointed with his whip and he led out the ten chieftains and he led them all out great and small and they charged and the four ranks of fighting men behind divided into two and marched up on the sides to meet at the front. Hu Yien Shu, seeing this, in great haste gathered together all his own men and horsemen and each man attacked and withstood his attacker.

And why was the victory not complete? Because in truth the horsemen in Hu Yien Shu's ranks were close upon each other. Every horse was clothed in armor and every man also, and naught could be seen of any horse save his four feet, and as for the man, naught could be seen of any man save his two eyes. But in Sung Chiang's ranks who wore any armor? None had aught save a shield of metal in front of him and ringing brass bells and pheasant's feathers. When the robbers let fly their arrows the arrows did but glance off the armor of the enemy. The horsemen of the enemy all had bows and arrows, and because of this the robbers did not dare to go near them. In mighty impatience Sung Chiang cried out, "Beat the gongs and call in the men!"

Then did Hu Yien Shu also retreat some five or six miles and encamp there.

Now when Sung Chiang called back his men he encamped to the west of the mountain, and the horses and men were put into order. Then he commanded the men who stood to the right and the left of him with their swords drawn, that P'eng Ch'i should be brought before him. And Sung Chiang looked at P'eng Ch'i to see what he was, and he rose and bade the fighting men to stand back, and he went forward himself and unbound P'eng Ch'i's ropes and led him into the tent. The two then sat down according to rank, and then Sung Chiang made obeisance. In great haste P'eng Ch'i returned the obeisance, saying, "This lowly one has been taken captive by your men and therefore I merit death, and why should you, Sir Warrior, make obeisance to me?"

Sung Chiang replied, "Such men as we have nowhere to rest our bodies. Now we are in that watery waste, and we are but escaping sorrow for the time, and the Emperor sends out his soldiers to seize us and according to law I should put forth my neck to be captured. But I fear lest death await me thereafter, and for this reason, though it be a crime, yet do I fight on. Wrong as I am, I dare to hope for your forgiveness."

Then P'eng Ch'i said, "Long have I known you were a righteous man and one who loved good deeds and to help those who are in need, but I did not know you were so righteous as this. If you do forgive me this useless life of mine, then ought I take this body of mine and with it serve you only."

Then on that very day did Sung Chiang appoint men to escort P'eng Ch'i The Eye Of Heaven to the great mountain lair and he commanded that the great chief Ch'ao Kai should see him and that he should be left in the lair. Then did Sung Chiang reward the fighting men and all the chieftains and they all took counsel together of the war.

Let it be told further. Hu Yien Shu having withdrawn his men into camp then took counsel with Han T'ao as to how to enter the great robbers' lair. And Han T'ao said, "Today these robbers seeing us massed together to withstand them made haste to come forward and fight against us. Tomorrow we must gather together all our men, for surely we can have a great victory."

Hu Yien Shu said, "I have already prepared to do this, and I did but wish to talk with you to see that we agree."

Then did he straightway send out his command that the three thousand horsemen should stand all in one great line in companies of thirty each, and every company of thirty horses should be linked together with chains. When the enemy were seen to approach if they were at a distance arrows were to be used; if they came near then spears were to be used and the soldiers were to charge among them. Thus were the horsemen to be divided into one hundred companies. The five thousand foot soldiers were to stand at the rear for aid. And he said further to Han T'ao, "Tomorrow we will not say anything to incite them. You and I will stay at the rear and watch. If battle breaks out, we will divide into three parts and charge forward."

When he had thus spoken they took counsel together and the next day at dawn they went out to battle.

Let it be told now of Sung Chiang. The next day he divided his horsemen into five parts and put them at the fore. Behind were the ten chiefs and on both sides were the ambushed men. The first chief to fight was Ch'ing Ming and first he abused Hu Yien Shu and commanded him to come forth to do battle. Then was the sound of shouting heard among the enemy but none came forward to fight.

Now the five companies to the fore were all placed in a straight line at the front. In the middle was Ch'ing Ming, at the left were Ling Ch'ung and The Ten Foot Green Snake, at the right were Hua Yung and Sheng Li. Behind them was Sung Chiang leading ten captains. Thus were horsemen and men placed everywhere closely. When they looked opposite at the ranks of the enemy there were about one thousand foot soldiers and they were beating drums and shouting battle cries, but there was not one who rode his horse forward to do battle.

When Sung Chiang saw this he began to doubt in his heart and he sent forth a secret command, "Let those in the rear retreat." Then he turned his horse and galloped to where Hua Yung was and there he looked about.

Suddenly he heard the sound of rockets bursting from the enemy's ranks and one thousand foot soldiers divided into two parts, and from among them were seen to come three companies of horsemen, and they came charging forward. From both sides of the horsemen came arrows flying, but those in the center carried spears.

Sung Chiang, seeing all this, fell into a great terror, and in great haste he let his own men fly arrows also. But how could they withstand the enemy? Every linked thirty of the horses all charged forward together and they must go forward whether they would or not. The hills and plains were covered with these horses as they came straight ahead and from the sides also. As for the five divisions of Sung Chiang's horsemen, when they saw the enemy thus they scattered and fled, nor could Sung Chiang's commands stay them. The horsemen and soldiers behind them could not stay them, and each ran for his own life. In great haste Sung Chiang also turned his own horse and fled as though winged and the ten chieftains surrounded him and fled also.

But from the rear there had already come upon them a company of horsemen, and they were led by Li K'uei and Yang Ling and they came forward to save Sung Chiang. They escaped to the water's edge and there was Li Chün, Chang Heng, Chang Shun and the three Juans, and these three chieftains of the water brought the boats to the rescue. In greatest haste Sung Chiang went into the boat and he sent forth a command, saying, "The chieftains are to be sent to rescue the others and bring them to the boats!"

Then those chained horses could but gallop to the water's edge and there the horsemen sent scattering arrows out, but because of the wooden covers of the boats, they could not prevail. In great haste the boats were then turned to The Duck's Bill Beach and they all went ashore. There in the water lair the soldiers were told off and more than a half had returned from battle. Most joyful of all was it that not one of the chieftains was missing. Although some of their horses had been lost, not a life had been taken. In a short time Shih Yung was seen, and Shih Ch'ien, Sheng Sing and The Goodwife Ku, and they were all running for their lives to the mountain.

Let it be told now of the foot soldiers. They all came charging forward and they destroyed as they came all of the houses and inns. Even such as we, had we been there and none to save us, we also would all have been seized captive. As for Sung Chiang, he asked one after the other of their welfare and he told off the chiefs and found there were six men who were wounded, Ling Ch'ung, Lei Heng, Li K'uei, Shih Hsiu, Sheng Sing and Huang Hsin. But among the lesser robbers such as were wounded and struck with arrows were beyond number, and Ch'ao Kai heard of this, and he brought Wu Yung and Kung Sun Sheng and they came down the mountain to inquire of it.

Now were Sung Chiang's eyebrows knotted together and his face was full of melancholy, so that Wu Yung exhorted him, saying, "Elder Brother, do not grieve. In war sometimes there is victory and sometimes loss, and it does not matter, and why should you grieve? I have thought of a good plan whereby we can break through the enemy's ranks."

And Ch'ao Kai sent forth a command and he commanded the fighting men upon the waters, saying, "Let the barricades be ready and the boats held behind it and let the waters about be guarded and all be ready whether by day or in the depths of the night."

Then he invited Sung Chiang to go up the mountain to rest. But Sung Chiang was not willing to go up the mountain. He did but encamp himself there on The Duck's Bill Beach, and he would only bid the wounded captains to be taken up the mountain to care for their ills.

Let it be further told. Hu Yien Shu had thus a great victory, and he returned to his own camp and he loosed the horses that were chained together, and all came to claim rewards for what they had done. It was not known how many of the robbers had been killed, but more than five hundred had been captured alive, and of horses they had seized more than three hundred.

Immediately then did he send one to go to court and announce the victory and while this was being done he took count of his soldiers.

Let it be further told also that the Commander Kao was at that very time seated in audience when he heard it announced from the gates, "Hu Yien Shu has won the victory over the robbers of the robbers' lair and he sends one to announce it."

Then was his heart greatly rejoiced. On the next morning he went to the Emperor's palace, and in all haste he spoke even out of his place. Then was the Son Of Heaven truly made glad and he rewarded the Commander with wine in his own imperial jars, sealed with yellow imperial seals, and with a robe of silk. Moreover, he sent a messenger to the camp of Hu Yien Shu to take reward for the soldiers of ten thousand strings of cash.

Then the Commander Kao received the imperial mandate and he returned to his own palace and straightway he appointed an official to bear the imperial mandate thither.

Let it be told now of Hu Yien Shu when already he knew that the Emperor had appointed one to come to him. He and Han T'ao went more than six miles to meet the royal messenger and they received him into the camp, and they gave thanks for the imperial grace and received their reward and when this was over they prepared a feast. And Han T'ao divided the money and rewarded the soldiers, and he told of the more than five hundred robbers who were captive in the camp and how they were but waiting until they had seized the robber chief and then they would send them all to the court and there let them be punished.

Then the imperial messenger asked, "How is it I do not see P'eng Ch'i?"

Hu Yien Shu replied, "Because he was so zealous to capture Sung Chiang he charged straight into the heart of the enemy's ranks and so was he captured. But the robbers did not dare come again. This humble one therefore commanded our men to attack them so that the mountain lair might be laid waste and the watery places made clean, and all the robbers captured, and all their dens destroyed. But on all four sides the lair is surrounded with water and there is no way by which we may enter. We can but look at them from a distance, and there is no way by which we may set their houses afire except with our fireballs and so destroy the robbers. Now long have we heard that in the capital there is one skilled at fireballs and he is Ling Chen, and his nickname is Thunder That Shakes The Heavens. This man makes fireballs most skillfully, so that the fireball can strike some four miles away. When the stones inside drop down the heavens split and the earth sinks and the hills fall and rocks burst asunder. If we can but secure this man, then can we vanquish the robbers. He has moreover excelling skill at weapons, and in shooting arrows, and in riding horses he is very able. When the royal messenger returns to the capital pray speak on this matter with the Commander and let that one be sent hither with all speed, and so perhaps in a day or two we can vanquish the robbers."

The imperial messenger promised this, and on that day he departed and there is naught to tell of his journey back. He returned to the capital and there he saw the Commander Kao and he told him respectfully how Hu Yien Shu begged for the help of Ling Chen so that a great glory might be established. The Commander heard to the end and he sent forth a command saying, "Let the one in command of the armory, Ling Chen, be fetched hither."

Now this Ling Chen was of ancestors from Yien Ling and he was the most skilled in that time of Sung at the making of fireballs, and because of this men all called him Thunder That Shakes The Heavens. Moreover he was skilled also in arms. At this time, therefore, Ling Chen came before the Commander Kao and he received the credentials of a general in war. Then he prepared his goods and his horse and he set forth.

Let it be told further that Ling Chen took the materials he needed for the making of fireballs and all he had of fireballs made ready and he put them upon carts. He took also with him his usual garments, armor, helmet, sword, and his goods and thirty or forty soldiers. So he left the eastern capital and he followed the road toward the robber capital, and he came to the camp and he went first to greet Hu Yien Shu and then he saw Han T'ao. And he asked how far the water lair was away and what of the road thither, and what the dangers were of the way to the mountain lair. He prepared three kinds of fireballs. The first was called wind fireballs. The second were gold wheel fireballs. The third were mother and son fireballs. He led out his men first to make these ready and then they went to the brink of the lake to set their racks in order and prepared for the firing of the balls.

Let it be further told of Sung Chiang as he was in the lesser lair upon The Duck's Bill Beach. He took counsel with the counselor Wu Yung as to the ways of breaking through the enemy's ranks, but they could think of no way. Then did a spy come to make report, "There is one skilled in fireballs, and he is of the eastern capital, and he is called Ling Chen and nicknamed Thunder That Shakes The Heavens. Today he is upon the shores of the lake preparing his racks ready to send forth fireballs, and they are all making ready to attack the lair."

Then Wu Yung said, "This matters nothing. All about our lair on all four sides is water, and the winding water ways are many. Moreover, the city of Wan Chi in the lair is very far from the water, and even though there were fireballs from all directions, how could they reach to the region of the town? Let us leave to the enemy this lesser lair of Duck's Bill Beach. We will see then how their fireballs come, and then we will take further counsel together."

So Sung Chiang left the lesser lair, and they all went into the great lair. Then Ch'ao Kai and Kung Sun Sheng met them in the Hall Of Meeting, and they asked, "How shall we withstand such a warfare as this?"

Before they had finished asking they heard already the sound of fireballs below the mountain. Three fireballs were let off one after the other. Two fell into the water, and the other fell exactly into the lesser lair on Duck's Bill Beach. Sung Chiang, seeing it, felt sorrow and melancholy return to his heart, and all the chieftains changed color. Wu Yung said, "If there be one who could bring this Ling Chen to the water's edge and so first capture him, then we could take counsel together as to how to break the enemy's ranks."

Ch'ao Kai said, "Then let Li Chün, Chang Heng, Chang Shun, and the three Juans come hither, and let these six take boats and go forth to action thus—and thus—. Upon the shore let Chu T'ung, Lei Heng, aid them thus—and thus—"

Let it be further told. The six chieftains upon the water, having received the command of their great chieftain, divided into two parts. Li Chün and Chang Heng first took with them some forty or fifty men able upon the water and they took two swift boats and they went secretly out among the reeds. Behind them Chang Shun and the three Juans brought more than forty small boats to aid them. It is again said of Li Chün and Chang Heng. They came to the opposite shore and they went straight to the racks and pushed them over, shouting as they did so. Then the soldiers in great haste made report to Ling Chen.

Then Ling Chen took two wind-and-fire balls and taking his weapon he mounted his horse, and he led out over a thousand men and they went out to pursue. Li Chün and Chang Heng led their men and went away. Ling Chen led his men in pursuit to the shore and the reeds and there he saw more than forty small boats placed and upon the boats more than a hundred water fighting men.

Now Li Chün and Chang Heng had already leaped upon the boats and on purpose they did not set sail. When they saw the soldiers and horses come they set up a shout and they all leaped into the water and as soon as Ling Chen and his horses and men were come they went forward to seize the boats. Chu T'ung and Lei Heng came from the opposite shore and they began to shout and to beat drums and gongs and Ling Chen seized many of the boats and he commanded all his men to come upon the boats and so charge across.

When the boats were come into the center of the lake then were seen Chu T'ung and Lei Heng upon the bank and they began to beat the gongs yet more loudly. Then out of the water at once did forty or fifty men spring, and they seized the rudders of the boats and the water rushed into the boats so that they overturned and all the soldiers fell into the water. In great haste Ling Chen in his boat made to turn back but the rudder was gone and he was lost upon the waters. Then from both sides of the boats came forth two chiefs and they laid hold upon that boat and the boat rocked heavily and overturned, and Ling Chen fell into the lake.

Now beneath him was Juan The Second and he seized him and he dragged him to the opposite shore and there were already chieftains upon that shore to meet them and they took a rope and bound Ling Chen, and they took him to the mountain lair. In the waters some two hundred soldiers were captured alive but as many were drowned. There were only a few who escaped with their lives and ran away.

Now when Hu Yien Shu knew of it in greatest haste he led men and horses in pursuit. But the boats had already all gone over to the Duck's Bill Beach. When he saw no one to be found he could but bear his wrath as best he could. But although he pondered angrily for a long time, yet he could do naught but lead his men and horses back.

Let it be further told then that the chiefs thus captured alive Thunder That Shakes The Heavens Ling Chen, and they took him up to the mountain lair and they sent men first to make report. Now Sung Chiang and all the chieftains then went down to the second pass to meet them. When he saw Ling Chen thus bound about with ropes he began to reproach the robbers, saying, "I bade you bring him with all courtesy to the lair and how is it you have behaved with such discourtesy?"

Ling Chen made obeisance of thanks for such grace as this, that though taken captive he was not to be killed, and Sung Chiang poured out wine of welcome for him, and when this was over he himself took Ling Chen's hand and led him to the lair. When they went into the lair and Ling Chen saw P'eng Ch'i also made a chieftain, he closed his lips and said not a word. Then P'eng Ch'i exhorted him, saying, "These two great chiefs Ch'ao and Sung act righteously for Heaven and they seek for heroes and they hope for the day when the state will bid them return and labor for the country. If I wait here now, it is to fulfill their commands."

Then did Sung Chiang return these compliments and Ling Chen answered, "Though I stay here for ever it would not matter save that my old mother and my wife are all in the capital. If there happens to be one who learns of me then they will suffer for it, and then what will happen!"

Sung Chiang said, "Pray do but let your heart rest. In a few days we will go and bring them thither."

Then Ling Chen gave thanks, "If the great chief can do this, when I die my eyes can close."

And Ch'ao Kai commanded, "Let a feast of welcome be prepared."

That day in the feasting of the great chiefs in the Hall Of Meeting, in the midst of the feasting Sung Chiang took counsel with the other chiefs as to how they might destroy the ranks of the enemy. Truly there was no good way. But The Gold Spotted Leopard T'ang Lung rose and he said, "This humble one has no skill, but I could try a plan. Only we must take a certain sort of weapon—and with a certain elder brother of mine we can break the armor of the horsemen."

Then Wu Yung asked, saying, "Good And Learned Brother, what sort of weapon is it you would use? And who is this wise elder brother?"

Then without haste and without impatience T'ang Lung forked his fingers together and he came forward and he told the name of the weapon and the name of the man. Truly

> It was as though in The City Of Jade a fabulous beast were caught,
> It was as though in The City Of Gold a faëry lion were sought.

What then was this weapon and what the name of this man of which T'ang Lung spoke? Pray hear it told in the next chapter.

Chapter 55

WU YUNG SENDS SHIH CH'IEN TO STEAL ARMOR. T'ANG LUNG DECOYS CH'Ü LING TO THE MOUNTAIN LAIR

IT IS SAID: At that time T'ang Lung said to all the chieftains, "The very ancestors of this humble one made their living by fashioning weapons. Because my father had this skill before me he was made an official in the city of Yien An and at the beginning of the dynasty there was but one who could fight with chained and armored horses. If such armor is to be broken, a certain weapon must be used, and this weapon is called the hook-bladed spear. I have a picture of this left to me from my ancestors. If you would have me beat it out, I will put forth my hand to do it.

"Now I can fashion the weapon but I cannot wield it. If one is to be found to wield it, there is only my cousin who can wield this hook-bladed spear. There is only that one whose house has known how to wield it from the times of our ancestors, and they have taught no others. Whether upon horse-back or whether on foot he knows how to do it and if he wields this weapon then in truth even the very devils are in fear!"

Before he had finished speaking Ling Ch'ung asked, "Is it not that Ch'ü Ling who is in the imperial armory?"

And T'ang Lung answered, "It is that very man."

And Ling Ch'ung said, "If you had not spoken of it, I would have forgotten. Truly in the use of spear and hook spears there is none under Heaven to equal him. I have often met with him in the capital and we have competed together in arms and we liked each other very intimately and well. But how can we fetch him and bring him up the mountain?"

Again T'ang Lung spoke, saying, "Ch'ü Ling's ancestors left him one precious thing, and there is nothing to equal it on the earth, and it is the most precious thing in his house. When I was in my apprenticeship I went with my father many times to see his sister, my aunt, at the eastern capital and I saw it there. It was a suit of armor made of the quills of eagle feathers bound about with metal. When this suit of armor was put upon the body it was both light and strong and no blade and arrow could pierce it. Men all say it is like a certain fairy beast of old. Though there were even princes who begged to see it, he would never let it be seen in any sort of disorderly fashion. This suit of armor is his very life, and it is kept in a small leathern trunk and this hangs upon a beam in his room. If we can think of some way to fetch this suit of armor here, so will he surely come also."

Then Wu Yung said, "If it be thus, what is there hard to do? If we had but a man like this with such skill as this here— I must use Flea On A Drum Shih Ch'ien to go forth."

At once Shih Chi'en answered, saying, "I do but fear that thing is no longer there. If it be truly there then good or ill I will bring it hither."

But T'ang Lung said, "If you do but bring the armor here, I swear I have a way to get him up the mountain."

Then Sung Chiang asked, saying, "And how will you decoy him up the mountain?"

T'ang Lung went to Sung Chiang and spoke a few words into his ears in a whisper and Sung Chiang laughed and cried, "How good and tricky a plan is this!"

Wu Yung said, "Let us take three men again and go together to the eastern capital. Let one go thither to buy the fire powder and the materials for making the fireballs and all that is in them, and let two go and find and bring here Ling Chen's household."

Now when P'eng Ch'i heard this he rose and said, "If there are those who go into the soldiers' camp to find my brother's household and bring them here, the whole city will know of it!"

Then Sung Chiang replied, "Let your heart rest. Pray do you two write letters and I will myself send them thither." And he called Yang Ling and said, "Take silver and gold and the two letters and take with you some of your comrades, and first go to the city of Ying and bring out the household of P'eng Ch'i. Let Shih Yung go also and buy such materials and powder as are needed for the fireballs, and then go to the eastern capital and bring out the household of Ling Chen. Li Yün shall be disguised as a merchant and he is to go with you all to the eastern capital to buy the stuffs for the fireballs and Yo Ho and T'ang Lung shall go with you. Shih Yung shall go and come with you, also."

But first they escorted Shih Ch'ien down the mountain. Then Sung Chiang bade T'ang Lung beat out the likeness of a hooked-bladed spear and Lei Heng was bade to oversee the matter.

Let it be said now that T'ang Lung made the hook-bladed spear and the ironsmiths in the mountain lair who fashioned weapons were commanded to make others like them, and Lei Heng saw to the matter, and no more need be told of it.

Then was a feast made in the great lair to speed those who went away and there were Yang Ling, Shih Yung, Li Yün, Yo Ho and T'ang Lung, and they took their farewell of the others and went down the mountain. The next day Tai Chung was sent down the mountain to spy out the land. It is hard to finish telling of all this in a few words, but it may be further told here that Shih Ch'ien left the region of the lair, and he carried with him hidden weapons and all that he needed to use and he went his way to the eastern capital and he found an inn and rested there. The next day he went into the inn, and he asked about among the city for the house of his teacher Ch'ü Ling. There were those who pointed it out to him, saying, "It is there inside the soldiers' quarters and it is the fifth house to the east and the gate is set in a black frame.—It is that one."

So Shih Ch'ien went into the gate of the soldiers' quarters and he first looked at the front gate and he turned aside into the alleys and found the back gate. There he saw a high wall, and inside that wall he saw two beautiful little storeyed houses. Beside them was a wooden pillar studded with gold. Shih Ch'ien looked for a while, and then he went back into the street and asked at the gate, "Is the teacher Ch'ü at home?"

The gateman answered him, "He does not come home until nightfall, for at early dawn he goes into the Emperor's palace to work."

Then Shih Ch'ien asked pardon for troubling him and he returned to his inn. He took out such things as he might need and put them about his person and he told the waiting man in the inn, saying, "It is more than half probable that I shall not return this night. I pray you to have an eye to the things in my room."

The man replied, "Do you but rest your heart and go on. This city is the city where the Emperor lives and there are no evil men here."

Then Shih Ch'ien went out and he bought himself some supper and ate it, and he went to the soldiers' quarters and to the right and to the left of Ch'ü Ling's home. But there was no good place where he might stay. But at last, seeing that the sky darkened with night, he went secretly into the soldiers' quarters. Now this night was in the time of the great dry cold of winter and there was no moon. Shih Ch'ien looked about and he saw beside a small temple to the god of wealth a great white pine tree. He put his two legs together and bit by bit he climbed up into the top of the tree, and he sat astride a branch as though upon a horse and without making a sound he looked beneath him.

Even as he watched he saw Ch'ü Ling return and go into his house. After this he saw two men come forth bearing lanterns and they locked the great gates of the barracks, and then each returned to his own house. Then he heard the sound of the drum and the gong beating out the first watch of the night. The clouds were chill and the stars were without lustre and slowly the dew turned to flowers of white frost. The great courts of the barracks were silent and soundless in the night.

Then did Shih Ch'ien come down out of that tree and he went to the back gate of Ch'ü Ling's house and he went to the wall, and with the least effort he climbed over it. When he looked about him inside, he saw a small yard. Then he went to the kitchen and stared into it. He saw a light within, and he saw there two slaves silently putting the room to rights. Then Shih Ch'ien came from around the pillar to the screen placed to keep winds away, and there he crouched. As he stared up at the house, he saw Ch'ü Ling and his lady sitting in their bedroom on either side of a brazier of coals warming themselves, and the lady held in her arms a child of six or seven years of age. Now as Shih Ch'ien looked into the bedroom he saw on the beams above a large leathern box tied and by the door of the room was hung a bow and bag of arrows, and a sword. Upon the clothes rack were hung garments of many hues. Ch'ü Ling called out to a slave, "Fragrance Of Peach Blossom, come hither and fold these garments for me!"

Then did a slave come from without and she went to a table and there she stood and folded a purple embroidered garment and she folded also a dark green and lined outer robe, and she folded also a pair of five-hued embroidered parted skirts and a flowery and colored head kerchief and a tie of stripes and green and beyond this a handkerchief. Besides this was a small kerchief in which was tied a girdle made of two strips of sealskin red in hue and set about with gold. All these she put in a bundle, and she placed it upon the rack near the fire.

All this Shih Ch'ien saw very well. About the second watch of the night Ch'ü Ling prepared himself and went to bed. His lady asked, "Do you go tomorrow to your duty?"

Ch'ü Ling replied, "Tomorrow the Son Of Heaven honors with his presence The Palace Of The Dragon. It is necessary to rise early at the fifth watch to go and wait upon him."

The lady heard this and she commanded her slave, saying, "My lord must rise tomorrow at the fifth watch to take up his duty. You must all rise at the fourth watch and prepare tea and sweetmeats."

Now Shih Ch'ien pondered to himself, "I can see very well that in the box there on the beams the armor must be placed. It will be well if I put forth my hand for it in the middle of the night, yet if I should make a noise and rouse them, I shall not get out of the city tomorrow, and would this not spoil a great matter? If I wait until the fifth watch it will not be too late."

He listened therefore and he heard Ch'ü Ling and his lady mount their bed and go to sleep. The two slaves spread their bedding outside the door. In the room a night lamp was lit upon the table. Then did the five persons all sleep. As for the two slaves, they had served all day and they were very weary at night and full of sleep, and they snored loudly. Shih Ch'ien came forward slowly and he felt in his person and brought forth a hollow reed and he thrust it through a hole in the window and blew out the light. When he saw it was about the time of the fourth watch Ch'ü Ling arose and he called to the slaves to come and prepare tea.

And the two serving maids rose up out of their dreams of their sleep. When they saw the lamp was out in the room they cried out, "Ai-yah! The lamp went out tonight!"

Then Ch'ü Ling shouted, "And if you do not go to the back and find a lamp, how long am I to wait?"

So the two maids opened the door and the stairs creaked as they came down. Now Shih Ch'ien heard this, and he passed quickly into the shadows of the trees and the pillar and he came into the darkness of the shadows of the back door. When he heard the slaves were about to open the back door and come out to open the gate of the wall, he went and hid in the kitchen, and he hid beneath the table there. One slave found a lighted spill and she brought it back and they closed the gate again and they came to the stove to light the fire. The other slave then went upstairs to light the fire of coals. In a short time the water boiled and she fetched a basin of it for her master to wash himself.

Ch'ü Ling washed his face and rinsed his mouth and he called out, "Heat some wine and bring it upstairs to me!"

So the slaves prepared meats and cakes and took them up also and after Ch'ü Ling had eaten he called, "Give my aide also to eat!"

Then Shih Ch'ien heard Ch'ü Ling come downstairs and call to his aide to come and eat and the aide took up the bundle and metal arms and he went to the gate, and the two slaves lit a lantern and escorted Ch'ü Ling outside the gate. Now did Shih Ch'ien come out from underneath the kitchen table, and he went upstairs and he climbed up by the corner of the window to the beam of the roof and there he lay upon the beam.

The two slaves again closed the gate and they blew out the lantern and they came up the stairs and took off their garments and once more they lay down to sleep. Shih Ch'ien, hearing the two again sleeping, once more put forth his reed and blew out the lamp. Then softly from where he was on that beam he untied the leathern box. Even as he was about to come down the lady awoke and she heard a sound and she called to a slave, "What is that noise up on the beam?"

Then Shih Ch'ien made a sound as though he were a rat and the slave answered, "Lady, do you not hear it is a rat squeaking? It is because the rats are fighting that there is such a noise."

Then Shih Ch'ien made a noise as though rats were indeed fighting and silently he came down off the beam and noiselessly he opened the door and taking up the box on his back he went slowly down the stairs straight outside, and so he came to the gate of the military quarters. There the watchman had already opened the gate at the time of the fourth watch and Shih Ch'ien with the leathern box on his back took opportunity of the crowd passing through and in a breath he was outside the city.

He came to the door of his inn, and it was but barely dawn. He knocked upon that door and he went into his own room and took his bundle and he found a rope and tied the bundle and box into one load on a pole across his shoulders. Then he paid what he owed for his room and he left the inn and turned toward the east, and he went some thirteen miles before he stopped at an inn. Then he went in and lighted a fire and prepared himself food to eat.

Suddenly he saw a man come hastening forward. Now when Shih Ch'ien looked he saw it was none other than The Magic Messenger Tai Chung. When Tai Chung saw that Shih Ch'ien already had the box they spoke together a few words softly and Tai Chung said, "I will take the armor first to the mountain lair and do you come slowly with T'ang Lung."

Then Shih Ch'ien opened the leathern box and he brought out that suit of armor made of eagle feathers linked with gold, and he put it in a bundle and Tai Chung tied it upon his person. When they were come out of the inn gate, he used his magic and went straight toward the robbers' lair. Then did Shih Ch'ien take the empty leathern box and he tied it openly upon his pole. After he had eaten and had paid for the fire he had made he took up his load and leaving the inn he went his way. When he had gone nearly seven miles he came upon T'ang Lung and the two went to a wine shop to take counsel together and T'ang Lung said, "Do you but come after me by this road. Whenever upon our way we pass by inns or wine shops if you see upon the gate a circle marked in white, why, then may you stay to buy meat and wine to eat, and only there may you rest. And you are purposely to put this leathern box where it may be seen. Then you are to go ten miles away and wait for me."

Then did Shih Ch'ien do as he was bid and T'ang Lung drank his wine slowly for a while and then he turned toward the eastern capital.

Let it be told now of Ch'ü Ling's house. At dawn the two slaves rose and they went upstairs and told the lady their mistress, saying, "We do not know how it is the doors are all open, but we do not see anything gone."

The lady then replied, "In the fifth watch I heard a noise on that beam but you said it was rats fighting. Do you then look to see that the leathern box is safe."

Then when the two slaves looked they could but cry bitterness, for they did not know where the leathern box was gone. The lady, hearing this, rose in greatest haste and she said, "Quickly send one to the imperial palace and tell my lord! Bid him to come with all speed and help us search."

Then in greatest agitation the slaves sent one to the palace and they sent one messenger after the other, but they all returned, saying, "The lord and all his peers have gone with the Emperor to his other palace, and about that palace stand imperial soldiers on guard and who can enter in? We can but wait until he of his own will returns."

Then were Ch'ü Ling's lady and the two slaves like ants caught upon a hot cauldron, and they ran hither and thither. They could not sup tea nor eat food, and at last they huddled together in terror waiting.

Now only when the twilight came did Ch'ü Ling take off his robe of office and he gave it to his aide to carry and taking up his metal weapon he went slowly home. When he came to the gate of the military quarter the neighbors said, "Your lady has suffered from thieves and she has been waiting for you to come and look into the matter, but you did not return."

Ch'ü Ling gave a start of fear and he hastened to his home and the two slaves met him at the gate and they said, "When our lord went out at the fifth watch a thief crept in and he took nothing but that leathern box tied upon the beam."

When Ch'ü Ling heard this he could but cry continually in bitterness, and his anger rose out of the depths of his belly to his lips. His lady said, "Truly I do not know when this thief could have come into the house."

Ch'ü Ling replied, "Nothing else would have mattered much except this one suit of eagle feather armor, which was left to me by four generations of my ancestors, and never was it lost before! There was one commander Wang who offered me three thousand strings of cash for it and I would not sell it. I feared lest I might need it sometime in a war, and lest something befall it I hung it high on that beam. Many a man has wanted only to see it and I have refused, saying I had it no more. Now when it is known that it is gone, everyone will laugh at me. Now that it is lost, what shall I do?"

And Ch'ü Ling could not sleep the livelong night and he thought to himself, "I do not know who it was who took it. It must be one who knew I had such a thing."

And the lady said, "I am sure it was at that time when the lamp went out that the thief came in and hid in the house. It must be that there is one who loved that thing of yours and since he could not buy it he hired a skillful thief to come and steal it. Seek someone then to search out the matter slowly and we will think of some way. But do not beat up the grass and frighten the snake away."

Now Ch'ü Ling heard this and at dawn he arose and he sat in his house and nursed his melancholy. At the time of the morning meal he heard someone knocking at the gate. Then his aide went out to ask for that one's name and he returned to make report, saying, "There is one at the gate from Yien An Fu and the court there, and he is the son of an official T'ang and his name is T'ang Lung and he comes to call upon you."

Ch'ü Ling heard this and he commanded that the guest should be brought within to see him. And T'ang Lung saw Ch'ü Ling and he bent his head in obeisance, and he said, "Elder Brother, have you been at peace here since we met last?"

Ch'ü Ling answered, saying, "I have heard that my uncle has returned to Heaven. As for me, I am bound as though a rope bound me by the cares of my officialdom, and your home is distant from mine and I could not go ever to ask after you. I do not know now what your occupation is nor where you live, nor whence you come at this moment."

And T'ang Lung said, "It cannot all be told in a word. Since my father died my fate has been evil as the times are evil, and I have wandered far and wide by river and lake. But now do I come straight from Shantung to inquire after my elder brother."

Ch'ü Ling replied, "Sit yourself down for a little while." And he commanded that meats and wines should be brought to welcome the guest. Then did T'ang Lung reach into his bundle and he brought out two strips of gold pieces shaped like leek leaves, and they weighed some twenty ounces and these he presented to Ch'ü Ling and he said, "My father when he was about to die left me these things and he said I was to give them to you, my Elder Brother, for a remembrance, but because I had no one whose heart and belly I knew and could trust, I could not bring them sooner. But this time I have come especially to bring them to you myself."

Then Ch'ü Ling said, "Deeply do I thank my uncle that he was thus thoughtful of me. But I have not performed a particle of filial duty toward him and how can I repay him?"

T'ang Lung replied, "Elder Brother, do not speak thus, for when my father was alive he thought much of your skill in arms. He did but hate it that the mountains were high and the waters wide so that we were not able often to see your face. Therefore did he leave this gold as a remembrance to you, my Elder Brother."

Then Ch'ü Ling gave thanks to T'ang Lung and he received the gold, and wine was prepared for T'ang Lung's entertainment. Nevertheless even in the midst of their wine drinking Ch'ü Ling's eyebrows were still knotted and he was still sorrowful. Then did T'ang Lung rise and ask, saying, "Elder Brother, why do you frown as though you were unhappy? It must be there is in your heart some sorrow that you cannot drive away."

Ch'ü Ling drew a sigh and replied, "Brother, you do not know, and it is hard to tell it in a word. There came a thief into my house in the night."

T'ang Lung said, "I do not know how much you have lost."

Ch'ü Ling said, "He took only one thing and it was that one thing left me by my ancestors, the eagle-feathered coat of armor, and it is named also like a faëry beast of old. Last night I lost this one thing and for this reason is my heart so sad."

And T'ang Lung said, "Elder Brother, I also have seen that coat of armor, and true it is that there was none other to compare to it. My father could never be done with praising it. But where did you keep it that a thief could steal it away?"

Ch'ü Ling replied, "I put it into a leathern box, and I bound it upon a beam in my sleeping room and truly I do not know when the thief entered and robbed me of it."

Again T'ang Lung asked, saying, "And what kind of a leathern box was it that held it?"

Ch'ü Ling answered, "It was a box of sheepskin painted red that held it and inside there was wrapped about it scented cotton wool."

Then T'ang Lung gave a start and he said, "A red sheepskin box? I have heard of it. Were there not cloud heads and trailing clouds embroidered upon it in white threads? And was there not in the center a lion holding a ball?"

Ch'ü Ling cried, "Brother, where have you seen it?"

Then T'ang Lung made answer, "Last night when I was ten or eleven miles from the city I entered a village wine shop to find some wine to drink and I saw a man with shining eyes and a thin dark face and upon his carrying pole I saw it. When I saw it I wondered to myself what it was and I asked myself what it could be that this leathern box held. When I left the inn I asked, 'Of what use is this leathern box of yours?' That fellow answered, 'It used to hold a coat of armor but now it has nothing but a few clothes.' It must be this very man! And I saw that the man had his leg lamed and he limped away step by step. Why should we not go therefore and pursue him?"

Ch'ü Ling said, "If we can catch him then surely it is Heaven itself that has sent me the chance!"

And T'ang Lung said, "If it is thus, then should we waste no time. Let us go and pursue him, therefore."

So Ch'ü Ling heard this and in great impatience he changed to his hempen boots and he took up his girdle knife and he took his sword and he went with T'ang Lung and the two of them went out by The Gate Of The Eastern Outer Court and they let out their strides and went with all speed in pursuit. Now as they went they saw ahead the gate of a wine shop which had upon it a circle marked in white and T'ang Lung said, "Let us stop here to drink a bowl of wine and ask at the same time about this man." So T'ang Lung went into the door and he sat down and he asked, "Sir Wine Shop Keeper, I would ask something of you. Was there not a bright-eyed, dark, lean fellow who came this way carrying a red leathern box?"

The keeper of the shop replied, "Last night there was such a fellow as this and he did carry a box made of red sheepskin. He had suffered a fall and hurt his leg and he limped along step by step as he went."

Then T'ang Lung said, "Elder Brother, you hear how it is!" And Ch'ü Ling listened but he could speak not a word. In all haste therefore did the two pay for their wine and they went out of the door of the wine shop. Ahead of them again they saw an inn and upon the frame of the door there was a circle of white, and again T'ang Lung stayed his feet and he said, "Elder Brother, I can walk no further. Let us, therefore, stop in this inn and tomorrow go on our way again."

But Ch'ü Ling answered, "I am an official, and if when they call the names I am not there then the court will reproach me on my return and what will come of it?"

T'ang Lung said, "But you need not trouble your heart over this—surely your lady will think of an excuse!"

That night they asked again in the inn and the serving man there answered, saying, "Yesterday night there was such a lean, dark fellow carrying a load and he did rest the night through in our inn. And he slept until this morning at dawn and then he went away asking the road to Shantung."

And T'ang Lung said, "Then indeed may we catch him."

Then did the two lay themselves down to rest for the night. The next day they rose at the fourth watch and they left the inn and again they wound along the road in pursuit. Wherever T'ang Lung saw a white circle upon a door frame there he stopped to buy wine and food and ask of the way, and at each place he said the same thing, and though Ch'ü Ling's heart grew impatient to return home, yet he could only go on with T'ang Lung in pursuit. At last seeing the sky darkening with night they looked and saw an old temple ahead of them. Under the trees of the temple sat Shih Ch'ien, and he had put down his load and sat there. T'ang Lung, seeing him, cried out, "Ha, it is well! Is not that Elder Brother's box there under the trees ahead, which once held the coat of armor?"

And Ch'ü Ling saw it and he rushed forward and with one grasp he seized Shih Ch'ien and he shouted out, "How great is your boldness that you dared to take away my armor!"

Shih Ch'ien said, "Stay—stay—do not cry out! Even though I have taken your armor now, what can you do about it?"

Ch'ü Ling shouted, "You mannerless beast, to ask what I will do about it!"

But Shih Ch'ien said, "Pray look and see in the box if there be any armor there."

Then did Ch'ü Ling open the box and look within but it was empty and he asked, "Where have you taken my suit of armor now?"

Shih Ch'ien replied, "Hear what I have to say. This humble one is surnamed Chang and I am the first in my family, and I am a man of the city of T'ai An. Now there is a rich man in that city and he seeks for the favor of one above him and he knew that you had in your house this suit of eagle-feathered, gold-mailed armor, and that you would not sell it. He sent me, therefore, and another man named Li The Third to go to your house and rob you of it, and he promised us ten thousand strings of cash for it. But I did not think I would fall down from that beam in your house and wrench my leg so that I could not walk. Therefore I told Li The Third to take the armor ahead and leave but the empty box here. Even though you want the armor, what has it to do with me? Even though you take me before a magistrate and have me beaten to death, I care naught! I will not say it was I who took it! But if you will forgive me, then I will go with you and fetch it again for you."

Now Chü Ling knit his brows and pondered for a long time but he could not decide what to do. At last T'ang Lung said, "Elder Brother, do not fear he will fly away. Do you but go with him and seek for the armor. If there be no armor, then you can go to the magistrate and ask for justice."

And Ch'ü Ling said, "You have spoken well, my Brother," and the three men went quickly to an inn and there rested.

Now Ch'ü Ling and T'ang Lung, guarding Shih Ch'ien between them, prepared to sleep. But Shih Ch'ien's leg was not really wrenched; he had only taken strips of cloth and bound them about his leg as though he were lamed. Ch'ü Ling, seeing he was lamed, did leave him half freed, thinking he could not escape, and so the three lay down together. The next morning they rose early to go on their way. All along the road Shih Ch'ien bought wine and meat and gave it to the other two. And again they went on for another day.

On that day along the road Ch'ü Ling felt a great impatience in his heart and he could but question and wonder whether his armor was still whole or not. Thus they went until they came to a place where ahead of them the road divided into three parts and there were two empty carts there. Behind them was a man who drove the carts and beside them a traveler. Now when this traveler saw T'ang Lung he bowed his head and made obeisance and T'ang Lung asked him, saying, "Brother, why have you come hither?"

That man answered, saying, "I have been doing my business in Chen Chou and I am about to return to T'ai An."

Then T'ang Lung said, "Naught could be better. We three have been looking for carts that we also might go to T'ai An."

That man said, "Do not speak of only three—even were there more still the carts would not be crowded."

Then T'ang Lung was greatly pleased and he brought Ch'ü Ling forward and told who he was, and Ch'ü Ling asked, saying, "Who is this man?"

T'ang Lung answered, saying, "Last year when I was in T'ai An and burned incense I came to know this brother. His surname is Li and his name is Yung and he is a righteous good man."

Ch'ü Ling said, "If it is thus—and this Chang The First cannot walk, therefore let us all mount into the carts. Bid the man drive the carts on."

Then did the four seat themselves in the carts and Ch'ü Ling asked, saying, "Chang The First, tell me what is the surname and the name of that rich man."

Now Shih Ch'ien refused him some three times and only at last he said, "He is a very famous lord surnamed Kuo."

Then Ch'ü Ling asked Li Yung, saying, "Has there ever been a great lord surnamed Kuo in that T'ai An of yours?"

Li Yung answered, saying, "That lord Kuo of my city is a rich man of the very first rank, and he likes best of all to be friends with imperial governors and he supports many idle persons in his house."

When Ch'ü Ling heard this he thought in his heart, "If there indeed be such a man as this, then nothing matters."

And he listened to Li Yung talk of fashions of wielding weapons and he heard him sing some songs, and thus unnoticed yet another day passed by.

They were now but about twelve miles away from the robbers' lair, and Li Yung was seen to stay the driver and bid him take a gourd and go and fetch wine and meat so they might eat and drink there in the cart. And Li Yung then reached into his garments and brought out a gourd and he poured out wine for Ch'ü Ling to drink first. Ch'ü Ling drank it down in a draught. Again Li Yung sent the man to fetch wine and again would he have given it to Ch'ü Ling to drink, but the driver's hand slipped and unwittingly the wine was all spilled upon the ground. Li Yung shouted out, "Go and fetch more wine!"

But suddenly Ch'ü Ling was seen to fall over in the cart, white froth dripping from his lips. Now who was this Li Yung? He was none other than Yo Ho, The Iron Whistle. The other three men then leaped down from the cart and they followed after the carts and came to the wine shop of Chu Kuei, and they carried Ch'ü Ling and placed him upon a boat and they all went to The Golden Sands and came ashore.

Now there had already been report made to Sung Chiang of this affair, and all the chieftains came down the mountain to meet them. And Ch'ü Ling began to awake out of his drugged sleep, and even as the others were about to use medicine to wake him, Ch'ü Ling opened his eyes and he saw all the crowd and he gave a start of fear and he asked T'ang Lung, saying, "Brother, why have you brought me hither?"

T'ang Lung replied, "Elder Brother, hear me speak. I hear now that the great chief Sung Chiang seeks goodly brave men from all parts, and so I came thither to seek my brother The Black Whirlwind Li K'uei so that I might go to the great lair and join them. But now are we attacked by the armored horses and men of Hu Yien Shu and we have no way to withstand them, and I bethought myself of the hook-bladed spear and how there is only you, my Elder Brother, who knows how to use it. Therefore did I make this plot that Shih Ch'ien should go first and steal your armor, and then I was to lead you hither. This man who pretended to be Li Yung put a drug in your wine. Pray, my Elder Brother, come up the mountain, too, and seat yourself in the chair of a chieftain!"

But Ch'ü Ling said, "If my brother has injured me thus—"

Then Sung Chiang came forward to make apology and he said, "I am but held for a time in this lair awaiting the command of the Emperor to come forth for forgiveness, and I long to use my strength for the state and I have no lust after robbing treasure and killing men, nor to do unrighteous and unforgiving deeds. Ten thousand times, therefore, do I hope that you, a noble official, will join me here."

And Ling Ch'ung came forward also bearing a wine cup to make apology, and he said, "This younger brother is here also, and I pray you not to refuse us."

But Ch'ü Ling said, "T'ang Lung, my Brother, you have led me hither. But at home my wife will assuredly be seized by the state, and what shall I do?"

Sung Chiang replied, "This is no great matter. Let the noble one's heart be at rest. It is all on my humble body. Surely on some day soon will I bring your household hither."

Then Ch'ao Kai, Wu Yung, and Kung Sun Sheng all came forward with such words of apology and exhortation to Ch'ü Ling and a feast was prepared for his welcome. Thus on the one hand were the lesser robbers to be taught how to use the hook-bladed spear and on the other hand Tai Chung and T'ang Lung went by night and by day to the eastern capital to fetch the wife and household of Ch'ü Ling.

Within ten days Yang Ling went to Ying Chou and there sought out the household of P'eng Ch'i. Shih Yung went to the eastern capital to seek out the household of Ling Chen. Li Yün bought five carts of powder for fireballs and brought it back to the lair. When yet more days had passed Tai Chung and T'ang Lung brought Ch'ü Ling's household up the mountain. Ch'ü Ling, when he saw his wife was come, gave a start of fear and he asked, "How is it you have come hither?"

His wife replied, "Ever since you went away you did not come home any more. When your name was called in the court I spent some bribe money and sent back an answer that you lay ill upon your bed and for this did you not come to answer for your name. Suddenly I saw this uncle T'ang and he brought back this eagle-feather armor and he said, 'We have found the armor, but my elder brother lies ill upon the way and he is about to die there in an inn.' And he told me and the child to come at once. He placed me upon a cart, nor did I know the way here for we wound hither and thither as we came."

And Ch'ü Ling said, "This brother of mine has done well and well enough but it is a pity he left my eagle-feather armor at home."

T'ang Lung said, "That I might please my elder brother, when the lady was upon the cart I turned about and plotted for the armor. I bade the slaves to put together all the treasure of the house and they made a bundle of it and I carried it here."

Then Ch'ü Ling said, "If it is thus, we can return no more to the eastern capital."

And T'ang Lung said again, "I have yet one more thing for my elder brother to know. Upon the road I met some travelers and I put your armor on myself and marked my face like yours and I said that I was you, and I robbed them of their goods. Sooner or later there will come a proclamation from the eastern capital that you are to be seized."

Then Ch'ü Ling said, "Brother, you have injured me no little."

At this Ch'ao Kai and Sung Chiang both came forward with words of apology, saying, "Yet if we had not done thus, then how would you, our Elder Brother, have been willing to come hither?" And quickly they set aside a house that Ch'ü Ling and his household might dwell there.

Then did all the chieftains take counsel together as to how they might destroy the armored horses and men. By now Lei Heng had already finished his task of overseeing the making of the hook-bladed spears. Sung Chiang and Wu Yung and the others then asked Ch'ü Ling that he would teach them all how to use this weapon and Ch'ü Ling said, "This humble one ought to tell how the spear is used and I should indeed teach all the chieftains concerning it."

Then he chose out one whose body was tall and strong. All the chieftains were there in the Hall Of Meeting to see the man whom Ch'ü Ling chose. Then indeed as he told of the ways to use this hook-bladed spear it was that

> Three thousand armored horses in a breath
> fell to the ground,
> On the day set by Heaven was a hero caught
> and bound.

How then did Ch'ü Ling teach the use of this hook-bladed spear? Pray hear it told in the next chapter.

Chapter 56

CH'Ü LING TEACHES THE ROBBERS HOW TO USE THE HOOK-BLADED SPEAR. SUNG CHIANG OVERCOMES THE CHAINED HORSEMEN

IT IS SAID: Ch'ao Kai and Sung Chiang, Wu Yung and Kung Sun Sheng and all the other chieftains met together in the hall and there they asked Ch'ü Ling to show them how to use the hook-bladed spear. Now as they all watched Ch'ü Ling, they saw how fine indeed he was for a man. His body was six feet and five inches tall and he had a round white face and he had a fine black beard divided into three parts and he had great breadth of shoulders and width of girth. When he had finished his choice of fighting men he came into the hall and he took up a hook-bladed spear and began to use it himself.

And when they saw it they all cried out in admiration. Then Ch'ü Ling began to teach the robbers, saying, "When you use this weapon from horseback the feints and postures must be made from the waist step by step. There are seven such feints. Of these seven three are pulling the weapon back, and four are thrusting it forward. Beyond these there is the blow forward and the blow to the side. In each feint there are nine postures. If the hook-bladed spear be used from afoot, then it is very useful, too. First take eight steps forward and then make four postures. This is as though you opened the enemy's gate. But after twelve steps change your feint. After sixteen steps, turn yourself about, draw back the spear and thrust, and whirl it. After twenty-four steps thrust the weapon up and then down, hook it to the east and thrust it to the west. At the thirty-sixth step guard well your own body and attack the enemy and those who bear strong arms against you. This is the right way to fight with the hook-bladed spear. There is a verse made concerning this and it says,

'Four thrusts and three pulls, seven feints all;
Nine postures full of magic thrall.
Twenty-four steps then to and fro,
Sixteen steps, and about we go!' "

Thus did Ch'ü Ling teach them how to use this weapon step by step and he asked all the chieftains to watch. As for all the fighting men, when they saw how Ch'ü Ling used the hook-bladed spear they were overjoyed and from that day on the strongest and best fighting men were chosen and they practised both day and night. The fighting men who fought on foot also were taught how to hide in the woods and how to crawl in grass, how to hook the feet of horses and how to snare them by the legs and how to use the three secret ways in ambush upon the ground.

In less than half a month there were thus taught some five hundred to seven hundred men in the robbers' lair. Seeing this, Sung Chiang and the other chieftains were greatly pleased and they prepared to overcome the enemy.

Let it be further told now of Hu Yien Shu. Ever since he lost P'eng Ch'i and Ling Chen he went forth every day on horseback and he led his horsemen to the water's edge to create confusion but Sung Chiang and the chieftains in the lair commanded the chieftains upon the water to guard well every shore. Now in the water were placed hidden stakes, and therefore Hu Yien Shu, although he blew bugles at the east and at the north of the mountain, yet could he find no way to go up, nor could he by any means approach the lair.

Then did those in the lair command Ling Chen to prepare many fireballs and they cast about for a day on which they might go down the mountain against the enemy and even those fighting men who had learned the ways of the hook-bladed spear were all used and ready.

One day Sung Chiang said to the chieftains, "I am but a man of narrow sight and I do not know whether my purpose suits itself to yours."

Wu Yung replied, "We would hear what you have to say."

And Sung Chiang said, "Tomorrow let us not use all our horses and fighting men, but let our chieftains fight with men on foot, for those famous warriors of old, Swen and Wu, have said that in fighting on a mountain the least costly way is to fight in woods and tangled grass. So let the fighting men go down the mountain on foot and let them divide into ten parts to meet the enemy. When they see the enemy horsemen charging forward, let the men run at random into the wild grass and the wood. There let them hide with their weapons and their hooks. Let ten who can use the hook-bladed spear be with ten who can use the long-handled hook. When they see the horses come near, with one stroke they can overthrow them, and then with the long-handled hook they can drag the riders down. Let this plan be used also not only upon the mountain but upon the plain. What think you of it?"

Wu Yung said, "Truly ought we to fight like this with our men hidden and so can we seize our enemies."

And Ch'ü Ling said, "Truly ought the hook-bladed spear and the long-handled hook to be used thus."

Then on that day did Sung Chiang divide the fighting men into ten divisions of infantry. Liu T'ang and Tu Ch'ien led one division. Mu Hung and Mu Ch'un led one division. Yang Hsiung and T'ao Chung Wang led one division, Chu T'ung and Teng Fei led one division, Hsieh Chen and Hsieh Pao led another division, and Chou Yuen and Chou Jun led a division, The Ten Foot Green Snake and Wang The Dwarf Tiger led a division, Shih Yung and Ma Ling led a division, Yien Shun and Chen T'ien Shou led a division, and Yang Ling and Li Yün led a division. These ten divisions of foot fighting men went first down the mountain to meet the enemy armies.

Then was Li Chün appointed and with him Chang Heng, Chang Shun, the three Juan brothers, T'ung Wei, T'ung Meng, Meng K'an and the nine water chiefs to bring the boats to meet and wait for the others. Again Hua Yung, Ch'ing Ming, Li Yün, Ch'ai Chin, Sheng Li, Ou P'eng, these six chieftains, led forth the horsemen. Li Chün was appointed and Chang Heng and they went down the mountain and around. Ling Chen and Tu Hsing were to do naught but send off the fireballs, Ch'ü Ling and T'ang Lung together to command those who used the hook-bladed spear. The chieftains Sung Chiang, Wu Yung, Kung Sun Sheng, Tai Chung, Lü Fang and Kao Shen were to take command of the horses and the sending forth of the signals. As for the other chieftains, they stayed to guard the lair.

When Sung Chiang had thus appointed all to their places, in the third watch of that night he sent forth first those who used the hook-bladed spear and they went across the river. There they divided into four directions and went into ambush. At the fourth watch the ten divisions of foot fighting men were ferried across. Ling Chen and Tu Hsing then went across with their fireballs, and they sought for a high place upon which to set up their racks and there they placed their fireballs. Ch'ü Ling and T'ang Lung took each his bag of bugles and went across the river also.

When dawn came Sung Chiang gathered together all the horsemen and they went down to the water and there they blew bugles and beat drums and shouted and their flags were waving in the winds. Now Hu Yien Shu was at this time in the midst of his camp when he heard a spy come to make report and then he commanded, "Let Han T'ao be sent forth as a vanguard and await us there."

Then did Hu Yien Shu straightway chain together the horses and he put on complete armor and he rode his black horse that had snowy feet and he took his two clubs and with all his great army of horsemen he charged toward the robbers' lair. Across the water he saw Sung Chiang leading a mighty horde of men. Hu Yien Shu commanded that his men were to be divided. Then did Han T'ao come to take counsel and he said, "To the south Sung Chiang has a great horde of robbers on foot and I cannot tell how many be there."

But Hu Yien Shu replied, "Do not ask how many are there! Charge forward with the horses!"

Then Han T'ao led out five hundred horsemen and he returned to his position of vanguard. Now to the southeast were seen another flock of banners and even as he was about to divide his men and go forward to attack them suddenly he saw to the southwest of the mountain again another flock of banners come forth and a shout of battle rose up. Again Han T'ao led his men back and he said to Hu Yien Shu, "To the south there are three companies of soldiers and they all bear the banners of the robbers' lair."

Hu Yien Shu said, "All these days they have not come out to fight with us. Surely there is some plot against us now."

Before he had finished speaking they heard the sound of an explosion to the north. Then did Hu Yien Shu fall to cursing and he said, "This fireball was assuredly set alight by that Ling Chen of ours, who has joined the robbers and they have commanded him to do it!"

When they all looked toward the north, again came forth three divisions of fighting men and Hu Yien Shu said to Han T'ao, "Now that there are robbers to the north and to the south, I will divide the soldiers with you. I will go and kill those to the north and do you go and kill those to the south."

Even as they were about to divide their men thus, they saw again four divisions come up out of the west. Then Hu Yien Shu grew agitated in heart and again he heard the sound of one explosion after another toward the north and the echo of it came straight there to the ridge. There was one great fireball that shattered into forty-nine lesser ones, and the name of such an one is called the mother and sons fireball, and the sound of it was terrible, and it was very fearful to see.

Then Hu Yien Shu's men without even going into battle became confused and Hu Yien Shu and Han T'ao and their men rushed in all four directions. As for the men of the lair, when they were attacked from the east they fled eastward, and when they were attacked from the west they fled westward. Hu Yien Shu, seeing it, fell into a mighty wrath and he led his men straight toward the north. As for Sung Chiang's men, they all ran away into the reeds. Hu Yien Shu in furious pursuit urged on his black horse with the snowy feet so that the earth whirled under him and the chained horses rushed on so that there was no holding them back and they all ran into the tangled reeds and into the wood.

Then was heard the blast of bugles in the wood and those with the hook-bladed spears all lifted up their hands together. The horses at the outer edges were first hooked, and naturally the center horses leaped and reared. Then did the robbers with the long-handled spears all come out and seize the soldiers fast—and there in the reeds the robbers had naught to do but bind their captives.

Hu Yien Shu, seeing that he had been deceived by this plot of hook-bladed spears and long-handled hooks, drew back his horse with all speed and going to the south he joined with Han T'ao. But before he knew it a great fireball fell from behind him and suddenly from here and there upon the whole mountain there were robbers pursuing him. Then were the imperial foot soldiers and the chained horsemen all taken in the tangled grass and the robbers seized them every one. As for Hu Yien Shu and Han T'ao, when they found they were taken thus in a plot, they beat their horses and looked in all directions for a way of escape. But they did not know that every path as well as wood and wild grass were full of the banners of the robbers.

At last Hu Yien Shu dared follow none of those roads and he could but go straight toward the northwest. When he had gone scarce two miles there rushed out upon him a pair of robbers and these two goodly fellows stood across his path. One of them was Mu Hung and the other was Mu Ch'un. They stretched out their two great swords and they roared out, "You vanquished warrior, do not pass!"

But Hu Yien Shu, maddened with his anger, lifted up his double clubs and he charged his horse down upon Mu Hung and Mu Ch'un. They fought some four or five rounds and then the two men went away. Then Hu Yien Shu did but fear that he had fallen into some other plot and he dared not follow them, and he went on the big road. But again from behind a ridge there rushed out another pair of robbers and these two goodly fellows stayed his path also. One was The Double Headed Snake Hsieh Chen, and the other was The Double Tailed Scorpion Hsieh Pao. They each carried brass forks and they leaped forward.

Then Hu Yien Shu lifted up his double clubs and came forward to withstand them, and when they had fought less than five or seven rounds

Hsieh Chen and Hsieh Pao lifted their footsteps and ran away. But Hu Yien Shu had pursued only a little way when from the sides of the path there were thrust out twenty-four hooks. Then Hu Yien Shu had no heart more for battle, and he turned his horse's head and he went to the great road to the northeast.

Suddenly there charged out upon him Wang The Dwarf Tiger and The Ten Foot Green Snake, husband and wife, and they stood in the way he must go. Hu Yien Shu, seeing the road before him was not smooth and that about him on all sides was high and tangled grass, whipped up his horse and lifted his clubs to kill a path through, and thus he forced his way. Then Wang The Dwarf Tiger and The Ten Foot Green Snake pursued him for a while but they could not come up with him and so Hu Yien Shu went away to the northeast. And he went bitterly defeated, his army scattered as the few small raindrops after a tempest.

Now did Sung Chiang sound the gongs and he recalled all his men and they went back to the mountain, and there each man made report of what he had done and each received his reward. Of these chained horses less than a half had their feet wounded by the hooks as they fell, and they took from these the armor and the skins and they used the carcasses for food. But the greater half of those good horses they led up the mountain and fed them, and they kept them for riding horses. As for the armored horsemen, the robbers captured them all alive and took them up the mountain. The five thousand foot soldiers were heavily beset on all sides and they tried to escape among the robbers and were waylaid by the hooks. Such as ran toward the water were captured by the robbers there and tied and taken upon boats and carried across the water and taken up the mountain. As for the horses and men that had been formerly captured by Hu Yien Shu, these all returned now to the lair. Even the wooden stockade Hu Yien Shu had put about his own encampment the robbers pulled up and carried to the lair, and they used it to build small camps in the watery wastes and marshes of the great lair. They built also two more wine shops to be like eyes for the robbers and spy out what was to be seen and Sheng Sing and The Goodwife Ku, Shih Yung and Shih Ch'ien were appointed to tend these wine shops.

Now Liu T'ang and Tu Hsing had captured Han T'ao and they bound him and brought him up the mountain. But Sung Chiang when he saw him come thus himself untied Han T'ao's ropes and he invited him to come into the hall and he spoke to him with all courtesy and gave him fine foods to eat, and he let P'eng Ch'i and Ling Chen reason with him that he also might join the robbers.

And this Han T'ao was also one among those seventy-two stars in the heavens and so was his spirit knit to theirs and then did Sung Chiang bid one write a letter and he appointed messengers to go to the city of Chen Chou and bring back the household of Han T'ao to come to the lair and join him.

Now Sung Chiang was greatly rejoiced that the chained horses had been overcome and that so many men had been captured and horses, too, and garments and armor and weapons and helmets, and every day there were feasts of congratulation prepared. He set also certain fighting men to guard that they might see when the imperial soldiers came out again and so they might be prepared. Of this no more need be told.

Let it be told now of Hu Yien Shu. He had lost many men and horses and he dared not return to the capital. Alone he went riding the great black horse with snowy feet and he tied his armor and garments of war upon his horse and he went fugitive, for in truth he was penniless, and he untied his girdle and sold it to get money for his food. As he went he thought to himself, "I never dreamed I would come to such a day as this, and whither shall I turn for refuge?" Suddenly he bethought himself, "There is that Mu Yung's house in Ch'ing Chou and we have met before and known each other. Why should I not go thither and take refuge with him? He has a younger sister who is concubine to the Emperor and I can reach perhaps the royal ear, and then again I will lead forth soldiers and take my revenge upon the robbers."

He went two days upon his way and when night came he was both hungry and athirst. Then he saw beside the road a wine shop, and he came down from his horse and he tied the horse to a tree before the door and he went into the wine shop. He put his whip upon a table and he sat down and he called out, "Bring wine and flesh hither!"

Then the keeper of the shop replied, "I do but sell wine here and if you want flesh go into the village and bid them kill a sheep. If you truly wish for it, then will this humble one go and buy it for you."

Then Hu Yien Shu reached into his bag by his waist and he brought out the silver he had from selling his golden girdle and he gave it to the inn-keeper and he said, "Go then and buy a leg of a sheep for me to eat, and buy a little hay also to feed this horse of mine. Tonight I will rest myself here in this house of yours, and tomorrow I will go on my way to Ch'ing Chou."

The keeper said, "Sir, though you sleep here it matters nothing, only I have no good bed."

But Hu Yien Shu said, "I am a soldier, and if I do but have a place to lie down it is well enough for me."

Then the shop keeper took the silver and he went himself to buy the sheep's flesh and Hu Yien Shu took the armor from his horse and loosened the girth and he sat there by the gate and waited half a day. At last he saw the wine shop keeper return, bringing the leg of a sheep, and Hu Yien Shu said, "Cook it! Buy also three measures of flour to make me bread and bring two measures of wine here."

So the wine shop keeper made the bread and cooked the flesh and heated the wine, and Hu Yien Shu washed his feet and he led the horse into a small room. And the wine shop keeper chopped up the straw for the beast to eat and at the same time he cooked the sheep's flesh. Now Hu Yien Shu first asked for the hot wine and he drank it for a while, and in a short time the meat was cooked and Hu Yien Shu bade the wine shop keeper to give it to him to eat and he commanded, saying, "I am an official in the imperial army and because I was vanquished in battle with the robbers I have come to Ch'ing Chou to the house of Mu Yung. Do you therefore care faithfully for this good horse of mine, for it was given me by the Emperor and its name is Black Horse Who Walks In Snow. Tomorrow I will reward you heavily."

The wine shop keeper replied, "I thank you, Sir. But there is one thing I would have you know. Not far from here there is a mountain and it is called The Peach Blossom Mountain and upon that mountain there is a band of robbers. The chief is called The Warrior Who Wars Against Tigers, Li Chung, and the second one is called Chou T'ung. These two have gathered together some five or seven hundred lesser robbers and they continually come hither to rob men's houses, nor can the imperial soldiers ever take them captive. Do you then sleep carefully in the night."

Hu Yien Shu said, "I have such strength as ten thousand men cannot withstand, and though all that horde came down, what would it matter to me? Do you but feed well this horse of mine."

Then he drank wine for a while and he ate his meat and bread, and the wine shop keeper spread a bed for him there in the shop and when it was made ready Hu Yien Shu went to sleep. Now because Hu Yien Shu was so weary with his melancholy and also because he had drunk a few cups too much of wine he lay down clothed as he was and he slept straight until the third watch of the night before he woke. Suddenly then did he hear the wine shop keeper begin to cry out from the back of the house. Hu Yien Shu, hearing it, leaped up in all haste and taking up his double clubs he went to the back of the house and he asked the keeper, "Why do you cry out?"

The wine shop keeper answered, "When I rose to feed the horse, I saw the earthen wall pushed over. Sir, your horse is stolen! In the distance about a mile away I see the flaming of torches and assuredly they have taken him thither!"

Hu Yien Shu cried, "What place is that?"

The wine shop keeper replied, "I see it is that road to The Peach Blossom Mountain and the robbers have stolen the horse and fled by that way."

Then Hu Yien Shu gave a start and he bade the wine shop keeper lead the way. But when they had gone in pursuit but a mile or so along the paths by the fields they could see no more the glare of the torches and they did not know whither the robbers were gone. Then Hu Yien Shu said, "And if this imperial gift horse is gone, what shall I do!"

The wine shop keeper replied, "Sir, do you go tomorrow and make report of it before the magistrate Mu Yung and ask that the imperial soldiers come out to seek it for only thus can you seize back again this horse."

But Hu Yien Shu could not rest for his melancholy and he sat up until the dawn. He bade the wine shop keeper to carry the horse's armor and he himself turned toward Ch'ing Chou. As he came into the city the sky was already darkening with night and he spent the night in an inn. At dawn the next day he went into the magistrate's court and he went to make obeisance to the magistrate Mu Yung. When the magistrate saw him he gave a start of fear and he asked, saying, "I have heard that you went out against the little robbers of Liang Shan P'o, and how is it you are here?"

Hu Yien Shu then told all that happened. When Mu Yung the magistrate heard of it he said, "Although you have lost many men and horses it was not indeed because of your own carelessness. It is because you fell into the plots of the thieves and what help was there for this! In this region which I, this small magistrate, control, there are constantly little robbers who come forth to maraud. Sir Warrior, if you are come here then do you lay waste that Peach Blossom Mountain and so take back again that imperial gift horse. And well it would be if you could lay waste the robbers in The Double Dragon Mountain and The Great Tiger Mountain also! Then would I use all my powers to make report of it to the Emperor and then would you be sent forth again with an army against the robbers of the great lair in Liang Shan P'o to take your revenge. How seems this to you?"

Hu Yien Shu again made obeisance and he said, "Deeply do I thank the most gracious one. If you can indeed work thus for me, then ought I not to fear death that I may return so great a good."

Therefore the magistrate Mu Yung bade Hu Yien Shu go to the guest hall to rest, and he bade him change his garments and eat. As for the wine shop keeper, he was told to go home alone.

After living there for three days Hu Yien Shu grew impatient to have his jade-like horse once more and again he came and begged the magistrate humbly that he would tell off soldiers for him. Then did the magistrate Mu Yung tell off soldiers and horsemen and he gave them over to Hu Yien Shu, and he gave him also a horse with a sky-blue mane. Then Hu Yien Shu thanked this gracious magistrate and he put on his armor and mounted the horse and he rode out leading the soldiers and horsemen and he went straight to The Peach Blossom Mountain.

Now let it be told concerning The Warrior Who Wars Against Tigers, Li Chung of The Peach Blossom Mountain, and of the other chief Chou T'ung. Ever since they had captured this inky-black horse with the snowy feet they had rejoiced and they had feasted every day in their lair. But on that day a spy came from the road and he made report, saying, "There come horsemen from Ch'ing Chou!"

Then Chou T'ung rose up and he said, "Elder Brother, do you guard the lair and I will go out and turn back the soldiers."

Then he counted off a hundred lesser robbers and he took his weapon and mounted his horse and he came down the mountain to meet the imperial soldiers. Now Hu Yien Shu led two thousand soldiers and horsemen and they came to the mountain and there they stood in rank. And Hu Yien Shu came out and he began to curse loudly, saying, "Ha, you little thieves and robbers, come out and receive your punishment from me!"

Now Chou T'ung scattered apart the fighting men he had and he lifted his weapon and let his horse free. Hu Yien Shu saw this and he urged his horse on to attack, and Chou T'ung charged on to meet him. The two horses met and the men fought less than six or seven rounds when Chou T'ung's strength began to fail and he turned his horse and went away toward the mountain. Hu Yien Shu pursued him for a while but he feared some plot and he came quickly back again and made encampment and he waited there.

Let it be told now of Chou T'ung. He went back to the lair and there he saw Li Chung and he said, "This Hu Yien Shu has great skill in arms and I cannot withstand him and I could but retreat up the mountain. If he should pursue to the very lair, then what shall we do?"

Li Chung said, "I have thought of something. There is a Temple Of The Precious Pearl there on The Double Dragon Mountain and there is a tattooed priest there called Lu Chi Shen and he has with him many comrades. Besides this there is one called The Blue Faced Beast Yang Chi and there is another one, a teacher called Wu Sung, and these are all such as ten thousand men cannot withstand. The best thing is to write a letter and send it by messenger thither to ask for aid. If they can save us out of this trouble, then will I be willing enough to say theirs is the greater lair and I will pay them every month a little tribute of some sort."

Chou T'ung replied, "Well do I also know there are goodly, noble men there. I do but fear the tattooed priest will remember that we fought him once and so now he will not come."

But Li Chung laughed and said, "You are wrong—he is a good and straight-hearted fellow; if there comes a man to him for aid, he will surely lead forth soldiers and come to save us."

Chou T'ung said, "Elder Brother, and you have spoken well, too!"

So he wrote a letter and he sent two robbers who knew how to carry out an affair, and they rolled down the back of the mountain and they followed the road to The Double Dragon Mountain. When they had gone two days they were already at the mountain, and the robbers there heard of what they had come to ask.

Let it be told now of that Temple Of The Precious Pearl. There were three chiefs there. The first was The Tattooed Priest Lu Chi Shen. The second was The Blue Faced Beast Yang Chi and the third was Wu Sung. At the gatehouse of the temple sat four lesser chiefs, one was The Gold Eyed Tiger Cub Shih En, and he was the son of a military official in the old city of Meng Chou, but Wu Sung had killed the whole house of the General Chang and Shih En could not seize him before he escaped, although it was his duty so to do, and therefore he escaped by night and became a wanderer by river and lake. Later his parents both died and hearing that Wu Sung was on The Double Dragon Mountain he went by night to that place to join him.

The second chief was called The Dagger Devil Ch'ao Cheng and he had gone to The Temple Of The Precious Pearl with Lu Chi Shen and Yang Chi, and first he had killed Teng Lung and then he joined them. The third was Chang Ch'ing and the last one The Female Savage, The Goodwife Sheng. These two were husband and wife and they were sellers of wheaten loaves stuffed with human flesh and their shop had been at the cross roads of Meng Chou. But because Wu Sung and Lu Chi Shen continually sent them letters to come thither they came also to join him.

Now when Ch'ao Cheng heard that there was a letter from The Peach Blossom Mountain he came to ask closely of it and he went into the temple to find the three great chiefs and he told them. Then Lu Chi Shen said, "When I left The Five Crested Mountain I went to a Peach Blossom village to stop for the night and how soundly I did beat a cursed fellow there! That fellow knows me very well, and he has even been up this mountain to drink a day's wine, and he swore me for his brother and he would have had me stay there to be chief. But I saw him to be a very stingy fellow and so I robbed him of his gold and silver drinking cups, and now he comes hither asking me to save him! Well, and let those little robbers of his come hither and let me hear what they have to say!"

Then Ch'ao Cheng was not long gone and he led those robbers to the door of the temple, and they cried out greeting and they said, "The magistrate Mu Yung has received a man who was vanquished by the robbers in the great lair at Liang Shan P'o and his name is Hu Yien Shu, and he uses two clubs. Now the magistrate has told him first to sweep clean away the robbers on The Peach Blossom Mountain and on The Double Dragon Mountain and on The White Tiger Mountain, and in all these several lairs, and then he will give him soldiers that he may go and revenge himself on Liang Shan P'o. Our chieftain now hopes ten thousand times that you will go down the mountain to save him, and when the trouble is over he will very willingly come hither to bring tribute gifts."

To this Yang Chi said, "We do but wish to guard our own lair and our own mountain, nor do we wish to go to the aid of others and it is partly also because we fear to injure some goodly wandering fellow and partly also lest he seize this Double Dragon Mountain from us and so put us to shame. Nevertheless let the four at the gate keep this lair and we three will go forth for the once."

Then straightway he told off five hundred robbers and more than sixty horsemen and each took armor and weapons and they went straight to The Peach Blossom Mountain.

Let it be told now concerning Li Chung. As soon as he heard the news from The Double Dragon men, he himself led out three hundred robbers and went down the mountain to meet them. And Hu Yien Shu heard of this and he led out with all speed a body of horsemen and he stood in the path, and whipping his horse he charged forward to do battle with Li Chung. Now Li Chung's ancestors were men of a small place near the city of Hao Chou and all his forefathers had trusted to arms for a living, and when they saw how tall and strong he was in body men called him The Warrior Who Wars Against Tigers. Now he came down the mountain to do battle with Hu Yien Shu, and yet how could even he overcome him? When he had fought some ten-odd rounds, he saw there was no escape for him and so he turned and led his men aside.

Hu Yien Shu, seeing how small was Li Chung's skill, hastily speeded his horse and pursued him. But Chou T'ung who had been watching from half way up the mountain, threw down stones as large as goose eggs. In great haste Hu Yien Shu turned his horse to rush down the mountain again when he heard his own soldiers call out in confusion. Then Hu Yien Shu inquired of them why they so shouted and the rearmost soldiers answered, "In the distance we see men and horsemen flying hither!"

Hu Yien Shu heard this and when he came among his soldiers to see he saw amidst a cloud of dust at the head of them all a big fat priest, and he rode a white horse and indeed it was that tattooed priest, Lu Chi Shen. From his horse this priest shouted mightily and he said, "Which is that cursed fellow who was vanquished by the great lair of Liang Shan P'o and who dares to come hither to frighten people?"

Hu Yien Shu replied, "And first I will kill you, you bald-headed donkey, and so slake the anger in my heart!"

Then Lu Chi Shen stretched out his long iron staff and Hu Yien Shu lifted up his double clubs and the two horses began to circle about each other and the men on either side shouted. The two fought more than forty rounds and it could not be told who was victor and who vanquished. Now Hu Yien Shu was truly a man of noble parts and in his heart he said, "This priest is truly a man of mighty skill!"

Therefore each one withdrew for the time with his men.

But Hu Yien Shu could not stay but for a little while, and again he urged his horse on to battle and he shouted loudly, "You robber priest, come forth once more! I will fight with you to victory or vanquishment!"

Even as Lu Chi Shen was at that time about to come forth on his horse Yang Chi called out, "Stay, Elder Brother! Watch me go and capture this man!" And drawing his blade, he urged his horse to the combat.

The two fought some forty or fifty times, and it could not be told who was victor or who vanquished. Again Hu Yien Shu secretly admired his opponent and he said to himself, "How is it there have come forth two such terrible ones as these? They are no common fellows of the greenwood!"

And Yang Chi also saw that Hu Yien Shu was a man of no mean skill in arms and he used guile and he turned his horse to retreat and galloped back to his men. Then Hu Yien Shu, holding the reins hard, did not go in pursuit and both sides withdrew their men. And Lu Chi Shen took counsel with Yang Chi, saying, "We ought not to stay so near the enemy's camp. Let us retreat some seven miles and then tomorrow we can come and do battle again."

Then leading the lesser robbers they went away and sought a near-by valley and there set up their camp.

Let it be told now concerning Hu Yien Shu as he sat in his camp and nursed his melancholy and in his heart he thought, "I had hoped that when I came here it would be to beat a path through a bamboo thicket and that I could seize these small robbers, and how is it I have come upon a pair as skilled as myself? How useless a life is mine."

Even as he sat in despair he saw a messenger sent from the magistrate Mu Yung's court, and he said, "Sir, you are commanded to lead the soldiers back to protect the city. Those robbers from The White Tiger Mountain, K'ung Ming and K'ung Liang, have led men and horsemen to the city to force open the gaol, and fearing there be trouble in the court, we have come especially to ask you, Sir Warrior, to return."

Hu Yien Shu, hearing this, took the opportunity to return with his soldiers that very night to the city of Ch'ing Chou.

On the next day Lu Chi Shen and Yang Chi again led out their lesser robbers and they went waving their flags and shouting aloud. But when they came to the foot of the mountain to see, there was not a soldier or a horse there. They gave a start of fear. Then did Li Chung and Chou T'ung, who were at the foot of the mountain, come forward and invited them into their lair, and made obeisance before the three chieftains and they invited them to come into their lair and they commanded that horses and sheep were to be killed and a feast prepared, and they sent spies down the mountain to spy out the news of the road.

Now let it be told of Hu Yien Shu as he led the soldiers back into the city. He saw a company of men and horses who were newly come to the edge of the city. The ones at their head were from The White Tiger Mountain and they were the sons of the lord K'ung and their names were The Curly Haired K'ung Ming and The Lone Fire K'ung Liang. These two because they had quarreled with a certain man killed his house clean of everyone great and small. Then they gathered together some five or seven hundred men and went away to The White Tiger Mountain. But because their uncle in the city, K'ung Ping by name, was seized by the magistrate and locked into the gaol, K'ung Ming and K'ung Liang came purposely with their robbers to attack the city of Ch'ing Chou and save their uncle.

Now they met Hu Yien Shu and his horsemen squarely and the two sides faced each other and shouted and prepared for battle. Hu Yien Shu let his horse free and came to the front of his ranks. The magistrate Mu Yung was in the tower of the gate of the city wall, and saw K'ung Ming take his weapon and send his command forth and they came to do battle with Hu Yien Shu. The two horses came and went, and they fought more than twenty rounds. Then Hu Yien Shu thought to show forth his prowess before the magistrate and he guessed that K'ung Ming had no great skill. Now K'ung Ming could but defend himself and wage no active battle, and as Hu Yien Shu attacked him furiously after they had fought a long time Hu Yien Shu captured K'ung Ming alive. Then K'ung Liang could but lead away the robbers and retreat.

The magistrate, seeing this from the wall tower, pointed with his fingers and commanded that Hu Yien Shu was to pursue him. As soon as the imperial soldiers charged they captured alive more than a hundred robbers, and indeed K'ung Liang suffered a mighty defeat and they scattered and fled in all directions, and that night they found an old temple and there rested.

Let it be told of Hu Yien Shu and of K'ung Ming whom he captured alive. He took K'ung Ming into the court and into the presence of the magistrate Mu Yung, and the magistrate was greatly pleased and he commanded that a large rack be fastened upon K'ung Ming and that he be put into the gaol with K'ung Ping and they were there together. Then he rewarded the soldiers and he feasted Hu Yien Shu and he asked how it was with The Peach Blossom Mountain. And Hu Yien Shu said, "But this thing would have been as easy as lifting a turtle out of a jar, had a company of warriors not come suddenly to their rescue. There were two among them who were one a great priest and the other a blue-faced fellow. Twice we fought but to no victory. Truly the skill in arms of these two is no common thing and they are no usual thieves in a greenwood, and so I could not capture them."

Then Mu Yung the magistrate said, "This priest is assuredly that one of Yien An, who worked with that old official there as a captain and his name is Lu Ta. Now he has shaved his head and become a priest and he is called The Tattooed Priest Lu Chi Shen. That big blue-faced fellow is a captain, too, from the eastern capital and he is called The Blue Faced Beast Yang Chi. There is one more and he is called Wu Sung, and he was the captain who killed a tiger upon The Ridge Of The Sun. These three now occupy The Double Dragon Mountain, and they rob men's houses and time and again they have withstood the imperial soldiers, and they have three or five of the captains sent out against them nor have any ever captured them."

Then Hu Yien Shu said, "I saw they were very skilled in arms, and if one be Yang Chi and one the captain Lu then indeed is their fame deserved. Most Gracious, rest your heart. Now that I, Hu Yien Shu, am here I can capture them all, one by one and alive, and bring them hither before you."

Then was the magistrate greatly pleased. When the feasting was over he invited Hu Yien Shu to go and rest in the guest hall and of this no more need be told.

Let it be told now of K'ung Liang as he led back his defeated men and horses. As they went along suddenly there came out from a wood a company of men on horseback. The first among them was Wu Sung. In great haste K'ung Liang came down from his horse and he made obeisance and he said, "Are you, Most Noble, without illness this day?"

In haste then did Wu Sung also return the courtesy. He lifted K'ung Liang up and asked him, saying, "I have heard that you, my Brother, are now on The White Tiger Mountain and many times have I thought to come and pay my respects but I have not, in the first place, been free to come down the mountain, and, second, the road thither is not easy to come upon. Therefore have we not been able to meet. But why have you come here today?"

Then did K'ung Liang tell him of the affairs of his uncle K'ung Ping and Wu Sung said, "Do not let your heart be ill at ease. I have six or seven brethren and now they are gathered together upon The Double Dragon Mountain. But today because Li Chung of The Peach Blossom Mountain was hard pressed by the magistrate of Ch'ing Chou, we came here to help him. Our two chiefs Lu and Yang came first with the lesser ones to do combat with Hu Yien Shu. But they fought for a whole day and we do not know why it was that Hu Yien Shu went away in the night. Those on The Peach Blossom Mountain kept us for the night and they gave us that black horse with the snow-white feet, and now I am taking back the first division of men and horses to the mountain, and Yang Chi and Lu Chi Shen follow after me. How would it be if I bade them go to the city and rescue your uncle and your brother?"

Then K'ung Liang made obeisance of thanks and Wu Sung waited for a while, and then he saw Yang Chi and Lu Chi Shen coming on their horses side by side. And Wu Sung led K'ung Liang to make obeisance before the two and he said, "Once at a certain time did Sung Chiang and I live in their village and we disturbed them much. Let us today count a good deed as first, and let us take our fighting men to Ch'ing Chou. When we have killed the magistrate Mu Yung and have taken alive Hu Yien Shu then let us take the treasure and the grain from those courts and bring them to our lair to use. What think you of that?"

Lu Chi Shen replied, "I think well of it, too."

Then they sent men to The Peach Blossom Mountain to make report and to say, "Bid our brother Li Chung bring out his men, and we three companies will all go together to Ch'ing Chou."

And Yang Chi said, "The city of Ch'ing Chou is very stout and the horses and men are strong. There is, moreover, that brave warrior Hu Yien Shu. It is not that I would seem afraid, but if we are to attack Ch'ing Chou together you must heed a few words of mine and then can we do the deed in a day."

Wu Sung replied, "Elder Brother, I would hear what you have to say."

Although what Yang Chi had to say was said in less time than it takes to eat a meal, yet because of this were the tiles upon the houses of the people of that city broken to bits so that the smoke came flying from the ruined roofs, and the heroes of the lair rubbed their fists together and struck their palms upon each other to do battle.

How then did Yang Chi tell Wu Sung that they were to attack Ch'ing Chou? Pray hear it told in the next chapter.

Chapter 57

THE THREE MOUNTAINS GATHER TOGETHER TO ATTACK CH'ING CHOU. ALL THE TIGERS TURN TO THE ROBBERS' LAIR

IT IS SAID: Wu Sung led K'ung Liang to make obeisance before Lu Chi Shen and Yang Chi and he implored them to save his brother K'ung Ming and his uncle K'ung Ping. Then Lu Chi Shen wished to gather together the horses and men of the three mountains and go forward at once, but Yang Chi said, "If we would attack Ch'ing Chou we must first gather together a great company of men and horses. I know the great name of Sung Chiang of the robbers' lair, so that by every river and lake he is called The Opportune Rain. Moreover, Hu Yien Shu is one of the enemies of that place. Let us, Brothers, then join together our men and horses with this brother K'ung. Let us wait here until all those from The Peach Blossom Mountain have come hither and then let us go together and attack Ch'ing Chou. Brother K'ung Liang, do you go this very night and seek out Sung Chiang, and by our united strength we can do the deed. This is the first plan. Since you, my Brothers, are all friendly with Sung Chiang, what think you of it?"

To this Lu Chi Shen replied, "Let it be thus, in truth. I have heard people say every day that Sung Chiang is a good man—today I have heard it said and tomorrow it will be said again, and pity it is that I have never met him! Everybody talks about him into my ear until I am fairly made deaf with the clatter, and truly I think he must be a very fine good fellow, since all under Heaven know his name. When before he was with Hua Yung in The Mountain Of Clear Winds I had the heart then to go and see his face but when I came there he was already gone, and so because I had no good luck I never saw him—and there was the end of it! Brother K'ung Liang, if you would save your brother, go quickly thither yourself and seek him and beg him to come. We will wait here and do battle first with those accursed."

K'ung Liang then called out the lesser robbers and bade them go with Lu Chi Shen, and he himself took but one to accompany him and he disguised himself as a merchant and that very night he went to the robbers' lair.

Let it be told further of Lu Chi Shen and of Yang Chi and Wu Sung. These three went into their lair and they bade Ch'ao Cheng and Shih En to bring a hundred or two more men down the mountain to aid them. When Li Chung and Chou T'ung of The Peach Blossom Mountain heard the news they brought forth their own men and they led out all they had, and they did but leave some thirty or fifty small fellows to guard the lair. The others they took down the mountain, and they gathered together there near Ch'ing Chou and they all attacked at once, and of this no more need be said.

Let it be told further of K'ung Liang. He left that region of Ch'ing Chou and winding his way he came to the robbers' lair and he stopped at Li Li's wine shop to buy wine to drink and ask of the road. Now Li Li looking upon them saw they were strangers and he asked them to sit down, and he asked, saying, "Sir Guests, from whence do you come?"

K'ung Liang replied, "From Ch'ing Chou we come."

Then Li Li asked again, saying, "Whom do you seek in the robbers' lair?"

And K'ung Liang answered, "I have one there whom I know and I come to seek him."

Again Li Li said, "But in that mountain there are only great kings living, and can you go thither?"

K'ung Liang replied, "I go to see the great Sung Chiang."

Then Li Li said, "If truly you come to see the chieftain Sung Chiang, I have here the rule of the way," and he commanded a serving man swiftly to bring the wine of ceremony to serve to the guest.

But K'ung Liang asked, "Yet we have never known each other and why do you treat me thus generously?"

Li Li replied, "Sir Guest, you do not understand. If there is one who comes to seek out our chief then it must be one of us and none other but an old friend, and how dare I not serve the wine of courtesy to him? Now I will go and make report of your coming."

K'ung Liang said, "I am the lord of that village near The Peach Blossom Mountain."

Li Li said, "I have heard our elder brother Sung Chiang speak often of your great name. Today we are rejoiced that you go up the mountain."

Then when the two had drunk the wine of ceremony Li Li opened the window at once and from that pavilion in the water he sent forth a singing arrow. Straightway out of the reeds they saw a small boat being ferried across by one of the lesser robbers and it came into the water pavilion. Then Li Li asked K'ung Liang to go down into the boat and they were ferried across to The Golden Sands where they came ashore, and then they went up to the pass. When K'ung Liang saw how strong and stout the three passes were and how the knives and weapons stood there like trees in a forest he thought to himself, "I have heard how prosperous this robbers' lair is, but I never thought it could be so great as this!"

Now there were already robbers who had gone to make report of their coming and in great haste Sung Chiang came down to meet them. When K'ung Liang saw him he hastened to fall before him in obeisance and Sung Chiang asked, saying, "Good Brother, why have you come hither?"

Now when K'ung Liang had finished his obeisance he let his voice out in loud weeping and Sung Chiang said, "Good Brother, what fearful thing is there in your heart which you cannot endure? Speak on, for it matters nothing. Even though there be fire and there be water, we will surely help you as with one strength. Good Brother, first rise!"

Then K'ung Liang replied, "Sir My Teacher, since you left us my old father has died and my brother fell into wrath with a rich man of our village and he killed that man's whole house, young and old. And the magistrate sought for him and pressed him hard and for this we went to The White Tiger Mountain and there gathered together some five or seven hundred men and there we robbed houses and despoiled our neighbors. But we had an uncle K'ung Ping in the city and him the magistrate Mu Yung seized and he had a heavy rack placed on him and bade him be thrown into gaol. For this did we two brothers go and attack the city and we hoped to save our uncle. Who would have thought that when we had but come to the city we should happen upon that Hu Yien Shu who uses double clubs? When my elder brother did battle with him he was captured and he was taken into the city and thrown into the gaol nor do I know whether now he be dead or living. As for me, I also was pursued for a while. But on the second day I came upon Wu Sung and he led me to meet his comrades. One is The Tattooed Priest Lu Chi Shen and one is The Blue Faced Beast Yang Chi, and they treated me as though they had known me long and they talked with me of how to save my brother. And Wu Sung said, 'I do ask these two chiefs, Lu and Yang, and Li and Chou of The Peach Blossom Mountain to gather together their horses and men that we may attack the city. Do you go by night to the great lair, therefore, and implore your old teacher Sung Chiang to come and help your uncle and brother,' and for this reason have I come hither this day."

Sung Chiang said, "If there is such an affair as this, then let your heart rest."

Then Sung Chiang led K'ung Liang to make obeisance before Ch'ao Kai and Wu Yung and Kung Sun Sheng and all the other chieftains and he said, "Hu Yien Shu has gone to Ch'ing Chou and he has hastened to the court of the magistrate Mu Yung. Now he has captured K'ung Ming and for this has K'ung Liang come hither to beg for aid."

Ch'ao Kai said, "Since they are two goodly fine fellows, and they are both men who do well and love righteousness and since you, my Brother, have been good friends with them long, why should we not go to their aid? Good Brother, do you prepare all therefore for going down the mountain and I will let you guard the mountain and this time I will go forth myself and do battle for you."

But Sung Chiang replied, "Elder Brother, you are lord of the lair and you may not yourself do as you would. This is my own affair. Since this one has come from afar to seek me—if I do not go—mayhap the hearts of these two brothers will be ill at ease if I do not go. But I would pray for several of the chiefs to go with me—"

Before he had finished speaking everyone in that hall cried out, "I—I—let it be I—I would serve like dog or horse—let me go with you!"

Then was Sung Chiang greatly rejoiced and on that day he entertained K'ung Liang well. Even as they were feasting Sung Chiang allowed The Iron Faced P'ei Hsüan to count off who should go down the mountain, and there were divided off five companies. The first company was appointed to Hua Yung, Ch'ing Ming, Yien Shun and Wang The Dwarf Tiger and they were to open the way as vanguard. The second company was appointed to Mu Hung, Yang Hsiung, Hsieh Chen and Hsieh Pao. The fighting men in the center were led by Sung Chiang, Wu Yung, Lü Fang and Kao Shen. The fourth company was led by Chu T'ung, Ch'ai Chin, Li Chün and Chang Heng. The last company was led by Sheng Li, Yang Ling, Ou P'eng and Ling Chen. Thus did Liang Shan P'o send forth five companies and there were in all twenty chieftains and there were three thousand horsemen. As for the other chieftains, they stayed with Ch'ao Kai to guard the lair.

Then did Sung Chiang bid farewell to Ch'ao Kai and he went down the mountain with K'ung Liang and through whatever town or city they passed he robbed no man of anything and thus they came to Ch'ing Chou. Now K'ung Liang went first to Lu Chi Shen to make report of the others coming and all those good fellows prepared a feast of welcome. When Sung Chiang and the others were come Wu Sung led forth Lu Chi Shen and Yang Chi and Li Chung and Chou T'ung and Shih En and Ch'ao Cheng, and they all came together and met. And Sung Chiang would give the place of honor to Lu Chi Shen and Lu Chi Shen said, "Long have I heard my brother's great name but never have I had the chance to bow before you. This day am I truly glad to know my elder brother."

Sung Chiang answered, saying, "So worthless as I be, how can I make any answer to this? Among the society of men I do constantly hear of your great virtues, my Teacher. Now today when I meet you, it is the good fortune of my whole life."

Then Yang Chi rose up and again he made obeisance and he said, "Once did I, Yang Chi, pass by Liang Shan P'o and the chieftains there would fain have had me stay but because at that time I was without any wisdom at all I would not stay. Now that today I have you here in my lair, it is the best thing under Heaven."

Sung Chiang answered, saying, "Your fame has spread abroad by every river and lake and pity it is that I have met you thus late."

Then did Lu Chi Shen feast them on every hand and he introduced this one to that until all were known to one another. On the second day Sung Chiang asked about Ch'ing Chou and whether there was now victory or defeat. Yang Chi replied, "Since K'ung Liang went away I have fought with them some three or five times and there has been neither victory nor defeat. There is but one man they lean upon in Ch'ing Chou and it is that Hu Yien Shu. If we could capture this one man the city could be as easily taken as if hot water were poured upon snow."

Then Wu Yung the counselor smiled and he said, "If you use strength with this man, you cannot overcome. We must use guile."

Sung Chiang asked, "And what guile shall we use to capture him?"

Wu Yung replied, "You must but do thus—and thus—"

Then was Sung Chiang greatly pleased and he cried, "How excellent a guile is this!"

That day the men and horses were made ready and they went forth early the next day and they came first to the region about the city of Ch'ing Chou. Now that city was encircled with the fighting men and the horsemen and they stood waving their banners and beating their drums and shouting. Then Mu Yung, the magistrate, heard report of it in the city and in great agitation he called for Hu Yien Shu to come and take counsel with him, and the magistrate said, "Now these thieves have gone to the robbers' lair and told Sung Chiang to come hither and what shall we do, then?"

Hu Yien Shu replied, "Most Gracious, let your heart rest. If these robbers have come here, then they have left behind them the strength of their own lands, for these men are only fierce when they fight about their own lair. Now that they are here, it is as though birds had left their nests and beasts their dens, and I will capture them one by one as they come. And how can they withstand me? Pray, Most Gracious, ascend to the city wall, and watch me kill them all."

Then in great haste did Hu Yien Shu put on his armor and his horse's armor, and he mounted his horse. And he bade the city gate to be opened and the drawbridge let down and he led out one thousand horsemen and set them in rank very near the city.

Then did a horseman come out from Sung Chiang's ranks and that man brought in his hand a wolf-toothed club and he lifted his voice and loudly he cursed the magistrate, saying, "You thievish governor who oppresses the people—you laid waste my whole home and now today do I come for my revenge!"

Now the magistrate Mu Yung recognized Ch'ing Ming and he fell to cursing also and he said, "You were an imperial official, nor did the Emperor ever injure you and why have you turned rebel? If I can capture you, I will cut you into pieces and into ten thousand bits! Captain Hu, put forth your hand and take this robber first!"

Now Hu Yien Shu heard this and he took up his double clubs and he urged his horse straight upon Ch'ing Ming. Ch'ing Ming also let his horse free, and flourishing his wolf-toothed club, he came to meet Hu Yien Shu. Truly these two warriors were very well matched and they fought to some forty or fifty rounds and still it could not be said who was victor and who vanquished. But the magistrate, fearing it would not be well if Hu Yien Shu fought too long, made great haste and he commanded that the gongs should be beaten and the soldiers withdrawn into the city, nor did Ch'ing Ming follow in pursuit. He returned and went to his own camp. Sung Chiang then commanded his forces to retire a mile or more.

Let it be told further of Hu Yien Shu. He returned into the city and he came down from his horse and he went to see the magistrate and he said, "I was even about to capture that Ch'ing Ming and why, Most Gracious, did you call back the soldiers?"

The magistrate replied, "I saw you had fought many rounds and I feared lest you be weary and therefore did I call back the soldiers. This Ch'ing Ming was once a fellow official of mine and he turned rebel together with Hua Yung but he cannot be despised as an enemy."

Then Hu Yien Shu said, "Most Gracious, let your heart rest. I will assuredly capture this unrighteous robber. Even now when I was fighting with him he was already using his club confusedly. Tomorrow do you, Most Gracious, watch me kill him straightway!"

And the magistrate said, "If you, Sir Warrior, are so fierce a hero as this, when you fight tomorrow then force a path for yourself. Now let three men be sent forth. Let one go to the eastern capital to implore aid, and let the other two go to the near-by towns and cities and gather together soldiers to come to our help and drive off these robbers."

Hu Yien Shu replied, "Most Gracious, how far a sight is yours!"

Then did the magistrate write letters imploring aid and he chose three captains and he sent them forth.

Let it be told now of Hu Yien Shu. He went back to his place of rest and he took off his armor to rest himself awhile. Before dawn was come there came a lesser captain who made report, saying, "To the north and outside the city there are three men upon horses and they are upon a hill there and looking into the city. The one in the middle wears a red garment and he sits upon a white horse, and of the two on either side of him I do but know that one of them is a certain Hua Yung. The one on the other side looks like a Taoist priest."

Then Hu Yien Shu said, "That one who wears the red robe is Sung Chiang and the Taoist must be the counselor Wu Yung. Do not any of you frighten them away. Only put on your armor and the armor upon your horses and come with me to capture them."

In haste did Hu Yien Shu put on his armor and mount his horse and he took up his double clubs and he led with him more than a hundred horsemen and carefully he opened the north gate and let down the drawbridge and leading the horsemen, he charged toward the hill. There he saw those three staring silently at the city and Hu Yien Shu whipped up his horse and rushed up the hill, but the three turned their horses' heads and went slowly away.

Then with all his strength he hastened ahead to where a few dried and dead trees stood and there he saw the three of them, their horses reined. Only then did Hu Yien Shu dare to go to the dead trees and suddenly he heard a shout arise. He had ridden to the edge of a pitfall and he and his horse fell headlong into the trap. Then from both sides of the pit there were thrust forth long hooks and staves, some fifty or sixty of them, and they first hooked up Hu Yien Shu and seized him and bound him and then they brought out his horse.

By this time the horsemen all were charging down and Hua Yung drew his bow and killed the first five or six of them. The ones at the back then turned their horses' heads and galloped away. Sung Chiang returned to his camp and there those to the right and to the left of him pushed Hu Yien Shu into his presence. But Sung Chiang looked at him and he rose swiftly and cried out, "Take those bonds from him and quickly!" And he himself supported Hu Yien Shu and helped him to be seated in the upper seat. Then did Sung Chiang make obeisance before him. But Hu Yien Shu asked, "Why do you do this?"

And Sung Chiang made answer, "How dares so humble an one as Sung Chiang rebel against the Emperor? It has all come about because the governors now love money too well and they oppressed me too bitterly and so was I forced to crime. Because of this I have taken refuge for the time in the mountain lair and I do but wait until the Emperor forgives me my crime. I did not think to rouse the imperial soldiers and to waste your godlike strength upon me for I do greatly esteem your high ability and if I have taken you today thus, I seek your forgiveness."

Then Hu Yien Shu said, "As for me whom you have captured, if I had died ten thousand deaths what would it have mattered! How is it then that you speak to me with such noble courtesy?"

Sung Chiang replied, "And how could such as I take a life like yours! Heaven knows what my heart is. I can but explain all to you and implore your pardon."

At this Hu Yien Shu asked, "Is it not your purpose, my Brother, that I should return to the capital and petition the Emperor to send forth an edict to forgive the robbers in that lair?"

But Sung Chiang replied, "And, Sir, how can you go? There is that Commander Kao who is of a very small, narrow heart and he forgets even a great mercy done him and he remembers every little fault a man may have. And you, Sir Warrior, have lost many men and horses and how can he not make you suffer for this crime? Now Han T'ao and P'eng Ch'i are all on the mountain in the lair. If it be so that you do not consider our lair too humble, I, Sung Chiang, would fain give my place there to you until such a time as the Emperor has need of you and sends out an edict of forgiveness. At such a time then you may put forth your heart to work for the Emperor nor will it be too late."

Then Hu Yien Shu lowered his head and knit his brows and so sat for a while in thought. At last because Sung Chiang had been so noble in courtesy and so full of reverence and because there was reason in what he said, he drew a deep breath and he knelt upon the ground and he said, "It is not that I am not loyal to my country but in truth it is because your righteousness exceeds that of every man and I cannot but follow after you. Therefore will I follow you, and I will even walk beside your horse as you ride, for now there is no road by which I can return to what I was."

Then was Sung Chiang full of joy and he invited Hu Yien Shu to come before the other chieftains and he asked Li Chung and Chou T'ung to bring forth that ink-black horse with the snowy feet and return it to Hu Yien Shu.

After this they all took counsel together as to how they might save K'ung Ming, and Wu Yung said, "There is but one way to do this and it is that Hu Yien Shu deceive them into opening the city gates. Then we need but put forth our hands and capture him. Moreover, this will prevent his ever returning."

And Sung Chiang heard this and he came in

apology to Hu Yien Shu and he said, "It is not that I covet at all what goods there are in that city but it is because the brother and the uncle of K'ung Liang are there in the gaol, and there is no way whereby we can save them, unless you, Sir Warrior, open the gates for us."

Then Hu Yien Shu answered, saying, "Since I have received such favor from you that you would even have me stay with you, then ought I to put forth my strength for you."

On that night there were appointed Ch'ing Ming, Hua Yung, Sheng Li, Yien Shun, Lü Fang, Kao Shen, Hsieh Chen, Hsieh Pao, Ou P'eng and Wang Ying, these ten chieftains, and they all disguised themselves as imperial soldiers and they went forth with Hu Yien Shu. In all there were eleven soldiers upon their horses and they came to the city and they went straight to the moat and Hu Yien Shu shouted out, "Open the gate there with all speed! I am escaping for my life!"

Then those on the city wall hearing his voice made report of it quickly to the magistrate Mu Yung. Now at this time Mu Yung was sunken in melancholy because of the loss of Hu Yien Shu and hearing it said that he had made his escape and was returned his heart was filled with joy and in all haste he mounted his horse and galloped upon the city wall. There he saw Hu Yien Shu and the ten horsemen with him, but he could not see his face. He could but recognize his voice. Then the magistrate asked, "How is it you have come back?"

Hu Yien Shu replied, "I fell into their pitfall and they captured me and took me to their camp, but those men who went with me stole that horse which was mine and gave it to me and so they have returned with me."

So the magistrate heard what Hu Yien Shu said and he commanded the soldiers to open the city gate and let down the drawbridge. And the ten chieftains came with Hu Yien Shu into the gate and they met the magistrate and immediately Ch'ing Ming gave one blow of his club and he struck the magistrate from his horse. Then Hsieh Chen and Hsieh Pao set fire to houses and Ou P'eng and Wang The Dwarf Tiger hastened into the city and killed the scattered soldiers. And Sung Chiang and a great company of horses and men, seeing the flames arise from the city, all came dashing thither and in all haste Sung Chiang sent forth the command that not one of the common people were to be hurt, but that the treasure and the stores of grain of the magistrate were to be seized. Then out of the gaol were rescued K'ung Ming and his uncle K'ung Ping and all his house and the fires were put out and the whole household of Mu Yung, young and old, were killed clean, and all his goods were divided among Sung Chiang's fighting men.

When dawn was come the robbers gave rice to such of the common people as had lost their houses by fire. The treasure and the stores of rice they had seized they placed into five or six carts. Moreover, they took more than two hundred good horses.

Then there in the court of Ch'ing Chou the robbers made a feast of congratulations and they asked the chieftains of the three mountains to join the great lair also. So Li Chung and Chou T'ung led their men back to The Peach Blossom Mountain and there they prepared all, men and horses and money and rice, and they went down the mountain, but first they set fire to the lair and destroyed it. And Lu Chi Shen and Ch'ao Cheng went back to The Double Dragon Mountain and with Chang Ch'ing and his goodwife they prepared their men and money and grain, and they also set fire to their lair.

In a few days the men and the horses of these mountains were all come together. Then Sung Chiang led this great company of fighting men and horses and he led them all to the great lair. And he sent forth Hua Yung, Ch'ing Ming, Hu Yien Shu and Chu T'ung, these four chieftains, to go ahead and open the way and they went through township and countryside, nor did they disturb anything at all. As for the people in the countryside, they came forth to meet them supporting their old and carrying their young, and they lit incense and knelt in reverence.

In a few days the great company came near the robbers' lair and the chieftains of the water came in boats to meet them, and Ch'ao Kai came down from the mountain leading his horsemen and his men on foot and they went to meet them at The Golden Sands. Then they all returned to the great lair and to the Hall Of Meeting and there they were seated. And a great feast of welcome was prepared to receive the newly come chieftains, Hu Yien Shu, Lu Chi Shen, Yang Chi, Wu Sung, Shih En, Ch'ao Cheng, Chang Ch'ing, The Goodwife Sheng, Li Chung, Chou T'ung, K'ung Ming and K'ung Liang, twelve chieftains newly come up the mountain.

When they were seated Ling Ch'ung told the story of how Lu Chi Shen had rescued him and Lu Chi Shen asked, saying, "After I left you, Sir Captain, there was not a day in which I did see your lady, and now what news is there of her?"

Ling Ch'ung replied, "After I killed Wang Lun I sent messengers back to seek after my family and I found my wife had hung herself because of the oppression of that son of the Commander Kao, and my father-in-law, because of his sorrow, fell ill and died."

Then Yang Chi told of what had passed in the old days with Wang Lün and they all said, "These things were writ thus by Heaven and they were fated so to be."

And Ch'ao Kai told of the affair of The Yellow Mud Ridge and they all sorrowed very much. That day they set aside for feasting and of this no more need be said.

Let it be told of Sung Chiang when he saw that the lair had now many more horses and men. How could he not rejoice? He bade T'ang Lung take charge of the iron smithery and make all sorts of arms and mail and chain armor. Hou Chien was to take charge of the making of banners both large and small and of the robes and the garments, the three-colored banners, the nine-starred banners, the four-starred banners, the five-starred banners, the twenty-eight-starred banners and such other banners as the flying dragon, the flying tiger, the flying bear and flying leopard and all others. He was also to see to the making of official sceptres, of white banners, red tassels and black umbrellas.

On all four sides of the mountain were put up watch towers and the wine shops on the west and the south passes were rebuilt so that those good fellows who came and went upon the mountain could be met at the one, and at the other news of the imperial soldiers could be spied out and listened upon. The wine shop to the east of the mountain was kept by Chang Ch'ing and his goodwife, since they had been formerly keepers of such a shop. The wine shop to the south was given to Sheng Sing and The Goodwife Ku. The wine shop upon the eastern road to the mountain had before been in the keeping of Chu Kuei and Yo Ho. The wine shop upon the northern road to the mountain was still given into the keeping of Li Li and Shih Ch'ien. About the three passes were built fresh stockades and certain chieftains were appointed to the keeping of them. When each had been appointed each took his place, and of this there is no more to be told.

Suddenly upon a day The Tattooed Priest Lu Chi Shen came and he said to Sung Chiang, "I have a friend and he is a pupil of Li Chung's brother, and he is called The Nine Dragoned Shih Chin. He is now upon The Little Hua Mountain in the county of Hua Ying and he is with a certain one nicknamed The Wily Warrior Chu Wu. There is another one also The Gorge Leaping Tiger Ch'en Ta and there is another yet called The White Spotted Snake Yang Ch'un. These four are there gathered together, and I do always long after them, and there has not been a day since I parted with them that they have not been upon my heart. Now am I fain to go there and see how they are and I will ask them to come hither and join with us. But I do not know what you will think of it."

Sung Chiang replied, "I also have long heard of their great names, and if you go to invite them hither, naught could be better. But if you go thus, you must not go alone. I will appoint our brother Wu Sung to go out with you for the once. He is a man of straight heart and he will be of the same mind with one like you who has renounced the world as priest."

Then Wu Sung said, "I will go with you, my Brother."

On that day they made ready their goods for the way, and Lu Chi Shen wore the garb of priest and Wu Sung disguised himself as his attendant. The two of them took farewell of all the other chieftains and went down from the lair. When they had passed The Golden Sands they went by day and slept by night and after days had thus passed they came to the region of Hua Chou and they went straight to that Little Hua Mountain.

Let it be told now of Sung Chiang. After Lu Chi Shen and Wu Sung had gone he could not let his heart be at ease about them. At last he sent Tai Chung to go after them and fetch news of them.

As for Lu Chi Shen and Wu Sung, when they had come to the foot of that mountain, there were some lesser robbers who leaped out of the roadside and stayed them and they asked, saying, "Whither do you two priests go?"

Then Wu Sung answered, saying, "Is not the lord Shih upon this mountain?"

A robber replied, "If it be that you seek after our great lord, then wait here a little while. I will go up the mountain and make announcement to our chieftain and then come again for you."

Wu Sung said, "Do you but say that Lu Chi Shen has come hither and has somewhat to say to him."

The robber was not long gone when Chu Wu was seen and Ch'en Ta and Yang Ch'un, these three, and they came to meet Lu Chi Shen and Wu Sung. But there was no sight of Shih Chin. Then Lu Chi Shen asked, saying, "Where is the great lord Shih and how is it I cannot see him?"

Then Chu Wu came forward and said, "Is this not Captain Lu of Yien An Fu?"

Lu Chi Shen replied, "I am he. This one who attends me is he who killed the tiger on The Ridge Of Ching Yang and his name is Wu Sung."

In all haste the three chiefs made bows and said, "Long have we heard of his name. But we have heard that you were upon The Double Dragon Mountain and why have you come hither today?"

Lu Chi Shen replied, "I am no longer upon The Double Dragon Mountain. We have gone to Liang Shan P'o to Sung Chiang in that great lair there, and today we came here on a purpose to seek out the great lord Shih."

Then Chu Wu said, "Since you are come hither, Honored Ones, then come up the mountain in our lair and there let this humble one tell you closely of what has befallen him."

But Lu Chi Shen cried, "If you have aught to say then say it quickly. If I do not see my brother Shih, how can I take the time to go to your cursed lair!"

And Wu Sung said, "This elder brother of mine is a man of very impatient heart. If you have something to say, it is better to say it with all speed."

So Chu Wu said, "We three humble ones upon the mountain have prospered greatly since the lord Shih came up the mountain. But one day he went down the mountain and he happened upon a painter and this man was a man of Ta Ming Fu, whose surname was Wang and his name I. He had vowed to paint wall pictures for a certain god in a temple called The Temple Of The Emperor Of The Golden Heaven and he went thither to fulfill his vow. Now he brought with him his daughter, whose name was Jade Branch, and we have a magistrate in our city, surnamed Ho, and he was once a follower of the prime minister. This magistrate is most wicked and covetous and he oppresses the people. It happened that he went on that very day to the temple to burn incense and who would have thought that he would notice how pretty a maid was Jade Branch, so that from that day continually he sent messengers to seek her for his concubine! But Wang I was not willing and at last the magistrate took the maid by force, and he exiled Wang I to a very far and evil place. His way passed by here and he happened to meet our lord Shih and Wang I told him of all this. Then the lord Shih rescued Wang I and brought him up the mountain and he killed the two guards who were with him. Moreover, he was fain to go into the court and kill that magistrate Ho, and he did not dream that the magistrate would have heard of this and bade men to seize him. Now he is in the gaol, and the magistrate is about to send out soldiers and horsemen to lay waste our lair, and here we be and without any way to escape."

Lu Chi Shen heard to the end and he said, "How dare this accursed magistrate act so without any virtue! How dare he be so fierce as this! I shall go and kill that thing!"

And Chu Wu said, "Pray come into the lair, Honored Ones, and there let us take counsel together."

But Lu Chi Shen was stout in his unwillingness, and Wu Sung put forth his hand and took hold of his staff and pointed at him with the other hand and he said, "Elder Brother, you do not see that the sunshine is already slanting across the treetops!"

Then Lu Chi Shen looked and he shouted out in his anger and they all went to the lair. And Chu Wu bade Wang I come out and make obeisance and he told again of how the magistrate had taken his daughter by force. Then the three chiefs killed cows and horses to welcome the guests. But Lu Chi Shen said, "My brother Shih is not here and therefore will I eat no mouthful of this feast. I will sleep the night only and then tomorrow I shall go and kill that thing in the court!"

Wu Sung replied, "Elder Brother, do not be in such haste as this. I will go back with you by day and by night to the great lair and we will tell Sung Chiang and we will lead forth a great company of horsemen to go and fight this man. Only then can we rescue our brother Shih Chin."

But Lu Chi Shen cried out, "And if we wait to go up the mountain and come back again then well I know his life will be gone!"

Wu Sung said, "And though you kill the magistrate yet how can you save the lord Shih? In truth I will not let you go thither alone!"

And Chu Wu exhorted Lu Chi Shen also and he said, "My Brother, pray still your wrath. What the captain Wu Sung has said is very right."

But Lu Chi Shen began to make a great uproar and he said, "It is all because of you cursed, slow-hearted men that my brother Shih has come to such a pass as this as to lose his very life! His life is in the hands of that magistrate and yet you have time for feasting and making merry!"

And how could any of them stay him by their exhorting? He drank half a cup of wine and he slept with his clothes on as he was. The next day he woke long before dawn and he took up his long staff and put on his priest's knife and he went away and no one knew whither. Then Wu Sung said, "He has not listened to us and there surely will something befall him."

And straightway did Chu Wu command two very knowing robbers to go and listen for the news of him.

Now let it be told of Lu Chi Shen. He went straight to the city of Hua Chou and as he went he asked by the way where the magistrate's court was. There were those who pointed it out to him and they said, "Go over that bridge and turn to the east and there it is."

So Lu Chi Shen went upon that bridge and there he heard everyone saying, "Priest, pray hide yourself, for the magistrate passes."

Then Lu Chi Shen said to himself, "I am even now seeking him and here he drops into my hand. Truly is he fated to die!"

Then did the horsemen in front of Ho the magistrate come pair by pair. Now this sedan in which the magistrate was sitting was a warm and padded one for the winter, and on either side of it were men who walked as guards, and in his hand each man carried a club or weapon or iron chain to guard. Lu Chi Shen, seeing this, thought to himself, "It will be hard to kill that accursed, and if I try and do not kill him they will laugh at me!"

Now Ho the magistrate looking through the window of his sedan saw Lu Chi Shen and he saw that the priest was fain to come near and yet did not. When he had passed over the bridge and come to the boundaries of his court and when he came down out of his chair he called to two of his guards and he commanded them, saying, "Do you go and invite that large fat priest there on the bridge and bid him come and eat with me."

The guards received this command and they went to the bridge and they said to Lu Chi Shen, "Our magistrate invites you to come and eat with him in the court."

Then Lu Chi Shen thought to himself, "This man ought to die by my hand, but I did fear that if I struck him just now I could not strike him dead and so I let him pass. Now even as I was about to go and seek him he comes hither to invite me!"

So he followed the guards and entered the court. There the magistrate had already commanded everything to be prepared. When he saw Lu Chi Shen come into the hall the magistrate said to him, "Put down your long staff and your knife and pray come into the inner hall and feast with me."

Now Lu Chi Shen was unwilling and at last the crowd about said, "But you are a priest and how little do you understand what you ought to do! How can you be allowed to take arms into the court of the magistrate?"

Then Lu Chi Shen thought to himself, "Even my two fists could beat that thing to powder," and so he put down his long staff and his knife and he went with the guards. Now the magistrate was at that time sitting in the inner hall and suddenly he put forth his hand and shouted, "Seize this shaven thief!"

Then from left and right there came forth four or five retainers and pulling and pushing they laid hold on Lu Chi Shen and seized him.

Even though he had been son of the King Of Heaven, how could he have escaped such a trap in the Earth, such a plot in the Heavens? Even though he had been the fiery-headed guardian god, how could he have come forth out of this dragon's watery lair, this tiger's den? Truly was it

> A flying moth darts into the flame and it is gone,
> A tortoise, angered, swallows the hook and its life is done.

What then of Lu Chi Shen's life when he had fallen into the magistrate Ho's hand? Pray hear it told in the next chapter.

Chapter 58

WU YUNG TAKES THE GOLDEN BELL BY GUILE. SUNG CHIANG MAKES A DISTURBANCE IN THE GREAT HUA MOUNTAIN IN THE WEST

IT IS SAID: So the magistrate Ho thus beguiled Lu Chi Shen into the inner hall and he shouted out, "Seize him!" and many of the retainers sprang forward and seized Lu Chi Shen and forced him there before the hall wherein the magistrate sat. Now the magistrate was about to question him when Lu Chi Shen was seen to fall into a mighty wrath and he cried out, "You adulterous thief, you who injure people—you dare even to take me and overthrow me!—Well, and if I die with my elder brother Shih Chin it will be good enough, but if I die, then my elder brother Sung Chiang will not forgive you for it! I will tell you now that there is no anger under Heaven which has not its revenge! Do you but give me back my brother Shih Chin and give me back the maid called Jade Branch and when I have taken her back to Wang I, then do you with all speed give back your place again to the Emperor so that you are no more magistrate! For I do think that such a thieving, rat-eyed man as you who does naught but lust after women ought not to be father and mother to the people! If you do these three things I bid, I will look upon you with the eyes of a god, but if you will say but half a nay, you need not think to repent later. Let me go first and see my brother Shih Chin, and then will I come back and talk with you!"

The magistrate heard this and he was so angry he could not speak. He could but stammer forth, "My heart told me this priest would be an assassin and truly is he one with Shih Chin! Such as this priest—look at him! Put him in the gaol and we will deal with him later! Assuredly this shaven donkey is even such an one as Shih Chin!"

Then without being beaten Lu Chi Shen had a great rack fastened upon him and he was thrown into the gaol of the condemned, and a letter was sent forth to the provincial court asking how to deal with his case. As for Lu Chi Shen's knife and his long staff, they were put in the magistrate's court.

Now the news of this thing stirred up the city of Hua Chou and the robbers' spies heard the news and they went as though winged and took the news up the mountain. Wu Sung was greatly frightened and he said, "We two came here on a mission to Hua Chou; now that one is captured how shall I go back and tell the chieftains?"

As he was in the midst of his perplexity there came one of the lesser robbers to say, "There is a chieftain here sent from the great lair and he is called Tai Chung The Magic Messenger. He is now at the foot of the mountain."

Then in great haste Wu Sung came down and

with Chu Wu the three gave greeting to each other, and Wu Sung told how Lu Chi Shen would not listen to his advice and so was seized and thrown into gaol. Now when Tai Chung heard this he gave a start of great fear and he said, "I can wait here no longer. I must go back to the mountain lair and make report to my elder brothers, so that they may with all speed send forth fighting men and save Lu Chi Shen."

And Wu Sung said, "I will do naught but wait here then for you and I do but pray ten thousand times that you, my Elder Brother, will go quickly and quickly return."

Then Tai Chung ate some vegetable food and he used his magic and he returned to the great lair. In three days he was come there and he came before the two chieftains, Ch'ao Kai and Sung Chiang, and he told of how Lu Chi Shen, because he would save Shih Chin, fell into the hands of the magistrate Ho. Now Ch'ao Kai heard to the end and in great agitation he said, "If our two brothers are fallen into such hardship how can we not go to save them? I cannot now delay but I will go myself this once."

Sung Chiang said, "Elder Brother, you are lord of this lair, and you are not free to go as you would. I will go in your place."

On that day there were three companies of horsemen prepared and they set forth. The first company was led by five chieftains and these were Ling Ch'ung, Yang Chi, Hua Yung, Ch'ing Ming and Hu Yien Shu, and they led out also a thousand armored horsemen and two thousand fighting men on foot, so that if they came upon mountainous roads difficult to pass they might make them smooth, or if they came to water they might make bridges. The chief of the second company was Sung Chiang and with him was counselor Wu Yung, and there were Chu T'ung, Ch'ü Ling, Hsieh Chen and Hsieh Pao, and there were six chieftains, and they led in all two thousand horsemen and men on foot. The last company was to attend to food for the horses and for the men and Li Yün, Yang Hsiung, Shih Hsiu, Li Chün and Chang Shun, five in all, were in command, and they also had on horse and afoot two thousand men.

So there were seven thousand men in all, and they left the mountain lair and they went straight to the city of Hua Chou. They went with all speed upon their way and in less than half a day they had gone more than half their way. It was first Tai Chung who went to take the news to those on The Hua Mountain, and there Chu Wu and the three of them prepared pigs and sheep and horses and they prepared good wine also and then they waited."

Let it be told further of Sung Chiang and his horsemen and fighting men. The three companies all went down from the great mountain lair and Wu Sung led Ch'en Ta and Chu Wu and the three of them came down from the mountain and made obeisance to Sung Chiang and Wu Yung, and then all the chieftains went up the mountain to the lair and seated themselves in rank. Then Sung Chiang asked concerning the city and Chu Wu made answer, "The two chiefs are seized by the magistrate Ho and locked into the gaol and they do but wait until the Emperor sends forth a clear mandate."

Then Sung Chiang asked Wu Yung, "What guile can we use to go and rescue them and what is the best guile?"

And Chu Wu said, "The city of Hua Chou is wide and broad and the moat about it is deep and very hard it is to attack it. We must use the guile that strikes from within and without together before we can succeed."

Then the counselor Wu Yung said, "Tomorrow let us go and see how that moat is. Let us take counsel together then."

And Sung Chiang drank wine until night and he longed for the dawn that he might go to see that city. But Wu Yung seeing him thus said, "Those in the city very well perceive that they have those two great tigers of ours now in their gaol, and will they not be prepared against anything? Therefore you may not go and see the city by day. Tonight the moon shines clear and bright. Let us go down at early nightfall and in an hour or two we will be there."

Therefore they waited until nightfall and Sung Chiang, Wu Yung, Hua Yung, Ch'ing Ming, Chu T'ung, in all five men upon horses, went down the mountain. They wound their way slowly along and by the end of the watch they were come to the place. There upon a high hill outside the city they reined in their horses and looked into the city of Hua Chou.

It was then about the middle of the second month of the year and the moon was bright as day and there was not a cloud in the sky and they could see that there were several gates to the city. And they saw that the walls of the city were high and that the lands within were very good and fair, and the moat about the city was deep and wide. They looked for a while, and in the far distance they perceived also that they could see that Western Hua Mountain. Now as Sung Chiang and the others looked, they saw that the city walls were stout and strong and the moat deep and wide and the whole place very impregnable, and they could think of no guile at all. At last Wu Yung said, "Let us return to the lair and there take counsel again."

So the five riding their horses went back by night to the lair, and Sung Chiang knitted his brows and hung down his head and upon his face melancholy was set. Then Wu Yung said, "I pray you send down some ten clever robbers that from afar they may listen and spy out what news there is."

Within the next two days therefore was seen a robber coming up the mountain and he made report, saying, "The Emperor sends a certain official of war to come hither with the royal hanging gold bell and he has sent him hither to this temple on our mountain to burn incense and he comes from the Yellow River to the Wei River."

Wu Yung heard this and he said, "Elder Brother, grieve no more—here is a place for guile!" And he commanded Li Chün and Chang Shun, saying, "Do you two do thus—and thus—for me and thus—"

But Li Chün said, "There is no one who knows the road, and if we could find someone to lead us in the way it would be well."

Then did The White Spotted Snake speak and say, "I, your humble brother, would fain go and help you, and what think you of it?"

At this Sung Chiang was greatly pleased and so the three went down the mountain. On the next day Wu Yung invited Sung Chiang, Li Yün, Chu T'ung, Hu Yien Shu, Hua Yung, Ch'ing Ming and Ch'ü Ling, in all seven men, to take five hundred men and go cautiously down the mountain. When they were come to the ferry of the Wei River, Li Chün, Chang Shun and Yang Ch'un had already gathered together ten-odd great boats and were there waiting. Wu Yung then commanded Hua Yung, Ch'ing Ming, Ch'ü Ling and Hu Yien Shu, these four to hide on the shore. Sung Chiang, Wu Yung, Chu T'ung and Li Yün went into the boats and Li Chün, Chang Shun and Yang Ch'un went each in a boat, and they hid along the banks of the river. There they waited for the night.

On the next day at dawn they heard in the distance the beating of drums and gongs and there came down the river the three imperial boats and on each was a yellow banner upon which was written, "The Minister Surnamed Su Appointed By The Sacred Order Of The Emperor To Burn The Imperial Incense."

Then Chu T'ung and Li Yün, each bearing his long staff, stood behind Sung Chiang. Wu Yung stood at the prow of the ship, and the minister's ship came near and the robbers put their boat in the way. Then out of the imperial ship came some twenty men in purple robes tied with silver girdles and they shouted out, "What boat is this of yours that dares to come in the way of a ship of the great minister?"

Then Sung Chiang held his weapon before him and he bowed low and called out greeting and Wu Yung stood there on the prow of the ship and he said, "This righteous man is Sung Chiang from Liang Shan P'o, and he waits here to speak to you with all respect and reverence."

Then did a small official, a purser who governed in the treasury, come forth out of the ship and he answered, saying, "This one here is appointed by the Emperor to go and burn the imperial incense in the temple of this mountain. If you are but robbers of Liang Shan P'o how dare you stay us?"

Now Sung Chiang was still bowed upon his boat and he did not rise and Wu Yung said from the prow of the boat, "But this righteous chief of ours wishes to see this one appointed by the Emperor for there is something we have to say to him."

Then the purser answered, "What sort of men are you? How dare you ask to see our high minister!"

Then did the guards cry out, "Speak no more!"

But Sung Chiang still was bowed, nor did he rise, and still did Wu Yung speak from the prow of the boat, saying, "We do but ask the high minister to come for a brief space to the shore so that we may take counsel with him."

Then the purser answered, "Do not speak like a fool and a barbarian! The minister is one appointed to a great mission by the Emperor himself, and how can he take counsel with such as you?"

Then did Sung Chiang rise up and he said, "If the minister will not see me, I do fear that these children of mine will do something to make him afraid." At this time did Chu T'ung shake the small banner that was hung upon his weapon and upon the shore Hua Yung, Ch'ing Ming, Ch'ü Ling and Hu Yien Shu came forth on their horses and they all held stretched their bows taut on the arrows, and they all came to the mouth of the river and there they stood fixed in line upon the shore.

Then did the men upon the minister's ship fall into a fright and they all ran and hid themselves in the shelter of the ship. The purser himself was afraid and he could but go into the ship and tell the minister of what was befallen them, and the minister could but come out himself and seat himself at the prow of the ship. Again did Sung Chiang bow himself in obeisance and he cried greeting and he said, "Such as we, we do not dare to behave lawlessly."

But the minister Su asked, "And why do you stay my ship then, Sir?"

Sung Chiang replied, "And how dare we stay you, the minister? I do but pray that you will come upon the shore, for I have something to say to you."

But Su the minister said, "Today I am especially appointed by imperial command to go and burn incense for the Emperor at The Western Mountain, and what can I have to take counsel with you, Sir? I am a high minister of the imperial court and how can I go thus carelessly upon the shore?"

Then did Wu Yung say from the prow of the boat, "If the minister be not willing I do but fear that these ones under me will not be willing—"

And again Li Yün shook the banner upon his weapon for a sign, and Li Chün, Chang Shun and Yang Ch'un all brought their boats forward straightway. When the minister Su saw this he was greatly frightened and Li Chün and Chang Shun took out their shining swords and held them in their hands, and they leaped across the boat and they put forth their hands once and immediately two of the minister's guards fell into the water.

Then did Sung Chiang shout forth, "Do not act like barbarians! You must not frighten this noble one!"

At this Li Chün and Chang Shun jumped, splashing, into the water and they fetched out the two guards again and put them on the ship, and they leaped upon their own boat again. But the minister was so afraid that his hands and feet were all in confusion, and Sung Chiang and Wu Yung both shouted out together, "Children, do you go away! You are not to frighten this honored one! We will take our time and persuade him to come ashore."

Then the minister Su said, "If you have aught to say then say it here, and it will be no matter."

But Sung Chiang and Wu Yung replied, "This is no place to talk. Pray come into our lair and there we will humbly say what we have to say. We have no heart to injure you. If we have aught of evil toward you then may the god of this mountain destroy us utterly!"

This time the minister had no other recourse but to ascend the shore and he could but leave the boat and do it. Then was a horse led forth from among the trees and the men helped the commander to mount and thus was he forced to go with the robbers. Sung Chiang and Wu Yung first commanded Hua Yung and Ch'ing Ming to go up the mountain with the minister; then Sung Chiang and Wu Yung mounted their horses also and they commanded that all those upon the minister's boat and the imperial incense and the imperial sacrifices and the hanging golden bell should all be brought up the mountain. There were left behind only Li Chün and Chang Shun and their men to watch the boats, and all the chieftains went up the mountain.

And Sung Chiang and Wu Yung came down from their horses and they went into the lair and they supported the minister into the Hall Of Meeting, and they gave him the seat in the center. On either side of him the chieftains stood, their swords drawn and in their hands. But Sung Chiang made four obeisances before the minister Su and he knelt before him and he said humbly,

"I was once a small official in the city of Yün Ch'en and because I was persecuted in the court and had not whither to escape there was no way left for me but to run to the mountains and become a robber, and now am I hiding from my trouble in the lair at Liang Shan P'o. I do but wait there until the Emperor commands me to come forth and serve my country. But now I have two brothers who without any cause at all have been seized by the magistrate Ho and put into the gaol. Now I would for the once borrow this imperial incense and this hanging golden bell and these guards of yours and go and play a trick upon that city of Hua Chou. When the affair is over, I will return all to you, and there can be no evil attached to your person. Pray let me know what your will is!"

Then Su the minister replied, "Though you take the incense and the hanging golden bell it matters little, but should the matter leak out, evil will come upon me indeed!"

But Sung Chiang made answer, "When you return, Sir Minister, to the capital, do you put it upon my person and there will be an end of it."

And the minister Su looked about on those men and he saw they were such as could not be refused and so he could but promise them, and Sung Chiang in all haste presented the bowl of wine and he gave thanks to the minister. Then did he take from the guards who had come with the minister all their garments and from among the robbers he chose out one who was handsome and strong and he had his beard shaved off and upon him he placed the minister's garments and this one he disguised as the minister, and Sung Chiang and Wu Yung disguised themselves as lesser officials like the purser. Hsieh Chen and Hsieh Pao and Yang Ch'un and Shih Hsiu disguised themselves as captains of the guards. The robbers all put on the purple robes and silver girdles of the guardsmen, and they took the imperial flags and the emblems and symbols of office and the sacrificial objects and they carried the imperial incense and the sacrifices and the hanging golden bell. Hua Yung, Ch'ü Ling, Chu T'ung and Li Yün disguised themselves as four guardsmen. And after this Chu Wu and Ch'en Ta and Yang Ch'un then tended the minister in the lair, and they gave food and wine to all who had come with him.

Then were Ch'ing Ming and Hu Yien Shu commanded to take with them a company of men and horses and Ling Ch'ung and Yang Chi were to take a company also and they were to divide their way to the city, and Wu Sung was to go first to the gate of the mountain temple to await them and when the whistle was blown, the plot was to begin.

But the story must not be told too long. The companies of men came down the mountain and went to the river and into the boats and so on their way, nor did they go to the city of Hua Chou, but they went at once to the temple and Tai Chung went first to announce their coming to The Temple Of The Highest Clouds. The abbot of the temple and those who tended the temple all went to the boats and brought the guests ashore. The incense and the sacrifices and all the imperial emblems were placed in order and the imperial incense was first put into the urn, and the priests in the temple lifted up the golden hanging bell and went ahead with it. And the abbot made obeisance to the false minister and Wu Yung said, "The minister fell ill by the way and he is very uneasy. Pray bring the covered sedan."

Then did those to the right and the left support the minister into the chair and they carried him into the very temple before the chair was set down. Then the false purser Wu Yung said to the abbot, "This is an especial mission from the Emperor and this incense and this golden hanging bell are brought to honor the god of this temple. How is it that the magistrate of this city does so despise us that he is not here to meet us?"

The abbot replied, "There are already those gone to tell him. I think he is now upon his way."

Before he had finished speaking, there came one appointed from the court of the city who brought with him some fifty or sixty retainers and bringing wine and sweetmeats they came to greet the minister.

Now though this lesser robber looked somewhat like the minister, he could not speak in the same way, and therefore was he said to be ill, and he was placed upon a bed and there he sat wrapped about with quilts. When these from the city saw that all the banners and emblems were those of the imperial court, how could they not believe them true? The false minister was twice told in all haste that these from the city came to give greeting, and they were led in and commanded to make obeisance at a distance from the sick minister. Seeing the minister but stretch forth his hand and say not a word his purser came forward quickly and began to reproach them thus: "This minister is the well-beloved statesman of the Emperor and though it were a thousand miles he does not fear to go forth on the imperial command and come hither to burn sacred royal incense. We did not think that he would fall ill upon the way. Now how is it that the magistrate of this city did not come forth to meet him?"

The under officer replied, "Although the vanguard did say the minister was coming yet we did not hear he drew near and for this did we not meet you and we did not dream the minister was already come to the temple. Our lord, the magistrate, would have come immediately. But because the robbers on The Hua Mountain have joined together with the robbers on Liang Shan P'o to attack the city and every day they prepare for it he has not dared to leave the city of Hua Chou, and so has he appointed me, his under officer, to come first to present the gift of the wine. Our lord will come straightway to see you."

Then did the purser say, "Our lord will not drink a drop of it. He does but bid your lord the magistrate come with all speed and make his obeisances."

Then did the under officer swiftly take the wine away again and he gave wine to such as had come with the purser, and the purser went in again to the false minister to make report, and he sought for the key and he led the under officer and they went and opened the lock and from the bag he brought forth the golden hanging bell, and he lifted it up on a bamboo pole and he bade the under officer to look at it closely. It was indeed a very fine golden hanging bell and it was made by a most clever goldsmith in the court of the eastern capital. It was set all about with seven colors of jewels and within it was set a red silk lantern. Truly was it such a bell as was hung in the center of the imperial temple, and if it had not come from the court of the Emperor how else could it have been so finely made? So the false purser gave it to the under officer to see, and again he locked it into its bag. Then the false purser took out also the imperial documents and he gave them to the under officer to see and he said, "Bid the magistrate come with all speed and choose a day for obeisance and sacrifice."

The under officer and those with him, seeing all these objects and documents, parted from the purser and they went straightway to the city of Hua Chou and there made report to the magistrate.

Let it be told further. Now was Sung Chiang secretly rejoiced in his heart and he said, "Although this magistrate is very wise and clever, yet have I deceived him until his eyes are not clear and his heart confused!"

By now Wu Sung was already standing outside the gate of the temple, and he bade Shih Hsiu hide a knife in his garments and come also to the temple gate to help Wu Sung with something. Tai Chung he bade disguise himself as a captain of the guard. The abbot of the temple then prepared some vegetable food for them to eat. Men were commanded to repair the temple.

Now while Sung Chiang was at leisure he went to look at the temple and in truth it was builded very well. The house was out of the usual and truly it was, although upon earth, yet like something from Heaven. Sung Chiang looked at it for a while and he went back again to the front of the temple and the gateman made report, saying, "The magistrate Ho is come."

Then Sung Chiang bade Hua Yung, Ch'ü Ling, Chu T'ung and Li Yün, these four guardsmen, each to take his weapons, and divide into two companies. Hsieh Chen, Hsieh Pao, Yang Hsiung and Tai Chung all bore hidden arms, and they stood to right and to left.

Let it be told now of the magistrate. He came leading more than three hundred men and he came before the temple and came down from his horse and they all crowded into the temple. The false pursers, Wu Yung and Sung Chiang, seeing that the magistrate came with more than three hundred men and that they all carried knives and weapons, shouted out, "This is the honored of the Emperor and idlers may not come in!"

Then did the crowd stay their feet and the magistrate Ho came in alone to make obeisance to the minister, and the pursers said, "The minister bids the magistrate come in to see him."

Then did the magistrate Ho come in to the hall, and looking at the robbers he bowed. The pursers said, "Magistrate, do you know you have committed a crime?"

The magistrate replied, "I did not know the minister was already come, and I do pray you will not fix crime upon me."

But the pursers said, "The minister has come by the command of the Emperor to burn incense here, and why did you not go to meet him?"

The magistrate answered, saying, "I did not receive the news that he was drawing near and it is true that I lost the chance to go and meet him."

Then did the false purser Wu Yung shout out, "Seize him!"

Hsieh Chen and Hsieh Pao, these two brothers, drew forth their swords with a swish and with the kick of a foot they overthrew the magistrate and cut off his head. Then Sung Chiang shouted out, "Brothers, put forth your hands, now!"

Soon were those three hundred who had come with him frightened into a daze and truly they could not move, and Hua Yung and the others all rushed forward together and in a short time the heads were tumbling about like beads off an abacus. Half of them rushed outside the temple gate and Wu Sung and Shih Hsiu came charging in with their knives and the robbers pursued them and killed them on all sides and there was not one left to return for those who came after them to the temple were all killed by Chang Shun and Li Chün.

Then in agitation did Sung Chiang command, "Quickly gather together the sacred incense and the golden hanging bell and put them upon the boats!"

When the robbers had pursued even to the city of Hua Chou they saw that already there were two columns of fire rising in the city, and they all rushed at once into the city. They went first to the gaol and rescued Shih Chin and Lu Chi Shen and then they beat open the treasury and robbed it of the treasure and they put it all upon carts. Lu Chi Shen leaped into the inner hall and he fetched his knife and his long staff. As for the maid Jade Branch, she had already jumped into a well and was dead.

Then did the robbers all leave Hua Chou and they got on their boats and returned to The Mountain Of Hua and they all went to make obeisance to the minister and they returned the sacred incense and the golden hanging bell and the banners large and small and they returned everything and they thanked the minister for his graciousness. Then Sung Chiang brought forth a plate of gold and silver and sent out to all, and it mattered not whether he was high or low whoever had come with the minister was given gold and silver. And a feast was made there in the lair to thank the minister and the chieftains all escorted him down the mountain.

When they had come to the mouth of the river they returned to the minister every boat and all he had had before, nor was one thing lacking and the men who had been with him were all returned also. Then Sung Chiang parted from Su the minister, and he returned up The Hua Mountain. There with the four chiefs he took counsel as to the gathering together of all the gold and silver in the lair, and then they set fire to the place and burned it. All the men and fighting men and horses and grain and hay all went toward the robbers' lair at Liang Shan P'o. Wang I was given money and he went his way to other parts and of him no more is known.

Let it be told further that the minister Su when he had gone down to his boat came to the city of Hua Chou and there it was already known that the robbers from the mountain had killed the magistrate and many of the soldiers and that all the treasure had been stolen. Of the city soldiers more than a hundred had been killed and all their horses had been robbed. In the temple also had there been many killed. The under officer of the court, therefore, was commanded to write a letter with all speed to tell the governor above, who might then tell the Emperor, and the letter told how Sung Chiang had robbed upon the highway the sacred incense and the golden hanging bell and thus he had deceived the magistrate into coming to the temple, and there killed him.

And Su the minister came to the temple and burned there the sacred incense and the golden hanging bell he gave to the abbot. That self-same night he returned with all speed to the capital and he memorialized the whole affair to the Emperor, and of this no more need be told.

Let it be told further of Sung Chiang. Thus he saved Shih Chin and Lu Chi Shen and he took the four good fellows from The Little Hua Mountain and at that time he divided all into three companies and so he returned to the great mountain lair, nor was anything robbed at all by the way.

Now Tai Chung went up the mountain first to make report, and Ch'ao Kai and all the chieftains came down the mountain to meet the others and with Sung Chiang they all went up into the Hall Of Meeting and there they gathered together and when they had all made greeting to one another, a feast of rejoicing was prepared.

The second day Shih Chin, Chu Wu and Ch'en Ta and Yang Ch'un took out their own moneys and made a feast to give thanks to Ch'ao Kai and Sung Chiang. In the midst of the feasting Ch'ao Kai said, "I have a thing to say and because my brother Sung Chiang has not for day upon day been in the lair I have not told of it, and yesterday because the four brothers were newly come, I did not speak out either. Three days ago Chu Kuei came up the mountain and he made report, saying, 'Near the great city of Hsü Chou there is a town and near this a mountain and upon it there is newly come a company of robbers and they have gathered together some three thousand and more men and horses. The chieftain at their head is surnamed Fan and his name is Lui and his nickname is King Of The Devils Who Roil Earth, and he can command the winds and call forth rains and he uses ways of fighting as a god does. Beneath him are two lesser chiefs and one is surnamed Hsiang and his name is Ch'ung and his nickname is The Eight Armed Lo Chao, and he can wield a great round shield and into it are thrust twenty-four flying knives. If he plucks out one of these knives there is not one man he misses at a hundred paces, and he holds in his hand also a spear pointed at both ends. There is yet another surnamed Li and his name is Kun and his nickname is The Heaven Flying God, and he wields also a round shield and into this shield are thrust twenty-four knives pointed at either end, and if he draws one forth and darts it at a man, there is not one he misses. In his hand he carries also a magic dagger. These three are sworn brothers and they stand on that Mountain Of Wild Grass And Rocks and they rob the countryside and they have taken counsel together and they plan a way whereby they can capture the great lair of Liang Shan P'o.' When I heard him say this I was suddenly completely filled with anger."

When Sung Chiang heard this he also was mad with his anger and he said, "How dare these robbers act so without law! I will go down the mountain once again and see—"

But just then The Nine Dragoned Shih Chin was seen to rise and he said, "We four brothers have but newly come to the great lair, nor have we done a service here so small as the half of a grain of rice. I would therefore lead out my own horsemen and go and capture these robbers."

Then Sung Chiang was greatly pleased and so Shih Chin counted out his own men and horsemen and together with Chu Wu, Ch'en Ta and Yang Ch'un they all put on their garments of war and they came to take farewell of Sung Chiang and go down the mountain. And they called the boats to The Golden Sands and they went straightway to the mountain. Within three days they could already see that mountain. Then Shih Chin drew in his breath and he asked Chu Wu, saying, "I do not know what this place is but I believe it is that place where the first Emperor of Han, before he was made Emperor, killed the white snake."

Chu Wu and the three of them then sighed also, and in a short time they were come to the mountain and the robbers who were spies upon that road went up and told of their coming.

Let it be told now of Shih Chin. He divided the men he had brought with him from Hua Mountain and he set them in place and he himself put on his own armor and he rode upon a horse as red as coals of fire. Then he went to the front of his ranks and he held across his saddle in his hand a three-pointed, two-bladed spear. Behind him came three chieftains and these were Chu Wu, Ch'en Ta and Yang Ch'un. These four good fellows reined in their horses and stood before the ranks. When they had been watching for a short time they saw come flying down from the mountain a company of men and horses. There were two fellows in the front and the foremost was a man of Hsü Chou and the county of P'ei, and his name was Hsiang Ch'ung. Truly enough did he bear a round shield. Behind it were the twenty-four knives and in his right hand he held a spear pointed at both ends. Behind him was one who carried an ensign. Upon this ensign was written four large characters, "The Eight Armed Lo Chao." The one behind was also a man of the county of P'ei, and his surname was Li and his name was Kun, and truly also did he bear a round shield and behind it were thrust twenty-four double-pointed knives. In his left hand he bore also the shield and in his right hand he held outstretched the magic dagger. Behind it was his ensign and upon it were written four large characters which were "The Heaven Flying God."

Thus did the two men come on foot down the mountain and they saw the opposing ranks and they saw Shih Chin, Chu Wu, Ch'en Ta and Yang Ch'un, the four astride their horses before their ranks. They made no great talk, but the robbers began to beat their drums and the two chiefs came whirling their great round shields and they came forward together.

Now Shih Chin could not withstand their coming and those behind him gave way, although those in front of Shih Chin held off the enemy. Then Chu Wu and his men began to shout and they all retreated some ten miles and more, and Shih Chin missed by but a very little a blow from one of the flying darts of the enemy. Yang Ch'un being slow to turn his horse, the beast was wounded, and Yang Ch'un leaped off and ran for his life.

Shih Chin then took count of his men and he had lost a half of them. And he took counsel with Chu Wu and he was even about to send one back to the great lair to beg for help when in the midst of his sorrow he saw a fighting man come and make report, "To the north on the great road there are clouds of dust and there must be some two thousand horsemen coming thither."

When Shih Chin looked from his horse to see what these were he saw the ensigns of the great robber lair and at the front of them all rode two great warriors and one was Hua Yung and the other was Ch'ü Ling. Then Shih Chin went to meet them and he said, "Hsiang Ch'ung and Li Kun came whirling along with their great round shields, and our horsemen and fighting men could not withstand them."

Hua Yung replied, "Our elder brother Sung Chiang when he saw you had come hither, could not let his heart rest and he repented it very heartily and so he sent the two of us to come hither to help you."

Then were Shih Chin and the others greatly rejoiced and they all joined their men together and encamped. On the next day at dawn as they were about to rouse their men to do combat, again one came, saying, "There on the north on the great highway there is yet another company of men and horses."

Then Hua Yung, Ch'ü Ling and Shih Chin all mounted their horses to see, and it was Sung Chiang himself and the counselor Wu Yung, Kung Sun Sheng, Ch'ai Chin, Chu T'ung, Hu Yien Shu, Mu Hung, Sheng Li, Huang Hsin, Lü Fang and Kao Shen, and they came with three thousand men and horses. Shih Chin told closely how hard it had been to withstand Hsiang Ch'ung and Li Kun and their flying darts and their whirling shields and how he had lost many men and horses. Then was Sung Chiang in great fear and Wu Yung said, "Encamp these men and horses now, and let us take counsel together again."

Now Sung Chiang was a man of impatient temper and he would fain have led his men out straightway to battle. He went to the foot of the mountain. It was already night and he looked up to the top of the mountain and it was covered with the light of blue-green lanterns. When Kung Sun Sheng saw this he said, "Those blue-green lanterns in that lair mean that there must be one there who knows how to use magic. Let us withdraw our men and horsemen for the present and tomorrow I will use a piece of magic whereby we can seize these two men."

Then was Sung Chiang greatly rejoiced and he sent forth the command, "Let the men and horsemen retire for seven miles and there set up camp."

On the morning of the next day Kung Sun Sheng set forth this magic. Truly thereafter

The Kings of Devils went humble to the robbers' lair
And all those heroic ones turned heart and soul there.

What piece of magic therefore did Kung Sun Sheng show forth?

Pray hear it told in the next chapter.

Chapter 59

KUNG SUN SHENG VANQUISHES THE DEVIL ON THE MOUNTAIN OF WILD GRASS AND ROCKS. CH'AO KAI IS WOUNDED WITH AN ARROW IN THE VILLAGE OF CHEN T'OU

IT IS SAID: So Kung Sun Sheng told Sung Chiang and Wu Yung of his magic and he showed it forth, saying, "This magic was used in the time of the three kingdoms of Han and there was a man named Kuo Liang and there was a way he set rocks in a row. Toward the four directions he divided his men into sixty-four companies and in the center he placed a great warrior, and these companies were so set as to seem to have four heads and eight tails. When they moved it seemed they marched to the left but in truth they turned to the right, and it was as though Heaven and Earth and winds and rain were shown forth there. When they stood they looked like dragons, like tigers, like birds, like serpents!

"Now when those three come down the mountain and charge toward us here, then let our men divide and let them come in and wait until they have come fairly to the camp. Then do you all but look at this ensign I have with seven stars upon it, and shape the men into the form of a serpent. Then I will use my magic to make these three men be caught in the midst of the camp so that they have no road either before or behind nor any gate to right or left. And let a pit have been dug to the north and slowly force them thither so that they must fall into it. Let men with long-handled hooks be ambushed there also and let them be ready to capture the enemy."

Now Sung Chiang, hearing this, was much pleased, and he sent forth a command that great and small were to fulfill this plan, and eight very fierce warriors were to stand to guard the lair. These eight were Hu Yien Shu, Chu T'ung, Hua Yung, Ch'ü Ling, Mu Hung, Sheng Li, Shih Chin and Huang Hsin. Then Ch'ai Chin and Lü Fang and Kao Shen were to lead the fighting men for the time. Sung Chiang and Wu Yung and Kung Sun Sheng went with Ch'en Ta to wave the banners. Chu Wu was told to lead out five fighting men and they were to stand upon a near hilltop and watch what went on in the camp and make report of it.

Now at this time it was about mid-morning and the fighting men that were left were set in the order planned, and the banners were waved and the drums beaten as call to battle. Then upon that mountain were seen from twenty or thirty places drums beaten until the earth thundered with the sound and the three chieftains all came to the foot of the mountain, and they divided their three thousand. The company to the left and to the right were led by Hsiang Ch'ung and Li Kun and the one in the middle who stood forth from those surrounding him was that King Of The Devils Who Roil Earth Fan Lui and he rode a black horse and he stood in front of the ranks. Now although this Fan Lui could use magic he could not wield weapons and when he saw Sung Chiang and about him his men gathered thick in all directions he was pleased in his secret heart and he said to himself, "Since you have set your men so, you do fall in my plot!"

Then he bade Hsiang Ch'ung and Li Kun, "If you see a wind arise then take five hundred men with whirling shields and darts and kill your way into their ranks!"

So Hsiang Ch'ung and Li Kun received his command, and each took up his round shield and the one took his double-pointed spear and the other his magic dagger and they waited for the sign that Fan Lui was to set. They saw that

Fan Lui sat still upon his horse and in his right hand he held his chained hammer that was like a shooting star, and in his left hand he held his magic dagger that was called King Of The Devils Who Roil Earth and he muttered a magic rune and he shouted out, "Speed!"

Straightway a mighty wind rose in all four directions and the sands flew past and stones moved. The heavens grew black and the earth was dark and the sun gave forth no more light. Then did Hsiang Ch'ung and Li Kun lead forth their five hundred men and they came charging forth.

Now when Sung Chiang and his men saw them charge thus they divided into two parts and Hsiang Ch'ung and Li Kun rushed into the very heart of the camp, and those at the sides let fly their arrows upon the enemy. But there were not more than forty or fifty men who came thus into the camp and the others all returned to their own side. Then when Sung Chiang saw that Hsiang Ch'ung and Li Kun had come thus into the very camp he commanded Ch'en Ta to wave the ensign of the seven stars, and then did those divided men form into the shape of a great serpent. Hsiang Ch'ung and Li Kun were there in the camp and they rushed to the east and to the west and they turned to the right and to the left but they could find no way of escape. Then Chu Wu from the hill waved a small banner and the two snared ones ran to the east, and Chu Wu waved his flag to the east, and if they ran to the west then he waved to the west.

Now Kung Sun Sheng, watching from a height, drew forth a magic dagger whose name was "The Most Ancient" and he murmured a magic rune and he shouted, "Speed!" and he used the mighty wind and sent it after Hsiang Ch'ung and Li Kun so that it roared in confusion about their feet.

Then those two there in the robbers' camp saw the heaven black and the earth grown dark and the sun give forth no more its light, and they saw no man or horse on any side, and there was blackness everywhere nor could they see one of those who had followed after them.

And Hsiang Ch'ung and Li Kun felt terror in their hearts and they did but seek for a way of escape, but in spite of a hundred efforts they could not find that way. Even as they were seeking they heard a mighty thunder clap and they stood and cried bitterness without ceasing. Suddenly they stumbled upon something and they turned head over heels into a great pit large enough to entrap horses. From both sides hooks soon had them fast and dragged them up and they were tied about with hempen ropes and their captors took them upon the ridge in triumph to show their prowess. And Sung Chiang pointed at them with his whip and his men charged down upon the three companies of the enemy, but Fan Lui had already turned and leading his men he went leaping up the mountain, but of his three thousand men and horses the greater half were lost.

Then Sung Chiang gathered together his men and all the chieftains were seated before the central tent and the fighting men led Hsiang Ch'ung and Li Kun before them. But Sung Chiang looked at them and in haste he commanded that their bonds were to be loosed from them and himself he poured a bowl of wine for them and he said, "Sirs and Brave Men, do not blame us for this. It cannot be but thus in war. This humble one, who am I, Sung Chiang, have long heard of the fame of you three great chieftains, and it has been my purpose to beseech you to come hither and join our company, but because no convenient opportunity has come for this, I have in error allowed the time to pass. But if you will not hold me wrong and if you will ascend to our mountain with us, then will I rejoice indeed."

Then when the two heard this they made obeisance to the very ground and they said, "Long have we heard the great name of The Opportune Rain but it has not been our fate to meet and make obeisance before you. Truly has our elder brother ever had great virtue. We ourselves did not know a good man, and it was as though we fought against Heaven and Earth. Now that you have captured us this day though we had died ten thousand deaths, it would have availed naught. And yet you turn about and treat us with such high courtesy! If you do not kill us, then will we reward your mercy with our service and we will not fear to die. As for that Fan Lui, if he has not us two, how can he live? Sir Chieftains, if you are willing to free one of us to go back, we will tell Fan Lui to come hither also and submit himself. But we do not know what you, Sir Chieftains, purpose."

Then Sung Chiang said, "Sirs and Brave Men, you need not leave even the one of you here as hostage. I do pray the two of you to go back together to your lair and in a few days I will hear your good news."

Then the two made obeisance and gave thanks and they said, "Truly are you a mighty warrior and if Fan Lui will not come hither we will seize him and bring him by force."

Sung Chiang, hearing this, was much pleased and he asked the two to come within and take food and wine and he gave them new garments to wear and he chose out two good horses and he bade his men return them their weapons and shields and he himself escorted the two out of the camp and on their way back to their lair.

Then the two men riding their horses could not have done with their gratitude for his mercy and they came straightway to The Mountain Of Wild Grass And Rocks. When the robbers saw them they were filled with fear and they met them and brought them to the lair. Fan Lui then asked the two how they had come and Hsiang Ch'ung and Li Kun said, "We are such men who, having fought against Heaven itself, do merit ten thousand deaths."

Then Fan Lui asked, "Brothers, why do you talk like this?"

So the two told of all Sung Chiang's goodness and Fan Lui said, "If Sung Chiang has so mighty a goodness as this such men as we must not rebel against Heaven. Tomorrow let us all go and give ourselves over to him."

The twain then said, "And for this did we come."

During that night they gathered together all they wanted from the lair and the next day at dawn the three went down the mountain together and they went straight to the front of Sung Chiang's camp and there they made obeisance to the very earth. But Sung Chiang lifted up the three men and he asked them to come into the tent and there sit down. When the three saw that Sung Chiang had no heart of doubt toward them one by one each told him all their heart and history. And they made obeisance before all the chieftains and they invited them to come up to the lair on The Mountain Of Wild Grass And Rocks and there they killed cows and horses and feasted Sung Chiang and all the chieftains and they rewarded the soldiers with money.

After the feasting was over Fan Lui made obeisance to Kung Sun Sheng as to his superior and Sung Chiang stood up and bade Kung Sun Sheng teach Fan Lui the magic called The Five Elements and The True Heart Of Heaven and so Fan Lui was greatly rejoiced.

In the midst of those days they brought forth their cows and their horses and what treasure and food there was in the lair and they bound their goods upon the beasts and when men and horses were so prepared they burned the houses and stockades in the lair and they went with Sung Chiang and his comrades and all their men and so they went to the robbers' lair at Liang Shan P'o, and of their journey there is naught to be told.

Thus did Sung Chiang with all his good comrades and the fighting men and horses get to the great lair, and even as they were about to ferry across they saw among the reeds near the highway a tall fellow gazing at Sung Chiang and he made obeisance. In great haste then did Sung Chiang come down from his horse and he lifted the man up and he asked, saying, "What is your honored surname and what your name and whence do you come?"

That fellow answered, saying, "This humble one is surnamed Tuan and I have a double name which is Ching Chu, but when men see this red hair of mine and my yellow beard they call me The Yellow Haired Dog. My ancestors were once men of Chu Chou and all my life I have lived by robbing the men of the north of their horses. In the spring of this year I went to the north and to a certain hill called Handle Of Spear, and there I robbed a very good horse, white as snow nor was there on its whole body a single hair of any other hue. From head to tail it was ten feet long and from its hoofs up it stood eight feet tall and that horse could run more than three hundred miles in a day, and it was famed through all the north and it was called White Lion That Shines In The Night. Now this horse was that one ridden by the son of the great king of the Chin country, but it was loosed there by the mountain and so this humble one came past there and robbed it. Long have I heard far and wide by river and lake of the great name of Sung Chiang, The Opportune Rain, but there has been no way whereby I could meet you. Now I would fain have given this horse to you, Great Chieftain, as an earnest so that I may come to you. But I did not dream as I passed by the town of Ling Chou and through the village of the family surnamed Chen that their fifth son would seize it from me. I said to him, 'But this horse belongs to Sung Chiang of Liang Shan P'o.' and I did not think that he would do what he did and fall into great curses. I, humble as I be, dared not to gainsay him, and I ran away and came hither on purpose to tell you."

Now as Sung Chiang looked at this man he saw that although he had in truth very curly reddish hair, yet he was a man above the common and he was pleased in heart and he said, "If it be so, pray come with me into the mountain lair and we will take counsel together."

Then did Sung Chiang lead this Tuan Ching Chu and they went into the boats and they went to The Golden Sands and there came ashore, and the great chief Ch'ao Kai and all the chieftains met them and brought them to the Hall Of Meeting, and Sung Chiang bade Fan Lui, Hsiang Ch'ung and Li Kun to greet all the chiefs, and Tuan Ching Chu was with them. Then was the drum in the guest hall struck and a feast of congratulation was prepared there.

Now Sung Chiang, seeing how there were now many men and horses added to the lair and how from all directions goodly men came to join them, bade the chiefs Li Yün and T'ao Chung Wang to oversee the building of new houses and the making of stockades about them.

And Tuan Ching Chu again told how fair a horse that was and Sung Chiang bade Tai Chung The Magic Messenger to go to the Chen village and spy out where that horse was. Tai Chung was gone some four or five days and he came back and he told all the chieftains, saying, "In that Chen village there are more than three thousand homes and there is one among them called The House Of The Magistrate. Now the elder in this house was once a man of the country of Chin and his name is the old lord Chen. and he has five sons and they are called the Five Tigers. The eldest is named Chen T'u, the second is named Chen Mi, the third is Chen So, the fourth is named Chen K'uei, the fifth is named Chen Sheng. These have a tutor who is named Shi Wen Kung, and one who aids him named Shu Ting. There in that village they have five or seven thousand men and horses and they have built a stockade and they have made more than fifty carts of war. And they have spread abroad their purpose that we and they shall not live at the same time, and they are determined to seize our chieftains to the very last man and so they are our enemies. As for that horse White Lion That Shines In The Night, it is now given to the instructor Shi Wen Kung to ride. But there is something yet more hateful than this. That man has made up a verse which even the children on the streets sing and they say,

> 'When we shake the bells for war
> Gods and devils fear the roar,
> Iron cart and iron chains,
> Strongly nailed with strongest iron,
> Have we made to waste the lair.
> We will seize the chief Ch'ao Kai,
> Living will we take Sung Chiang,
> Living also seize Wu Yung.
> Here be we Five Tigers Chen,
> Known to all beneath the heavens!'

There is not one who does not sing this and truly it is so it cannot be borne any longer!"

When Ch'ao Kai heard this he was full of a mighty anger and he said, "How dare these beasts act so without any law! This time will I assuredly go forth myself and if I cannot seize these beasts, I will not return to the mountain. I will use five thousand men and horses and I will appoint twenty chieftains to go down the mountain with me, but the others are to remain with Sung Chiang and guard the mountain."

On that day therefore did Ch'ao Kai call forth Ling Ch'ung, Hu Yien Shu, Ch'ü Ling, Mu Hung, Chang Heng, Yang Hsiung, Shih Hsiu, Sheng Li, Huang Hsin, Yien Shun, Teng Fei, Ou P'eng, Yang Ling, Liu T'ang, Juan The Second, Juan The Fifth, Juan The Seventh, P'ei Sheng, Tu Ch'ien and Sung Wan, in all twenty chieftains, and they led with them three companies of horsemen down the mountain.

Now Sung Chiang and Wu Yung and Kung Sun Sheng and all the chieftains went so far as

The Golden Sands, and as they were drinking wine together there blew up a mighty wind and it snapped off the pole of the banner Sung Chiang had had newly made. When they saw this every man's face changed its hue and Wu Yung, seeing it, said, "Elder Brother, even as you lead forth the fighting men the wind arises and breaks off the pole of our banner and this is a very evil thing for war. Better then would it be if you delayed for a few days and then went forth to do battle with those men."

But Ch'ao Kai replied, "There are ever winds and clouds rising out of the heavens, and what is there strange in it? If we do not take advantage of the warmth of spring and if we do not go and if we wait until their strength is waxed great and then we go forth to wage our war with them, it will be too late. Do not stay me. This time I shall go forth the once, whatever befall!"

How could Wu Yung alone restrain him? So Ch'ao Kai led forth his men and they ferried across the waters, and Sung Chiang returned to the mountain lair and secretly he bade Tai Chung to go down the mountains and spy for what might befall.

Let it be told now of Ch'ao Kai as he led forth his five thousand horsemen and the twenty chieftains, and they came near to the village of Chen and opposite them were the stockades and on that day he led forth his chieftains mounted upon their horses and they went to look at that village. Now as these goodly fellows reined in their horses and looked about them they saw a man seated upon a horse come flying out of a willow wood and with him were seven or eight hundred men. In the midst of them was a goodly fellow and it was the fourth son of the family of Chen who was named Chen K'uei, and in a great voice he shouted forth, "You are those small thieves of Liang Shan P'o, and you are rebels against the Emperor! I shall seize you and drag you to court and claim my reward! Heaven gives me this chance and why do you still sit astride your horses, and to what hour will you sit there waiting?"

Then did Ch'ao Kai fall into a mighty wrath, and when he turned his head to look there was a warrior who leaped out upon his horse and it was none other than that goodly fellow of the mountain lair, The Leopard Headed Ling Ch'ung. The two whirled their horses about and they fought more than twenty rounds and Chen K'uei perceived that he could not overcome Ling Ch'ung. Therefore he drew back his weapon and turned his horse and went back into the wood, and Ling Ch'ung held his horse and did not pursue him. Then Ch'ao Kai led his men back into their encampment that they might take counsel together as to how to attack the village of Chen. And Ling Ch'ung said, "Tomorrow let us go to the mouth of the village and there stir up battle and we will see what they have of skill and men and then we can take counsel again."

The next day therefore as soon as dawn came Ch'ao Kai led the five thousand horsemen to the mouth of the village of Chen and there was a wild but level plain there. When they had formed themselves upon that they struck the drums and shouted their cry of battle. Then from the wall of the village there sounded the noise of fireballs and a great company of men and horses came forth. In a line in front of them were seven good fellows and in the center of them was that instructor Shi Wen Kung. To the left of him was the assistant instructor Shu Ting, and on the right was the old lord of the Chen family, and Chen T'u. To the right beyond were Chen Mi and Chen K'uei and to the left beyond were Chen Sheng and Chen So, and they were all armored from head to foot. Then the instructor Shi Wen Kung turned himself and thrust his arrows into their quiver and the horse upon which he sat was that White Lion That Shines In The Night. In his hand he bore a square battle axe.

Then three blows were struck upon the drum and from among the ranks of the Chen village there were seen to come forth several carts and they were placed before the ranks. And Chen T'u pointed at the enemy and he began to curse, saying, "You thieves and rebels against the Emperor! Do you not see our carts for prisoners? If I kill every one of you yet would I not be called a good fellow! I shall catch you every man alive and fasten you into these carts and take you to the eastern capital, and only thus will the power of the Five Tigers be shown forth! Turn to us quickly, then, and kneel before us and there may yet be a way for you!"

But Ch'ao Kai when he heard this was full of great wrath and he lifted his weapon and he urged on his horse and he dashed at Chen T'u and all his men rushed forward as one. Then were the men on both sides fighting and struggling in confusion and gradually step by step the men and horsemen of the Chen family were forced back into their village, and Ling Ch'ung and Hu Yien Shu rushed to the east and to the west killing as they went, but seeing that the roadways were not good, they hastened back and withdrew their soldiers. On that day both sides lost many men and many horses.

Then Ch'ao Kai went back to his camp and there was in truth sorrow in his heart. All the warriors besought him, saying, "Elder Brother, pray ease your heart and open it wide. Do not close melancholy within and so harm your body. When our elder brother Sung Chiang sallied forth with the men there were times when he too was vanquished. Come what may, we will conquer and return to the lair. In the confusion of battle today both sides lost men and horses, nor did we only lose. Why then should you be so sorrowful?"

But still Ch'ao Kai was melancholy and there was no joy in him. Thereafter each day for three days he went out to do battle but each day there was not one of the enemy to be seen.

On the fourth day there came suddenly two priests and they came to Ch'ao Kai's tent there to make obeisance and the fighting men led them into the tent. And the two priests knelt down and made report, "We are two priests set to watch the temple on the mountain and our temple is continually harassed by the Five Tigers of the Chen family. They come thither to destroy and there is nothing of gold or treasure which they have not asked of us. Now we two know very well where they are and where they go and how they come in, and we know it all. Therefore we have come hither today on a purpose to make our obeisance before the great chieftain and we will lead you to where they are encamped, that you may go in and seize them. If they can all be driven out, then happy will we be."

Now Ch'ao Kai heard this with much pleasure and he invited the two priests to be seated and he gave them wine and food. There was only Ling Ch'ung who, seeing it, exhorted Ch'ao Kai, saying, "Elder Brother, do not heed what they say. It may be there is a plot in what they say."

But Ch'ao Kai replied, "And how could two priests be willing to lie like that? Long have we of Liang Shan P'o done such deeds as are good nor have we robbed the lands through which we passed, and what enmity have these two with us that they should come hither to deceive? Doubtless the Chen family cannot conquer us at any odds, and why do you suspect these? Brother, do not have a suspicious heart and so perhaps lose the chance of a great deed. I will go forth myself this night."

Then did Ling Ch'ung beseech him bitterly and he said, "Elder Brother, do not go forth at this time. I will take half the men myself and go forth to their camp. Do you but stand outside to aid me if need comes."

But Ch'ao Kai made answer, "And if I will not go, who will be willing to lead them? Do you stay outside with half the men for aid."

Then Ling Ch'ung asked, "Elder Brother, and whom will you take for this battle?"

Ch'ao Kai replied, "Count out ten chieftains and divide two thousand five hundred men and let them go." And the ten chieftains were Liu T'ang, Hu Yien Shu, Juan The Second, Ou P'eng, Juan The Fifth, Yien Shun, Juan The Seventh, Tu Ch'ien, P'ei Sheng and Sung Wan.

On that night when these had eaten they took the bells from the horses and the men put each a bit of wood in his mouth and when the night was at its blackest hour they went silently with the two priests and they went straight to that temple. Now when Ch'ao Kai looked at it he saw it to be a very ancient temple and he came down from his horse and went within, and he saw there were no priests there. Then he asked those two priests, "How is it that in so large a temple there is not one priest?"

The priests replied, "Those beasts of the Chen family have so troubled them they have driven them all away and in despair they went every man to his own home again. There is but an old abbot here and a few attendants who live behind the temple in the court of the pagoda. Leave your horse and your men here now and wait until the end of the watch when we will lead you to the camp."

Ch'ao Kai asked, "And where is their camp?"

The priests replied, "They have four encampments, but the north camp is where the Chen brothers are with their men. If you destroy that one camp then are the others vanquished also."

Again Ch'ao Kai asked, "And when can we go?"

The priests replied, "It is now but the second watch of the night. Wait until the third watch and they will be all unprepared."

So Ch'ao Kai listened then and he heard the sound of the watch being beaten in the streets of the village, and after a while he could hear it no more. Again he heard the sound of the half watch, and after this he heard no more. Then the priests said, "Now they are all asleep and we can go."

So the priests led the way, and Ch'ao Kai led with him some of the warriors and they mounted their horses and they led with them the fighting men and left the temple. When they had gone less than two miles they could not see the two priests in the darkness and the men in front dared not go on, for as they looked about them they saw the roads leading in all directions nor could they see any house at all. Then were the fighting men agitated and they went to make report to Ch'ao Kai and Hu Yien Shu gave the order to turn back with all speed. But when they had gone less than a hundred paces they heard the mingled sounds of drums and gongs and there was such a shouting as shook the very earth. Suddenly they saw torches flaming everywhere.

Then did Ch'ao Kai and his warriors seek for a path of escape and they had but gone two bends of a road when they fell upon a company of horsemen and from these came scattered arrows. With a slash one of the arrows struck Ch'ao Kai full in the face and he fell from his horse. But the three Juan brothers, Liu T'ang, P'ei Sheng, these five chieftains, risked their lives and they ran forward and lifted Ch'ao Kai upon his horse again, and they fought their way through to the village. At the mouth of the village Ling Ch'ung and the others were waiting to aid them, and only then could they make a stand. The two armies there opposed fought untill dawn and then each returned to its camp.

Now when Ling Ch'ung returned and counted the men, of the chieftains, Yien Shun, Ou P'eng, Sung Wan and Tu Ch'ien had one by one escaped with their lives. Of the two thousand five hundred men and horses who had been led forth there were left but one thousand and two or three hundred and they returned to the camp only because they had followed Hu Yien Shu.

Now when all the chieftains came to see Ch'ao Kai they saw the arrow had struck full into his cheek, and when it was pulled out the blood flowed so freely that Ch'ao Kai fell to the ground and when they looked at the arrow there were three letters upon it which said "Shi Wen Kung." Then Ling Ch'ung called out, "Bring forth that medicine for wounds which is called The Golden Spear!"

But this arrow was a poisoned arrow and Ch'ao Kai had received the poison into himself and already he could not speak. Then Ling Ch'ung commanded that he be put into a cart and he bade Liu T'ang and the three Juan brothers and Tu Ch'ien and Sung Wan to go back first with Ch'ao Kai to the great lair. As for the other fourteen chiefs, they were to take counsel together in the lair. Then Ling Ch'ung said, "Tonight our chieftain Ch'ao Kai returns to the lair, and we did not dream such a thing would come to pass. It is because of that sudden great evil wind. We ought therefore to gather together our men and return with all speed also. Yet we must wait for the command of our elder brother Sung Chiang to come down to us before we can return, for having but half completed our victory over this Chen village, it will not be well if we depart."

Thus in the fifth watch of that night when the sky was turning faintly to dawn the fourteen chieftains were there in the camp sighing and full of unease and they were fain to do this and that and yet nothing seemed well for them to do. Suddenly they saw a man of theirs come in from the road who made report, saying, "There are in front of us four or five ranks of horsemen who are charging hither and I cannot count how many torches there are."

Ling Ch'ung heard this and all the chieftains sprang on their horses and it was true that on all sides the mountains were alight with the flare of torches and it was as bright as day with their light. On all four sides the sounds of shouting came to the camp. Then Ling Ch'ung led the chieftains and they did not go out to do combat, but they took up their camp and with all their men they retreated. Behind them the horsemen of the Chen family pursued with all vigor and thus one army retreated and the other fought, and only when some twenty miles had been passed did they separate.

When the robbers counted their number once more they had lost some five to seven hundred men. After such a great vanquishment they retreated with haste into the paths they knew and they returned to the great mountain lair.

When all the chiefs had crossed the waters and ascended the mountain they went to see how the chieftain Ch'ao Kai was. Already he could take neither water nor rice, and he ate no food at all, and his whole body was swollen and Sung Chiang stayed continually by his bedside mourning and weeping, and all the chiefs stood about the curtains of his bed. In the third watch of that night Ch'ao Kai's illness grew yet more grave. Then he turned his head and he looked at Sung Chiang and he gave command thus: "Good Brother, do not blame me for what I say. Whoever captures that one whose arrow smote me, let that one be chief of the lair."

When he finished his speaking he closed his eyes and so he died.

Now all the chieftains had heard what Ch'ao Kai said as he died. But as for Sung Chiang, when he saw that Ch'ao Kai was dead he let his voice out in mighty weeping and he wept as though for his own parents. Then the chieftains led him out exhorting him to come and do what remained for him to do, and Wu Yung and Kung Sun Sheng exhorted him, saying, "Elder Brother, do not grieve thus. The birth and death of man are certain and fixed, and why then grieve so bitterly? Pray come now and do the great deeds that must still be done."

So Sung Chiang ceased his weeping then and he commanded that fragrant water be fetched to wash the corpse and that garments and head covering be put upon it. When this was all done, the corpse was brought into the Hall Of Meeting and thither the chieftains came to make sacrifice.

Then inner and outer coffins were made for the dead chieftain and he was laid in it and he lay in state in the Hall Of Meeting, and over him was hung a spirit canopy of silk. At the head of the coffin was placed a spirit tablet and upon it was written, "The Spirit Tablet Of The Great Lord Of Liang Shan P'o, The Heavenly King Ch'ao Kai."

From Sung Chiang down every chieftain wore deepest mourning and the captains and lesser robbers wore upon their hats the signs of mourning. And Ling Ch'ung took that arrow and he placed it at the head of the coffin as a sign of sacrifice. Within the lair was set up a long scroll of cloth upon which was writ the tale of Ch'ao Kai, and the priests from temples near the great lair were called in to sing their chants of the dead and so escort the soul of Ch'ao Kai to the regions where it must go.

Every day Sung Chiang led all those of the lair in mourning nor had he heart to attend to any affairs. But Ling Ch'ung and Wu Yung and Kung Sun Sheng and all the other chieftains took counsel together and they said, "We will choose Sung Chiang as lord of the lair and we will all obey his commands."

On the morning of the next day incense and flowers and candles were prepared and Ling Ch'ung was first and he went with the others and they asked Sung Chiang to come into the Hall Of Meeting and there they sat in their places. And Ling Ch'ung opened the matter and he said, "Elder Brother, hear what I humbly say. 'The state may not for one day be without a sovereign nor a house for one day without a head.' Our chieftain Ch'ao Kai has returned to Heaven, and how can our lair be without a lord? All within the four seas have heard of your great name, our Elder Brother. Let us therefore choose a lucky day and on that day do you become lord of our lair, and we will all obey your good commands."

But Sung Chiang made answer, "At the hour when The Heavenly King Ch'ao Kai died he commanded, 'Let him who captures Shi Wen Kung be the lord of the lair.' This command you do all know. There the arrow is still, and can you forget it? I have not yet taken revenge nor have I wiped away our hatred and how can I take this place therefore?"

Then Wu Yung said, "Although Ch'ao Kai The Heavenly King did so speak, and although that man has not yet been captured, yet we cannot for a single day be without a lord in our lair. If you will not take this place, my Elder Brother, which of these men who are all beneath your hand dare take it? These men are of one heart toward you nor is there one who dares speak otherwise. Therefore take this place for the time, Elder Brother, and wait until another time for some other plan."

So Sung Chiang replied, "Sir Counselor, you have spoken very well. For the time then will I take this place. When on another day revenge has been made and the anger wiped away he who takes captive Shi Wen Kung, whoever he be, he shall have this place."

Then did Li K'uei, The Black Whirlwind, cry out from where he stood to one side, saying, "Elder Brother, I say do not speak of being only lord of our lair, for if you were to be the great Emperor of Sung you could be him very well!"

Then did Sung Chiang reply in great wrath, "This black fellow again speaks like a fool! And if you speak so foolishly again I will cut out that tongue of yours!"

But Li K'uei replied, "But I did not say I would not have you be him—I said I would have you be Emperor, and why do you say you will cut my tongue out?"

Then Wu Yung said, "This fellow understands nothing. The others among us are not so foolish as he. Pray cease your wrath, then, and think of greater things to be done."

Now when Sung Chiang had burned incense, Ling Ch'ung and Wu Yung led him to the highest seat and they placed him there in the center. At the left and the seat next in rank was Wu Yung, and the right and the third seat was Kung Sun Sheng. To the left again sat Ling Ch'ung, and to the right again was Hu Yien Shu. When Sung Chiang was thus seated, all took their places and then Sung Chiang said, "This humble one does not but for the time being sit in this seat, and I do it only that I may serve you, my Brothers. We have the same heart and mind, like limbs upon the same body are we, and thus united must we work righteousness for Heaven. Now in our lair have we many men and many horses nor can we compare ourselves to what we once were. I do therefore ask you, my Brothers, to divide yourselves into six camps and let us change the name of this Hall Of Meeting to the Hall Of Loyalty And Righteousness. To the four sides of this hall let four camps be built, and on the back of the mountain let two lesser camps be made. To the front of the mountain where the three passes stand there is an encampment upon the water, and there are the two small encampments upon the shores. I do pray you, my Brothers, that you will divide yourselves and go to govern these camps. In this Hall Of Loyalty And Righteousness I myself will live in the first place. Wu Yung shall have the second, the third shall be given to Kung Sun Sheng, the fourth to Hua Yung, the fifth to Ch'ing Ming, the sixth to Lü Fang, and the seventh to Kao Shen.

"In the camp to the left the first place shall be given to Ling Ch'ung, the second to Liu T'ang, the third to Shih Chin, the fourth to Yang Hsiung, the fifth to Shih Hsiu, the sixth to Tu Ch'ien and the seventh to Sung Wan. In the camp to the right the first is to be Hu Yien Shu, the second Chu T'ung, the third Tai Chung, the fourth Mu Hung, the fifth Li K'uei, the sixth Ou P'eng, the seventh Mu Ch'un. In the camp to the front the first is to be Li Yün, the second Ch'ü Ling, the third Lu Chi Shen, the fourth Mu Sung, the fifth Yang Chi, the sixth Ma Ling, the seventh Shih En. In the camp to the rear the first is to be Ch'ai Chin, the second Sheng Li, the third Huang Hsin, the fourth Han T'ao, the fifth P'eng Ch'i, the sixth Teng Fei, the seventh Hsüeh Yung. In the camp upon the waters the first is to be Li Chün, the second Juan The Second, the third Juan The Fifth, the fourth Juan The Seventh, the fifth Chang Heng, the sixth Chang Shun, the seventh T'ung Wei, the eighth T'ung Meng. In the six camps there are to be in all forty-three chieftains.

"To guard the first pass upon the mountain there are appointed Lei Heng and Fan Lui. To guard the second pass are appointed Hsieh Chen and Hsieh Pao. To guard the third pass are appointed Hsiang Ch'ung and Li Kun. To the small camp upon The Golden Sands are to go Yien Shun, Chen T'ien Shou, K'ung Ming and K'ung Liang, and these four men are to be there as guards. In the small camp upon the beach called The Duck's Bill there are to be Li Chung, Chou T'ung, Chou Yuen and Chou Jun, and these four are to guard there. Of the two small camps to the rear of the mountain there is one to the left upon dry land and there are to be Wang The Dwarf Tiger, The Ten Foot Green Snake and Ch'ao Cheng. In the right camp and it is also upon land, there are to be Chu Wu, Ch'en Ta and Yang Ch'un and these six must guard the rear of the mountain.

"In the Hall Of Loyalty And Righteousness in the room to the east the one in change of letters shall be Siao Jang; the one in charge of rewards and punishments shall be P'ei Hsüan. The one in charge of the seals shall be Ching Ta Chien. He in charge of the moneys is to be Chiang Ching. In the room to the right the one in charge of the fireballs shall be Ling Chen. He in charge of the boat building shall be Meng K'an. He in charge of the making armors is Hou Chien. He who shall tend to the building of the walls of the lair is T'ao Chung Wang. In the rooms behind the hall there are men who must labor also and the one who is to be chief of the building of houses is Li Yün; he in charge of the iron smithery shall be T'ang Lung. He in charge of the making of wines and vinegars shall be Chu Fu. In charge of the preparing of meals and feasts shall be Sung Ch'ing. In charge of miscellaneous goods are Tu Hsing and Pei Sheng.

"There are at the foot of the mountain four wine shops whose purpose it is to spy. These are already given to Chu Kuei, Yo Ho, Shih Ch'ien, Li Li, Sheng Sing, The Goodwife Ku, Chang Ch'ing and The Goodwife Sheng. In charge of the horses from the north there shall be Yang Ling, Shih Yung and Tuan Ching Chu.

"All these I have appointed, and now let every man begin his duty, and let no one disobey me."

From that time when Sung Chiang became lord of that lair, did all those chieftains in the mountain lair, both great and small, follow him with a single heart.

On the next day Sung Chiang took counsel with all the chieftains and he said, "I had the purpose to seek revenge for The Heavenly King Ch'ao Kai and to lead out soldiers to fight this village of Chen. But then I bethought myself that although a man has lost his parents yet can he not do all he will. We must wait the hundred days of mourning and then go forth with soldiers."

So the chieftains obeyed what Sung Chiang had said and they remained in the mountain lair and every day they did good deeds in that they had chants read in memory of Ch'ao Kai.

One day they invited thither a priest whose name was Ta Yuen and he was the abbot in a great temple called the Temple Of The Beautiful Dragon at the city of Ta Ming Fu, which was under the rule of the northern capital. In his wandering he came past this mountain, and so he was asked to come to be one of the priests to chant in the lair. Now in the midst of idle talk while they were at a meal Sung Chiang asked this priest concerning what famous people were at the northern capital and that priest replied, "Sir Chief, how is it you have not heard of The Jade Ch'i Lin of Hopei?"

Sung Chiang heard this and suddenly he bethought himself and he said, "See how I do forget things even before old age is come! In the northern capital there is indeed a great and rich man surnamed Lu and his double name is Chün I, and his nickname is The Jade Ch'i Lin. There are three men in Hopei who have great fame and he is one among these three. His ancestors were men of the northern capital. And how skilled he is in arms! There is none equal to him under Heaven in the use of the club and the staff. If we could gain this man to our lair what further sorrow could there be in my heart?"

Then Wu Yung smiled and said, "And why do you let this desire pass, my Brother? If you long for this man to come to our lair, what is there hard about it?"

Sung Chiang answered, saying, "But he is the richest man in the city of Ta Ming Fu, and how can we gain him here to be a robber?"

Wu Yung replied, "I have long thought on that man also, but in these few days I have somewhat forgot him. I will use some small guile or other and beguile that man into coming to our lair."

Then Sung Chiang said, "Men do all call you The Great Intelligence and truly is this name a good one. Dare I ask what plot it is that you will use so that you can beguile him into coming up the mountain?"

Then without haste and without speed Wu Yung told forth his plot and because of this Lu Chün I left behind his treasures of silks and of flowers and of jewels and he came to the pools where dragons are and to the dens where tigers live. Truly was it

For one man who became a robber chief
A mighty people suffered wars and grief.

How then did Wu Yung beguile Lu Chün I to come to the mountain lair? Pray hear it told in the next chapter.

Chapter 60

WU YUNG BEGUILES THE JADE CH'I LIN. CHANG SHUN BY NIGHT DISTURBS THE GOLDEN SANDS

IT IS SAID: Now when this priest of the temple called The Beautiful Dragon spoke of the most excellent one called The Jade Ch'i Lin, Lu Chün I, and gave his name to Sung Chiang, Wu Yung said, "I will trust to this tireless three-inch tongue of mine and I will talk Lu Chün I into coming to the mountain, and it will be as easy as though I thrust my hand into a bag and brought up what I wished. I do but lack a special hideous fellow to go with me."

Before he had finished speaking there was seen The Black Whirlwind Li K'uei and he cried out in a loud voice, saying, "Elder Brother, and my Chieftain, I, your brother, will go with you!"

But Sung Chiang shouted out, "Brother, stay! If there are to be fires lit in front of winds or if men are to be killed behind words, or if houses are to be robbed, or if any city or town is to be attacked, then we can use you very well. But this is a very nice, dainty plot and how can a man like you go forth to do it?"

Li K'uei said, "Well and you need not make an ado! If you do hold me too hideous and you hate me because of it, well—and I will not go!"

Then Sung Chiang said, "It is not that I despise you, but there are many in Ta Ming Fu now who catch robbers and I do fear lest there be one who sees what you are and so may you lose your life for naught."

But Li K'uei cried out, saying, "It is naught to me! If I do not go it matters naught, but I think there is no other suited to the counselor's purpose."

Then Wu Yung said, "If you will obey me in three things I will take you with me. If you cannot obey them, then stay behind in the lair."

At this Li K'uei cried, "You need not say only three things—though there are thirty yet would I do them all!"

But Wu Yung said, "Here is the first thing. Your desire for drinking wine is like a mighty fire but from today on you must leave off drinking, and you may drink no more until you return. The second thing is that you must disguise yourself as a Taoist attendant priest and follow me, and whatever I tell you you are not to disobey. The third is the hardest of all. From tomorrow on you are to be silent and talk no more and you are to pretend that you are deaf and dumb. If you can fulfill these three things, then will I take you with me."

Then Li K'uei said, "Not to drink wine, and to pretend to be a Taoist—these I can do, but to shut this mouth of mine and say nothing is like being stifled to death!"

But Wu Yung replied, "If you open your mouth once there will trouble come of it."

So Li K'uei said, "Well, and it is easy, too. I will put a copper penny in my mouth as a dead man does and I can do it."

Then all the chieftains laughed and how could they exhort him more? On that day a feast was made in the Hall Of Loyalty And Righteousness to speed them on their way and that night each went to his rest.

On the next day at dawn Wu Yung prepared his goods for the journey and he bade Li K'uei make himself into a Taoist attendant priest and take up the load and go down the mountain. And Sung Chiang and all the chieftains escorted them to The Golden Sands and there he thrice commanded Wu Yung, saying, "Take every heed and do not let this Li K'uei make any sort of misstep."

Then Wu Yung and Li K'uei bade farewell to the chieftains and Sung Chiang and the others returned to the lair.

Let it be told further of Wu Yung and Li K'uei. The two men went toward the northern capital and they were gone for four or five days and every day when the night fell they went into an inn and there rested, and as soon as day was light they set forth again. Upon that whole way Wu Yung ruled Li K'uei very bitterly hard. When they had thus gone for several days they came to an inn on the outskirts of the northern capital and there they stayed. Now on that night when Li K'uei went into the kitchen to prepare food he struck a serving man of the inn with such a blow from his fist that the fellow spat blood. Then the serving man went in to tell Wu Yung and he said, "That deaf and dumb Taoist follower of yours is too fierce. Today I did light the stove a little late, and he struck me so I spat blood."

In great haste then did Wu Yung make apologies and he gave the man some ten strings of cash with which to heal himself and Wu Yung himself reproached Li K'uei, and of this no more need be told.

But after the night was passed when they rose the next day at dawn and had prepared some food and eaten it, Wu Yung called Li K'uei into his room and he commanded him, saying, "You would have your way and come with me and yet all the way along you have been a worry to me fit to be my death! Today when we go into the city do you remember it is no place to play the clown and you are not to make me lose my life."

Li K'uei said, "And do I not know this very well?"

But Wu Yung spoke again, "I will set a secret sign for you. If I shake my head then you are not to move."

When Li K'uei had given his promise the two made ready there in the inn and then went into the city. Now Wu Yung wore a black silk handkerchief that came to his eyebrows and he wore a black-edged white silk Taoist robe, and about his waist he tied a girdle of many colors, and on his feet he wore square-toed black cloth boots. In his hand he carried a staff with a bell on the end, and the staff was made of brass melted with gold. And Li K'uei wore false brownish hair and into the sides he thrust two bone pins upon which to coil the hair and he wore a short reddish-black robe of coarse cloth, and about his waist he tied a girdle of mixed hues. Upon his feet he wore a pair of rough mountain shoes, and he carried a staff higher than his head. Upon the staff hung a paper sign upon which was written,

"To have your life and fortune told,
The price is but an ounce of gold."

When the two had thus disguised themselves they locked the door of their room and they left the inn and they came to the southern part of the city. Now these were the times when there were robbers in every part of the land and in every least small town or city there were imperial soldiers to seize them. This northern capital was the chief place in Hopei and the governor was the one surnamed Liang who guarded that place very well with a great army, and how could there be aught but the most perfect order?

But let it be told further of Wu Yung and Li K'uei. These two went swaying as they walked in seeming idleness and they came to the city gate and there were some forty or fifty soldiers there and they surrounded the officer who sat there as guard to the gate and Wu Yung came forward and made obeisance and the officer asked him, saying, "Sir Scholar, from whence have you come?"

Wu Yung answered, saying, "This humble one is surnamed Chang and named Yung. This attendant of mine is surnamed Li and we travel far and wide telling fortunes for a living, and we come hither to this place to cast horoscopes for people." And he brought forth from his person a false passport, and he gave it to the officer to see.

Then several men spoke and said, "But this cursed Taoist attendant's eyes do look like a very robber's eyes!"

Now when Li K'uei heard this he was angry and was even about to do battle when in great haste Wu Yung shook his head and Li K'uei hung his head. Then Wu Yung made apologies to the officer and he said, "It is hard for this humble one to tell all in a few words. This attendant of mine is both deaf and dumb, and he is but wild fierce strength. But he is one of our family and I could do naught but bring him forth with me, although such as he understands nothing of how to behave. I pray you will forgive him."

Then he bade the officer farewell and went on his way, and Li K'uei followed behind him, but as he followed he lifted his feet very high and put them down very slowly and thus they went into the heart of the city. Then Wu Yung shook the bell upon the staff in his hand and he chanted a rune and he sang,

"Kan Lo early became great,
Chi Ya was so very late.
Yien Huei died at thirty-two,
P'eng Chu lived eight centuries through.
Fan Tan dwelled in poverty sore,
Shih Ch'ung had all he wanted and more.
Thus life is never the same for all,
Some are great and some are small.
The year, the month, the day, the hour—
When men are born, I know their dower."

And he cried, "Here is your fortune! Here is your life foretold! What your birth, what your death, what your riches, what your poverty—if you would know your future, then give me but an ounce of gold!"

When he had thus cried out he again shook the bell, and there followed after him some fifty or sixty of the little children of that city, laughing as they ran. Thus going to and fro Wu Yung came to the gates of the treasury house of the lord Lu, and nodding his head and ringing his bell he passed by and then he came back again, and behind him the children followed in ever greater crowds.

Now the lord Lu was at that very hour sitting in his treasury and he was watching those in the treasury as they cared for his treasure when he heard the sound of many people in the streets and he called his chief treasurer and he asked, saying, "Why is there this ado upon the street?"

The treasurer replied, "Truly it is a merry sight. There upon the street is a Taoist who is a fortune teller and he is come from other parts and there he is on the street doing his business, and for an ounce of gold he will tell a man's life. But who would spare the money? There is an attendant who follows after him, a very filthy hideous fellow to see, and the way he walks is like no way at all, so that the children follow after him laughing."

Then Lu Chün I said, "If this man speaks so high, he must have very high learning too. Bid him come hither for me."

In great haste therefore the treasurer went out and called, "Sir, the honorable lord calls you."

Wu Yung asked, "And what honorable lord is it who calls me?"

The treasurer replied, "It is the honorable lord Lu."

Then Wu Yung went with his attendant and they lifted up the curtain and entered into the hall. Then Wu Yung bade Li K'uei sit upon the high, goose-backed seat to wait, and he turned toward the front, and then made obeisance before the lord Lu. Then Lu Chün I rose and returned the obeisance and asked, "Sir, where is your honored village and what is your high surname and what your noble name?"

Wu Yung answered, "This humble one is surnamed Chang and my name is Yung, and my nickname is Heavenly Mouth, and my ancestors were men of Shantung. I have a way whereby I can foretell a man's life before ever he is born, and I know when he is to be born and when he is to die, but I ask for an ounce of gold before I am willing to tell."

Then Lu Chün I invited Wu Yung to come into an inner small room and there they seated themselves in place. When they had drunk tea Lu Chün I commanded his treasurer to go and fetch an ounce or two of shining gold for the fee and he said, "I do pray you, Sir Teacher, to tell what my fate is to be, and whether it be good or ill."

Wu Yung replied, "Pray then give me your hour, year, month and day so that I can tell it."

But Lu Chün I said, "Sir, a nobleman asks only what his evil fate is to be, not what his fortune. You need not tell me how I shall be rich—only tell me how it is with me now. I am now thirty-two years old. I was born in the first year of the cycle, in the second moon of that year and the third day and in the fourth watch at the time of the rabbit."

Then Wu Yung brought out a handful of

iron symbols for fortune telling and he shook them once together and took up one of them and he shouted out mightily in astonishment and he cried, "How strange a thing!"

In sudden fear Lu Chün I asked, "What strange and fearsome thing is there now in this life of mine?"

Wu Yung said, "Sir, it is so strange that if I tell you you will blame me for it."

But Lu Chün I said, "But I would pray you, Sir Teacher, to tell me, who am a man confused, and though you tell me it is evil it matters naught."

So Wu Yung said, "In this life of yours it can be seen that in less than a hundred days there will be the curse of blood splashed out; nor can you longer keep your treasure. You will have already died under another's sword!"

Then Lu Chün I laughed and said, "Sir Teacher, you have made a mistake. I live within the northern capital and I have been rich from my childhood up nor for a hundred generations have the men of my house committed a crime against the Emperor, nor has there ever been a woman twice married. Moreover, I have ever been careful in the carrying on of my affairs. I have never done that which is against law, and what was not mine I have not wanted. How then can there be the curse of spilled blood?"

Then did Wu Yung's face change its hue and he returned the piece of gold and stood up and went away, and he sighed and said, "Men under Heaven do ever wish to hear only what is in accordance with their own desire and what suits them and sounds fair. Let be—let be, then!

'I have pointed the road both clear and straight
He turns upon me with looks of hate.'

Well, and I will go, then!"

Then Lu Chün I said, "Sir Teacher, cease your wrath. I did but speak in merriment, for in truth I do desire to hear what you have to teach me."

Wu Yung said, "It has ever been that plain talk is hard to believe."

But Lu Chün I said, "I do desire to hear you. I do but hope you will keep nothing hidden from me."

So Wu Yung said, "The fortune that is yours is altogether good except there is this one year which is contrary to the year of your birth and so this evil fate is there, and it lies within the next hundred days, and your head and your body are fated to lie in two different places. This destiny comes assuredly from Heaven nor can you escape it by any means."

Lu Chün I asked, "And can there be no way to hide myself from it?"

Wu Yung again shook the iron symbols and to himself he muttered, "There is but one way and it is to go to the southeast which corresponds upon the horoscope to fire, more than three hundred miles away, and there can you hide from this trouble. There though you may suffer a little, it will be but little."

Lu Chün I said, "If I can only escape this trial then will I reward you heavily with every sort of treasure."

Then Wu Yung said, "I have four rhymes of verse regarding the period of your birth. I will say them and do you write them upon the wall. If later it happens as I have said, then you will know I have a very magic lore."

So Lu Chün I called for brush and ink and there he wrote upon the wall at a place as high as his head and Wu Yung spoke the four lines and he said,

"A nobleman stands in a boat on the lake,
Turns he here or there his fear to slake?
Turns he here, turns he there, none comes to help or save,
Robbers, darkness, storm and winds—all he can but brave!"

Now when Lu Chün I had finished writing this, Wu Yung put away the things with which he had told the fortune and making obeisance he turned to go. But Lu Chün I stayed him, saying, "Sir Teacher, sit awhile and go after the noon."

Then Wu Yung answered, saying, "Much have I received of your favor, but I fear to delay my business and I will meet with you another day," and again he gathered himself to depart.

So Lu Chün I escorted him to the threshold and Li K'uei took the divining staff and they went outside the gate. Then Wu Yung bade farewell to Lu Chün I and leading Li K'uei they went straightway out of the city, and so returned to the inn. There they paid for their rooms and their food and put together their goods and bundles. Li K'uei took up his sign and they went out of that inn. As they went out Wu Yung said to Li K'uei, "Now is this great affair ended. We will hasten by night to the mountain lair, and there prepare to receive Lu Chün I. Sooner or later he will come."

Let it not be told now of Wu Yung and Li K'uei as they returned to the lair, but let it be told of Lu Chün I. After he had escorted Wu Yung to the gate, he stood at the door of his house every night and there alone he looked at the heavens, and there was no joy in him. Sometimes he talked to himself and truly he did not understand what was come upon him.

One day he could bear it no longer and he said to the treasurer, "Bid all those who are doing my business for me to come hither for counsel."

In a short while they were all come. Now the one who was the chief in his house was surnamed Li and named Ku and this Li Ku was a man of the eastern capital and he had come there once to the northern capital to seek a friend. But not finding his friend and it being deepest winter, he fell frozen outside of the gate of Lu Chün I's house, and Lu Chün I saved his life and nourished him in his house. Then seeing him to be a prudent careful man and that he could write and count, Lu Chün I bade him stay to serve in the house. Within five years Lu Chün I had raised Li Ku to be chief steward and all was in his hands both within and without the house, and he had beneath his hand some forty or fifty men. Within and without the house he was called by all the Chief Steward Li.

On that day all the stewards both great and small came to the hall and there made obeisance and Lu Chün I saw them and he said, "How is it I do not see that man of mine?"

But before he had finished speaking, there came a man forward and he was more than six feet tall and he was some twenty-four or -five years of age. His beard was parted into three parts and covered his mouth, and his waist was very slender and his shouders very broad. Upon his head he wore a kerchief made into a turban the hue and the shape of a quince. He wore a robe of silver-white color, with a large round collar, and around his waist was a spotted red girdle. On his feet he wore high boots of yellow leather. Behind his head was a gold circle, and over his ear was thrust a flower.

Now this man was a native of the northern capital, and from his childhood he had been orphan and he had been nurtured in the home of Lu Chün I until manhood. Seeing that his flesh over his whole body was white as snow Lu Chün I had called a very skilled tattooer and he had the youth's whole body tattooed with a pattern, so that he looked like a carven pillar of jade, and there was none to compare to him. Yet not only was his body so beautiful, but he could blow a flute and play a lute, and he could sing and he could dance, he could guess riddles and he could embroider with a needle and twisted hempen cords and there was nothing he could not do and nothing he was not able to do. Moreover he could speak the language of every place, and he knew the language of every trade and business. Truly in every skill there was none to compare with him. He used a triple-arrowed cross bow. Whenever he went forth to hunt he never once returned empty, for every time his arrow flew forth the thing he hunted fell to the ground. If he went for a day's hunting when he returned at night it was with a hundred and more birds. If he went forth to a match where men compared their skill, every prize was his. Truly was he so wholly wise, so wholly clever, that if the head were spoken of in a matter, at once he knew the tail also.

Now this man was surnamed Yien and he was the eldest in his house, and his official name was Ch'ing. The people of the northern capital all called him The Prodigal. He was a man trusted by Lu Chün I, and on this day he came forward to the hall and gave greeting there, and he stood to the right of Lu Chün I and Li Ku to the left. Then Lu Chün I began to speak, saying, "On a day past I had my fortune told and within a hundred days my blood must flow. I can but go to the southeast more than three hundred miles away and there hide. Now I have bethought myself of a place where I may go, and it is called the city of T'ai An at the foot of the great T'ai Mountain. A temple is there and the god of that temple governs birth and death and the sorrows of man. I shall go thither to burn incense and so have forgiveness of my sins and escape from my sorrows, and at the same time I can flee this curse upon me. More than this, I can in the third place do a little business and see what the country is and what are the hills and waters." And he said to Li Ku, "Do you therefore hire for me ten carts and put within them the merchandise of Shantung. Then prepare our belongings and come forth with me. As for Yien Ch'ing, he shall be steward in the house and do you today tell him all he must know of it, for within three days I shall set forth."

Then Li Ku said, "My Master, you do make a mistake in this. The proverb says, 'Fortune tellers sell their ware—true or false, what do they care!' Do not listen therefore to the foolish talk of those fortune tellers. Even though you stay in your home, what harm can come to you?"

But Lu Chün I replied, "My fate is writ. Do not oppose me. If truly there come a curse then will it be too late to escape it."

And Yien Ch'ing said, "Master above me, pray hear my few and foolish words. This road which goes to T'ai An of Shantung goes of necessity past the great robbers' lair of Liang Shan P'o. Now within that lair there are Sung Chiang and a great band of robbers who fight and rob, nor can the imperial soldiers go near there at all. If my lord would go to burn incense then wait, I pray, until more peaceful times. Do not believe the foolish talk of that fortune teller the other day, for I think it may be an evil man from that very lair who made himself like a fortune teller and so came to deceive my lord. It is a pity I was not at home yesterday. If I had been at home in two words or three I would have found out the truth of that Taoist, and I would have pierced his disguise and made him a laughing butt."

But Lu Chün I said, "Do not the two of you speak like fools! Who would dare to come and so deceive me? What do those male and female robbers there matter to me? I do but hold them as grass and if I should go forth alone to seize them and show forth the skill of war I used to know then would I be called a very clever warrior—"

Before he had finished speaking his lady came out from behind the screen and she exhorted him also, saying, "Husband, I have listened to you now for a long time. From ancient times it has been said, 'To go even a third of a mile from home is not so well as remaining at home.' Do not therefore heed the foolish talk of that fortune teller. Do not cast aside this great house of yours. Do not in your fright go to do business in that very den of tigers and nest of dragons. Stay at home and prepare a room and sit yourself there and make your mind clean of every thought and worry and sit upon a high seat in meditation and there can come no ill to you."

But Lu Chün I said, "And what can a woman know? My decision is made and fixed, and let there be no more of all this talk."

Again Yien Ch'ing said, "Because of your greatness, I have learned many ways with weapons. It is not that I praise myself, but let me go forth with you for the once. If there should come forth any robbers by the way I could overthrow some thirty or fifty of them. Let Li Ku stay to be steward and guard the house, but let me go forth with you and serve you, my Master."

Lu Chün I replied, "But I do not know how to do this buying and selling and I would take Li Ku with me, for he understands it very well, and he will put forth his strength for me. For this I leave you at home as steward, for there will be others who can write the accounts for you. I do but bid you stay as chief in the house."

Then Li Ku said, "This humble one who am I have a little illness and my feet are swollen and truly I cannot go forth on a long journey."

Now Lu Chün I heard this and he was full of anger and he said, " 'A thousand days the Emperor nurtures his soldiers and all for one day's battle!' I would have you go with me this once, but you are full of excuses. If there be one more who opposes me now I shall let him taste of this fist of mine!"

And Li Ku was afraid and he could but look at the lady, and the lady could but walk slowly away. As for Yien Ch'ing, still less could he say more. Then they all scattered. Li Ku could but hold back his anger and he set about preparing for the journey. He hired ten carts and he hired ten carriers and he hired some forty or fifty drivers for the carts and he put all the goods into the carts and when all the merchandise had been bound up Lu Chün I himself prepared his own goods. On the third day he burned a paper god of luck and he laid his commands upon all in his house, men and women. That night he bade Li Ku to call two serving men to prepare all for going out of the city with him and Li Ku went also. As for the lady, when she saw the carts depart she went into the house weeping.

Now on the next day at the fifth watch Lu Chün I rose and he washed himself and he changed to new clothes throughout and he ate his early morning meal. Then he took out his weapons and went into the inner halls and there he burned incense before the tablets of his ancestors and he took his farewell of them and he went out of the gate at once and set upon his journey. He bade his lady look well to the house and he said that at most in three months and at least in fifty or sixty days he would return. His lady said, "Husband, take care upon your way and do you as often as you can send letters back."

When she had finished speaking she let the tears fall from her eyes and she made obeisance to him. Then Lu Chün I commanded Yien Ch'ing, saying, "Do well all that there is to be done and do not go forth and make quarrels over some small cause, small as three tiles or a single room."

And Yien Ch'ing replied, "Since you go forth now, my Master, how could I dare not be careful in all things?"

Then Lu Chün I took up his staff and he went outside the city and there Li Ku took the staff from him and Lu Chün I said, "Do you take the two men and go ahead, and if there is a clean inn prepare a meal and there wait for me. As soon as the carts and the carriers arrive let them eat, and so will we not waste time upon the journey."

Then Li Ku took a staff also and he went ahead with two serving men. Lu Chün I and several of his underlings came behind the carts walking.

Now as they went Lu Chün I saw the mountains were clear against the sky and the waters very bright and the road was wide and smooth and his heart grew cheerful and he said, "Had I stayed at home, how could I have seen so fair a scene as this!"

When they had gone thus nigh upon twelve miles Li Ku met his master, and when they had eaten sweetmeats and had eaten their noon meal, Li Ku again went ahead and again they went some ten or eleven miles and so to an inn. Again Li Ku met the men and the carts and the horses and prepared food. When Lu Chün I came to the inn he put aside his staff and hung up his hood and unfastened his girdle knife and he changed his shoes and hose and he took food, and more need not be told of this.

The next morning he awoke at dawn and a fire was lit and food prepared. When all had eaten the carts were prepared and the beasts also and again they set forth on their journey. From this time on they journeyed thus by day, sleeping by night, and so they went for many days.

One day they came to a certain inn to eat and sleep. When dawn came and they were about to set forth again a serving man of the inn was seen to come forward and say to Lu Chün I, "I would have you know a thing, Sir Guest. Less than seven miles from this inn is the mouth to that great robber lair. Upon the mountain is the robber king, Sung Chiang, and although he does not injure those travelers who come and go, yet pass by silently and softly, and make no great ado as you go over this hill and that."

Lu Chün I heard this and he said, "If it be thus —" and he bade one of his men to bring the box where his garments were held and open the lock of it and bring a bundle out of it. From this bundle he took out four white silken banners and he asked the serving man for four bamboo poles and upon each he tied a banner. Now upon each banner were written seven letters and they were writ thus,

"The brave and generous Lu Chün I,
Though fierce and dangerous this place be,
He comes with treasure of gold and jade.
If his carts be emptied, he is not afraid,
For he shall from these mountains take
Treasures more fair his palace to make."

Now when Li Ku and the serving men and the carriers saw this they all cried out bitterness, and the serving man asked, saying, "Must it not be, Sir Guest, that you are a relative of the great robber king Sung Chiang?"

Then Lu Chün I replied, "I am a rich man of the northern capital and what relation can I

WU YUNG BEGUILES THE JADE CH'I LIN

have with these robbers? I am come especially to seize Sung Chiang!"

The serving man said, "Sir Guest, speak more softly—do not drag me into this! It is not matter for play. Even though you had ten thousand men and horsemen you could not go near them."

Then Lu Chün I made answer, "You do but pass your wind! Such as you are among the thieves."

But the serving man put his hands to his ears and he would listen to no more, and the carriers and carters were all frightened into a daze. Li Ku and the treasurers knelt upon the ground and they prayed humbly, "Master, have pity upon us all and spare us our lives so that we may return again to our homes. Better would this be than to let that king of death destroy us!"

But Lu Chün I shouted, saying, "And what do you know? How can a sparrow do battle with an eagle? I have bethought myself that now this skill that I have learned all my days has never been bought by any. Today I have come by luck upon such a chance as this and if I do not sell it now, what do I wait for, then? In those bags in my cart is no great merchandise. There are only many hempen ropes. These robbers are doomed to die and they shall fall into my hand. With each blow of my sword one shall fall, and then you all are to bind them and cast them for me into the carts. If the goods are lost it is nothing, but prepare the carts for the robbers, for we shall seize the chief of the robbers himself and take him into the city. When I go thither to claim my reward then will the skill of my whole life be made known to all. If there is one of you who will not go with me I will kill him first here and now."

Then were four carts placed in front and upon them were placed the four banners. The six other carts followed behind, and that Li Ku and the others weeping and wailing could but let Lu Chün I have his way.

And Lu Chün I brought forth his sword and he held it with his staff and he bound them together with a triple knot and he hastened after the carts and he went on the road toward the robbers' lair. As for the others, when they saw the rugged mountainous road they went a step and trembled a step with fear. But Lu Chün I would but go on in all haste. They set forth at dawn when they rose in the morning and marched until the fourth watch in the day. Then far in the distance they saw a great wood where there were thousands of trees and hundreds so large that two men could not reach around them. They were but just come to this wood when they heard the shrill sound of a whistle. Li Ku and the others were so frightened they knew not where to hide, but Lu Chün I commanded them to put the carts at one side and the carters and the others all hid under the carts crying out bitterness. Then Lu Chün I shouted out, "As soon as I knock them down you are to bind them for me—"

But before he had finished speaking they saw coming out of the edge of the wood some four or five hundred robbers and they heard the sound of a drum beating from the rear and again there were some four or five hundred robbers coming from the rear. Then there was the noise of a rocket in the wood and suddenly there leaped out a fine fellow and in his hands were double axes and he lifted his voice and he shouted out, "Lu Chün I, do you know that Taoist's deaf and dumb serving man?"

Lu Chün I then bethought himself all at once and he shouted out, "I have ever had the thought that I would come and seize you robbers and for this have I come a-purpose this day. Bid Sung Chiang come down straightway from the mountain and make obeisance to me, for if he does not I shall in this moment make every one of you to die, nor will I leave one."

But Li K'uei laughed mightily and he said, "Sir, today our chieftains have decided what your life is to be. Do you but come quickly then and sit yourself in one of the great chairs."

Then was Lu Chün I filled with wrath and he took up his sword and rushed after him. Now Li K'uei in the wood darted to the east and dodged to the west. Then did the more mighty anger rise in Lu Chün I and with enormous strides he leaped into the wood. Li K'uei ran as though winged into the thicket of the pine wood and Lu Chün I pursued him past the other side of the wood, and there was no one to be seen. Now even as he was about to return he heard a company of men come out of one side of the pine wood and one man cried in a loud voice, "Sir, do not go! It was hard for you to come hither, and now pray stay with me awhile. Do you know who I am?"

When Lu Chün I looked to see it was a great fat priest who wore upon his person a black priestly robe and he carried an iron staff. Lu Chün I shouted, "From whence do you come as priest?"

Lu Chi Shen laughed mightily and he said, "I am that tattooed priest Lu Chi Shen and now I follow the commands of my chieftain and I am appointed to come hither to meet you as you escape from your evil fortune."

Then was Lu Chün I sorely confused in heart and he began to curse the priest mightily and he said, "You bald-headed donkey, how dare you be so mannerless?" And lifting up his sword he went toward Lu Chi Shen. Then Lu Chi Shen lifted his iron staff and he came forward to meet him and the two had fought less than three rounds when Lu Chi Shen parried Lu Chün I's sword and then retreated. But Lu Chün I followed after him and even as he pursued Wu Sung came out from among the robbers and he carried two priest knives and he hastened straight forward, and he cried out, "Sir, do you but come with me and so will you not go where blood must be spilled!"

Then Lu Chün I dared not answer a word and he fought Wu Sung. Again they fought less than three rounds when Wu Sung retreated. Then Lu Chün I laughed with a great ha-ha, and he said, "I will not pursue you, you fellows who are not worth mention!" But before he had finished speaking he saw a man at the foot of a ridge of the mountain and this man called out, "Sir, do not boast of yourself. Have you not heard it said, 'Men fear destitution, and iron fears the fire'? This fate that we have set for you is as changeless as the eight letters of destiny and whither will you go?"

Then Lu Chün I shouted out, "And who are such as you?"

That man smiled and said, "I am Liu T'ang, The Redheaded Devil."

Then Lu Chün I shouted, "Do not go, you robber!" and lifting up his sword he rushed to cut down Liu T'ang.

Now they had but fought three rounds when one came out from the side and cried in a loud voice, "Sir, Mu Hung, He Whom No Obstacle Can Stay, awaits you here!"

Then did Mu Hung and Liu T'ang each with a sword both fight against Lu Chün I but even in the midst of their fighting and before they had fought three rounds they heard the sound of footsteps behind them. Lu Chün I shouted and Liu T'ang and Mu Hung leaped backward several paces. When Lu Chün I turned quickly to see who that man was behind him he saw it was Li Yün, The Eagle Who Smites The Heavens. These three chieftains then stood in a triangle to fight Lu Chün I. But Lu Chün I was not in the least afraid and the more he fought the more strong he grew.

Even as they were in the thickest of the combat they heard the sound of a drum upon the crest of the mountain. Then did the three chieftains each make a feint and the three of them all retreated and went away.

As for Lu Chün I, he was now in a complete sweat and he did not dare go in pursuit. He ran out of the wood therefore to look for his men and his carts. But he could not see the ten carts nor the beasts nor the men. Then Lu Chün I sought out a high ridge and he looked in all four directions and there in the far distance at the foot of a ridge he saw a company of robbers and they were driving before them the carts and the beasts and Li Ku and the men were bound one to the other and following after them and with the beating of drums and gongs they were taken to the other side of the wood.

This Lu Chün I saw and the fire of anger rose mightily in his breast and the smoke of his anger came out of his nostrils and lifting his sword he rushed in pursuit. But when he was not far from that ridge he saw two men who cried out, "And whither do you go?"

Now one of those was The Beautiful Bearded Chu T'ung, and the other was The Winged Tiger Lei Heng. When Lu Chün I saw them he began to curse in a loud voice and he cried, "You accursed robbers, you have taken my good carts and my beasts and my men!"

Then Chu T'ung smoothed his long beard with his hands and he laughed greatly and he said, "Sir and Lu Chün I, how is it you do understand so little? I have often heard our fighting men tell of this way of telling fortunes, and they say you can fly hither but never fly away again. Since it has come to such a place as this, better it is that you sit in the great chair of a chieftain."

But when Lu Chün I heard this he fell into mighty wrath and he took up his sword and Chu T'ung and Lei Heng each took up his sword. When they had fought less than three rounds the two turned about in retreat. Then Lu Chün I thought to himself, "I must needs seize one of them at least before I can ask again for my carts."

Then regardless of his life he rushed to the ridge and the two good fellows lost sight of him. They did but hear the sound of drums and of flutes upon the mountain. When they lifted their heads to look the wind was fluttering the newly risen banners and upon them were embroidered four letters, "Righteousness Is Done For Heaven." Then they turned and looked again and they saw a red embroidered umbrella beneath which sat Sung Chiang. To the left of him was Wu Yung, to the right was Kung Sun Sheng, and there were walking beside them some sixty or seventy men and together they cried to Lu Chün I, "Sir, we do rejoice that you are well."

But when Lu Chün I saw this he was the more angry and he pointed at them and he cursed them. Then Wu Yung exhorted him, saying, "Sir, pray cease your wrath. Our chieftain Sung Chiang has long counted your life precious and he did appoint me to go myself to your house and lead you to come to our lair so that together we might work righteousness for Heaven. Pray do not hold us as strangers therefore."

But Lu Chün I began to curse mightily and he said, "You robbers without any cause, how dare you deceive me thus?"

Then did Sung Chiang bring out from behind him Hua Yung and he brought out his bow and set an arrow to it and he looked at Lu Chün I and shouted forth, "Lu Chün I, do not trust to your own skill—see first the magic arrow of Hua Yung!"

Before he had finished speaking he had sent forth an arrow and it struck off the red plume from Lu Chün I's hat. Then Lu Chün I gave a leap of fear and he turned himself about to go away. Now was the thunder of the drums upon the mountain enough to shake the very earth and The Fire In The Thunder Clap Ch'ing Ming and The Leopard Headed Ling Ch'ung were seen leading a company of men and horses, their banners waving, and they dashed out of the eastern part of the mountain. Again was seen Hu Yien Shu and Ch'ü Ling leading also a company of horsemen, and waving their banners and shouting together they came marching from the western side of the mountain.

Lu Chün I was so terrified he knew not where to turn. He saw, moreover, that the sky was darkening to night and his feet ached and he was hungry and truly he was so confused he could not choose a path by which to go. At last, seeing a small path leading through a ravine, he went thither. It was now the hour of twilight and the mists lay like water over the land and they hid the mountains. The light of the moon was faint and the stars shone many and bright, nor could he see which was wood and which was wild grass. Thus gazing about him he came to a place and truly "if he had not come to the borders of Heaven, he had come to the ends of Earth." When he lifted his head to look about he saw all about him reeds standing and there was a great flowing waste of water.

Then did Lu Chün I stay his feet and he looked to the heavens and he drew a sigh and said, "It was because I would not listen to what men said and so today have I come to such a pass."

Now even as he stood there grieving he saw a fisherman in the reeds rowing a small boat and coming forth and the fisherman brought his boat near the shore and called, saying, "How daring are you, Sir Traveler! This is the exit of the great robbers' lair and how have you come here in the night?"

But Lu Chün I replied, "It is because I lost the right way and I could find no place where to lay my head. Save me, therefore!"

The fisherman said, "If you take a wide turn from here there is a village, but you will not find it in less than ten miles. More than this, the paths are very tangled and winding and the way is hard to find. Yet if you would go by water, there is but a mile or two. If you give me ten strings of cash, I will ferry you over."

Lu Chün I said, "If you will ferry me across and find me an inn in that village I will give you more money than that."

Then that fisherman rowed his boat to the shore and he helped Lu Chün I to come into it and he pushed the boat off with his long hook pole and they went over a mile or two of water. Suddenly they heard a noise in the reeds ahead of them as of boats coming, and a small boat came out swiftly as though winged and upon that boat were two men. The one in front was stark naked and he held a wooden pole. The one behind moved an oar. The man in front pushed the boat crosswise and he was singing a mountain song and he sang,

"A hero I who cannot read,
I live in a lair where robbers breed,
For a tiger fierce have I set my bow,
For bait for a faëry whale I go."

When Lu Chün I heard this he gave a start of terror and he dared not speak. Again he heard a sound from the left among the reeds and again came forth two men rowing a small boat and behind them there was the sound of the creaking of the oars. The man in the front set the boat crosswise also and he also sang a mountain song and he sang,

"Though but a rascal I may be,
Good men I kill not, but leave them free.
I put my hand to my leopard's crest
—The Jade Ch'i Lin and I are abreast!"

Now Lu Chün I heard this and he could but cry bitterness. Then he saw the small boat come forward from the center as though it flew and at its prow stood a man and he turned upside down his iron-tipped wooden pole and he sang a mountain song and he sang,

"A nobleman stands in a boat on the lake,
Turns he here or there his fear to slake?
Turns he here, turns he there, none comes to help or save,
Robbers, darkness, storm and winds—all he can but brave!"

When the songs were over the men on the three boats together cried greeting. The one in the middle was Juan The Second, the one to the left was Juan The Fifth, and the one to the right was Juan The Seventh. Those three small boats came crowding forward together, and Lu Chün I thought to himself in his heart, "And I do not know how to swim!" and he cried out, "Fisherman, take me quickly to the shore!"

Then that fisherman roared out a great ha-ha of laughter and he said to Lu Chün I, "Above are the blue heavens, below are the green waters, I was born upon a river, I came to the robbers' lair, in the third watch I do not change my surname, in the fourth watch I do not change my name and my nickname is The Dragon Who Roils Rivers, and my name is Li Chün! If you, Sir, will still not come to join us, you will lose your life and for naught!"

Then was Lu Chün I in great terror and he shouted out, "If you live, then do not I—if I live, then not you!" and he took up his sword and thrust it forward to the very nest of Li Chün's heart.

Li Chün seeing the sword, so thrust his oar, overturned himself backward into the water and he fell with a splash. And the boats turned round and round in the water circling and Lu Chün I's sword fell into the water. Then was a man seen to come out of the water from behind a boat and he called out, "I am White Stripe In The Waves Chang Shun!" and he clung with one hand to a boat and with his feet he kicked the waves.

Thus he turned the boat over and its bottom was upturned to Heaven and Lu Chün I was thrown into the water. Truly was it,

Thus was a dragon felled, for a phœnix spread a net,
Thus for a Heaven-shaking hero traps were set.

How was it in truth with Lu Chün I's life? Pray hear it told in the next chapter.

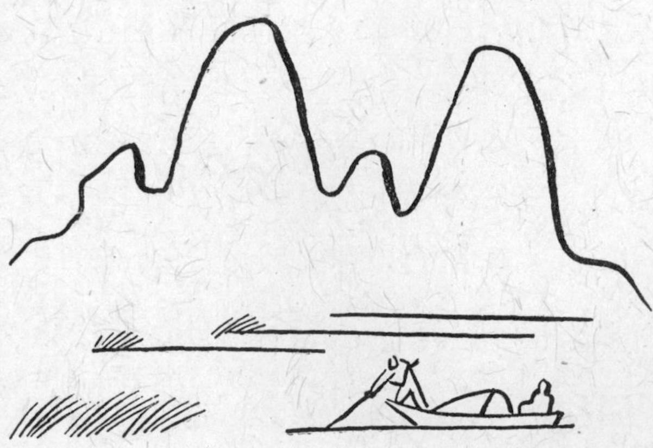

Chapter 61

YIEN CH'ING LETS FLY A LONE ARROW AND SAVES HIS LORD. SHIH HSIU LEAPS FROM A BALCONY ON THE EXECUTION GROUND

IT IS SAID: Now although this Lu Chün I was a very fearsome man in skill yet he could not swim and he was thrown into the water by Chang Shun, when that one overturned the boat. Then Chang Shun beneath the water seized Lu Chün I about the waist and carried him to the shore. Now there were already torches flaming upon the shore and there were some fifty or sixty men waiting there and they received Lu Chün I upon the shore and encircled him about and they unfastened his girdle knife and took off all his wet garments. They were then about to take ropes to bind him when Tai Chung The Magic Messenger gave forth a command. He bid them come thither and he said, "Do not hurt at all the honored person of this lord Lu Chün I."

And a man came forward with a bundle and within the bundle were silken clothing and an embroidered coat and he put them upon Lu Chün I, and eight robbers came forward carrying a sedan and they supported Lu Chün I into it. In the far distance were seen now some twenty or thirty pairs of red muslin lanterns and the light from them shone upon a great company of men and horses, and beating drums and playing lutes they came forward in greeting.

Now the ones at the front were Sung Chiang, Wu Yung and Kung Sun Sheng, and behind them were all the chieftains, and they were then seen all to come down from their horses. In great haste then Lu Chün I came down out of his chair. But Sung Chiang knelt first and behind him all the chieftains one after the other knelt down also. Lu Chün I then knelt upon the ground and he said, "Now that I am captured I do only pray you will kill me quickly."

But Sung Chiang smiled and said, "I pray the honored one to sit in his sedan."

So they all mounted their horses again and with the sound of drums and the music of lutes they went up the mountain and they came before the Hall Of Loyalty And Righteousness and there they dismounted again. Then was Lu Chün I invited into that hall and the lamps and candles were lit until the hall was filled with their light and Sung Chiang came forward to make apologies and he said, "Long has this lowly one heard of the great name of the honored one and it has been like thunder in my ears. Today it is my joy that we meet and it is the joy of my whole life. These my brothers have but now troubled you very much, and ten thousand times I beg your forgiveness."

Then Wu Yung came forward also and he said, "The other day I was only obeying the commands of my brother chief, for he bade me go myself, Honored One, to your house, disguised as a fortune teller and so by guile lead the honored one up the mountain so that we might all together work righteousness for Heaven."

Then did Sung Chiang invite Lu Chün I to sit in the first seat but Lu Chün I laughed loudly and he said, "Then there was nothing to kill me had I stayed in my house! Now that I have come hither today I do think that I have no hope of life. If you are to kill me, then kill me, for why do you play with me?"

Again Sung Chiang smiled in apology and he said, "Truly would I not dare to play with you. Truly do I revere your power and your goodness. My reverence has been so deep it has been like hunger and thirst to me, nor has it been thus for but a day. So did I make this plot to lead you hither, Honored One, to be our chieftain and day and night will we all hear your commands."

But Lu Chün I replied, "Speak no more! Easy it is for me to die, but how hard to do what you ask!"

Then Wu Yung said, "Let us wait until another day and then let us take counsel."

So a feast was prepared to welcome Lu Chün

I nor had Lu Chün I any recourse and he could but drink down a few bowls of wine in silence, and afterwards the robbers invited him to go into an inner hall and there rest.

On the next day Sung Chiang killed horses and cows and he commanded a mighty feast to be prepared and he invited Lu Chün I to come forth to feast. Three times and four times he would have Lu Chün I take the seat of honor at the table. When the wine had passed for a while Sung Chiang rose and he held up his wine bowl in both hands and he made apologies, saying, "Yesterday night we did offend you very sorely, Honored One, and greatly do we hope for your forgiveness. Although our mountain lair is but a poor, small place so that it is not fit resting place even for your horses, yet consider the meaning of these two words, loyalty and righteousness. I would give up my place to you and I pray you will not refuse it."

But Lu Chün I replied, "Ha, Sir Chief, you are wrong! In me there is no sin all my life long, and I have a little wealth too, and I am a citizen of the country of Sung and though I die I shall be a loyal shade of the great country of Sung. Had you not spoken those two words, loyalty and righteousness, I might today even have let be and done what you ask. But if you speak of loyalty and righteousness, then may my hot life-blood be spattered forth first!"

Wu Yung said, "Sir, if you will not, then hard it will be for us to force you to it! It would be keeping your body only for we could not keep your heart. Yet it was very hard for my brothers and for me to fetch you hither, and if you will not join us, nevertheless stay with us for a few days at least and then we will take you to your home once more."

But Lu Chün I said, "Since you cannot make me stay, why do you not free me at once? I do fear those in my household will be full of unease."

Wu Yung made answer, "This is easy. Let us bid Li Ku take the carts back first, and what will it matter if you delay a few days?"

Then Wu Yung asked the steward Li Ku, "Have you yet all your carts?" and Li Ku answered, "I lack nothing at all."

Sung Chiang then brought out two great pieces of silver and gave them to Li Ku and he gave two lesser pieces to the serving men. To the ten carters he gave ten ounces of white silver. Then did they all make obeisance of thanks and Lu Chün I commanded Li Ku, saying, "You know all my bitterness. Go back therefore to my home and tell all to my lady and say to her that she is not to grieve. If I do not die, I shall return."

And Li Ku said, "Since these robber chiefs have loved you with such mistaken love, though you stay here for two months it matters nothing," and he took his farewell and went out from the hall.

Then quickly Wu Yung rose and he said, "Sir, enlarge your heart and sit here for a while. I will escort Li Ku down the mountain and return."

So Wu Yung mounted a horse and he went ahead and waited at The Golden Sands. In a little while Li Ku and the serving men and the carters all came down the mountain and Wu Yung and some five hundred lesser robbers encircled them on both sides and they sat down beneath the willow trees there and Wu Yung called Li Ku before him and he said, "Your master has already arranged all with us. He will now sit in the second place. Before ever he came up the mountain I wrote four lines upon the wall of his house, and I will tell you now the meaning of those eighteen letters written upon that wall. There is one letter at the beginning of every line. The first word of the first line is Lu, the second word of that is Chün, and the third I. These four lines of verse do show forth that Lu Chün I will turn robber. Today you already know he has come up the mountain. It was my first purpose to kill you all. But I feared it might appear too evil of us and so I have let you go free now to return to your homes and you are to tell the people in the capital, 'My lord will never return.' "

Then Li Ku and the others knelt in obeisance and Wu Yung commanded a boat to be fetched and to be ferried across. Then did the whole company go into the boat and they hastened back to the northern capital.

Now the story divides into two parts. Let it not be told first of how Li Ku and his company returned home but let it be told of Wu Yung as he returned to the Hall Of Loyalty And Righteousness, and entered again to the feast. Each man said nothing but he drank his wine in silence and they did not part until night. On the second day a feast was again prepared in the lair and Lu Chün I said, "I do thank you, Sir Chieftains, that you did not kill me. Yet if you had killed me it would have been better, too, for alive it does seem as if in each day I passed a year. Today I must depart."

And Sung Chiang said, "All ignorant as I am, it has been a great joy to me that I have known you, Honored One, and in a few days I shall bring forth my own silver to make a feast. Let us therefore talk for a while together, heart to heart, face to face. I pray you do not refuse me."

Again a day passed and on that day Sung Chiang was host and on the next day Wu Yung was host and on the next day Kung Sun Sheng was host. But the story must not be told too finely. Of the thirty and more chiefs each was host day after day in turn, and thus the time passed, and light and moonlight followed each other like flowing water. When more than a month had passed Lu Chün I was filled with impatience and again he would have taken his departure, but Sung Chiang said, "It is not that we would force you, Honored One, to stay here. If in truth you are impatient to return, wait a few days and we will have a few poor feasts of farewell for you."

On that day Sung Chiang again used his own silver and made a feast of farewell. Then did all the chieftains say, "Our elder brother has used ten parts of reverence in the manner in which he has treated you, the honored Lu Chün I, and such as we ought therefore to use twelve parts. Will you, therefore, eat only of our elder brother's feast? How is it you 'hold a brick of value, and despise a lesser tile'?"

Then Li K'uei called out from among them loudly and he said, "I did for your sake suffer a deal of silent anger when I went to the northern capital to ask you hither and if I give you a feast of farewell, will you say you will not eat it? If you will not, then I will run my head against yours and I will fight to the very death!"

Then Wu Yung laughed mightily and he said, "I never did see such a way as this to invite a guest! I will implore the honored one to consider your warm purpose and stay yet a few days more."

Thus without knowing it there passed four or five more days, and at last Lu Chün I was determined to depart. Then was Chu Wu seen to come leading a company of the chieftains and he came before Lu Chün I and he began to speak, saying, "Although we are brothers newly come to the lair, yet we do serve our great chieftain also, and is there any poison hidden in our feast we would give to you? If you, Lu The Honored One, see something strange there and you will not eat what is ours, it would not matter for me alone, but I do fear the lesser brothers might do something and it might be very ill for you."

Then Wu Yung rose and he said, "You are not one of you to be troubled. I will beseech the honored one for you, that he may stay yet a few days more, and what is there about it that he cannot do? It is ever said, 'To beg a man to feast is never aught but kindness.' "

So Lu Chün I could not withstand them all and he could but stay yet a few more days. In all he thus stayed some thirty to fifty days, and since the time he left the capital in the fifth month without knowing it he had soon spent two months in the robbers' lair, and the golden winds of autumn began to blow, and the dew fell chill like drops of jade. It was already mid-autumn, and Lu Chün I longed with all his heart to depart and he told this to Sung Chiang. And Sung Chiang smiled and he said, "This is very easy. Tomorrow we will take you to The Golden Sands."

Then was Lu Chün I filled with joy. On the next day he was given again his weapons and all the chieftains gathered together and escorted him down the mountain. Sung Chiang gave him a plate of gold and silver, but Lu Chün I smiled coldly and said, "And from whence does this treasure in your lair come? Tell me before I can take it. Yet if I have no money how can I return and how can I do without it? But once I get to the northern capital what money is left I do not want."

And Sung Chiang and the chieftains escorted him to The Golden Sands and there they parted, and of this no more need be told.

The story now is not of Sung Chiang and the

others. Let it be told of Lu Chün I. He let free his steps and by day and by night he went homeward to the capital and he went thus some ten days before he reached the capital. But darkness drew on and it was too late to enter the city, and so he spent the night at a village inn. The next day at dawn Lu Chün I left the village and he went as though winged into the city.

Now when he was about a third of a mile away he saw a man clothed in ragged garments and a torn head kerchief and when he saw Lu Chün I he began to weep aloud. When Lu Chün I lifted his eyes to look, he saw it was that serving man of his, Yien Ch'ing, and he asked him, saying, "And why are you like this?"

Yien Ch'ing replied, "This is not the place to tell it."

Then Lu Chün I turned into a corner behind an earthen wall and he asked closely into the cause of this and Yien Ch'ing answered, "After my lord went away in less than half a month Li Ku came back and he said to our lady, 'The lord has joined the robbers in that great lair of Liang Shan P'o and he sits there as second chieftain.' And that very hour he went to the magistrate's court and so announced it. Now he lives with your lady as one, and he hates me and so I am turned against him. All the goods and treasure of the house he has sealed up and he has driven me out of the city. More than this, he told my friends and my relatives that if there were one who received me into his house to rest there, he would use half his possessions to go to law against that man. Therefore could I stay no longer in the city and I could but come outside the city and earn my living by begging. But it was not that I could not go elsewhere, but I thought that my lord could not by any means have become a robber, and so I stayed even in extremity, and I waited here to see my lord once more. If you, my lord, have truly come from the robbers' lair, then hear what I say; return with all speed to that lair and then seek some other way to set matters aright, for if you enter the city, you will come to harm."

Then Lu Chün I shouted, "My lady is no such person as this! Do not stand there and pass your wind!"

But again Yien Ch'ing said, "My lord, you have not eyes in the back of your head, and how could you see it all? You have ever been interested in things of war and in tests of strength and the like, nor have you ever sought the lusts of women. Long ago my lady had that to do with Li Ku, and today they have closed the door and they live together as man and wife. If you return thither, my lord, you will feel the poison of their hands."

Then was Lu Chün I in a great wrath and he shouted and he cursed Yien Ch'ing, saying, "For five generations has my house lived in the northern capital, and who is there who does not know me? Li Ku must have several heads and several brains to dare do such a thing as this! Is it not rather that you have done some stupid thing and so today you turn about and come and say this? I shall return to my home and ask the truth and there will not be an end of it with you!"

Then Yien Ch'ing began to weep and he crawled upon the ground and he laid hold on the lord's garments. But Lu Chün I kicked him aside with his foot and in great strides he went toward the city. He went into the city and straight to his house. There he saw his stewards all terrified at his coming, and Li Ku came forward in haste to greet him and he invited him to come into the hall and he bowed his head and made obeisance before his master. Then Lu Chün I asked where Yien Ch'ing was, and Li Ku answered, saying, "Master, I pray you do not ask, for assuredly it cannot be told in a word. You have suffered much on the way, and rest yourself, therefore, and then I will tell you."

Then his lady came suddenly, weeping, running from behind the screen and Lu Chün I said, "Lady, I see you again. Pray tell me therefore where Yien Ch'ing has gone."

His lady replied, "I pray my husband will not ask, for truly it is hard to tell it all in a word. You have suffered weariness and winds and cold by the way, and wait until you are rested and I will tell you."

Then Lu Chün I's heart began to doubt and though he died he would ask what was to do with Yien Ch'ing. But Li Ku only said, "I pray you, my Master, to change your robes and do reverence before the tables in the ancestral hall and when you have eaten it will not be too late to tell you."

Then was food prepared for Lu Chün I to eat

and even as he was about to take up his chopsticks he heard a great noise of voices at the front gate and at the back gate and two or three hundred runners from the magistrate's court came rushing in. Lu Chün I was frightened into a daze, for those runners bound him with ropes and as he walked a step they beat him and thus they forced him to the court and to the Hall Of Judgment.

Now this was at the hour when the governor Liang sat in audience and to the right and to the left of him there stood in rows men who looked as fierce as tigers and wolves and they led Lu Chün I into the middle of the hall. At the side knelt also his lady and Li Ku. Then did the governor shout out mightily, "You thing that you are, you were once a righteous man of the capital, and how is it you went and turned a robber in the great lair at Liang Shan P'o and sat there in the place of second chieftain? And here you come again to stir up trouble within the city to join with those who are outside! And I have caught you at it! What have you to say?"

Lu Chün I replied, "This lowly one has ever been but a fool. Wu Yung of that robbers' lair came as a false fortune teller, and false words came from his lips and he confused my clear heart, and thus was I deceived into that lair, and there I was held though gently treated for more than two months. Then did I long most bitterly to come out again that I might return to my home, and there has been no other meaning in me at all. Let my heart be mirrored before you clearly, O Most Gracious!"

But the governor Liang shouted out, "And how can you explain it thus? If you had not been of a heart with them there in the robbers' lair, how could you have stayed there all these days? Here are Li Ku and your own lady who make accusation against you, and they have confessed for you, and how can it be false?"

Then Li Ku said, "My Master, since you have come to this pass, it is better to acknowledge it. There is writ upon the wall of our house a verse which that long-haired rebel wrote. It is true witness against you, and you need not say much else."

Then his lady said, "It is not that we would injure you. It is that you may implicate us. The proverb says, 'If one man turns rebel against the throne, nine generations must suffer from it.' "

Then Lu Chün I began to cry out against his evil fate, but Li Ku said again, "Master, you ought not to cry out against your fate. If it is your true destiny then can you not escape it; if it be not your destiny then escape must be easy. Confess, therefore, the sooner, and so spare yourself suffering."

And the lady said, "Husband! Our family affairs cannot be brought into the governor's court. If indeed this thing be true then can you not deny it. If you have committed this crime, then you have taken my life. Pity is it that our flesh and our skin can feel pain and can suffer but what pain does the stick that beats you feel! Confess, therefore, for if you confess you will receive but a certain punishment."

Now Li Ku had spent money high and low, and a lesser judge surnamed Chang came forward and he said, "This man is thick-skinned and his very bones do refuse to take the blame. If he is not beaten how will he be willing to confess?"

And the governor said, "You have spoken truly." And he gave a shout, "Beat him!"

Then the underlings to the right and to the left bound Lu Chün I and without a word they beat him until his skin burst open and his flesh hung in shreds, and his good blood flowed everywhere. He fainted away three or four times and at last he could bear no more. Crawling there on the ground he sighed and he said, "I am fated to die by violence, and therefore I will say it is I."

Then did the judge Chang take the paper upon which were written the words of this confession and he had fetched a rack of more than a hundred catties and it was fastened upon Lu Chün I's neck and he was locked into the gaol, and those who saw him thus in the court could not endure to see it.

On that day he was pushed into the gaol doors and he was placed in the center of a room and there he knelt, and his guard sat upon the brick bed.

Now the small official who had brought him there was in charge of the executions in two courts, and he was surnamed Ts'ai and his name was Fu. He had lived for long in the northern capital and because of his swift skill with weapons he was called The Iron Arm. The one who stood beside him was his own brother and he was a lesser guard and all his life long he liked to wear a flower in his hair and so the men of those parts carelessly called him The Single Flower, Ts'ai Ch'ing. He carried an iron staff and he stood beside his brother. And Ts'ai Fu said, "Take this condemned prisoner into the other gaol. I will go home and then come back again." And Ts'ai Ch'ing led Lu Chün I away.

Now Ts'ai Fu had risen and gone out of the gate of the gaol when he saw a man come from around the wall at the front of the court. In his hand he carried a vessel of rice and his face was wet with tears. Ts'ai Fu recognized him for The Prodigal Yien Ch'ing and Ts'ai Fu asked him, saying, "What do you do here?"

Then Yien Ch'ing knelt on the ground and the tears fell from his eyes like scattered pearls, or like seed beans sown over a field, and he said humbly, "Sir Gaoler and my Elder Brother, have pity on my master Lu Chün I, who has been beaten for a false accusation, for I can give him no money for food while he be in gaol. I have begged only this half vessel full of rice outside the city so that I may stave off my master's hunger for the moment. Sir, can you not do a kind—"

But before he had finished speaking his grief choked him and he fell upon the ground. Then Ts'ai Fu said, "I know of this matter. Do you but go and take this rice to him to eat."

Then Yien Ch'ing made obeisance of thanks and went on into the gaol to take the rice. And Ts'ai Fu went over a bridge. Suddenly he saw a small serving man out of a teashop come before him and make obeisance and say, "Sir, there is a guest in the upper room of our house and he waits there to have speech with you."

So Ts'ai Fu went to that upper room and when he looked he saw it was that steward Li Ku. When each had made obeisance Ts'ai Fu asked, "Sir Steward, what have you to tell me?"

Li Ku replied, "Adultery cannot be hidden, for though evil be hidden yet must it out. All that I do you know. Tonight in the night do you 'cut off the future and cover the past.' I have naught for a gift except these fifty pieces of gold in the shape of leek leaves, which I would present to you, though it be too lacking in respect for you. As for the others in the court, I will go myself and reward them, nor need you pay any heed to them."

But Ts'ai Fu laughed and said, "Have you not seen the stone tablet in the midst of the court and how it says, 'Men may be deceived but Heaven knows all'? That thing in which you deceive others I know already though you fear I do not. You have taken all his riches and you have taken his woman for yourself. Now you would give me fifty pieces of gold to take away even his life! But if the governor should find it out then indeed could I never suffer so great a penalty!"

Li Ku said, "I see you do hold the money too little. I will give you fifty ounces more."

But Ts'ai Fu said, "Sir Steward, you do think to feed your cat with its own cut-off tail. Has this famous rich man of this city, Lu Chün I, no more than a hundred pieces of gold? If you would have me fell him, it is not that I would force you, but I must ask you for five hundred pieces of gold!"

Then Li Ku said, "I have all the gold here and I will give it all to you. I do but ask that tonight you will finish the deed."

At this Ts'ai Fu took the gold and he hid it in his person and he stood up and said, "Come tomorrow morning to carry away the corpse."

Then Li Ku bowed in thanks and he went away rejoicing, and Ts'ai Fu went back to his house. But he had but just entered the door when he saw a man lift up the reed curtain and come in and he called out, "Sir, do you do well?"

When Ts'ai Fu looked to see he saw that man was one altogether beautiful and he wore his clothes very perfectly and he wore a round-collared robe of the dark hue of a crow's wing, and he wore a belt with medallions of jade the color of mutton fat. About his head was a turban the shape of a certain bird and his shoes were studded with jewels. When this man came in he made obeisance before Ts'ai Fu and in haste Ts'ai Fu returned the courtesy and he asked, saying, "Sir, what is your high surname and what your business with me?"

That man replied, "Let us go within to talk."

So Ts'ai Fu asked him to come into a small room where they could talk together and they seated themselves and that man began to speak, saying, "Sir, do not be frightened at what I have to say. I am a man of Ch'ang Chou and my surname is Ch'ai and my name is Chin, and I am a descendant of the Emperors of the dynasty before this and my nickname is The Little Whirlwind. Because I love to do righteousness nor do I care for riches I know many of the good fellows under heaven. Only I did not foresee that because of a crime I committed I would have to flee to the robbers' lair at Liang Shan P'o. Today I have received the command of my elder brother Sung Chiang and he has bade me come hither to hear news of the honored Lu Chün I. Who would have thought this evil governor, these filthy small officials, this adulteress, this adulterer, would all join together to do him hurt, so that now he is in the gaol doomed for death! His life now is like a shred of silk and it is all in your hand, and heedless of my own life I have come to your house to tell you. If you spare his life I will regard you with the forgiving eyes of a god, nor shall I ever forget your goodness. But if you have an error so large as the half of a grain of rice my great warriors will come to your city and my fighting men to your moats and without regard whether the men in this city be good or ill or young or old they will beat open the city and kill them every one. I have long heard you are a good and righteous man and I have nothing else to give you except that here are a thousand ounces of yellow gold. If you would capture me then I pray you bring ropes here and bind me nor will I frown at all."

When Ts'ai Fu had listened to this he was so frightened that his body was covered with chill sweat and he could not make answer for a long time. Then Ch'ai Chin rose and said, "When a good man has aught to do he must be decided and so I pray you answer."

So Ts'ai Fu answered, saying, "I pray you, Sir Brave, return. This lowly one has a way."

Then Ch'ai Chin made obeisance and said, "Since you have so nobly promised, I will surely repay your great grace."

And he went out the gate and he called for those who had come with him and he brought out the yellow gold and he gave it to Ts'ai Fu, and when he had said farewell, he went away. The men who came with him were Tai Chung and there was one other who could not walk.

Now when Ts'ai Fu had received this news, he did not know what to do. For a long time he meditated. At last he went back into the gaol and he told his brother all that had happened, and Ts'ai Ch'ing said, "Elder Brother, you are commonly a man quick to make up your mind, and in so small a thing as this, what is there hard? The proverb says, 'To kill a man blood must be seen; to save a man, he must be saved to the end.' Assuredly if there be a thousand ounces of gold in this, let us use it high and low. The governor Liang and the judge Chang are both covetous men. If they receive our bribes they can surely save Lu Chün I's life. In some way or other they will punish him by exile, and whether he can be saved or not will rest on those good fellows in the robbers' lair, for our part in the matter will be ended."

Then Ts'ai Fu said, "Brother, truly your purpose is the same as mine. Do you therefore first place Lu Chün I in a good place and night and morning give him good wines and good food and give him also the news of this."

So Ts'ai Fu and Ts'ai Ch'ing, these two, when they had taken counsel together and had thus decided, used bribes high and low and secretly always and thus all was arranged. Now on the next day the steward Li Ku, seeing that his plan was not carried out, went to Ts'ai Fu's house to reproach him. Ts'ai Ch'ing answered him, "We were even about to put forth our hands to kill him, but the governor Liang was not willing, for he had already commanded that Lu Chün I's life was to be spared. Do you therefore arrange it with the upper officials and have a command sent down to us, and then we can do it, and what will there be hard about it?"

In haste did Li Ku send bribes to the upper officials, and the governor Liang said to those who brought him the bribes, "But this is such an affair as belongs to the gaolers. Would you have me put forth my own hand to such a deed as this? He will be dead of a surety in a day or two."

Thus did both sides refuse to do the deed. As for the judge Chang, he had already received goodly sums of money and wilfully he changed the day in the official mandate. At this Ts'ai Fu came again to speak and he urged that the affair be settled with all speed. Then Chang The Judge came with the mandate to the governor who said, "And how should we decide this matter?"

And Chang The Judge replied, "As this small one sees it, Lu Chün I, although he is accused, is yet without true sin. Although he did live for many days in the robbers' lair, yet this is but comparable to some misdemeanor and it is not a real crime. According to custom he should but be beaten forty times and exiled a thousand miles. But I do not know what the governor's decision is."

Then the governor Liang replied, "Sir Judge, you have discerned very well, and it is just what I also think."

Immediately therefore he bade Ts'ai Fu to go into the gaol and bring forth Lu Chün I and then and there he had the great rack taken from Lu Chün I's neck and he gave him his former confession to read and the sentence that had been laid on him. Then was Lu Chün I beaten forty strokes, and an iron, two-leafed rack weighing about twenty catties was placed on him and it was fastened upon him there in the hall. Then Tung Ch'ao and Hsieh Pa were appointed to guard him and lead him forth in exile to a far island in the sea.

Now these men Tung Ch'ao and Hsieh Pa were before underlings in the court of K'ai Feng Fu and they it was who guarded Ling Ch'ung to Ch'ang Chou. Since they had not been able to kill Ling Ch'ung on the way thither, after they returned to the Commander Kao, they were without reason branded and sent into exile to this northern capital, and there the governor, seeing they were very able, ready men, bade them stay there in the court of judgment, and so on this day he appointed these two to guard Lu Chün I.

Thus they went forth bearing the official mandate and they took Lu Chün I and they left the court and they put Lu Chün I into the room where exiles from abroad came and each man returned to his home. There they prepared what goods they needed for the journey and they made ready to depart immediately.

Now when Li Ku came to know of this he could but cry bitterness and he invited the two guards to come and talk with him privately. So Tung Ch'ao and Hsieh Pa went there to a wine shop and Li Ku met them and he asked them to come into a room to talk. There he spread forth wines and foods to entertain them. After they had drunk three bowls of wine, Li Ku opened his eyes and said, "I will not deceive you and I will tell you openly that Lu Chün I is an enemy of mine. Now that he is exiled to that island the road is very far, nor has he a penny of money, and if you take him there you do but spend your own money for travel, nor however fast you go can you return in less than three or four months. I have nothing I can give you either now, and here are only two great pieces of silver to press in your hands. At most go two marches and at least one or so, and there turn aside to some convenient place and take his life. Dig out the gold brand from his face and bring it back for me to see as proof of the deed. When I see it, then I will give to each of you fifty ounces more and of gold. Then do you but make a written report that he died upon the journey, and I will go to the court and myself arrange the matter."

At this Tung Ch'ao and Hsieh Pa looked at each other in silence and then Tung Ch'ao said, "I do but fear it cannot be done."

Hsieh Pa said, "Elder Brother, this honored one Li Ku is a great man and very well known. If when we do this for him some hardship comes out of it for us we must ask him to look out for us then."

Li Ku said, "I am not such a man as forgets a favor done or a good deed received. Later I will reward you both."

Then Tung Ch'ao and Hsieh Pa received the silver and they said farewell and went home and fetched their bundles. In the night they set forth and Lu Chün I said, "I do suffer very much where I was beaten today—let me stay until tomorrow to set forth."

But Hsieh Pa fell to cursing him and he said, "Shut your accursed mouth, then! It is very evil fate for one like me that I even see so poor a man as you! To come and go to that island is more than two thousand miles and how much money is needed for the travel, nor have you a penny! What would you have us do?"

Then Lu Chün I besought him, saying, "Look down upon me with pity now since this sudden evil fate has befallen me!"

But Tung Ch'ao began to curse him a little also, saying, "Rich men such as you were would not spend a penny, and now Heaven has opened its eyes and rewarded you speedily for your evil. But do not hate us, and we will help you on your way."

So Lu Chün I could but keep down his anger whatever they said and he could but set forth upon the journey. They went out of the east gate of the city and then Tung Ch'ao and Hsieh Pa both hung their bundles and their umbrellas upon Lu Chün I's rack and as they went they spoke sometimes well and sometimes very evilly to Lu Chün I and thus they went.

When they saw the sky would soon be dark, they had already gone some fifteen miles and ahead of them was a village. There they sought an inn and rested, and the serving man led them into a small inner room, and they put down their bundles and Hsieh Pa said, "We lords, we suffer very much as such men of labor as we must be, and how can we serve a common criminal? If you would eat, then go quickly and light the fire."

Then Lu Chün I, bearing his rack, could but go into the kitchen, and he begged a little grass of the serving man. This he tied into a bundle and he went to the front of the earthen stove to light the fire. But the serving man washed the rice for him and cooked it, and he washed the bowls and chopsticks also. Now Lu Chün I was son of a rich man and such work as this he could not do at all. Moreover the grass was damp and would not burn, and it went out altogether. When he blew upon it with his breath the smoke filled his eyes. As for Tung Ch'ao, he could but mutter curses.

When at last the rice was cooked the two guards took it all away, nor did Lu Chün I dare to beg for any of it to eat. The two ate for a while and they gave to Lu Chün I what cold rice was left and he ate it up. Then for a while Hsieh Pa fell to cursing him without ceasing, and when the meal was over he bade Lu Chün I go again and heat water to wash their feet. Only when the water was hot did Lu Chün I dare to go and sit down in the room.

Then the two guards washed their feet and they took a bowl of very hot water and they forced Lu Chün I to wash in it. Even as he had taken off his straw sandals Hsieh Pa pushed his two feet into the boiling water, and the pain was an agony for Lu Chün I. And Hsieh Pa said, "Yes, and we lords do tend you and you turn about and make an angry face like this!" Then the two guards went and slept upon the bed. As for Lu Chün I, they took an iron lock and chain and they locked him behind the door.

When the fourth watch was come the two guards rose and they bade the inn's serving man prepare food and they ate themselves full and tied up their bundles and were about to set forth again. But Lu Chün I when he looked at his feet saw they were all blisters so that he could scarcely stand. On that day there was rain and it had rained for many days so that the road was slippery, and when Lu Chün I walked a step he slipped a step and fell. Then Hsieh Pa lifted his club and beat Lu Chün I without mercy, and Tung Ch'ao pretended to beg him to stay. Thus all along the way did the guards bemoan their fate.

They left the village inn and had gone some three miles when they came to a great wood and Lu Chün I said, "Truly this lowly one can walk no further. Have pity on me, therefore, and let us rest awhile."

Then the two guards led him into the wood. It was near dawn and there was no one to be seen and Hsieh Pa said, "How weary are we two with such early rising as this! But if we rest awhile in this wood we do fear you will escape."

Lu Chün I replied, "Even though I had wings now I could not fly."

But Hsieh Pa said, "Do not try to fool us. Wait until I bind you." And he took from his girdle a hempen rope and he bound it about Lu Chün I's belly and he tied it upon a pine tree, and he twisted Lu Chün I's two feet about also and bound them to the tree. And Hsieh Pa said to Tung Ch'ao, "Elder Brother, go and stand outside the wood. If any man chances to pass, then do you give a cough for warning."

Tung Ch'ao said, "Elder Brother, if you put forth your hand, then put it forth quickly."

Hsieh Pa said, "Let your heart rest. Go and watch outside the wood."

When he had finished speaking he took up his club and he looked at Lu Chün I and he said, "You are not to blame the two of us. The steward of your house, Li Ku, bade us kill you upon the way. Even though you went to the far island you must die, and better it is if you die the earlier. When you go among the shades, then do not take revenge upon us. A year from today you will have been dead a year."

Lu Chün I heard this and his tears fell like rain and he bowed his head to receive his death and Hsieh Pa lifted his club in his two hands, and he raised it ready to bring it down upon Lu Chün I's skull.

Now Tung Ch'ao was outside and he heard a thud and he took it that Lu Chün I was dead. But when in haste he went in to see, Lu Chün I was still bound as he had been upon that tree and Hsieh Pa lay stretched out beneath it, and the club was thrown to one side. Tung Ch'ao said, "Here is something very strange! Was it not that you used too great a strength and so fell backwards?"

But when he went forward to lift up Hsieh Pa, how could he do it? He did but see blood flowing from Hsieh Pa's mouth and from the hollow of his heart there protruded three or four inches of a very slender arrow. Even as Tung Ch'ao was about to shout out he saw a man seated in a tree to the east, who cried, "Speed!" and suddenly Tung Ch'ao felt an arrow in his own neck and his feet were thrust up to the sky and he fell.

Then that man leaped lightly down from the tree and he took out a small sharp knife and he cut the ropes that bound Lu Chün I and he split open his rack, and there beneath the tree he embraced Lu Chün I and he let his voice forth in great weeping. When Lu Chün I opened his eyes to look at him, he saw it was that young man Yien Ch'ing, and he cried out, "You—is it not our spirits that meet thus?"

But Yien Ch'ing answered, "I came with these two from the gaol and thus I came here, nor did I think they would put forth their hands suddenly like this in the wood. But I have killed them now with my two arrows. Did you see it, my Master?"

Lu Chün I said, "Although you have saved my life, yet you have killed these two guards, and this is to make the crime still greater and now it fills the Heaven. Where can we go, therefore?"

Yien Ch'ing replied, "After all, it was Sung Chiang who injured you thus, and today if we do not go to his lair, where else can we go?"

Lu Chün I said, "But these welts where I was beaten have festered and the blisters on my feet are broken, and I cannot so much as touch the earth."

Yien Ch'ing replied, "Yet we cannot delay. I will take you on my back, my Master."

In great haste, therefore, his heart beating and his hands confused, he kicked the two dead bodies aside, and he took his bow and arrows and thrust his knife in his girdle and he took up his club. Then lifting Lu Chün I upon his back he went straight toward the east. But when he had gone about three miles, he could go no further, and he saw a small hamlet and an inn there, and he entered into it and sought for a room where they might rest, and he bade food to be prepared quickly for they were sore hungered. Thus for the time these two rested there.

As for the travelers by that way, when they saw two guards lying in the wood, killed by arrows, they told the chief man upon the street of the village and he told the head man of the village and he went to the court in Ta Ming Fu to make report of it. Straightway an officer was sent to see who the dead were, and it was seen that indeed they were Tung Ch'ao and Hsieh Pa, the guards. Then the governor Liang was told, and the chief of the robber catchers was appointed and he was given a certain number of days in which to catch the murderers. The other underlings of the court came also to see and as soon as they saw the arrows, they knew they were the arrows of Yien Ch'ing. There could be no delay, and a hundred or two of the men from the court went here and there putting up proclamations, and they told what manner of men were Lu Chün I and Yien Ch'ing, and they told it forth in every village and hamlet far and near and in every inn and in the streets and market places and in men's homes, so that everyone might look and see and aid in the capture.

Now Lu Chün I was at this very time in the inn nursing his festering wounds and truly he could not walk and he could but live on there. As for the serving man in that inn, he heard there had been a murder for there was not one who did not talk of it. When he saw the picture of these two men, his heart began to be full of doubt and he went and told the head of his neighborhood, and he said, "In my inn there are two men who are very strange and they do not act like common men. But I do not know whether or not they be these two."

Then the head sent a man to see.

Now Yien Ch'ing having nothing for food had gone out to a near place with his bow and arrow to seek for a bird or some wild fowl or animal, and he was about to return when he heard the village suddenly full of shouting. Yien Ch'ing hid in the wood and peered out and he saw two or three hundred men from the court, some with spears and some with swords, and they encircled Lu Chün I whom they had bound and placed in a cart, and they pushed the cart away. Yien Ch'ing would have charged out to save him, but he had no weapons, and he could but cry bitterness. To himself he thought, "If I do not go to the robbers' lair and tell it to Sung Chiang, and beg him to come and save him, will it not be that I lose my master his life?"

He went straightway, therefore, and by night, and he was hungered and he had not a penny upon his person, and he came to a hummock of earth and stood upon it. About him were many scattered trees, and there he slept until dawn the next day. He woke with his heart full of melancholy, and he listened to the magpies clattering and shrieking on the branches above him and to himself he thought, "If I could shoot one down, I would beg some water from the villagers and cook it and I could eat it and ease my hunger somewhat."

When he had come out of the wood and lifted his head to see, those magpies turned toward Yien Ch'ing and called, and silently Yien Ch'ing took his bow and he made a vow to Heaven and he looked up into the empty spaces above him and he prayed and said, "I have but this one arrow left. If my master's life is to be saved then let that finest bird fall when my arrow flies. But if it be that my master's life is destined now to end, then let the bird fly away when my arrow comes near."

He fitted his arrow to the bow and he cried, "O God Of My Desire, do not deceive me!"

The string of the bow sang and it struck full into the tail of that bird and carrying the arrow the bird flew to the foot of the hummock. In great strides Yien Ch'ing went thither, but he did not see the bird, but he saw two men come forward. The one who came first wore a turban shaped like a pig's snout, and behind his head were two curling pieces of gold. He wore an incense-colored silken robe, and about his waist was a girdle speckled with gold. Upon his legs were soft cloth hose, long and half way to his thighs, and upon his feet were hempen shoes, and he carried a staff as high as his eyebrows. The man behind him wore a white straw hat made in an old fashion and in such a shape as to keep off the dust, and he wore a robe of a corded, tea-colored silk. About his waist was tied a girdle of deep purple and on his feet he wore a pair of strong leather shoes. He carried a bundle of garments on his back and in his hand he held a short staff. In his girdle was thrust a sword.

These two men who came thus passed by Yien Ch'ing shoulder to shoulder. When Yien Ch'ing turned himself to see them he thought to himself, "I have truly not a penny, and why should I not knock those two down and take their bundle from them? Then I could go on to the robbers' lair." And he put his bow away and he turned himself and went back.

Those two went on, their heads bowed. Behind them followed Yien Ch'ing and he thrust out his fist and struck the hindmost man, and he fell with a thud. Yien Ch'ing was about to strike the one in front, but that man raised his spear and with a blow he struck down Yien Ch'ing, and he struck full upon Yien Ch'ing's leg and overturned him upon the ground. Then the hindmost man clambered up and he put one foot upon Yien Ch'ing's body and with his hands he drew out his sword and was about to bring it down upon Yien Ch'ing's face, but Yien Ch'ing cried in a mighty voice, "Good Fellow, it matters nothing if I die, but it is a pity if there be left no one to take my message!"

Then that man did not let his sword down, and he stayed his hand and he lifted up Yien Ch'ing and he asked, "And what message does such a thing as you bear?"

Yien Ch'ing said, "And why do you ask me?"

Then the man in front jerked Yien Ch'ing's hand and the tattooed marks upon his flesh showed forth, and in great haste he asked, "Are you not some fellow in Lu Chün I's house, that fellow The Prodigal Yien Ch'ing?"

Yien Ch'ing thought to himself, "Whether I turn right or left I must die, and so I will speak but the truth. If I am killed, then will I meet my master among the shades!" and he said aloud, "I am that Yien Ch'ing of the house of Lu Chün I."

When the two men heard him say this, they stared at him steadfastly and Yang Hsiung said, "Well it is he has not killed you already! If you are indeed Yien Ch'ing do you know who we two are? I am a chieftain of Liang Shan P'o, and I am The Sick Kuan So Yang Hsiung, and he is The One Who Heeds Not His Life Shih Hsiu. Today we obey our chieftain and he has sent us to the northern capital to seek news of Lu Chün I. Our counselor Wu Yung and Tai Chung with him follow after us down the mountain, and they do but wait for this news."

When Yien Ch'ing heard these were Yang Hsiung and Shih Hsiu he told them all that had happened before, and Yang Hsiung said to Shih Hsiu, "If it is like this, I will go with this brother Yien Ch'ing up the mountain to make report of it, and we will think of some other way. Do you go on alone to the northern capital and then return and tell what you hear."

Shih Hsiu said, "It is best so." And he felt in his bosom and brought forth a wheaten cake and some dried flesh and gave it to Yien Ch'ing to eat. Then he gave his bundle to Yien Ch'ing to carry, and Yien Ch'ing went that very night with Yang Hsiung up the mountain. There they saw Sung Chiang and Yang Hsiung told him closely of all that had befallen and Sung Chiang was greatly afraid and he took counsel with all the chieftains concerning some plot they could make.

Let it be told now of Shih Hsiu. He had but the clothes he wore upon him and he came outside the city of the northern capital and it was near night and he could not enter the city. He stayed the night outside therefore and the next morning after he had finished his breakfast he came to the city and there he found everyone sighing and every man grieved. Shih Hsiu's heart began to misgive him and he came to the market place and there he asked those who did business, and an old man answered him, saying, "Sir Traveler, you do not know, but we here in the capital had a certain Lu Chün I, and he was a very true great rich man, but he was taken by the robbers in Liang Shan P'o, and when he escaped home again he was seized by the court, and now he has been exiled to a very far isle. And we do not know how, but halfway upon the journey his two guards were killed. Last night Lu Chün I was brought back again and today just after the noon he is to be brought here into the market place and killed. Sir Traveler, will you come and see?"

When Shih Hsiu had heard this, it was as though icy water had been poured over his head. He went at once to that place of slaughter, and there he saw a wine shop with an upper storey. Shih Hsiu then went into that upper storey, and he sought for a small place from whence he could see the street.

The serving man in that wine shop came and asked him, saying, "Sir Guest, have you invited others, or do you eat alone here?"

Then Shih Hsiu opened his eyes very strange and wide and he said, "Bring a great bowl of wine and a great piece of flesh, for what cursed asking is this?"

The serving man gave a start of fear and he poured two jugs of wine and cut a great piece of flesh, and brought them there. Then Shih Hsiu ate and drank for a while, but he had not sat long after eating when he heard a commotion rise on the streets below and in the wine shop. Shih Hsiu went to the window to see, and there he saw every householder closing his doors and every shop closing also, and the serving man came upstairs and said, "Sir Guest, are you drunk yet? There is a man to be killed below. Quickly reckon the money for your wine and go elsewhere to hide!"

Shih Hsiu said, "And what cursed thing do I fear? Go down quickly or this lord will strike you!"

The serving man dared say no more and so he went down the stair and away. In a short time the sound of drums and gongs filled the street to the very heavens. When Shih Hsiu looked out from his window in the upper room, there at the cross roads the people encircled in crowds the execution place. In the midst were more than ten pairs of executioners with their swords and spears, and they guarded the prisoner, and thus they brought Lu Chün I bound and he knelt before the wine shop. There The Iron Arm Ts'ai

Fu took the executioner's knife and The Single Flower Ts'ai Ch'ing held to Lu Chün I's rack and he said, "Lu Chün I, you must take care that you understand. It is not that we two brothers could not save you, but it is that you yourself have done what is wrong. In The Temple Of The Five Gods we have already prepared a place for you. Let your shade go thither, then, and there rest."

When he had finished speaking, there cried out one from among the crowd, "The hour is come!" Then was Lu Chün I's rack opened from off his neck and Ts'ai Ch'ing held his head and Ts'ai Fu had already lifted the knife high. The official who was in charge of the execution then read in a loud voice the cause for the prisoner's death, and the crowd shouted.

Then Shih Hsiu from his upper room in the midst of this shouting took out his knife from his girdle and he shouted also with the others and he shouted, "All the good fellows from the great lair are here!"

Then Ts'ai Fu and Ts'ai Ch'ing unbound Lu Chün I and freed him and they went away. Shih Hsiu leaped down from that upper room and grasping his steel knife in his hand he cut down men as though they were melons and cabbages and he killed as he went and he killed some ten-odd men. Then laying hold on Lu Chün I he went toward the south.

Now Shih Hsiu had never known the streets of the northern capital and Lu Chün I was so terrified he could not walk. Therefore when the governor Liang heard the news he was greatly afraid and he appointed his own chief captain to take out horsemen to go everywhere and close the city gates. He bade all his men to gather together also, and however a good hero one might be, how could he go over so great a wall and past such fortresses as were there? Truly was it that

Not teeth nor claws had he to burrow through the ground,
Nor wings to fly in the blue Heaven had he found.

How then did Lu Chün I and Shih Hsiu escape with their lives? Pray hear it told in the next chapter.

Chapter 62

SUNG CHIANG AND HIS FIGHTING MEN ATTACK TA MING FU. KUAN SHENG SEEKS A WAY TO SEIZE THE ROBBERS' LAIR

IT IS SAID: At that time these two, Shih Hsiu and Lu Chün I, were in the city, nor did they have any path for escape, for from all four sides men and horsemen came about them. The soldiers from the court had hooked poles and hempen ropes and they all came together. Pity is it that two men cannot withstand a host, for these two were both taken captive, and they were led before the governor and he cried, "Bring hither that thief who robbed the one to die!"

Then was Shih Hsiu held there before the hall and he opened his eyes very wide and strange and he began to curse in a mighty voice and he cried, "You are a slave, and you are slave of a slave! I have obeyed the command of my elder brother, and sooner or later he will bring his fighting men and he will fight your city and make it into level ground! And he will take his sword and cut you into three pieces. He bade this lord, who am I, come first to tell you!"

Thus Shih Hsiu there before the hall cursed the governor a thousand and ten thousand times for a slave, and those who heard him were terrified and fled. Now the governor Liang heard him and he lowered his head and fell into thought, and he commanded that a great rack be brought with all speed and put upon the two prisoners and that they be placed in the gaol for the condemned. Then he bade Ts'ai Fu "guard them with all care, and let no mistake be made." As for Ts'ai Fu, he desired to win the favor of the robbers, and he put the two prisoners into one gaol and guarded them and he brought good wine and good flesh for them to eat, and he fetched it in all haste, and so these two did not suffer any great deal.

Let it be told now of the governor Liang. He commanded a newly come magistrate surnamed Wang to see to this matter. Of those who had been injured in the city, there were some seventy or eighty who had been killed, and those who were wounded in the head or in the limbs or feet were countless. To all who had their names reported in the court the governor Liang gave money. When this was done and the dead bodies burned, on the second day there were those who came from within and without the city and they said, "We have received writings without any name, and there are many tens of these writings, and they are from the robbers' lair, nor dare we hide them. We do but bring them hither to the court."

The governor took the writing and he read, "The righteous one Sung Chiang of Liang Shan P'o announces to the court at Ta Ming Fu and to the governors high and low there, and he says, 'Lu Chün I is a great good man of the earth and now we do invite him to come upon our mountain so that together we may work righteousness for Heaven. Why have you taken bribes like fools, and so injured a righteous man? I sent Shih Hsiu first to tell you, nor did I think you would turn about and capture him also. If you protect their two lives and if you bring forth to me the two adulterers, then I will ask no more. But if you turn about and wilfully injure those innocent ones who are to me as my arms and legs and as my wings, and this without any cause, then will I bring forth all my men from my lair and I will come out against you, and we will come with hearts seeking revenge. At that hour we will not ask who is good or who is evil, but we will kill them all. Whether stone or jade all shall be destroyed. Those who oppress others and who are covetous, those who deceive the people, those who are fools and stubborn and who will not hear what others have to say, these we will destroy, and Heaven and Earth will help us in the deed, and gods and devils will come to our aid. Merry and laughing will we come and joyful will we go away again. You who are righteous men and virtuous women, who are sons reverent to parents and grandsons dutiful to ancestors and all you people who do your duty and you who are careful and you who are not covetous governors, do not fear our coming but proceed steadfastly with your work. Now to all do I proclaim my purpose.' "

When the governor Liang had finished reading this, straightway he sent for the magistrate Wang to come and take counsel with him, and he said, "And how shall we prevent such a thing as this?"

Now this magistrate was a very weak, unready man, and hearing all this fierce talk, he said humbly to the governor, "The Emperor has already sent his soldiers many times against this horde in the robbers' lair, and always in vain, and how much more vain, therefore, are the soldiers of this one city! If these men who are ever reckless of their lives, come here with their fighting men and if the imperial soldiers cannot come to save us, then are we lost indeed. If you do what this humble one would suggest, then let us save the lives of these two men and let us write a memorial to the Emperor and let us write also to the commander Ch'ai so that he may know it and then let us send forth the soldiers of our city against the robbers' lair, and so will we be prepared against surprise. Thus can we preserve this city and guarantee it against trouble, and soldiers and people will remain unharmed. But if we kill these two men I do fear these robbers will send their fighting men against our city and we will have no soldiers to save us, and moreover the Emperor will blame us and besides the people will be in such fear that the city will be in a turmoil and that will be very truly evil."

The governor Liang heard this and he said, "Sir Magistrate, what you have said is very right," and he first commanded the gaoler Ts'ai Fu to come thither and he said, "These two thieves we have are not the common sort. I do fear if you treat them too hardly they will die, and yet if you are too easy they may escape. You two brothers, therefore, must guard them night and day, and if you must be hard then be hard, and if easy, then easy, and take care to guard them very well at whatever they do. Let there be not one time when you are not careful for them."

SUNG CHIANG AND HIS FIGHTING MEN ATTACK TA MING FU

Ts'ai Fu heard this and he was secretly pleased for this was how his heart would have it. So having received the governor's command, he went into the gaol and there he comforted his two prisoners and of this no more need be told.

Let it be told now of the governor. He called his soldiers together and his horsemen and his two generals who were named Wen Tah, The Great Knife, and The Heavenly King, Li Ch'eng, and the two both came before the hall to take counsel. The governor then told them closely of all the affair of the robbers' lair and the letter that was addressed to none, and he told them also of what the magistrate Wang had said. When the two had heard through to the end, Li Ch'eng answered, "And I do think such little wretched thieves will never dare to leave their lair, and why, Most Honored, do you so waste yourself in thought upon them? Though I be a very dull and unskilled fellow, yet have I had my living these many years from the Emperor, and I have had no way of returning my gratitude. Now would I labor like any dog or horse and I would lead out soldiers from the city and go against that lair. If these little robbers do not come we will take counsel otherwise. But if those robbers are fated to be already near the end of their years and their lives fated to be cut off and they come out against us then, although it is not that I boast of my small self, yet truly I swear I will not let one of them return again to his home."

When the governor Liang heard this he was greatly pleased and straightway he had fetched satin embroidered with gold and with such stuffs he rewarded his two generals. Then the two gave their thanks and departed, and each went back to the camp to rest.

The next day the general Li went into his tent and he called his captains and lesser officers and from them there came forth a man very handsome and full of dignity and it was one named So Ch'ao and he was nicknamed The Swift Vanguard and he came forth to meet the general. Then Li Ch'eng commanded, saying, "Sooner or later that robber Sung Chiang will come forth and he comes to attack our city. Do you therefore tell off soldiers and horsemen and let them go some ten miles from the city and there encamp. I will come after you with more soldiers."

So Ch'ao received the command and on the next day he told off soldiers. Now the name of that place ten miles away was The Valley Of The Flying Tiger and he set the camp near the mountain. On the next day Li Ch'eng led out his captains and his aides and they and their men went some eight miles out of the city to a place called The Ridge Of Elms, and there they set their camps. All about them they placed knives and spears and all about for a long way they put down barricades of wood and on three sides they digged pits.

Then did the soldiers wait in all impatience for the battle, rubbing their palms together in their impatience, and all the captains were of the same heart. They did but wait until the robbers came out of the lair so that they might achieve glory in the battle.

Let the story be divided into two parts. Now this writing which was written to no one man, was because Wu Yung, the counselor, having heard the news that Yang Hsiung and Yien Ch'ing had brought and that of Tai Chung also whom he had sent to go and spy out what befell Lu Chün I and Shih Hsiu and when he heard that they were both captured, he wrote this false proclamation and had it pasted upon bridges and upon the walls of the streets and this he did to save the lives of these two men Lu Chün I and Shih Hsiu. And Tai Chung returned to the lair and he told to the chieftains all that had happened.

When Sung Chiang heard he was in great fear and he had the drums beat there in the Hall Of Righteousness And Loyalty and all the chieftains great and small seated themselves in rank. Then Sung Chiang opened the talk and he said to Wu Yung, the counselor, "Sir, you had before a very good clever plot whereby to decoy Lu Chün I up this mountain. But we did not think that he would suffer thus this day and we have let our brother Shih Hsiu suffer in it too. What other guile can we think of now so that we may save them?"

Wu Yung replied, 'Brother Chieftain, let your heart rest. I am a man of no gifts, but I will take this opportunity to take all the food and the treasure of the city of Ta Ming Fu for us to use here in our lair. Tomorrow is a very lucky day. I pray you, therefore, Brother Chieftain, to divide one-half of the chiefs to guard the lair and let all the others go out together to attack the city." Then did Sung Chiang call The Iron Faced P'ei Hsüan, who was judge of the lair, and he said, "Appoint which men are to go and which are to stay, for tomorrow we set forth."

Then The Black Whirlwind Li K'uei said, "These two great axes of mine for long have done no business. When they hear this talk of attacking the city they are very pleased there where they stand in the hall. Elder Brother, set aside five hundred little robbers for me and we will charge against that city and we will make it a place of scattered pieces of flesh. And we will save out Lu Chün I and Shih Hsiu, and thus I will spit out of me, too, all the old anger I have had in me since that time I was deaf and dumb. Only if you will but let me carry the thing through to an end, can I be happy and eased!"

But Sung Chiang replied, "Brother, although you are very brave and fierce, yet this court and city are not like others. This governor Liang is son-in-law to a high ruler and beneath him he has also two generals, Li Ch'eng and Wen Ta, and these are such men as thousands cannot withstand, and they are not enemies to be lightly considered."

But Li K'uei shouted in a great voice, "Elder Brother, that other time you did know very well how quick my tongue is to speak and yet you would have me go as a man deaf and dumb. Today you very well know I love to kill men, and you will not bid me go and be vanguard. And if you use men like this, is it not as though you as good as killed me, The Iron Ox?"

Then Wu Yung said, "If you would go, then you shall be the vanguard and you shall have five hundred robbers to go with you. Go then and attack the first camp. Tomorrow go down the mountain."

On that night Sung Chiang took counsel with Wu Yung and they appointed the men and P'ei Hsüan wrote a proclamation and sent it to every part of the lair and without delay every man went to fulfill his own part that had been set for him to do.

Now it was the time of the year when autumn changes into winter, and it was a time easy to put on garments of war and the horses were fed fat and strong with waiting, and the fighting men, since they had long not been in a war were filled with lust of battle. Truly was it a time to seek glory after long idleness, and there was not one who did not love Heaven and rejoice in Earth. They all prepared their arms and saddled their horses and when the bugle was once blown they all went straightway down the mountain.

The first company was led by The Black Whirlwind Li K'uei and he led forth five hundred men on foot. The second company was led by The Double Headed Snake Hsieh Chen and after him came The Double Tailed Scorpion Hsieh Pao and The Curly Haired K'ung Ming and The Lone Fire K'ung Liang, and they led forth a thousand robbers on foot. The third company was led by The Ten Foot Green Snake and beside her was The Female Savage The Goodwife Sheng and The Female Tiger The Goodwife Ku, and they led forth a thousand men on foot. The fourth company was led by Eagle Who Smites The Heavens Li Yün and beside him were The Nine Dragoned Shih Chin and The Lesser Yü Ts'e Sheng Sing, and they led a thousand robbers on foot.

The leader of the central company had for great chief Sung Chiang and beside him was Wu Yung, and there were four chiefs for guard who were The Lesser Duke Lü Fang and He Who Is Like Jen Kuei Of Old Kao Shen, and The Sick Warrior Sheng Li and He Who Rules Three Mountains Huang Hsin.

The company in front of Sung Chiang was led by The Fire In The Thunder Clap Ch'ing Ming, and beside him were Victor In A Hundred Battles Han T'ao and The Eye Of Heaven P'eng Ch'i. The chief of the company behind Sung Chiang was The Leopard Headed Ling Ch'ung and beside him were The Magic Iron Flautist Ma Ling and The Red Eyed Lion Teng Fei.

The chief of the company to the left of Sung Chiang was The Double Clubs Hu Yien Shu and beside him were Eagle In The Clouds Ou P'eng and The Five Hued Tiger Yien Shun. The chief of the company to the right of Sung Chiang was Little Li Kuan Hua Yung, and beside him was The Gorge Leaping Tiger Ch'en Ta and The White Spotted Snake Yang Ch'un.

He who brought the fireballs was Thunder That Shakes The Heavens Ling Chen and he controlled also the rations for the men. He who was chief of the spies was The Magic Messenger Tai Chung.

When the chieftains and their fighting men were all thus appointed each to his place they went on together and they went that very day. There were left behind that one who aided the warriors Kung Sun Sheng and Liu T'ang, Chu T'ung and Mu Hung, these four chiefs, and they with fighting men and horsemen stayed to guard the lair. Upon the three passes and the watery parts of the lair there were Li Chün and the others to guard and of this no more need be told.

Let it be told now concerning So Ch'ao as he was there in The Valley Of The Flying Tiger. There he was encamped and he saw a horseman coming to him as fast as a flying star and he came and said, "Sung Chiang and his fighting men and horsemen, great and small, and I cannot count how many there be of them, are but ten miles or so away from our camp and they are coming near."

So Ch'ao heard this and he went as though winged to tell Li Ch'eng who was there in the camp by the elm trees. Li Ch'eng heard and he sent a horseman into the city to tell it. He had prepared for himself a war horse and he went to the camp where So Ch'ao met him and there they talked closely together. The next day they rose and ate at the fifth watch and when it was light they pulled up camp and went away. First they came to the village of the Yü family and there they stayed and arranged their men and set forth fifteen thousand men and horsemen.

Li Ch'eng and So Ch'ao put on their whole armor and beneath an upraised banner they sat prepared, reining in their horses. When they looked to the farthest east they saw in the distance a cloud of dust and there were more than five hundred men speeding forward as though winged. The good fellow in front of them was The Black Whirlwind Li K'uei and in his hands he held his double axes and in a mighty voice he shouted, "Know me for a good fellow from the mountain lair, your black lord!"

Li Ch'eng looked at him as he sat upon his horse and he and So Ch'ao laughed loudly and he said, "They do talk every day of these good fellows from the robbers' lair and here is such a little filthy thief as this! How can he be spoken of at all! My General Of The Vanguard, do you see this one? Why should we not first seize this little thief?"

And So Ch'ao laughed and said, "It is not necessary for me to go—there are others for such glory as this—"

Before he had finished speaking there came out a warrior from behind So Ch'ao's horse and his surname was Wang and his name was Ting and in his hand he carried a long spear and he led out a hundred horsemen of whom he was captain and he charged past as though winged. They charged into Li K'uei's fighting men and in the instant of impact scattered them in four directions. Then So Ch'ao leading his own men pursued them past the village of the Yü family, when suddenly from behind a ridge of the hills there came forth the sound of drums and gongs and it filled the heavens and there came forth two companies of horsemen. To the left were Hsieh Chen and K'ung Liang and to the right were K'ung Ming and Hsieh Pao and each of them led out five hundred robbers and they all came charging and killing as they came.

Only then was So Ch'ao afraid, when he saw they had horsemen and fighting men set ready like this, and he pursued no more but turned his horse about and retired. Then Li Ch'eng asked him, saying, "How is it you have not brought the thief?"

So Ch'ao replied, "I followed him over the hill and was even about to capture him, but this man had from the beginning others to support him, and when these supporting men all came out together, it was very hard to put forth my hand against him."

But Li Ch'eng said, "And what is there to fear about such little thieves as these?" And he led out all his own men and dashed forward against the robbers.

Suddenly he saw in front of him banners waving and he heard the shouts of many men and there was a thunder of drums and the clatter of gongs and there was yet another company of horsemen and upon the chiefest horse there sat a woman warrior and upon the red silken banner above her there were written in great gold letters these words, "The Beauty Who Is The Ten Foot Green Snake." At her left was The Goodwife Ku and at her right The Goodwife Sheng and they led more than a thousand horsemen, and among these were men both short and high and every size and shape and there were men from every place and province. Li Ch'eng, seeing this, said to So Ch'ao, "And what use are such fighting men as these? Go forward then and do battle with them and I and my men will encircle them about on all four sides."

Therefore So Ch'ao having received this command took his gilded battle axe in his hand and spurring his horse he went at the enemy. But The Green Snake, reigning back her horse, retired, and she went into a deep valley of the hills and so away. Then Li Ch'eng divided his men and horsemen and pressed in on all four sides.

Suddenly there came out a company of horsemen and they roared so that the very earth shook. It was Li Yün, The Eagle Who Smites The Heavens, and to his left was Shih Chin and to his right was Sheng Sing and they came thundering over the ground. Li Ch'eng retreated in greatest haste to the village of the Yü family when to the left there rushed forth Hsieh Chen and K'ung Liang and from the right there rushed forth K'ung Ming and Hsieh Pao and leading their men they came charging forth again to do battle. Then did the three women warriors again turn their horses and come forward and they followed behind, and thus pursued Li Ch'eng's soldiers were scattered in four directions and cast down. Even as he was about to gain his own camp The Black Whirlwind was there to stay him. Li Ch'eng and So Ch'ao pushed through the crowd of their men and sought for a path of escape for themselves. When they had come there to the camp their soldiers had already fallen in countless numbers, nor did Sung Chiang and his men go in pursuit. He gathered his men together and let them rest awhile and then they put down camp.

Let it be told now of Li Ch'eng and So Ch'ao. In great haste they sent messengers into the city to tell the governor Liang of what had befallen and that selfsame night the governor again sent out Wen Tah and he bade him take forth his men with all speed and save the day. Li Ch'eng went forth to meet him and there in the camp by the elm trees they took counsel together as to what guile they might use to overcome the enemy. And Wen Tah smiled and said, "Such a war as this is as though you did have a little itch upon your body and what does it matter?"

That night they took counsel together as to what they would do. The next morning they rose at the fourth watch and ate and at the fifth watch put on their armor and as soon as it was dawn they sent forth their soldiers and when the battle drum had sounded thrice they took up camp and went to the Yü village ahead. There they saw Sung Chiang and his men and horsemen come rushing at them like the wind. Wen Tah then commanded his men and horsemen to part and he commanded his men to let fly arrows from their bows and crossbows and so stay their feet in approach.

Then straightway did there come forth one from among Sung Chiang's ranks who was a mighty warrior and upon his red banner was written in great silver letters, "The Fire In The Thunder Clap, Ch'ing Ming," and he reined his horse there in front of the ranks and he lifted his voice and shouted, "You filthy little lords of Ta Ming, hear what I have to say! Long have I wished to come against this city of yours, save that I did fear to hurt the people. Give us Lu Chün I and Shih Hsiu sound and safe and give us that man and woman who are adulterers and I will take my men away and do no more battle, nor do I come to deceive you. But if you are foolish and wilful and will not do what I ask, then speak forth quickly what you have to say for yourselves!"

When Wen Tah heard this he was full of a mighty anger and he cried, "Who will pit his strength against this thief?"

Before he had finished speaking So Ch'ao had already galloped out on his horse and he stood in front of the ranks, and in a great voice he shouted, "You were once an officer of the imperial throne and what harm did the Emperor ever do you? You wilfully would not be a good man and you turned robber. Today when I have seized you I will cut you into ten thousand pieces!"

Now Ch'ing Ming heard this and it was as though coals were heaped upon a fire and oil poured upon the flames. He spurred his horse and rushed forward and holding aloft his wolf-toothed spear he charged on. So Ch'ao freed his horse and galloped against him. But the horses were evil and they circled about each other and would not stay, and the two warriors being men of very impatient temper fell into fighting, and all the soldiers shouted their battle cry. And the warriors fought more than twenty rounds and it could not be told who was victor and who vanquished.

Then did Han T'ao come out from Sung Chiang's ranks and there sitting on his horse he fitted an arrow to his bow and when he saw So Ch'ao come near he sent the arrow singing forth and it struck into So Ch'ao's left arm. Then So Ch'ao dropped his battle axe and turned his horse and retired into his own camp, and Sung Chiang pointed with his whip and all his men great and small dashed forward together, and they fell upon So Ch'ao's men. Truly then "dead bodies covered the wilderness and blood flowed in rivers." Thus was a mighty victory won and the robbers pursued past the Yü village and there straightway they seized the camp in the elms.

That night Wen Tah hastened as though winged to The Valley Of The Flying Tiger and there he counted over his men and there were a third of them gone.

Now Sung Chiang had his men gathered together upon The Ridge Of The Elms and Wu Yung said, "When soldiers have been vanquished their hearts are very certainly filled with fear. If we do not take hold of this opportunity to pursue them hard then it may be that their spirit of revenge will rise up again and we cannot in any short space seize the victory again against them."

And Sung Chiang answered, "Sir Counselor, your words are very fitly spoken," and immediately he sent forth a command that on that very night his best fighting men and bravest captains should go forth in four companies and they charged forward.

Let it be told further that when Wen Tah had hastened to The Valley Of The Flying Tiger he sat there in his tent panting and of a sudden a lesser captain came to make report and he said, "There upon the mountain to the east fire blazes forth."

Then Wen Tah leading out with him soldiers mounted on horses went to the east to see, and there he saw mountain and plain indeed red with the fires, and upon the western mountains also fire began to blaze. Wen Tah then hastened with his men to the west and as he went he heard behind his horse the sound of a shouting loud enough to shake the earth. When he looked to see he saw the great chief at the head of those who shouted was Hua Yung and he led with him certain chiefs and these were Yang Ch'un and Ch'en Ta and they came charging forth out of the fires to the east. Wen Tah in that instant felt his heart fill with fear and he led his men and went away.

Then out of the fires in The Valley Of The Flying Tiger there came forth a company and the one at their head was the great chief Hu Yien Shu with his two swords and he led with him the chieftains Ou P'eng and Yien Shun and they charged out straightway. Thus did these two companies come forth together with all their strength and the shouting from the rear grew yet more great and the glare from the fires yet more bright. Then came forth yet another great chieftain and it was The Fire In The Thunder Clap Ch'ing Ming and he led with him Han T'ao and P'eng Ch'i and countless beyond number were those men who shouted and the horses who neighed as they ran.

Then Wen Tah's soldiers and horsemen were thrown into the mightiest confusion and they hastily took up camp and fled. Again did the shouting break forth ahead of them as they fled and the glittering flames danced back and forth and Wen Tah and his soldiers seized any road they could for escape. And they heard great explosions that shook the very heavens and the foundations of the earth were shaken. It was Thunder That Shakes The Heavens Ling Chen, and he came out leading with him his men and they came out of a small bypath and there they lit their fireballs. Out of the thunder were seen torches flaring and in the light of the torches there was a company of horsemen who stood across the way. He in front of this company was The Leopard Headed Ling Ch'ung and he led with him Ma Ling and Teng Fei and these cut off the path of retreat. On all four sides there arose now the sound of throbbing drums and the high flames spread to the skies and all the soldiers fled in all directions and each ran for his own life.

Wen Tah, his great sword in hand, fought most bitterly and so forced a way through for himself, and at that instant he came upon Li Ch'eng and they joined their men together and fighting every step they pressed on. Thus it went until dawn came and only then did they reach the city.

Now when the governor Liang heard of this he was so terrified that of his three souls two he lost and of his seven earthly spirits for the time he had but the one left. In great haste he counted off soldiers and he went out of the city and met those returning vanquished and when they were all come into the city the gates were closed tightly and guarded so that none went out.

On the next day Sung Chiang and his horsemen came to pursue and they went straight to the east gate and there made camp and they prepared to attack the city.

Let it be told now that the governor Liang gathered many together in his court to take counsel with them as to how they could be saved. And Li Ch'eng said, "Now that this robber Sung Chiang's men have come to our very gates great danger is upon us, and if we delay we are lost. Let the governor therefore write a letter to tell of our extremity and let a trusty messenger be chosen to go by night to the capital and give the letter to the prime minister there and thus it will be told the sooner to the Emperor and he will send his best soldiers to come hither to fight with us. This is the first best way. The second is that a proclamation be sent forth to all parts to tell the cities about us and the towns also that they are to send forth soldiers straightway to our aid. The third way is that the magistrate of this city is to command certain of the citizens to go upon the walls and there aid in guarding the city. Let them prepare great logs of wood and stones and repeating bows and arrows and lime bottles and burning filth and let them prepare thus by night and by day. Only thus can the city be made safe."

The governor replied, "This letter we will write at once but who will go forth with it?"

And he appointed a certain great warrior named Wang Ting to take the letter and the warrior put armor upon himself and every weapon he might need. There were appointed also certain horsemen and they took forth the secret letter and the city gate was opened and the drawbridge let down and he went as though winged toward the eastern capital and the horsemen told the proclamation about through the near cities and towns, that they were to send aid. The magistrate Wang was commanded to gather together the people of the city and they went upon the city walls to guard and of this no more need be told.

Let it be told further of Sung Chiang. He divided out his fighting men and he led them out and encircled the city and they put down camp on the three sides of east and west and north. Only the south gate was left open. Every day thereafter did he lead his men against that city, and he sent word to the great lair for food and fuel that they might entrench themselves at the city for he had set himself that he would break open that city and deliver out of it Lu Chün I and Shih Hsiu.

Li Ch'eng and Wen Tah day after day brought soldiers out of the city also to do battle but they could not gain the victory, and the wound that So Ch'ao had in his arm from the arrow was yet unhealed.

Let it be told no further of Sung Chiang and his men attacking the city; rather let it be told first of that great warrior Wang Ting as he carried the secret letter to the prime minister. He and the two with him went straight to the prime minister's house and there they came down from their horses and the guardsman at the gate went in to announce their coming and the prime minister commanded that they were to come before him.

They went therefore into the inner hall and there they made their obeisances before him and when it was done they presented the secret letter and the prime minister tore open the envelope. When he had read the letter he grew greatly afraid and he asked closely and Wang Ting told

KUAN SHENG SEEKS A WAY TO SEIZE THE ROBBERS' LAIR

all of the affair of Lu Chün I and he said, "Now Sung Chiang is outside the city with his fighting men and how mighty are his looks! Truly can we not withstand him. There in the village of the Yü family, upon The Ridge Of The Elms, and in The Valley Of The Flying Tiger in all three places they do battle . . ."

When he had told all the prime minister said, "You have suffered much on so long a journey on your horse. Pray therefore go into the official inn and there rest yourself and wait until I have gathered together my ministers and taken counsel with them."

Again did Wang Ting say humbly, "Most Gracious and Counselor Of The Most High Emperor, the city is now in as precarious a situation as a pile of eggs heaped upon each other. By morning or night it must fall. If that whole province of Hopei be lost, then indeed what will come of it? I do hope that the most gracious, the prime minister, will immediately send forth soldiers to destroy the robbers utterly."

The prime minister replied, "You need speak no further. Pray go now."

Wang Ting went therefore and straightway the prime minister called for his ministers to summon all the officers of state to come thither with all haste to discuss a matter of highest import. In a short time the great official T'ung Kuan came forth leading the three commanders of the capital with him and they came into the hall of audience of the prime minister. There the prime minister told them in detail of the trouble in the northern capital and he said then, "What guile can we use now and what good warriors shall we use so that we can drive away these robbers and so save the city and the state?"

When he had finished speaking all looked at one another astounded and each was colorless with fear. Then was seen the commander of the infantry to bring forth one from behind him and it was a captain of his court who was guard there and stayed off all enemies. His surname was Hsüan and his name was Tsan and he was in charge of the horsemen and the soldiers in that court. Now the face of this man was as black as the bottom of a cauldron and his nostrils pointed toward the sky and his hair was kinked and his beard was red. He was eight feet tall and the weapon he used was a steel sword. Indeed his skill was far above the common man's. He had once been son-in-law to a prince who was son of the Emperor, and so men called him The Ugly Prince or The Ugly Warrior. Because he had once been victor in a competition with repeating bows the Emperor's son had loved him for his skill and so had sought him for son-in-law. But who would have thought the princess held him too hideous for husband, and so filled was she with her hatred of him that after a while she died of it and for this the man could rise to no high place. He was only a guardsman captain.

But now he could not hold himself back and he came out from the ranks where he stood and he said, "This little warrior who am I, when I was at my home I had a certain friend and this man was one descended from that one called Kuan Kung who lived in the times of The Three Kingdoms. This man's surname is Kuan and his name Sheng and he is grown the very image of that ancestor of his. He uses also a scimitar called The Green Dragon. Men call him Kuan Sheng Of The Great Sword. He is a chief of the guard in a place called P'u Tung and it is so small a place for so great a one that it seems his very destiny is gone awry. From childhood he has studied books of war and very well he knows all things of war. Among ten thousand there is not one to compare with him. If he be asked hither with proper gifts and courtesies and he be given reverence and lifted to a high place then will he sweep clean that robbers' lair and he can destroy all of these robbers and so will the country be safe and the people be at peace. I pray humbly that such a command may be sent forth."

When the prime minister heard this he was filled with joy and he sent forth this very man as messenger and he was to take the letter and by that same night go to P'u Tung and with every courtesy he invited this Kuan Sheng that he would come to the capital city and there take counsel on the matter. The ministers then departed.

But the story must not be told too finely. Hsüan Tsan took the letter and mounted his horse again and went forward and he had with him some three or five followers. In less than a day he came to the front of the court of the magistrate in P'u Tung and there he came down from his horse. On that day Kuan Sheng was with Hao Ssŭ Wen there in the court and they were speaking of many men who had risen afore time and were now gone down and they heard it said that from the eastern capital had there come a messenger with a letter. Kuan Sheng then made haste and he with Hao Ssŭ Wen came out to meet the messenger and when the rites of courtesy had been performed he invited Hsüan Tsan to come into the hall and be seated. Then Kuan Sheng asked, saying, "Old Friend, long have we not met. And why have you come this long distance today?"

Hsüan Tsan answered him, saying, "Because the robbers from the great robbers' lair at Liang Shan P'o have come against the city of Ta Ming Fu and in the presence of the prime minister I raised your name as of one who could come straightway and manage this affair. I have said you had a way to make the state sound again and that you have the skill to make soldiers retreat from attack and to kill a warrior who came to do battle. Therefore have I the mandate of the Emperor and the command of the prime minister and with it I bring silks of five hues and a horse ready saddled and with every courtesy I beg you to set forth at once. Brother Warrior, indeed you may not refuse. Pray set your affairs in order and make ready at once to go to the capital."

When Kuan Sheng heard this he was full of pleasure and he said to Hsüan Tsan, "This brother here is surnamed Hao and he has a double name which is Ssŭ Wen, and he is my sworn brother-friend. His mother when she had conceived him was visited by a god in a dream and so was his destiny fixed and he is called now by the name of that god. There is not one of the eighteen ways of war which this brother of mine does not know, and yet it is his evil fate that he is still here and none have seen his ability. Now why should he not be allowed to go with me and save the state?"

Then Hsüan Tsan was pleased enough and he urged them to set forth at once.

And Kuan Sheng gave his commands to his household and he took with him some ten-odd of the tall fellows who come from Kuangsi and he prepared his weapon and his horse and his helmet and his goods and that very night he set forth with Hsüan Tsan and so they came to the eastern capital, and they went straightway to the prime minister and there came down from their horses. The guard at the gate went to announce their coming and the prime minister knew of it and he commanded that they be brought thither to him.

Hsüan Tsan then came into the hall of state leading with him Kuan Sheng and Hao Ssŭ Wen. When their obeisances had been made they took their stand outside the door and the prime minister looked at Kuan Sheng and in truth he was a very fine handsome man. He had a great body eight and a half feet tall and his silky beard fell in three parts. His eyebrows were so long they stretched clean across his temples and his eyes slanted to the heavens, and his face was the hue of red dates and his lips were as red as vermilion. The prime minister was greatly pleased and he asked him, saying, "How many green springs have you passed?"

Kuan Sheng answered, saying, "This small warrior has lived thirty and two years."

The prime minister said, "These robbers from the robbers' lair have encircled the city of Ta Ming Fu, and I would ask you, Sir Warrior, what plan of guile you may have against them so that we may drive them away?"

Kuan Sheng then replied humbly, "Long have I heard that these robbers held those waters for their lair and that they do ever go out into the countryside and frighten the people and maraud everywhere. Now that they have left that den of theirs of their own will it is that they seek for their evil fate to fall upon them. Now if we go to save the city of Ta Ming Fu it is but to disturb the people there for no use. I pray that I may be given some tens of thousands of good soldiers and I will go first and seize the lair at Liang Shan P'o and then go and take those robbers and thus shall I divide head from tail so neither can aid the other."

When the prime minister heard him speak thus he was deeply pleased and he said to Hsüan Tsan, "This guile is like that guile used in times of old when the kingdom of Wei was attacked so that the soldiers of Chao might come to their aid and so be caught in battle and it is a guile after my own heart."

And immediately he commanded the captains

and generals of his court to send thither all good soldiers of the two provinces of Shantung and Hopei to the number of fifteen thousand and Hao Ssŭ Wen was to be vanguard, and Hsüan Tsan was to bring up the rear. As for Kuan Sheng, he was to appoint each of the soldiers to his place and duty. The commander of the foot soldiers who was Tuan Ch'ang was to give out food for men and horses and send largess to the soldiers before battle. Straightway were they to set forth and they went with great swords and spears toward the robbers' lair.

As for the robbers, it was as though the dragon had left his home in the sea and how could he ride the clouds? It was as though a tiger left his hills and descended to the plains and how could he there open his great fangs and spread his great claws? Truly was it,

Because he coveted the full autumn moon
He lost the shining gem he had in his own room.

What then befell the men and horsemen whom Sung Chiang led forth? Pray hear it told in the next chapter.

Chapter 63

HU YIEN SHU DECEIVES KUAN SHENG ON A MOONLIT NIGHT. SUNG CHIANG SEIZES SO CH'AO UPON A SNOWY DAY

IT IS SAID: Kuan Sheng of P'u Tung on that day when he took his farewell of the prime minister led with him fifteen thousand men and horses and he parted them in three companies and he left the eastern capital and went toward the robbers' lair.

The story now must be divided into two parts. Let it be told of Sung Chiang first and of the warriors with him. Every day together they attacked the city and how could Li Ch'eng and Wen Tah dare to come out to oppose them? Nor had that deep and sore wound in So Ch'ao's arm yet healed itself and therefore was there none to come out and withstand the robbers. Then Sung Chiang, seeing that they could not break into that city with their united attack, fell into melancholy. They had long left the lair and yet there was no hope of victory.

It happened that on a certain night he sat in the center tent of the camp and there was a candle lit before him and he fetched the heavenly books he had been given. Even as he was in the midst of reading them there came in suddenly a little captain who made report, saying, "The counselor has come."

Then Wu Yung came into the tent and he said to Sung Chiang, "Our fighting men have encircled the city for a very long time and how is it there comes no one to the rescue of this city from all this countryside about? Nor does any come out of the city to do battle, either. There were three horsemen who galloped out of the city a few days ago and surely it was that the governor Liang sent out to the capital for aid and his father-in-law the prime minister would assuredly send out soldiers for his aid and among them assuredly there would be very able warriors, too. If haply he uses that guile of old when the kingdom of Wei was besieged and the army of Chao deceived into coming to their aid then they would not come hither first but they would go to our great lair and take that. Then what would befall us? Brother, we must think of this also. Let us first bid our fighting men to make all ready so that they may retreat, but not all together—"

Even as they were in the midst of their talk there was seen to come Tai Chung The Magic Messenger and he came and made report that the Prime Minister Ts'ai in the eastern capital had sent for the fourth descendant of the god Kuan, Kuan Sheng of P'u Tung, The Great Sword, and he was bringing with him an army of soldiers and he came as though winged to the lair, nor could the chieftains there decide what they ought to do. And he said, "I pray that you, my Brother Chief, may quickly gather together the fighting men and return with all speed. But let us first dispel this danger that threatens at the mountain."

Then Wu Yung said, "Although it be thus, yet we must not be in haste. Tonight let us send first the men on foot and let the two companies of horsemen stay and let them hide in ambush on either side of The Valley Of The Flying Tiger. When the city knows that our men are retreating they will surely come in pursuit. If we do not use this way our men will fall into confusion."

Then Sung Chiang said, "The words of the counselor are fitly spoken," and he sent forth a command and he bade Little Li Kuan Hua Yung lead out five hundred fighting men and go and hide at the right side of The Valley Of The Flying Tiger. The Leopard Headed Ling Ch'ung was to lead five hundred also and go to the left of the valley. Again he bade The Double Clubs Hu Yien Shu to lead forth twenty-five horsemen and among them was to go Ling Chen and he was to take his fireballs and torches and when they were some three miles from the city, when they saw the soldiers come in pursuit they were straightway to light their fireballs. Then were the ambushed soldiers to rise up together and fall upon the soldiers, and they were to be scattered like the rain and like clouds and if they were scattered then there need be no war waged, but let them be pushed gradually back. As for the men on foot, they were to rise in the middle of the night and go according to order and they were to march out in such ordered companies until the mid-morning of the next day. Those who watched Sung Chiang from the city wall saw the robbers carrying their banners and their weapons and in confusion and haste they seemed to take up camp and go away and it seemed to those who watched that the robbers were returning to their lair. This was all seen clearly from the city wall and it was told the governor that he might know of it and they said, "Today the robbers have retired every one."

When the governor heard this he straightway took counsel with his generals, Li Ch'eng and Wen Tah, and Wen Tah said, "It seems to me that the rescue armies have gone to attack their lair, and they fear, these robbers, that they will lose their den, and so in all haste they return to it. Let us take advantage of the hour, therefore, and go in pursuit of them and kill them, and surely we will be able to seize Sung Chiang."

Before he had finished speaking there came a horseman galloping in from outside the city and he said, "There is news from the eastern capital that armies have been sent to attack the robbers' lair. If the robbers retreat then we may fall to in all haste and pursue them."

Then did the governor Liang command Li Ch'eng and Wen Tah each to take with him a company of horsemen and to go out from east and west and pursue Sung Chiang and the robbers.

Let it now be told of Sung Chiang. As he led out his fighting men to return he saw the soldiers from the city in pursuit and he fled as though for his life. On the other side Li Ch'eng and Wen Tah pursued beyond The Valley Of The Flying Tiger when suddenly behind them they heard the sound of bursting fireballs. Then did the two generals give a start of fear and when they reined in their horses to see what befell them they saw the banners appear behind them in ranks and there arose the sound of drums beaten as for battle. Before they could move to any action from the left there came Little Li Kuan Hua Yung and from the right The Leopard Headed Ling Ch'ung and each led out five hundred horsemen and from both sides they came charging forward.

Then Li Ch'eng and Wen Tah saw they had fallen into a trap and in all haste they turned their soldiers to retreat. But suddenly before them there came forth Hu Yien Shu and he led a company of horsemen and straightway they fell into desperate battle so that soon the two generals had lost their helmets and their robes of war hung in tatters and they were pushed back to the very city. There they took refuge behind the closed gates and they came forth no more.

Then the robbers returned according to their plan but when they were about to come to the lair they came upon The Ugly Warrior Hsüan Tsan and he with his company stood across their way. Then Sung Chiang bade the robbers stand and there they made camp, and he sent one secretly by small bypaths and across a secret ford to go up the mountain and there make report, and they made a covenant with the fighting men on the water to help each other.

Let this be told now. In the water lair Chang Heng and his brother Chang Shun took counsel together and Chang Heng said, "Ever since we two brothers came to this lair we have done no great noble deed. Now The Great Sword Kuan Sheng from P'u Tung leads forth three companies of soldiers and they come against this lair of ours. Let us go, therefore, we two, in the night and take his camp by surprise and capture that Kuan Sheng and gain a great glory for ourselves and so draw our breath freely before all our brother chieftains."

Chang Shun replied, "Elder Brother, you and I have but these men who fight on the water and if we go unaided then will we go in vain and men will laugh at us."

But Chang Heng said, "If you are so careful as this then in what year and in what moon can we ever gain any glory. If you will not go there, let it be an end of it, for I will go this night alone."

Then Chang Shun exhorted his brother most earnestly, but on that night Chang Heng counted out fifty and more boats and on every boat there were three or five men and every man wore soft armor and in his hand each man carried a bamboo spear, and each man bore a knife the shape of a lily leaf. By the dim light of the moon in the silence of the falling dew they went on their boats to the shore and it was then at the time of the second watch.

Let it be told now that Kuan Sheng was at this time in the central tent of his camp and he had a lamp lit and he read a book and there came a little captain who was a spy by the roadside and he bent his head and whispered, "In the creek where the reeds are flowering there are some forty or fifty small boats and every man on them carried a spear and they are hidden in the reeds on either side of the way. I do not know what purpose they have, and therefore have I come to make report of it."

Kuan Sheng heard this and he smiled a cold smile and he turned to the tall warrior who stood beside him and he said a few words in a low voice.

Let it be told further of Chang Heng. He led out his two or three hundred men and hiding in the reeds and creeping as they went they came full to the side of Kuan Sheng's tent and they pulled up the barricades that were placed about it and went into the midst of camp. When they saw the light of a lamp shining brightly in the central tent there was Kuan Sheng twisting his long beard and he sat and read a book. Then was Chang Heng secretly rejoiced and holding his spear he dashed into the tent. Suddenly there was the sound of a drum beating on either side of the tent and all the soldiers began to shout as though Heaven and Earth had fallen and as though the mountains had toppled and rivers had rushed loose and Chang Heng was so terrified he ran away dragging his spear behind him.

Then the soldiers hidden on all four sides rose up and Chang Heng could not escape nor any one of his two or three hundred soldiers and they were captured every one and bound and they were dragged into the tent where Kuan Sheng sat. And Kuan Sheng looked at them and he smiled and cursed them, saying, "You senseless little thieves, how dare you come and spy upon me? Ha, let this Chang Heng be put into a prisoner's cart, and as for the others let them be put under guard! We will wait until we have captured Sung Chiang and then we will take them all together to the capital."

It will not be told further now of Kuan Sheng having captured Chang Heng but of the three Juan brothers in the water lair. They were taking counsel together and they sent one to Sung Chiang to know what his commands were. Then they saw Chang Shun come thither and he made report, saying, "My brother would not hear this younger brother's bitter pleading but he would go and try to take Kuan Sheng's camp by surprise and without knowing it he was captured and now he is fastened in a prisoner's cart."

Juan The Seventh heard this and he began to shout aloud and he said, "We brothers live and die together and we must help each other in any evil and danger! You are own brother to him and how was it you let him go alone so that now he has been captured? If you will not go and save him then we three brothers will go ourselves."

Chang Shun replied, "But I had not received our chieftain's command and so did I not dare to go."

But Juan The Seventh replied, "If you do wait until the command comes your brother will already be chopped into pieces as fine as earth."

And Juan The Second and Juan The Fifth both said, "Spoken truly!"

Now Chang Shun could not withstand these three and he could but let them have their way. On that night, therefore, at the fifth watch they counted off all the chieftains of the water lair, great and small, and to each one was given more than a hundred boats and they all went straightway to the camp of Kuan Sheng. The soldiers on the shore looked and saw the boats of war come swarming like ants to the shore and in great haste they made report of it. But Kuan Sheng smiled and said, "What stupid serving men are these!" And again he turned his head to the warrior who stood beside him and again he said a few words in a low voice.

Let it now be told of the three Juans. They led the robbers and Chang Shun came behind and all shouting together they dashed forward. There they saw the lamp brightly shining in Kuan Sheng's tent in the midst of the camp but no one was there. Then were the three Juans suddenly afraid and they turned themselves to go away. But suddenly there was the loud beating of drums without the tent and on both sides there rose horsemen and foot soldiers in eight companies and they were encircled. Round as a winnowing basket or as a three-sided dustpan, thus roundly were the robbers encircled on three sides.

Chang Shun, seeing the outlook was evil, leaped first into the water with a splash. The three Juans seized a path by force and came to the water's edge but already the soldiers had come upon them and hooked spears flew out and the loaded chains also and Juan The Seventh was captured and dragged away alive, his head down and feet anyhow. And Li Chun and T'ung Wei and T'ung Meng came forward reckless of their lives and rescued Juan The Second, Juan The Fifth and Chang Shun.

It will not be told now of how Juan The Seventh was captured and how he was put into a prisoner's cart. Let it be told rather of how the water robbers told of it to the great lair, and Liu T'ang bade Chang Shun to go by water to Sung Chiang's camp and there tell of what had befallen. Then Sung Chiang took counsel with Wu Yung as to how they could force Kuan Sheng to retreat and Wu Yung said, "Let us wage battle with him tomorrow and see who is victorious and who vanquished."

But even as they were in the midst of their planning they heard a sudden sound of drums beaten on all sides in confusion. Now it was none but The Ugly Warrior leading all his soldiers and coming straight upon Sung Chiang's camp. Sung Chiang led out all his fighting men and there beneath the banners of The Ugly Warrior a very bitter battle was about to be waged. Then Sung Chiang asked, "My Brothers, which of you will go against him?"

And Hua Yung was seen to whip up his horse and come forward bearing his weapon and he went straight toward The Ugly Warrior and The Ugly Warrior came to meet him, brandishing his sword as he came. Back and forth they went and to and fro and they fought ten rounds thus when Hua Yung made a feint and turned his horse about and made as if to go away. The Ugly Warrior pursued and Hua Yung hooked his weapon to his saddle and taking out his bow and arrow he turned himself half about and stretched out his ape-like arm and let fly an arrow straightway as he turned. The Ugly Warrior heard the twang of the bowstring and instantly the arrow was come. But he flung out his sword and there was a clatter and the arrow struck the sword.

Then Hua Yung seeing this one arrow was not enough, again brought forth another and seeing also he was nearer now to his enemy than before he aimed it full to The Ugly Warrior's breast. But The Ugly Warrior bent himself over very far and again the arrow went harmlessly past him. Yet the Ugly Warrior, seeing how great was Hua Yung's skill with bow and arrow, did not dare to pursue him more and he turned his horse about and went away.

Hua Yung, seeing he was not pursued, turned his own horse about and quickly went in pursuit of The Ugly Warrior. Again he took out the third arrow and he aimed it at the back of his enemy's heart and again he sent it forth. He heard a clang and the arrow had struck on The Ugly Warrior's backplate, and in all haste The Ugly Warrior urged on his horse and galloped into his own ranks. From thence he sent men to make report to Kuan Sheng and when Kuan Sheng knew of it he commanded a soldier, saying, "Bring my horse with all speed."

Then he stood suddenly and seized his Green Dragon Spear and he mounted his fire-red horse and parting the curtains of his camp he galloped straightway to where his soldiers were massed. Sung Chiang, seeing how far above all others was Kuan Sheng in his looks, pointed him out with admiration to Wu Yung and he turned himself again to his chieftains and said, "This warrior is true hero and his fame is not false."

But at this Ling Ch'ung grew very angered and he shouted out, "We brothers ever since we have come to the great lair have fought some fifty to seventy battles great and small, nor have we been once vanquished. Why do you shame us before ourselves this day, therefore?"

When he had said this he took up his weapon and went out and he went straight to Kuan Sheng. When Kuan Sheng saw him he gave a great shout and said, "You little thief out of the marshes, I did not seek this little war of my own will! Bid Sung Chiang come forth for I have something to ask of him. Why has he turned rebel against the Emperor?"

Now Sung Chiang heard this beneath the banners and he cried out to Ling Ch'ung to stay and he gave rein to his own horse and he galloped out to the front of the camp and there he bowed to Kuan Sheng and he said, "I am but a petty clerk of Yün Ch'en, whose name is Sung Chiang, and I come into your presence with all reverence. Ask therefore as you will of any crime I have committed."

Then Kuan Sheng shouted, saying, "If you are but a petty clerk then how dare you turn rebel against the Emperor?"

Sung Chiang answered, saying, "Because the Emperor is too lacking in all wisdom and because he allows evil governors to rule the state nor will he let a just and righteous man come forth as a governor. In every court and in every post there are naught but evil covetous officials, and they injure the common people under Heaven. I, Sung Chiang, and these my brothers do work righteousness for Heaven therefore, nor have we any other purpose than this."

Then Kuan Sheng shouted in a mighty voice, "It is clear enough you are but a robber and what Heaven do you work for and what righteousness is it you do? Heaven's soldiers are the Emperor's soldiers and they are here, and do you dare still stand and say smooth words to me and wear that fair face before me? If you will not come down from that horse of yours and suffer yourself to be bound then will I make your bones into powder and your flesh into dust!"

But suddenly that Fire In The Thunder Clap Ch'ing Ming hearing this gave a great shout and he took that wolf-toothed club of his and he freed his horse and galloped straightway forward. Ling Ch'ung shouted loudly also and he lifted his weapon and galloped forward on his horse as though winged and the two warriors attacked Kuan Sheng together and Kuan Sheng met them both. The three then whirled in the dust of battle, dim as shadows upon a lantern. But Sung Chiang suddenly began to point with his finger and he commanded that the gongs should be beaten and the fighting men recalled. Then Ling Ch'ung and Ch'ing Ming turned their horses and came back and they cried out, saying, "We were even about to seize this thing and why have you recalled us from battle, O Elder Brother?"

Then Sung Chiang cried out in a great voice and he said, "Good Brothers, such as we must work with loyal hearts and in just ways, and to fight one enemy with two warriors is not according to my will. Even though we seized him now yet would his heart not acknowledge our rightness. In my sight this Great Sword is a very honorable brave man and he is a loyal statesman. Moreover, his ancestor has become a god and is worshipped in every house. If this man receives any hurt from us then will I give up my seat."

When Ling Ch'ung and Ch'ing Ming heard this their color changed and each man retired. On that day both sides recalled their men.

Let it be told now of Kuan Sheng. He returned to his camp and he came down from his horse and took off his armor and he thought in his heart "I used all my strength against those two warriors and almost I was overcome by them when Sung Chiang recalled his men. I do not know what purpose he had." And he bade a soldier to bring out the two prisoner carts in which Chang Heng and Juan The Seventh were imprisoned and he questioned them, saying, "Sung Chiang is but a petty clerk of the city of Yün Ch'en and why do such as you follow him?"

Then Juan The Seventh answered him, saying, "Our elder brother is far famed in the province of Shantung and in the province of Hopei and he is called The Opportune Rain, Sung Chiang. Such as you know a righteous man and how can you not know him?"

Then Kuan Sheng bowed his head and answered never a word, and at last he bade one take the carts away.

That night in his room whether he sat in his chair or laid himself upon his bed he was ill at ease and he rose and went out of his tent and looked at the moon. The cold hue of night spread over the heaven and the flowers of frost covered the earth and Kuan Sheng sighed without ceasing.

Suddenly there was a spy who came forward to say, "There is a bearded warrior and he rides alone and in his hand is but a whip and he comes hither and would see you."

Kuan Sheng inquired, "Did you not ask who he was?"

The spy replied, "He has neither arms nor weapon and he will not tell his name and he says only that he has come to see you."

Then Kuan Sheng said, "If it be so, then bid him come hither to me."

In a short time the warrior came to the tent and he bowed before Kuan Sheng and Kuan Sheng turned to the warrior and he pushed up the wick of the lamp and looked again, and it seemed that he knew somewhat the man's looks and he asked who it was. That man answered, "Pray bid these to your right and left that they go out for a space."

Then Kuan Sheng laughed loudly and replied, "A great warrior lives in the midst of ten thousand soldiers and if these ten thousand be loyal and of one heart with the warrior shall he not use them as he does his own hand? These in my camp, both high and low and great and small, are all loyal men, able to keep what secret I tell them, and whatever you have to say, say on without fear."

And that man said, "I am that little warrior Hu Yien Shu and once I led out the chained horses in the imperial army and I went out against the robbers in their lair. But who could know that they would injure me so that I lost my war with them and I could not return to the capital nor see my Emperor more. Yesterday I heard you were come, Sir Warrior, and truly was I rejoiced. This morning Ling Ch'ung and Ch'ing Ming would have seized you but Sung Chiang speedily recalled his men lest the honored one might be wounded. That one in truth has ever had a heart loyal to the Emperor and pity it is that the other robbers will not follow him in it! Even now he did take counsel with me secretly that he would urge these robbers to declare themselves loyal to the Emperor. If you, Sir Warrior, will listen to what he says, tomorrow in the night mount your horse and with light bow and short arrows ride straight to the robbers' lair and take Ling Ch'ung and those robbers alive and send them to the capital. Thus will not only you gain the glory but Sung Chiang and I also can redeem ourselves of the crime we have committed."

When Kuan Sheng heard this he was full of joy and he invited Hu Yien Shu to come into the midst of the tent and there he poured out wine for his entertainment. Then Hu Yien Shu told in detail how Sung Chiang held righteousness and loyalty higher than all else and how great a pity it was that now he was caught in this den of robbers and held. And Kuan Sheng spread apart his beard and drank wine, and he smote his knee and pitied Sung Chiang. Of this no more need be told.

Let it be told further of Sung Chiang. On the second day he led out his men to battle and Kuan Sheng took counsel with Hu Yien Shu and he said, "Although we have this plot tonight, yet today we have a victory, too, over these."

And Hu Yien Shu borrowed a suit of armor and he mounted his horse and they went together out to battle. Then did Sung Chiang fall to cursing Hu Yien Shu loudly and he said, "We did not injure you in any way in our lair and why did you steal out in the middle of the night?"

Hu Yien Shu answered, "You stupid, small thief, what great deed can you do?"

Then Sung Chiang called for Huang Hsin, He Who Rules Three Mountains, and he went straight toward Hu Yien Shu and the two horses faced each other and passed to and fro. Before they had fought ten rounds Hu Yien Shu lifted his club and struck Huang Hsin down from his horse as though he were dead. Then was Kuan Sheng filled with joy and he bade all his soldiers great and small to charge forward and kill the robbers. But Hu Yien Shu said, "They must not be pursued to death for that Wu Yung has very strange and unknown guile. If we pursue them and kill them doubtless we shall fall into some trap."

And Kuan Sheng heard this and immediately he recalled his soldiers, and they all went into the camp again. When he was come into his own tent once more he poured forth wine for Hu Yien Shu and he asked what manner of man Huang Hsin was upon that mountain and Hu Yien Shu replied, "This man was once an officer in the Emperor's courts and he was an official in Ch'ing Chou, and he turned robber at the same time with Ch'ing Ming and Hua Yung. Commonly he is not in accord with Sung Chiang and today Sung Chiang would have him come out and do battle with me because he hoped to have him killed."

Then was Kuan Sheng pleased again and he sent down a command, saying, "Let the captain Hao Ssŭ Wen bring up the rear while I myself lead out five hundred horsemen and I will carry a light bow and short arrows and Hu Yien Shu shall lead the way. We will set forth in the second watch of the night and at about the time of the third watch hasten straight to the camp of Sung Chiang and a rocket will be set off for a sign. Then those within shall rush out and those without rush in and we will all go forward together."

On that night the moonlight was like day for brightness, but before the sun was set the soldiers had their armor ready and on, and the bells were taken from the horses' necks, and the soldiers wore their soft armor, and in every man's mouth was a bit of wood to keep him silent and they all mounted their horses. Hu Yien Shu led the way first alone and all the others followed after him. They went along a small mountain path, and they had gone about the space of half a watch when they came upon some thirty to fifty fighting men, and they asked in a whisper, "Is this not the warrior Hu who comes?"

Then Hu Yien Shu shouted out, "Speak not a word but follow after me!"

And Hu Yien Shu let his horse free and went on and Kuan Sheng followed behind. Again they came around a mountain by a small path and suddenly Hu Yien Shu was seen to point with his weapon and far in the distance was seen a red lantern. Then Kuan Sheng reined in his horse and he asked, "What place is that with the red lantern?"

Hu Yien Shu replied, "That is the central part of Sung Chiang's company. Let us urge on our men and horses."

When they were come near to that red lantern suddenly they heard the sound of a rocket bursting and all the soldiers went forward with Kuan Sheng and they charged forward. When they were come beneath that red lantern and looked about them they saw not a man. When they called Hu Yien Shu they did not see him either. Then was Kuan Sheng in great fear for he knew that he was fallen into a trap and in much haste he turned his horse about.

But from the mountains on four sides of him he heard the beating of drums and gongs and now truly was he so filled with fear that he fled in any path he could without heeding which he chose. And so did every soldier flee for his life. Now when Kuan Sheng had turned his horse in such haste he had but a few horsemen who went with him and they galloped out of the mouth of a divide, and suddenly they heard behind them again the sound of a rocket. From four sides the long hooks were thrust forth and they dragged Kuan Sheng down from his horse, and he was robbed of his sword and his horse and his garments and his armor were torn. Those in front of him pushed him back and those behind him encircled him and they seized him and took him into the central camp.

Let it be told now of Ling Ch'ung and Hua Yung. Each led forth a company of fighting men and they encircled The Ugly Warrior and there under the light of the great moon the three horses charged together. When they had fought somewhat less than twenty or thirty times The Ugly Warrior felt his strength gone and he turned his horse and went away. Suddenly from behind him there dashed out a female warrior and she cast a net made of ropes of the five colors and she caught The Ugly Warrior in it and dragged him from his horse. The foot soldiers dashed forward but they were taken captive every one and they were led to the great camp where Sung Chiang was.

Now does the story divide into two again. On this side Ch'ing Ming and Sheng Li led out a company of horsemen to seize Hao Ssŭ Wen and they came upon him face to face by the way. And Hao Ssŭ Wen beat his horse and loudly he cursed, "You robbers—you low thieves, he who stands in my way I will kill! He who runs away I will let live!"

Then was Ch'ing Ming filled with anger and he whipped up his horse and brandished his wolf-toothed spear and he went at Hao Ssŭ Wen. The two horses came together and when they had fought countless rounds, Sheng Li came from the side. Then Hao Ssŭ Wen grew afraid and he ceased using his sword in any ordered fashion and with one push of his weapon Ch'ing Ming thrust him from his horse, and the fighting men shouted out and ran forward to seize him.

Again came Eagle Who Smites The Heavens Li Yün, and he led forth robbers great and small and they dashed forward into Kuan Sheng's ranks and first they rescued Chang Heng and Juan The Seventh and such robbers as had been captured from the water lair, and they took back again such horses and goods and hay as had been taken from them. Then they went everywhere about and wherever they saw soldiers hiding they called them out and bade them not fear. And Sung Chiang recalled all his men and they returned to the mountain lair.

By this time there was faint dawn in the east.

There in the Hall Of Righteousness And Loyalty they seated themselves according to rank and there were brought before them Kuan Sheng, The Ugly Warrior and Hao Ssŭ Wen, one by one. Sung Chiang looked at them and in great haste he came down from his place and he abased the men who held them and he bade them be gone and he himself untied his enemies' bonds and he supported Kuan Sheng to his own central seat and there he bowed before him to the ground and he knocked his head upon the ground in sign of his desire for forgiveness and he said, "We reckless fools who have had to escape for our lives, have in our heedlessness injured the great warrior who is noble as the lordly tiger, and for this we beg a thousand times forgiveness!"

Then Hu Yien Shu came forward and he asked forgiveness also for his fault and he said, "This lowly one did but receive a command from above and I dared not do other than I have done. Ten thousand thousand times do I beg to be forgiven for my guile, Sir Warrior!"

Kuan Sheng, looking about on these chieftains, perceived how deep was the bond of brotherhood between them and he turned his head and looked at the other two, The Ugly Warrior and Hao Ssŭ Wen, and he said, "Now are we seized and brought hither, and what shall we do, then?"

And the two answered, saying, "We will hear any command."

Then Kuan Sheng said, "I am in such shame now that I can never return to my Emperor and I do but beg to be put early to death."

But Sung Chiang answered, "And why do you speak thus? If you do not despise us who are so small and lowly then let us together work righteousness for Heaven. But if you will not, I dare not force you to stay and at this very hour will send you to the capital."

Then Kuan Sheng said, "Truly is it right that men have praised the righteousness of Sung Chiang, for he is righteous. When a man is born upon the earth and the Emperor sees him for what he is, he is loyal to the Emperor; if friend sees him truly, then he is true to friend. Today am I moved by all I see and I would be a small follower beneath your command."

Then was Sung Chiang filled with joy and on that day he commanded that a feast be prepared and he sent forth messengers to bid the soldiers who had escaped to come back and fear no longer and thus he gained some five to seven thousand men and horses more. If any among them had parents or wives and children, straightway he gave them silver and bade them return again to their homes. And he bade Hsüeh Yung go to P'u

Tung with a letter to Kuan Sheng's house and bid them all come thither to the lair. Of this no more need be said.

Now in the midst of their wine drinking suddenly Sung Chiang bethought himself of Lu Chün I and Shih Hsiu and how they were yet in the gaol in the northern capital and his tears began to fall. Then Wu Yung said, "Brother, you should not grieve. Assuredly have I a way. Let this night pass and tomorrow we will send out men to fight against the capital and surely the thing can be done."

And Kuan Sheng rose and said, "There is not a way whereby I can repay the loving kindness you have given me, and I would therefore lead the vanguard of this company."

Then was Sung Chiang greatly rejoiced, and on the next day he sent forth a command that The Ugly Warrior and Hao Ssŭ Wen were to go to help Kuan Sheng, and Sung Chiang gave him the men they had led before, and these were vanguard. There was not one lacking of the chieftains who had gone aforetime against that city and again they went forth, and he added to them Li Chün and Chang Shun and they took with them garments for fighting in the water, and thus in their order they went again to the capital.

Let it be told here that the governor Liang was in the midst of that city and he had but just invited So Ch'ao to come and feast with him, since now his wound was newly healed. It was a day when the sun was dull behind the clouds and the north wind blew in gusts and suddenly a spy galloped in on his horse and he made report, saying, "Kuan Sheng, The Ugly Warrior, and Hao Ssŭ Wen and a company of horsemen have all been seized by Sung Chiang, and they have already joined the robbers, and now the robbers have come near from the great lair."

The governor Liang heard this and he was so terrified that his eyes were staring and his mouth ajar and he started and overturned his wine cup and cast his chopsticks upon the ground. Then did So Ch'ao say, "I have suffered already from that secret arrow of a robber and today will I revenge myself."

Then the governor Liang poured forth a cup of hot wine for So Ch'ao and he commanded thus, "Do you lead a company of soldiers and horsemen outside the city and Li Ch'eng and Wen Tah shall follow behind with their armies to aid you."

Now this was the time of the second moon of winter and day after day there was a mighty wind and Heaven and Earth changed their hue. The hooves of the horses were frozen with ice and metal armor was like a coat of ice. But So Ch'ao left the feasting place and went straightway to The Valley Of The Flying Tiger and there put down camp.

On the next day Sung Chiang went out with his guard and with Lü Fang and Kao Shen he went to a high place and he watched Kuan Sheng do battle. When the drum had been beaten thrice then Kuan Sheng went forth and opposite to him So Ch'ao came forth on his horse. When So Ch'ao saw Kuan Sheng he did not know him. But the soldiers who had come with him said, "This one who comes is The Great Sword, Kuan Sheng, who is newly turned robber."

So Ch'ao heard this but he said never a word. He did but charge forward to combat and Kuan Sheng whipped his horse on also and lifted his weapon. The two had fought less than ten rounds when Li Ch'eng saw by the way So Ch'ao used his battle axe that he could not overcome Kuan Sheng and he came forth with his two swords and the two of them fought against Kuan Sheng. On the other side The Ugly Warrior Hsüan Tsan and Hao Ssŭ Wen, seeing Li Ch'eng come forth, each took up his own weapon and they came forward to do battle.

The five horses were crowded together and Sung Chiang saw it from the high place and he pointed with his whip and all the fighting men rushed forward. On that day Li Ch'eng's army suffered a great defeat, and the same night they retreated into the city. Behind them the robbers pursued to the very foot of the city wall and there they set up camp.

On the next day the black clouds came down from the sky and the heavens seemed sad and daily the earth cracked with the cold. So Ch'ao alone led out a company against the robbers. Wu Yung saw this and he commanded them to go and pretend battle with him. If he did come into the camp they would seize advantage and press after him, and in this way So Ch'ao seemed to gain a victory and went back to the city pleased.

On that night the clouds were yet more heavy and the wind blew the more bitter. When Wu Yung went out of the camp to see, snow was already falling heavily. Then he bade the fighting men go on foot to the mountains and there on a narrow path beside a stream they were to dig a deep pit, and they were to cover it with earth. The snow fell the night through and when again he looked out the next day the snow was deep enough to cover a horse's knees.

Let it be told now of So Ch'ao. He beat his horse and rode upon the city wall and he looked down and saw that all the robbers seemed in some fear and they ran hither and thither east and west. Then quickly he called off three hundred horsemen and of a sudden he rushed out of the city. Sung Chiang's men parted and ran in all directions, and he commanded Li Chün and Chang Shun to put on their soft armor and mount their horses and take their weapons and come forward to meet the enemy. Even as they had begun battle with So Ch'ao they suddenly threw down their weapons and galloped away, and they purposely led So Ch'ao toward the pit that had been digged.

Now So Ch'ao was a man of impatient heart and how could he stop to see the trap? In that spot there was on one side a road, and on the other side the stream. Li Chün leaped from his horse into the water and he looked ahead and called, "Elder Brother Sung Chiang, run quickly!"

So Ch'ao heard this and he recked nothing of himself and he went ahead as though winged and behind them there was the sound of a rocket. Then did So Ch'ao and his horse fall into that digged pit and all the robbers who were ambushed came out. Even though So Ch'ao at this hour had had three heads and six arms must he have been wounded sorely and in many places. Truly was it

> Under the silvery snow lay the circle of a trap,
> Under the smooth jade snow lay the secret
> hidden pit.

How was it then with So Ch'ao's life? Pray hear it told in the next chapter.

Chapter 64

THE SPIRIT OF THE PAGODA MOVING HEAVENLY KING CH'AO KAI APPEARS AS A GOD. WHITE STRIPE IN THE WAVES CHANG SHUN TAKES HIS REVENGE UPON THE FACE OF THE WATERS

IT IS SAID: Thus Sung Chiang took advantage of this deep snow and he made a plot and so seized So Ch'ao, and the other soldiers and horsemen galloped into the city, and the thing was told in the great capital. When the governor Liang heard of it he grew afraid even though he would not, and he sent out a command, saying, "Let every warrior stay within the city on guard, nor may any go forth to battle."

Then it came into his heart to kill Lu Chün I and Shih Hsiu straightway, and yet he feared to anger Sung Chiang and for this reason force his anger yet higher, nor could the imperial army come forth immediately to save him. Thus did his sorrows heap upon him and he could but bid his officers guard the two well. Again he sent word to the capital that he would do whatever the Emperor willed.

Let it be told further now of Sung Chiang. He went into his camp and into his own tent and there he sat himself down and soon his men brought So Ch'ao before him. When Sung Chiang saw him he was filled with pleasure and he shouted to the soldiers to withdraw and himself he loosened his bonds and he invited him to come within the tent. There he poured forth wine for him, and with good words he comforted him and he said, "Look at us who were brothers, and you will see that the greater half of us have once been soldiers for the Emperor. If you do not despise us, Sir Warrior, I beg you to help me and let us together work righteousness for Heaven."

Then Yang Chi came forward and he made obeisance to So Ch'ao and the two talked together of what had happened since they last met and they held each other's hands and they let their tears flow, and since matters had come to such a pass there was naught for So Ch'ao except to join the robbers. Then was Sung Chiang overjoyed and again he commanded that a feast be spread there in his tent to celebrate the day.

On the next day the robbers took counsel as to how they would attack the city. It was a thing to do in several days, nor could the city be suddenly forced open. Now was Sung Chiang melancholy for a while and his joy went from him and on that night he sat alone in his tent. Suddenly there came upon him a gust of cold wind and it blew so upon the flame of the lamp that it went no larger than a bean is, and where the wind blew there appeared in some strange cloudy mist the form of a man. Then Sung Chiang lifted his head and looked—and it was The Heavenly King Ch'ao Kai! He made as though to come in and yet he did not and he called out, "Brother! What do you here?"

Sung Chiang gave a start of terror and quickly he rose and asked, "Elder Brother, from whence have you come? I have not yet taken revenge for your death and therefore my heart is not at ease day or night. There has ever been some matter to be done day after day and from then until now I have had no opportunity. Today your spirit appears to me thus and surely it is to reproach me for some cause."

Then Ch'ao Kai made answer, saying, "Brother, you do not know. I am sworn bond-brother with you and today I came especially that I might save you, for today that which you bear upon your back is about to come forth and there is none who can save you from that curse except only one who lives in the south, a lesser star among the brotherhood. Brother, once you said in the thirty-six ways of escape none is better than to run away. If today therefore you do not run away with all speed, for what do you wait further? If some unknown evil comes upon you then what will you do? Do not blame me if at that time I do not come to save you."

Then Sung Chiang came to ask again and more clearly and he hastened forward and asked, "Elder Brother, here your spirit is in this place and I hope ten thousand times you will speak forth the truth."

But Ch'ao Kai replied, "Do not talk overmuch. Only prepare yourself and return to the lair. Do not delay. Now am I gone."

Then suddenly Sung Chiang seemed to come out of a dream and indeed it was as though he had been in some far faëry country. He invited Wu Yung to come into his tent and Sung Chiang told him all his dream, and Wu Yung said, "If indeed it was The Heavenly King who showed his ghost we cannot but believe what he has told. Now the season is winter and the earth is frozen and it is not easy either for our men or our horses to stay on here. Truly ought we therefore to return at once to the lair and wait until winter is ended and the spring come and the snow is gone and the ice melted. Then let us come again against this city nor will it be too late, either."

But Sung Chiang answered, "Sir Counselor, although what you have said is true enough, yet there are our brothers Lu Chün I and Shih Hsiu suffering in the gaol and a day for them is as though a year passed and they do but hope for us, their brothers, to come and save them. If we do not return, perhaps those evil ones will even take the lives of these two. Truly in this is it hard to go forward and hard also to retreat. What shall we do, therefore?"

Their counsel together could not be finished.

The next day Sung Chiang seemed weary and worn and his body was fevered and his head ached as though an axe had split it and when he lay upon his bed he could not rise. And all the chieftains went into his tent to see him and Sung Chiang said, "I do feel my back is very hot and sore."

When they all looked at his back there was a place as large as a pot upon his back, red and swollen, and Wu Yung said, "This illness, if it be not an outer illness, comes from deep within. Once I read a physician's book and I read that if a gruel were made of green pea meal the poison from this illness could not enter into the heart. Quickly then let us seek this remedy and prepare it for our brother to eat. If in such a great camp of men as this we cannot at once find a physician—"

Then did Chang Shun say here, "When this lowly one was by the river of Ching Yang my mother had such an illness as this on her back and a hundred medicines could not cure her. At last we invited a certain doctor of Nanking who was called An Tao Ch'uan and when his hand fell on that illness straightway it disappeared. From that time on we were grateful for his goodness and if I had but some silver I would have sent it to him. Now seeing how heavy is this same illness of my elder brother none can heal him save that one man. Only the road from here thither is very far, nor can one go there in a few days. For his sake, therefore, I can but go this selfsame night."

Wu Yung said, "Our elder brother Sung Chiang has dreamed that our elder brother Ch'ao Kai told him he would suffer a hundred days of hardship and none could heal him save one from the south where Nanking is. It must be this very man."

Then Sung Chiang said, "Brother, if you have such a man as this, go for me quickly and do not refuse to suffer for me but remember first our loyalty to each other. Go then this very night and seek this man and save my life."

So Wu Yung commanded that one hundred ounces of gold shaped like leek leaves should be fetched to give the doctor and that there should be beyond this twenty or thirty ounces of silver for use upon the journey and he commanded Chang Shun to set forth that same day and good or ill that he must bring the physician back with him nor could there be any delay at all. And he said, "Let us now take up the camp and return to our lair and let us meet this physician there. Brother, return with all speed."

Then Chang Shun parted from them all and he took his bundle on his back and went forward on his way.

Let it be told now of the counselor Wu Yung. He gave forth a command to all the chieftains and he said, "Recall the fighting men with all speed and take up camp and return to our lair. Let Sung Chiang be placed upon a cart and let us set forth this very night. As for the enemy in the city, they have suffered once when we withdrew and they will guess that again we do plan some guile and surely they will not dare to come in pursuit."

Thus did Wu Yung recall the robbers.

Let it be told now of the governor Liang. When he heard that again the robbers had withdrawn in truth he did not understand why it was. Then Li Ch'eng and Wen Tah said, "That Wu Yung is very full of guile and we can but guard our city with all care and let them go."

Now the story divides into two parts. Let it be told of Chang Shun. In his desire to save Sung Chiang he ran the night through. It was now the end of winter and if it did not rain it snowed and the road was very hard to go. But Chang Shun did not heed the wind and snow and he recked nothing of his life save to go on. Alone he hastened to the side of the river Yangtse and when he looked for a ferry boat there was not one. Then could Chang Shun but cry bitterness and there was nothing for him except to walk along beside the river. Suddenly he saw smoke rising from among the ruined reeds upon the river's bank and Chang Shun cried out, "Ferryman, quickly bring the ferry hither and carry me across!"

Then was there a sound of rustling in the reeds and there came forth a man. On his head was a great rain hat and he wore a coat of grass against the rain and he asked, saying, "Sir Traveler, whither do you go?"

Chang Shun answered, "I would ferry across the river and go to Nanking on a very important matter and I will give you more than the usual boat fee. Ferry me across, therefore."

Then that ferryman said, "To ferry you across is easy enough but the night comes, and even though you crossed the river, there is no inn where you may rest. Sleep, therefore, in my boat and when the fourth watch comes and when the wind has died down and the snow ceases to fall then will I ferry you across. Only you must give me the more silver for it."

Chang Shun said, "You have spoken very truly too." And he went with the ferryman into the reeds and there upon the bank was tied a small boat. Beneath the mats which made its roof there was a thin young man cowering over a pot of coals. The ferryman helped Chang Shun upon the boat and Chang Shun went into the cabin and he took off the wet garments from his body and he bade the thin youth dry them over the fire. Then he himself opened his bundle and brought out his bedding and he rolled it about himself and laid himself down. Then he called the ferryman and said, "Have you wine for sale here? If I could buy some it would be well, too."

The ferryman answered, "Wine there is no place to buy, but if you wish food, then eat a bowlful."

So Chang Shun sat up again and he ate a bowl of rice and again he laid down his head and was asleep. Now because he had suffered such hardship these several days and because he was so proud in himself and feared nothing he slept for several hours. But that thin youth sat there with his hands over the coals and he pointed his lips at Chang Shun and he said softly to the ferryman, "Elder Brother, did you see?"

Then the ferryman crept forward and he pinched the bundle beneath Chang Shun's head and he perceived that there was something there like silver and gold. He shook his hand and whispered, "Do you go and loose the boat and it will not be too late if we go out into the middle of the river to kill him."

Then the youth pushed aside the curtain and he leaped upon the shore and he loosed the rope and leaped again upon the boat and he took the bamboo pole and pushed the boat from the shore and set the oar in its socket and there was the sound of the oar squeaking as he rowed. And the ferryman took the rope into the cabin and softly he bound it about Chang Shun and then he went behind some boards back of the bed and fetched out a long knife. At this moment Chang Shun awoke, but both his hands were tied down and he could not move and the ferryman took the knife in his own hand and he pressed him down with the other. Then Chang Shun besought him, saying, "Good Fellow, spare me my life, and I will give you all my gold!"

But the ferryman answered, "The gold I will have—and your life will I have also!"

Then did Chang Shun cry out continually and he said, "Do you but let me die whole and then will my spirit not come to seek you out after I am dead!"

The ferryman replied, "This I can do." And he put down the knife and he threw Chang Shun with a splash into the water. But when the ferryman went to open the bundle and looked into it he gave a start when he saw how much silver and gold was there. He knitted his brows together and he said to the thin youth, "Fifth Brother, come in, for I have somewhat to say to you."

Then the youth came in and the ferryman gripped him with one hand and with the other he raised his knife and cut the young man's head off clean and he pushed him into the water, and the ferryman wiped away the blood from the boat and he rowed the boat away himself.

Let it be told now of Chang Shun. He was such a man as could live for three or five nights under the water and here he was pushed all at once into the river. There in the water he gnawed loose the bonds that bound him and he swam to the southern bank. Now when he was come there he saw the light of a lamp shining in the midst of the woods and he climbed up the bank then and dripping as he was he hastened into the wood to see what it was. It was a village wine shop, where the keeper had risen in the middle of the night to brew his wine and from the cracks in the wall the light of his lamp leaked out. When Chang Shun called to him to open the door he saw an old man and he bent his head and made obeisance. Then the old man said, "Surely you are not he who leaped into the river to save your life when you were robbed?"

Chang Shun answered, "Truly do I not think to deceive you, Old Sir. This lowly one came down from the mountain and I was going to Nanking on business. When night was come I had reached the river and there I searched for a boat, and I did not think to come upon two evil men. They have taken my clothing and all my silver and gold and they cast me into the river. But I could swim and I escaped with my life. Grandfather, save me, therefore!"

The old man heard this and he led Chang Shun into the midst of an inner room and he gave him a quilted coat and took off from him his wet garments to dry by the fire and he poured some hot wine for him to drink. Then the old man said, "Fellow, what is your surname? And if you be a Shantung man for what have you come hither?"

Chang Shun replied, "This lowly one is surnamed Chang and the physician surnamed An of Nanking is my brother and I have come on a purpose to see him."

Then the old man asked, "When you were coming from Shantung did you pass by the great robbers' lair?"

Chang Shun replied, "I did come by that very place."

Then the old man said, "That great chieftain Sung Chiang there does not rob those who pass by, neither does he take men's lives and he does but work righteousness for Heaven."

Chang Shun said, "The chieftain Sung Chiang holds highest of all loyalty and righteousness and he does no harm to good men. He does but hate evil governors and their evil followers."

The old man said again, "I have heard that Sung Chiang and such as are with him are truly very kindly men, and that they save the poor and old. And how is he not like these robbers we have here! If *he* were but to come here how happy would the people be! Then would we not eat bitterness from the ceaseless oppression of these wicked governors of ours and their evil followers, who ever give us no peace!"

Now Chang Shun when he had heard this said, "Grandfather, do not be afraid. This lowly one is none other than White Stripe In The Waves Chang Shun. Because my elder brother Sung Chiang has fallen ill of a great wen upon his back he bade me bring a hundred ounces of yellow gold and come hither to invite the physician An. Who would have thought that I would deem myself so mighty a robber as to fall asleep on the boat thinking nothing and so have been bound by these two evil thieves and cast into the river? But I bit my bonds loose and so came hither."

Then the old man said, "If you are one of the good fellows from there, I will bid my son come out that he may see you."

In a little while there came out a slender young man from within and when he saw Chang Shun he made obeisance and he said, "This lowly one has long heard the elder brother's great name but I have had no good fortune and so I have not met you. This humble one is surnamed Wang and I am the sixth in my family, and because I run and leap so quickly when I walk men all call me The Lively Devil. All my life I have loved well to swim in the water and to use a staff. Once I did seek teachers but I never found one greatly skilled enough to teach me, and now I sell wine here upon the river's bank to make my living. I know those who did rob you but just now. One was Cut The River In Twain Chang Wang and that other young man was a man of the township of Hua T'ing and he is called The Oily Mudfish Swen The Fifth. These two men are ever on this river robbing. Elder Brother, let your heart rest. Live here for a few days and wait until these come hither to drink wine and I will take revenge for you."

Chang Shun said, "Much do I thank you for your goodwill, my Brother. But for my elder brother Sung Chiang's sake I would fain be but a day in returning to the mountain lair. I do only wait until the dawn comes, and then will I hasten into the city to invite the physician An. When I return I will speak with you again."

Then did Wang The Sixth take out his own bundle of new garments and he gave them all to Chang Shun to change and he killed a fowl and he poured out wine to make a feast for him. Of this no more need be told.

On the next day the sky was clear and the snow gone, and Wang The Sixth again gave some ten-odd ounces of silver to Chang Shun and bade him go on then into the city of Nanking. So Chang Shun went into the midst of that city and he went to The Bridge Of Elms and there he saw the physician An at his own door selling medicines. Chang Shun went in and he saw the physician and he put his head down and made obeisance. When the physician An saw Chang Shun he asked him, saying, "Brother, many years we have not met. What wind has blown you hither?"

Then Chang Shun followed him within and he told him the whole story of how he had disturbed the city of Ching Chou and how he had followed Sung Chiang to the lair, and he told how Sung Chiang had fallen ill of a wen upon his back and so he was come on purpose to invite the physician and he said, "When I had come into the midst of the river Yangtse I did almost lose my life, and for this I have come empty handed, for I truly lost all I brought."

Then An The Physician said, "If it is Sung Chiang of whom you speak, and he is held a good man in all the world, the most important thing for me is to go and heal him. But since that stupid woman of mine died, I have no other near relative in my house and I cannot go far away. For this I may not go forth."

Then did Chang Shun beseech him bitterly and he said, "If you refuse me, Elder Brother, and you will not go, then I also will not return to the mountain."

Then An The Physician said, "Let us take counsel further."

In a hundred ways therefore did Chang Shun beg him and only then did An The Physician give his promise.

Now this An The Physician for long had been coming and going with a certain courtesan of the city of Nanking whose name was Ling Ch'iao Lu, and at this time their love had just come to its full heat. On that night therefore he led Chang Shun with him to the courtesan's house and there wine was set forth and the courtesan made obeisance to him as brother-in-law. After they had drunk thrice and five times and when they were almost drunken An The Physician said to the courtesan, "I will sleep here in your house for the night and tomorrow I will go forth early with this brother of mine to the mountain. If I am gone long it will be a month, and if I am gone for a little while it will be some twenty days before I return and then I will come back and see you."

But that courtesan answered, "I will not have you go indeed, and if you do not heed what I say then enter my door no more."

Then An The Physician said, "But my bag of medicines is all filled ready and I have but to set forth. Tomorrow shall I go. Enlarge your heart a little, therefore, and be at peace, for even though I go I will not linger for many days."

But the courtesan pouted and she put forth all her sweet wiles and she wept and threw herself upon the man's bosom and she said, "If you do not think of me—well, go then—and I will stay here and curse you until your flesh flies off in ten thousand bits!"

Now Chang Shun heard these words and he hated the woman and he hated himself because he could not swallow her down like a mouthful of cold water. He saw the night grew late and there was the physician fallen down in a mighty drunkenness so that he went into the courtesan's room and laid himself down in her bed. Then the courtesan came out and bade Chang Shun be gone and she said, "Do you return alone. I have no place here for you to sleep."

Chang Shun replied, "I will wait until my elder brother wakes from his wine and then we will go together."

And the courtesan could not move him to be gone and she could but let him lie in a small room by the gate.

Now Chang Shun's heart burned with melancholy so that the pain was like that of boiling oil in him, and how could he sleep? At the time of the first watch there came one to knock on the gate and when Chang Shun peered through the crack he saw a man run in and speak of something with an old woman who lived with the courtesan as her mother, and the old woman asked the man, saying, "You have not come for a long time and where have you been then? Tonight the physician has made himself drunken and he sleeps there in her room. And now what can be done?"

That man replied, "I have ten ounces of gold here to give to her to make a hairpin and earrings for herself. Old Woman, have you no way to help me that I may see her for a little while?"

Then the old woman said, "Do you but stay there in my room and I will bid my daughter come."

Now while Chang Shun looked there in the light of the lantern he saw this man was none other than the ferryman called Cut The River In Twain Chang Wang, for he was such an one as who when he found gold upon the river somehow he came and spent it in this courtesan's house. When Chang Shun saw this he could not keep his anger down and when he listened further he saw the old woman setting forth a feast there in her room and she called to the courtesan to come out and feast with Chang Wang. And Chang Shun was about to leap forward and yet he feared, too, to make some mistake and let the thief escape somehow.

At about the time of the third watch the two

servants in the kitchen were also drunken and the old woman was staggering and falling to east and to west and she stared at the lamp with glazed and drowsy eyes. Then silently did Chang Shun open the door of the room and he went to the kitchen and he saw a chopping knife shining with oil there on the earthen oven and he saw the old woman lying drunken on a bench beside the oven. Then he went into the kitchen and he took up the chopping knife and first he killed the old woman. But the chopping knife was not over sharp and when he went to kill the servants he cut only the head of one when the edge of the knife turned. Those two were just about to set up a cry when his hand fell opportunely upon an axe that was there for splitting wood and he lifted it up and with a blow apiece he killed them both.

But now the courtesan heard the ado and she opened the door in great haste and she met Chang Shun full. He lifted the axe in his hands and he split her between the breasts and she fell to the ground. Then Chang Wang, seeing the woman lie dead in the light of the lamp, pushed open the back window and he leaped out and down the wall and so he went away. Then did Chang Shun repent himself sorely that he had not had time to kill the man also when suddenly he bethought himself how Wu Sung had written his confession in blood upon the wall. Straightway he cut off the edge of one's coat and he dipped it in blood and he wrote upon the whitewashed wall and he wrote, "I who killed all these am An The Physician." This he wrote in some scores of places. Then he waited until dawn was nearly come when he heard An The Physician awake from his drunkenness in the inner room and he called, "Where is that woman of mine?"

Chang Shun answered, "Elder Brother, speak no word. I will let you see that woman of yours."

Then An The Physician arose and he saw there the four dead bodies and he fell into such terror his flesh seemed dead on his bones and he trembled so he could not stand. Then Chang Shun said, "Elder Brother, do you see what you have written?"

An The Physician answered, "Ai, and how you have put bitterness upon me!"

Chang Shun said, "There are but two ways for you and you may choose which you will. If there comes a great stir then I will escape and you must go and suffer for their lives. But if you would have no trouble come of it then let us fetch the bag of medicines from your house and let us go this very night to the lair and so save my elder brother. Choose, therefore, which of these two ways you will choose."

An The Physician said, "Brother, you are such an one as uses too cruel ways to force his will, and your own life will be cut short some day thereby."

And they took advantage of the coming dawn and Chang Shun gathered together the moneys he needed for the way and he went with the physician to his house and they opened the locks and pushed the door and they fetched the medicines and then went out of the city and straight they went to Wang The Sixth's wine shop. Wang The Sixth met them and he said, "Yesterday Chang Wang passed by here and it is a pity you did not meet him, Elder Brother."

Chang Shun replied, "But I have met that thing not long since, too, but it is a pity that I had not time in which to kill him. Yet I have a great thing now to do and how have I time to take my small revenge?"

Before Chang Shun had finished speaking Wang The Sixth said to him, "That thing Chang Wang is coming even now."

Then Chang Shun said, "Do not frighten him at all and let us watch where he goes."

Then they saw Chang Wang go to the river's edge and busy himself with his boat. And Wang The Sixth called, saying, "Elder Brother Chang, pray leave your boat here that two friends of mine may ferry across!"

Chang Wang replied, "If they want the boat then let them come at once."

This Wang The Sixth told Chang Shun and Chang Shun said to the physician, "Brother An, do you lend me your garments, and I will change my clothes for you to wear, and then we will go upon the boat."

But the physician asked, "What does this mean?"

Chang Shun answered, "Assuredly I have a meaning. Ask nothing therefore."

So An The Physician took off his garments and he gave them to Chang Shun to wear and Chang Shun put on the other's turban and his wind hood and his round hat and his mantle. Then Wang The Sixth took on his back the bag of medicines and they went to the side of the boat and Chang Wang poled the boat close to the shore and the three went aboard. Chang Shun went to the back part of the boat and he pulled up the planks of the back of the boat, and the chopping knife was still there. Silently he took it up and went back to the cabin. Chang Wang poled the boat away and there was the sound of the squeaking of the oar in its socket. Again they came to the midst of the river and there Chang Shun took off his upper garment and he gave a shout, "Ferryman, come here quickly! See, here in the cabin there are the stains of blood!"

Chang Wang said, "Sir Traveler, do not make merry with me." Thus he spoke and while he spoke he came into the cabin. But Chang Shun seized him by the bosom and he gave a yell, "You robber! Do you know that traveler who came that snowy day to ferry across the river?"

Chang Wang stared at him and he could not make a sound. Then Chang Shun shouted, "Such as you! You have tricked me of my hundred pieces of gold and you would have had my life, too! Where is that thin youth you had?"

Chang Wang replied, "Good fellow, I had a heap of gold and I feared he wanted to share with me and then I would have less and for this I killed him and I cast him into the river."

Then Chang Shun cried, "You thief and robber, lord that I am, I was born beside the river at Ching Yang and I grew there beneath The Little Orphan Island and I was a weigher for fish sellers and my name was spread abroad under Heaven. But because I made a turmoil in the city now I live for the time in the great lair at Liang Shan P'o and I do follow Sung Chiang, the chieftain, and wherever I am under Heaven none can withstand me, and where is there one who does not fear me? Such as you to deceive me into coming into your boat—and you bound my two hands and you cast me into the heart of the river! If it had not been that I am one who can live under the water, would you not have had my life? Today we meet again by fate and I will not forgive you." And he pulled the man toward him and threw him into the cabin and he took the rope that stayed the boat to shore and he bound the ferryman, hands and feet together, until he was hoof-shaped and turning to the great river he cast him in and he shouted, saying, "Thus have I spared you too a blow of the knife!"

Wang The Sixth saw this and he sighed in pity. But Chang Shun took out from the inner part of the boat all the ferryman's store of gold and all his odd pieces of silver and he tied them all into his bundle. Then the three rowed the boat to shore and Chang Shun said to Wang The Sixth, "Good Brother, this mercy which you have showed to me I will repay whether I live or die. If you do not despise us then close your wine shop, you and your father, and hasten to our lair and join with us all. Yet I do not know what your heart says."

Wang The Sixth answered, "Elder Brother, what you say is after my own heart."

When they had finished speaking they made ready to part and Chang Shun and An The Physician changed their garments again and they went ashore to the northern side of the river and there Wang The Sixth said farewell and rowing the small boat he went back alone and he made ready his possessions and hurried thither.

Let it be told now of Chang Shun and of An The Physician when they had come upon the northern shore. They carried the bag of medicines and went straight on their way. Now this physician was a man of learning and so he could not walk with ease and he had gone but ten miles or so when already he could walk no more, and Chang Shun sought out a village inn and he bought some wine for him to drink. In the midst of their drinking they saw a traveler come from without and he came in and stood before them and he called out, "Brother, why have you come so late as this?"

When Chang Shun looked to see it was that Tai Chung Of The Magic Strides and he had disguised himself as a traveler and had come thither with all speed. With all speed too Chang Shun showed him the physician and he asked, "How fares it with our elder brother Sung Chiang?"

Tai Chung replied, "Our elder brother lies now in delirium and no rice nor water can pass his lips. Even as we watch him he seems dying."

Chang Shun heard these words and the tears flowed from his eyes like falling rain. Then An The Physician asked, "And how is the color of his blood and what the hue of skin and flesh?"

Tai Chung replied, "His skin is dark and dry and he cries out from morning to night and his pain is unceasing, and we cannot say when he must die."

Then An The Physician said, "If his flesh and skin can still feel pain then he can be healed. But I do fear we will delay too long."

Tai Chung said, "This is easy." And he took out his magic letters and he tied them upon the physician's legs. Then Tai Chung himself took the bag of medicines and he commanded Chang Shun, saying, "Do you come on slowly and alone. I will go on ahead with this physician."

Then the two left the village inn and they used the magic and went on first.

Let it now be told of Chang Shun. He rested in this inn for several days and then of a sudden he saw Wang The Sixth coming with his bundle and he came by with his old father. Chang Shun went to meet them and his heart was filled with great joy and he said, "I do wait on purpose for you here."

Then was Wang The Sixth filled with fear and he said, "Elder Brother, how can you still be here? Where is the physician?"

Chang Shun said, "Tai Chung The Magic Messenger came hither to meet him and the two have gone on first."

Then Wang The Sixth and his old father went on with Chang Shun and so they went toward the robbers' lair.

Let it be told now of Tai Chung. He led The Physician An and he used his magic and by night they went to the lair and there the chieftains met him, great and small, and they circled about him in the room where Sung Chiang lay. When they looked at him as he lay upon his bed there was but a small faint breath in his mouth and he lay well-nigh dead. But the physician first counted off his pulse and he said, "Do not fear, Sir Chieftains. His pulse says there is naught to fear, although the illness lies heavy on his body. But as to that great last thing, death, there is no fear. It is not that I boast of myself with great words but within ten days he will be again as he was."

Then all of them when they heard it said thus they all made obeisance.

And An The Physician first took the leaves of mugwort and set it burning and he put these on the wen for poultice and he drew the poison forth and then he used ointments and on the ointments plasters. Within he used medicines which when they were eaten would force the poison out and grow new flesh. Within five days Sung Chiang's skin turned lighter and more pink and soft and it was tender once again. In no more than ten days, although the hole of the wen had not yet closed, yet he could eat and drink as ever he did.

Then was seen Chang Shun leading Wang The Sixth and his father, these twain, and they came and they made obeisance before Sung Chiang and all the chieftains, and Chang Shun told them all that had befallen him upon the river and how upon that same river he had taken his revenge. Then did all the company praise him and they cried, "So might we all unknowing have lost you, our Brother!"

Now Sung Chiang's illness was but newly well and he talked to them all, weeping as he spoke, and he took counsel with them how he must go and attack that city Ta Ming Fu and save out Lu Chün I and Shih Hsiu. But An The Physician exhorted him, saying, "Sir Chieftain, your wen is not yet wholly closed, and you cannot go about as you would. If you go hither and thither you cannot soon be well."

And Wu Yung said, "You need not trouble yourself about this, Elder Brother. Do you but nourish your own self and nurse yourself until you are strong as once you were. I, although I be a man of little worth, yet will I seize this time of spring newly come, and surely will I beat open that city of Ta Ming Fu and save the lives of Lu Chün I and Shih Hsiu, these twain, and I will seize and bring hither to the lair those two who are in adultery. Thus will I take revenge for you, my Brother."

Then Sung Chiang said, "If you will truly take revenge for me then I, if I must die, may close my eyes in peace."

Wu Yung then went to the Hall Of Righteousness And Loyalty and sent forth the call.

Because of this the midst of the city of Ta Ming Fu became a pot of flames and a wood of weapons. Before the court of the governor Liang that place was changed into a mountain of heaped dead and the blood flowed like a sea. Truly was it

He spoke and smiled, and devils and gods felt
their galls burst loose with fear;
And here and there he sent his good men, and
they held him very dear.

How then did the counselor Wu Yung go to vanquish that city of Ta Ming Fu? Pray hear it told in the next chapter.

Chapter 65

SHIH CH'IEN BURNS THE HOUSE OF THE JADE CLOUD. WU YUNG TAKES THE CITY OF TA MING FU BY GUILE

IT IS SAID: Wu Yung said to Sung Chiang, "Today do we rejoice that you are healed and that we have this physician An here in the lair to heal you and this is ten thousand fortunes for us in the lair. When you are lying on your bed, my Brother, this younger brother, who am I, sent men continually to the city of Ta Ming Fu to hear the news there. Day and night is the governor Liang there afraid and he is filled with melancholy and he does but fear lest our men and horsemen go thither to attack him. And I have sent men to the city, and without the city and within they have pasted everywhere proclamations signed by no name that tell the people not to be troubled nor afraid, for there is but one on whom we take revenge and there is but one who owes us aught, and when our fighting men come to that city, we shall have a certain place to go. Therefore is the governor Liang yet more afraid. He has heard, too, that Kuan Sheng has joined himself to us and even more the prime minister dares not mention this before the Emperor, and so he has said to some that he will seek soon a chance for the robber chieftain to turn loyal to the throne again, and so there will be an end of trouble for us all. For this the prime minister continually sends letters to the governor Liang that he is to protect the lives of Lu Chün I and Shih Hsiu and he is to save their lives to serve as hand or foot."

Now when Sung Chiang heard this he would fain have hastened his men down to attack the city, but Wu Yung said again, "The winter will soon be over and spring will come and soon it will be The Feast Of Lanterns, and it is an old custom of the city of Ta Ming Fu to light many lanterns for the day. I will take this opportunity and I will send men ahead and bid them hide there in the city before the day comes, and we will send many fighting men to attack from the outside, from within and without, and so we can overcome that city."

Sung Chiang answered, "This plan is truly very wise, and I do pray you, Sir Counselor, to carry it out."

Then Wu Yung said, "The thing of first importance is that a fire be lighted in the midst of the city for a sign. Who among you, my Brothers, dares go for me first to light that fire?"

Then was seen one to come from across the way and he said, "I would go." When they all looked at him it was Flea On A Drum Shih Ch'ien and he said, "Once when I was a child I went to Ta Ming Fu and there is a storeyed house there in the midst of the city and it is called The House Of The Jade Cloud. Above and below in this house there are more than a hundred rooms and eye can see that it will be a very merry place on that night of The Feast Of Lanterns. I, your younger brother, will first go secretly into that city and on the night of the feast day I will climb up that house and set a fire blazing for a sign. Then may you, Sir Counselor, lead the horsemen into the city."

Wu Yung said, "Thus would my heart do also. Tomorrow when the day begins to dawn then go down the mountain first. On the night of the feast when the first watch begins, set fire there on the house and it will be to your glory."

So Shih Ch'ien promised, and having this command he went his way. On the next day Wu Yung appointed Hsieh Chen and Hsieh Pao to disguise themselves as huntsmen and they were to go into the city of Ta Ming Fu and go to the houses of officials there and take all sorts of game. On the night of the feast day when they saw the sign of the fire rise they were to go before the court of the governor and hold those back who would go forth to spread the alarm. And these two received their command and went forth.

Again did Wu Yung appoint Tu Ch'ien and Sung Wan that they were to disguise themselves as rice merchants and they were to push a wheelbarrow and go into the city and seek an inn. On the night of the feast day when they saw the sign of the fire they were to go first to the eastern gate and seize it. And the two received the command and went their way.

Once more did Wu Yung appoint K'ung Ming and K'ung Liang and they were to disguise themselves as beggars and they were to go into the midst of a busy street and there lie down to sleep under the eaves of some house. When they saw the fire rise from The House Of The Jade Cloud they were to be ready to help anywhere there was need. And these two received the command and went their way.

Again did Wu Yung appoint Li Yün and Shih Chin that they were to disguise themselves as travelers and they were to go to an inn outside the east gate of the city and there rest. When they saw the sign of fire rise in the midst of the city they were to go and kill the guards of the gate first and take the gate and so make a way of escape. And these two received their command and went their way.

And Wu Yung appointed Lu Chi Shen and Wu Sung that they were to disguise themselves as wandering priests, and first they were to go to a temple outside the city and lodge there, and when they saw the fire in the city rise for sign they were to go outside the south gate and there hold it against the enemy soldiers and do battle and obstruct their way as best they could. And these two received the command and went their way.

And again Wu Yung appointed Chou Yuen and Chou Jun that they were to be travelers and sellers of lanterns and they were to go straight into the midst of the city and seek an inn and rest there. When they saw the first fire rise in the house in the city they were to go and wait before the gaol and there lend aid. And these two received the command and went their way.

Again Wu Sung appointed Liu T'ang and Yang Hsiung that they were to be runners of a court and they were to go and stay before the court of the magistrate in the city, and when they saw the signal fires rise they were to lay hold on any who went out to make report of it, and so confuse them that head could not aid foot nor foot the head. And these two received the command and went their way.

And Wu Sung invited the teacher Kung Sun Sheng that he would disguise himself as a Taoist called a "Wandering Cloud," and he bade Ling Chen follow him as attendant, and he was to take with him every kind of wind and fire and thunder to set forth in the heavens and they were to go into the city to some lonely empty place and there wait. When they saw the signal fire rise then were they to set fire to their rockets. And these two received their command and went their way.

Again Wu Sung appointed Chang Shun and with him Yien Ch'ing that they were to go into the city by the water gate and they were to hasten straightway to the house of Lu Chün I and seize the two adulterers.

And he appointed Wang The Dwarf Tiger and Sheng Sing and Chang Ch'ing and The Goodwife Hu and The Goodwife Ku and The Goodwife Sheng that they were to disguise themselves as three country couples and they were to seem to go into the city to see the lanterns, and they were to seek out the house of Lu Chün I and set fire to it.

And again he appointed Ch'ai Chin and with him Yo Ho, that they were to disguise themselves as captains and go straight to the gaolers, the brothers Ts'ai, and save them both.

Thus did the chieftains each receive his command and each went his way.

Now this was the beginning of the first month of the year and it need not be told how the good fellows of the robbers' lair one by one went down the mountain. Let it be told of the governor Liang of the city of Ta Ming Fu. He bade one fetch Li Ch'eng and Wen Tah and the magistrate Wang and others and they took counsel concerning the matter of The Feast Of Lanterns. The governor Liang said, "According to our old custom we will light many lanterns to celebrate the feast and so make merry with the people, and we will do altogether as the custom is in the eastern capital. But twice the robbers from the lair at Liang Shan P'o have come into our city, and we do fear that they may come again and make trouble. In this small official's mind it is better to forbid the lighting of the lanterns. But what think you all?"

Then Wen Tah said, "Yet I do think those robbers have secretly retreated. Everywhere upon the streets there are proclamations pasted with no names signed and this they have done because they are driven to it and have no other way. Assuredly they have no plans beyond. Sir Governor, why are you then so melancholy? If this year we let no lanterns be lit and the spies of those robbers hear and know of what we do they will surely laugh at us and shame us. Therefore send forth your mandate and tell the people that they may light more lanterns than they did last year and that they may add certain merry plays, and in the midst of the market they may make a false fairy fish mountain on which there are lanterns and let all be done as it is in the eastern capital and let the merrymaking last the whole night through, and let it begin on the thirteenth day of the month and last through to the seventeenth, and let there be these five nights of lanterns and bid the magistrate count the people and let not one be lacking. And do you go forth yourself upon the streets, Sir Governor, clad in your holiday robes and make merry with the people. As for me, I will lead a company of horsemen outside the city and I will go to The Valley Of The Flying Tiger and there stand, and be prepared for any plot the robbers make. And bid the general Li to take a company of armored horsemen and circle about the city and spy out, so that the people may fear nothing."

And when the governor Liang heard this he was greatly pleased and all the governors having taken counsel decided what to do and straightway they sent forth proclamations and announced all to the people. Now this city was the greatest city in that province of Hopei and all who came in and went out of the country passed through it, and so there was much commerce coming from other parts there, and the merchants of the world settled there thick as fog or as clouds. When it was heard that the lantern feast was to be celebrated, then all the merchants came flocking thither and in every street and alley and in every market place those who must oversee counted out the people. The rich people made every sort of play with lanterns and each house hastened to buy lanterns to hang before the doors, and those who went far went even to a hundred miles and those who went near went thirty miles or so. Because of this every year there were those who sold lanterns who came to the city to do business and before the door of every house a pavilion was made of mats and there the lanterns were hung, and every house longed to hang the best lanterns and fire off the finest rockets.

Within the doors a tent was put up like an umbrella and there screens of five colors were placed and lanterns and rockets, and on the four sides were hung famous words of famous men written down and old curiosities and toys. All in the city, whether upon the great streets or on the small, in every house might light its lanterns.

At the governor's courts, beside The Chou Bridge, there was raised the fairy fish mountain and there were circled about it two dragon lanterns, one red and one yellow, and every scale of those lanterns was a little separate lantern, and out of the mouths of the dragons flowed pure water and it flowed into the stream beneath the bridge. Around the mountain and below and above it there were lighted countless lanterns.

In front of The Temple Of The Brass Buddha there was yet another fairy mountain made and upon it crawled a green dragon and around it were thousands and hundreds of flower lanterns. At The House Of The Jade Cloud there was also a fairy mountain and upon it crawled a white dragon and about it the lanterns lit were countless.

Now this wine shop was famous over the whole province and it was held the first of all.

Its roofs were three-eaved and its beams were most cunningly carved and the pillars also. Truly was it most finely built. There were, upstairs and down, more than a hundred rooms and there was music and merrymaking in that house both day and night, and the sound of lutes and every sort of music filled the ears without ceasing.

In the city every Taoist temple and Buddhist temple and every temple to any god and every monastery, each had its lanterns lit to wish good harvest for the year.

As for the brothels and the houses and the courtesans, they need not even be mentioned, being but the more full of lanterns and of merriment.

Now the spies from the robbers' lair heard this news and they took it to the mountain, and when Wu Yung knew it he was very glad, and he went and told it all to Sung Chiang. Then Sung Chiang was fain himself to lead fighting men against the city but when An The Physician saw this he said, "Sir Warrior, your wound is not yet closed, and indeed you may not yet stir as you would, for if a little anger rises in you then will you not be soon healed again."

Then Wu Yung said, "I will go forth this once for you, my Elder Brother."

Straightway then with The Iron Faced P'ei Hsüan he counted off eight companies of men. The first company was led by The Great Sword Kuan Sheng and with him was The Guardian Star God Hao Ssŭ Wen, and this company was to go as vanguard and behind him was to come He Who Rules Three Mountains Huang Hsin as aide, and all the company were horsemen.

The second company was led by The Leopard Headed Ling Ch'ung and with him were The Magic Iron Flautist Ma Ling and The Red Eyed Lion Teng Fei and behind him for an aide was Little Li Kuan Hua Yung, and all this company also were horsemen.

The third company was The Double Clubs Hu Yien Shu and he led with him Victor In A Hundred Battles Han T'ao and The Eye Of Heaven P'eng Ch'i and behind for aide was The Sick Warrior Sheng Li and all this company were horsemen.

The fourth company was The Fire In The Thunder Clap Ch'ing Ming and he led with him Eagle In The Clouds Ou P'eng and The Five Hued Tiger Yien Shun and behind him Ch'en Ta, The Gorge Leaping Tiger, came as aide. All were horsemen.

The fifth company were foot fighting men and the chief was He Whom No Obstacle Can Stay Mu Hung and with him were The Devil Faced Tu Hsing and The White Faced Goodman Chen T'ien Shou.

The sixth company was on foot and the chief was The Black Whirlwind Li K'uei and with him were The Pursuing God Of Death Li Li and The Dagger Devil Ch'ao Cheng.

The seventh company on foot was led by The Winged Tiger Lei Heng and with him were The Gold Eyed Tiger Cub Shih En and The Lesser One Whom No Obstacle Can Stay Mu Ch'un.

The eighth company on foot was led by King Of The Devils Who Roil Earth Fan Lui and with him were The Eight Armed Lo Chao Hsiang Ch'ung and The Heaven Flying God Li Kun.

These eight companies of horsemen and fighting men on foot were to go each on its own way and they prepared to set forth straightway, nor would they delay an instant.

On the fifteenth day of the first moon Wu Yung said, "At the second watch on the night of the fifteenth day of the first moon you are all to come to the city of Ta Ming Fu, and horsemen and foot fighting men are all to go thither."

Then did those eight companies go down the mountain as they had been commanded. As for the other chieftains, they all stayed with Sung Chiang to guard the mountain.

Let it be told further. Now Shih Ch'ien went over the city wall into the city, but none of the inns in the city would receive a man alone and without goods, so he could but walk the streets by day and when night came he went into The Temple Of The God Of The Eastern Mountain and there he slept beneath the pedestal of the god. On the thirteenth day of the first month he went about in the city to look and to see, watching those who put up pavilions and hung lanterns and in the midst of his watching he saw Hsieh Chen and Hsieh Pao carrying their wild game and walking about in the city staring. He came, too, upon Tu Ch'ien and Sung Wan as they came out of a brothel.

On that day Shih Ch'ien went to The House Of The Jade Cloud to see how it was and there was K'ung Ming, his hair flying and unbound and on his body an old torn sheepskin and in his left hand a staff and in his right hand a bowl and there he was all covered with filth and grime, begging of those who passed. When he saw Shih Ch'ien he made a secret sign that they were to go to some lonely place to talk and Shih Ch'ien said, "Elder Brother, such a big fellow as you—and your face all red and white—does not look like a beggar. There are many runners from the court here in the city and perhaps they will see through you and then will a great cause be lost. Elder Brother, better would it be if you hid!"

Before he had finished speaking he saw another beggar coming and he came from beside the wall and when they looked at this one it was K'ung Liang. And Shih Ch'ien said to him, "Elder Brother, and here your snow-white face is leaking out! You do not look like any suffering, starving man either! With such a face as this surely some evil will come."

He had but finished saying this when suddenly behind him two men laid hold of him by the hair and they shouted, "And a good thing this is you do!"

When Shih Ch'ien turned to look there were Yang Hsiung and Liu T'ang. Shih Ch'ien said, "You would frighten me to death, I swear!"

But Yang Hsiung said, "Do you all come with me," and he led them to a lonely spot and there he blamed them, saying, "You three, how are you so stupid as this and how was it you fell to talking there? Well it was that it was we two who saw you. If you had been seen by those sharp-eyed, quick-handed runners from the court then would not a great cause have been lost? We two have seen all, and you, my Brothers, need go no more about the streets."

K'ung Ming said, "Chou Yuen and Chou Jun yesterday sold lanterns upon the street. Lu Chi Shen and Wu Sung are already outside the city in a temple, and better it is to talk no more, but let each go to his place and set about his business."

Thus the five finished their talk and they all went before a certain temple and there they came upon a Taoist as he came out of the temple. When they lifted their heads to look at him it was Kung Sun Sheng and behind him was Ling Chen as attendant. The seven all bowed in understanding and then each went his way alone.

Thus the time for the feast approached and the governor Liang first commanded the general Wen Tah to lead out horsemen and go outside the city and to The Valley Of The Flying Tiger and there stand and be prepared against the robbers. On the fourteenth day then Li Ch'eng was himself to lead out five hundred mailed horsemen and completely armed, both man and horse, they were to encircle the city as guard.

Now the next day was the fifteenth day of the first moon and the very day of the feast and it was a day both fair and clear and the governor Liang's heart was filled with pleasure. Before evening had come the round clear moon leaped up into the sky and it filled the winding city streets with molten gold and the people were crowded breast to back, shoulder to shoulder. Flowery rockets and wheeling fire crackers and all such things were finer than they ever were in other years. On this night the gaoler Ts'ai Fu commanded his brother Ts'ai Ch'ing to guard the great gaol and he said, "I will but go home a little while and look and then come back again."

But he had scarcely entered in his door when he saw two men run swiftly in. The one in front looked like some lord of war and the one behind him like his serving man. Now as he looked at the pair under the light of the lanterns Ts'ai Fu knew the one for The Little Whirlwind Ch'ai Chin, but he did not know the one behind was The Iron Whistle Yo Ho. Ts'ai Fu invited them to come within and there were wines and meats spread ready and straightway he invited them to eat. But Ts'ai Chin said, "It is not needful to give us wine. I have come hither to ask an important thing of you. Lu Chün I and Shih Hsiu have received your protection and for this we thank you much. Tonight I ask that I may have the chance to see them for a little while, and take advantage of the merrymaking of the feast. I pray you to trouble yourself to lead us thither and do not refuse us."

Now Ts'ai Fu was an officer and already he guessed some eight parts of their plan. If he refused then perhaps if later the robbers were victorious he would have lost all the favor he had gained with them and so lose also the lives of his whole house. He had no way therefore but to take upon himself the burden of a danger great as seas of blood. He took out some old clothes and he bade the two put them on and disguise themselves as runners of the court and to change their turbans too. Then he led them into the gaol and it was about the time of the first watch of the night.

Now Wang The Dwarf Tiger and The Ten Foot Green Snake and Sheng Sing and The Goodwife Ku and Chang Ch'ing and The Goodwife Sheng, these three disguised as country couples, mingled among the crowds, chattering and laughing as country folk will and they went toward the east gate. Kung Sun Sheng and Ling Chen carried a deep basket made of withes of a tree and they went to The Temple Of The City Devil and there sat down beneath the veranda. Now this temple was beside the magistrate's court. Chou Yuen and Chou Jun, carrying their lanterns, walked about the city. Tu Ch'ien and Sung Wan, each pushing a barrow, went straight to the front of the governor's palace and mingled in the confusion of the crowd.

The court where the governor Liang lived was in the great street by the eastern gate. Liu T'ang and Yang Hsiung, each carrying his club and carrying secret weapons too, came to The Bridge Of Chou and sat on the two sides. Yien Ch'ing, leading Chang Shun, came from the water gate into the city and they came in and hid. Of these no more need be said.

Soon in the drum tower the second watch rang out. Let it now be told of Shih Ch'ien. He carried a basket and within it was every sort of fireball and torch to set fire here and there. Upon the basket were stuck some toys and he went behind The House Of The Jade Cloud. He went upstairs and there from a room he heard the sound of flute and song and the throbbing of a drum and the tinkle of the castanets, and the house was filled with every sort of music, and there were young men calling and laughing and making merry uproar and they were all upstairs looking at the lanterns.

Shih Ch'ien went upstairs also and he pretended to be a toy vendor and he went into every room to look. Then he came upon Hsieh Chen and Hsieh Pao and they carried their hunting forks and on them were hanging rabbits, and they came and went before the rooms. Then Shih Ch'ien said, "The time has come and how is it we hear nothing from without?"

Hsieh Chen said, "We two were but just now before the house and we saw one go by upon a horse whose business it was to tell the news, and doubtless the men and horsemen have come. Let us but go on and do what we have to do."

Before he had finished speaking there arose a shouting in front of the house and one cried, "The robbers have come outside the western gate!"

Then Hsieh Chen commanded Shih Ch'ien, "Go quickly now! We must go before the governor's court and help there," and he hastened thither.

When he reached the court he saw the vanquished soldiers all come rushing into the city and they said, "The robbers have seized the camp of the general Wen Tah by stealth and those robbers have all come into the city, men and horsemen, and Li Ch'eng is even now upon the city wall watching it!"

When this was said there came Li Ch'eng on a swift horse to the court and he commanded that straightway soldiers be counted out and he commanded that the city gates be closed so that the city might be guarded.

It is further said now that the magistrate Wang himself led out his more than a hundred men and with long racks and with chains they were prepared for any who made turmoil. When they heard this news in great haste they went to the front of the governor's palace.

Now let it be told of the governor Liang. He was at that very hour sitting at leisure in his court and he was drunken. The first time it was told him that robbers were come from the great lair, he was not much afraid. But in less than half a watch's time there came horsemen galloping as swift as shooting stars and one after another they brought the same report and he grew so full of terror he could not speak a word except to cry without ceasing, "Make ready my horse—make ready my horse!"

But before he had finished speaking there was

seen to burst from The House Of The Jade Cloud a fire that spread to heaven and the light of that fire covered the light of the moon and truly was it a mighty fire. The governor Liang saw it also, and in all haste he mounted his horse, and even as he was to go to see it, he saw two tall fellows pushing two barrows and they put them down in the midst of the road. Then they went and fetched a hanging lantern and set fire to the barrows and straightway fire rose.

Now as the governor Liang would have gone to the eastern gate there came forth two more tall fellows and they said, "Li Yün and Shih Chin are here," and they took up their swords and came charging forward in great strides and they so frightened the guards of the gate that they ran away, although they did wound some ten-odd of those who were nearest their hands. Tu Ch'ien and Sung Wan met them as the two others came and the four joined themselves together and they held the east gate. Then the governor Liang, seeing the outlook was evil for him, led with him his followers who had come with him and they ran with all speed to the south gate. But at that gate this one and that said, "There is a great fat priest who whirls an iron staff in his hands and a tigerish-looking other priest who pulled out two swords and they came charging into the city, yelling as they came."

Then the governor turned his horse about again and he went once more to his court. There he saw Hsieh Chen and Hsieh Pao twisting their three-forked iron spears and there they were striking east and striking west. Then the governor dared not go before them and in haste he turned aside into the court of the magistrate Wang. Now at this moment the magistrate was passing to his door and Liu T'ang and Yang Hsiung brought down their clubs together upon the head of this one and split his skull so all his brains gushed forth, and his eyes burst out from their sockets, and he died there upon the street.

Then did the guards and the runners of that court run each for his own life and in agitation the governor turned his horse again and he galloped to the west gate. But even as he passed The Temple Of The City God, he heard the sound of fireballs bursting and the heavens thundered and the earth shook. Chou Yuen and Chou Jun, in their hands bamboo poles, were setting fire to the eaves of houses. From a certain brothel Wang The Dwarf Tiger and The Ten Foot Green Snake came dashing out. Sheng Sing and The Goodwife Ku took out their secret hidden weapons and helped there at that place also.

Before The Temple Of The Brass Buddha Chang Ch'ing and The Goodwife Sheng hastened forth and they climbed upon the fairy mountain and there they set fire.

By this time in the city all the people were running hither and thither like rats and wolves, and in every house there was the sound of weeping like gods and devils mourning. On all four sides there were ten-odd places where the flames leaped to heaven nor could it be told any more which direction was which, for all were alike.

Let it be told now of the governor Liang. He galloped to the west gate and there he met with the soldiers of the general Li Ch'eng. In all haste they went to the city wall to the south and there they reined their horses by the drum tower and looked about. They saw that city full of horsemen and of fighting men, and on their banners were written, "The Great Sword Kuan Sheng." In the midst of the shining flames Kuan Sheng ran hither and yon and everywhere and he showed forth all his strength and skill of war. To his left was Hsiang Ch'ung, to his right was Hao Ssŭ Wen. Behind him was Huang Hsin, urging on the men and horses.

Like the wings of the wild goose, those armies came on and already they were come beneath the south gate.

Now the governor Liang could not go out of the city and with Li Ch'eng he hid beneath the north gate. There again they saw the fire very bright and there were fighting men and horsemen without number. It was The Leopard Headed Ling Ch'ung galloping up and his weapon held horizontally before him. To the left of him was Ma Ling, to the right of him Teng Fei, and behind him was Hua Yung, urging on the men and horsemen, and they all came dashing forward as though on wings.

Again the governor turned to the eastern gate, and there in the midst of many flaming torches he saw He Whom No Obstacle Can Stay Mu Hung, and to the left of him was Tu Hsing and to the right of him Chen T'ien Shou, and these three goodly fellows were in front, their swords in their hands, and leading more than a thousand men they charged into the city. In terror the governor Liang dashed to the south gate and there reckless of his life he forced a way through. Beside the drawbridge the torches were all alight, and he saw The Black Whirlwind Li K'uei, and to the left of him Li Li and to the right of him Ch'ao Cheng. Li K'uei was stark naked and in his hands he grasped his two battle axes and he came as though flying from the moat, and Li Li and Ch'ao Cheng with him.

Now Li Ch'eng was in front of the governor and he slaughtered a bloody pathway before him and so they leaped out of the city and guarding the governor round about they went on. But suddenly they heard a great uproar of war cries at the left of their way and out from the flare of torches ablaze they saw a countless number of horsemen. It was Hu Yien Shu, he who bore double clubs, and he whipped up his horse on which he sat and brandishing the clubs he charged full upon the governor Liang to seize him. Then Li Ch'eng lifted his two swords and came forward to meet him, but in truth at that time he had not the heart to do battle and he turned his horse and would have gone away.

But to the left was Han T'ao and to the right P'eng Ch'i, and they came forward from both sides, and Sheng Li was behind urging on the horsemen. With all their strength united they made a charge and in the midst of the battle there hastened up from behind them Hua Yung and he put up his bow and fitted his arrow to it and let fly upon a captain who aided Li Ch'eng, and this man turned over and fell from his horse. Li Ch'eng saw it and he let his horse gallop away as though on wings. In less than half the time it takes for an arrow to fly he heard the sound of drums upon his right hand and the glare of lights pained his eyes with their brightness and it was The Fire In The Thunder Clap Ch'ing Ming and his horse came leaping up and he was whirling his weapon as he came. He brought with him Yien Shun and Ou P'eng and behind him Ch'en Ta came charging also. Li Ch'eng was covered with blood and now he stayed and now he went, and guarding the governor Liang he forced his way through.

Now the story divides in twain. Let it be told of what befell in the city. Tu Ch'ien and Sung Wan went to the home of the governor Liang there to kill his whole house great and small. Liu T'ang and Yang Hsiung went to kill the whole house of the magistrate Wang. K'ung Ming and K'ung Liang had already come out from the wall of the gaol and they had climbed into the gaol. Chou Yuen and Chou Jun were in front of the gaol and there they held fast all who came or went.

In the great gaol Ch'ai Chin and Yo Ho, seeing the signal fire rise, said to Ts'ai Fu and Ts'ai Ch'ing, "Have you two brothers seen it or not? Then how long do you wait?"

Now when the gaoler Ts'ai Ch'ing looked there from the side of the gate where he was, Chou Yuen and Chou Jun had already opened the gate of the gaol and they cried out loudly, saying, "The good fellows of the robbers' lair are all here! Send out safely to us our two brothers Lu Chün I and Shih Hsiu!"

In great haste Ts'ai Ch'ing went to tell this to Ts'ai Fu, but K'ung Ming and K'ung Liang had already leaped down from the wall, and they paid no heed to whether the two brothers would or no. The robber Ch'ai Chin took out his knife and went to open the racks of the two prisoners. Thus he freed Lu Chün I and Shih Hsiu.

Then Ch'ai Chin said to the gaoler Ts'ai Fu, "Come with me quickly to your home and care for those of your household."

When these were all come out of the gate of the gaol Chou Yuen and Chou Jun met them and joined with them. The brother gaolers Ts'ai Fu and Ts'ai Ch'ing went with the robber Ch'ai Chin and they went to their house and made all safe. Lu Chün I and Shih Hsiu, K'ung Ming, K'ung Liang, Chou Yuen and Chou Jun, these five brothers, all hastened straightway to Lu Chün I's house and they went thither to seize Li Ku and the woman.

Let it be told further thus. Now when Li Ku heard that the good fellows of the robbers' lair were leading horsemen into the city and also when he saw the fire rising in all four directions, it was just at the time when he sat in the house and he had felt on himself an evil omen and it was that the skin about his eyes twitched of its own will and he could not help it. Then he took counsel with the lady and they tied together some gold and silver and jewels and costly stuffs and they put it on their backs and hastened from the gate.

Suddenly they heard all the gates along the street burst open and truly they did not know how many people rushed out. In all haste the two turned themselves about and rushed into the house again and went and opened the back gate. When they had come around the corner of the wall they came to a canal and tried to find a hiding place. There they saw upon the banks the robber Chang Shun, and he called in a mighty voice, "Where does that woman go?"

Now was Li Ku's heart full of terror and he leaped into a boat to hide. Even as he was about to rush into the cabin of the boat he saw yet another man put forth his hand who came out and he laid hold of the knot of hair upon Li Ku's head and he shouted out, "Li Ku, do you know me?"

Now Li Ku heard it and it was the voice of Yien Ch'ing, and in great haste he cried out, "Good Little Brother, I have never had any quarrel with you, and do not put me forth upon the shore."

But Chang Shun upon the shore had already seized the lady and he held her under his arm and he dragged her to the side of the boat and Yien Ch'ing seized Li Ku and they all went toward the eastern gate.

Let it be told further. Lu Chün I hastened to his house and he did not see that Li Ku or his lady. Then he told those who were with him to take all his goods and his gold and his silver and all his precious things and bring them forth and put them upon carts and take them to the lair and there divide them.

Yet further be it told that Ch'ai Chin the robber and the gaoler Ts'ai Fu went to the gaoler's house and brought out all his goods and all his household that they might all go together to the lair upon the mountain. Ts'ai Fu said then, "Great lord, I pray you save all the common folk of this whole city. Do not let them suffer."

And Ch'ai Chin heard this and he went to seek the counselor Wu Yung and when he had found him, although Wu Yung with all speed gave forth the command yet the city was already half destroyed.

By this time the sky was bright with full dawn. Wu Yung and Ch'ai Chin went into the city and beat gongs to call the robbers out and all the chiefs went to meet Lu Chün I and Shih Hsiu and they went together to the court of the governor Liang, and there Lu Chün I and Shih Hsiu told them all how greatly they had gained by the favor of the two brother gaolers and how their lives had already been saved by them. Now Yien Ch'ing and Chang Shun had already brought thither Li Ku and that lady. Lu Chün I saw them and he told Yien Ch'ing to place them in prisoners' carts and guard them himself and wait until later judgment. Of these no more need be said.

It is said again that Li Ch'eng, guarding the governor Liang, went outside the city to escape their troubles and they came full upon Wen Tah leading back his vanquished soldiers and they put their men together and went toward the south. But in the midst of their going there rose a cry from the soldiers in front and it was that King Of The Devils Who Roil Earth Fan Lui. To the left of him was Hsiang Ch'ung, and to the right of him was Li Kun, and they led three companies of good fighting men on foot and they were brandishing their winged weapons and their winged swords and they came charging forward. Behind them was Lei Heng The Winged Tiger and he led with him Shih En and Mu Ch'un, and each led a thousand fighting men on foot, and they ran forward and cut off the path of escape. Truly was it

> The prisoner freed must to his gaol again be led,
> The sick man healed must lie again upon his bed.

How was it then with these companies of robbers? Pray hear it told in the next chapter.

Chapter 66

SUNG CHIANG REWARDS THE VICTORIOUS ROBBERS. KUAN SHENG OVERCOMES TWO WARRIORS OF WATER AND OF FIRE AND LEADS THEM TO THE LAIR

IT IS SAID: At that time the governor Liang and Li Ch'eng and Wen Tah in all haste gathered together their remaining vanquished soldiers and turned to the south and at that very time also they came again upon two companies of fighting men on foot and there was slaughter in front of them and behind. But Li Ch'eng and Wen Tah guarded the governor Liang and they fought on reckless of their own lives and they withstood many charges and at last escaped with their lives and they went straight toward the west.

Now Fan Lui and Hsiang Ch'ung and Li Kun could not catch them in pursuit and so with Lei Heng and Shih En and Mu Ch'un and the others they all went into the city to receive further commands.

It is said again that the counselor Wu Yung sent down his command from the midst of the city and on the one hand proclamations were sent forth to reassure the people and on the other hand the fires were put out. The whole households of the governor Liang and Li Ch'eng and Wen Tah and the magistrate Wang were killed, such as were to be killed, were killed, and such as were to escape, escaped, nor did Wu Yung care what befell them more. But he opened the treasury of the city and the silver and gold and precious things that were there were all placed upon carts. The granaries were opened also and rice was given to all the common folk of the town and what was left was put upon carts and it was taken back to the lair to be used when it was needed. All that had been commanded to be done by chieftain, horseman, and by fighting man, was now complete. And Li Ku and the lady were nailed into prisoners' carts. Then the horsemen were divided into three companies and they all went back again to the mountain lair, and Tai Chung was sent first to tell the news to the great chief Sung Chiang.

Then Sung Chiang gathered together all the chieftains left in the lair and they went down the mountain to meet the others and they all went up together to the Hall Of Loyalty And Righteousness. And Sung Chiang saw Lu Chün I and he bent his head down and made obeisance. In greatest haste Lu Chün I returned the courtesy and Sung Chiang said, "I have not done well. I thought to ask you, Sir and Noble, to come up the mountain and join together with us here but I did not think to throw you in such hardship as you have had to bear. Almost have I lost you your life. But I have suffered as though my heart were cut in many pieces and I called on Heaven to save you and only so have we met again today."

Then Lu Chün I bowed in thanks and he said, "Above me I trust to your power, mighty as a tiger's, and beneath me, I thank the great loving-kindness of these my brother chieftains that you put your strength together and saved this mean body of mine. Though I spread my liver and my brains upon the ground before you, yet could I not repay what you have done for me."

Then he asked Ts'ai Fu and Ts'ai Ch'ing, the brother gaolers, to come and make obeisance before Sung Chiang and he said further, "If it had not been for these two, then this lowly life of mine could never have been saved to come hither."

Then would Sung Chiang fain have had Lu Chün I sit in the chief seat. But in great fear Lu Chün I answered, "What manner of man am I? How could I dare to be chief of this great lair? I would but walk beside your stirrup, Elder Brother, and hold your whip while you ride, and be a little serving fighting man and so repay your grace in saving my life. This is my highest happiness and fortune."

Again and again did Sung Chiang invite him, but how could Lu Chün I be willing to seat himself there? Then was Li K'uei seen to shout out to Sung Chiang, "Elder Brother, there is only your one heart that is not straight! You were willing to take the first place that other day and now you would give it to another. Is this cursed chair made of gold that it must be given first to this one and then to that? Do not rouse my temper so I shall come bursting forth!"

But at this Sung Chiang roared, "Such as you!"

In great haste Lu Chün I made obeisance and he said, "If you force me bitterly to have the seat, my Brother Warrior, then must it be that I cannot stay here long."

Again Li K'uei shouted out to Sung Chiang, "If you were an Emperor, my Elder Brother, and Lu Chün I your prime minister, and we brothers all living in a palace with you, then might we have all this turmoil! But we be only robbers living in a watery waste and let us go on as we were and call an end of it!"

But now Sung Chiang was so angry at this that he could not speak a word, and so Wu Yung exhorted him, saying, "Pray let us bid Lu Chün I to go to the house at the east and there rest and let us hold him for the present as a guest. Later when he has gained some glory then we will give him the chief seat for his own."

Only then would Sung Chiang stay his pleading. So he bade Yien Ch'ing to rest there with Lu Chün I and he appointed another house for the two brother gaolers and their families. Kuan Sheng's household Hsüeh Yung had already brought thither.

Then Sung Chiang commanded that a mighty feast be prepared to reward the horsemen and the men who fought on foot and those who fought on water and all the chieftains great and small and the robbers went each to his own place to feast. There in the Hall Of Loyalty And Righteousness the feast was prepared and all the chieftains high and low showed the fullest courtesy each to the other and they all drank wine and made merry. At last Lu Chün I rose and he said, "The adulterer and the adulteress have been seized and they are here and they await their judgment."

Then Sung Chiang smiled and answered, "Truly I had forgot them. Bid them be brought hither."

So the robbers beat open the prisoners' carts and they brought the two to the front of the hall and they tied Li Ku to the pillar to the left and the lady they tied to the pillar to the right. Then Sung Chiang said, "Let us not ask into the sin they have committed. Do you, Sir, set your own judgment on them."

Then Lu Chün I took a short sword in his hand and himself he walked down that hall and he cursed mightily, saying, "Wicked woman—thievish weak reed of a man!"

And he cut the breasts of the two open and he dug out their hearts and he cut their flesh in pieces and dragged the dead bodies out and cast them aside to be buried. Then he came back into the hall and bowed his gratitude to all, and all the chieftains gave him their congratulations, and they praised him without ceasing.

Let it be told no more now of the great feast in the robbers' lair or how the three companies of fighting men on horse and land and water were rewarded. Let it be told rather of the governor Liang. When he heard that the robbers had gone back to their lair he and his generals led back their vanquished soldiers to the city and he went into the city and looked at his home. Out of ten of his household eight or nine were dead, and there in the street he wept with those who were left. When the armies came from the surrounding cities to succor the city the robbers were already gone, and he bade each one recall his soldiers.

But the lady of the governor Liang had hid in the inner flower garden and so she had escaped with her life and she bade her husband write a memorial to the Emperor and a letter to the prime minister that it might be known what had been done so that the sooner generals and their soldiers might be appointed to come out and destroy these robbers and wreak revenge. Then the people who had been killed were counted and there were more than five thousand, and those who were sorely wounded were beyond number. Of soldiers in all armies more than thirty thousand had been killed. This was all written and the messenger sent forth upon his way.

In less than a day the messenger came to the eastern capital before the palace of the prime minister and the guard went in to announce it. And the prime minister commanded him to be brought in and the messenger went into the audience hall and presented his papers and the memorial for the Emperor, and he told the whole tale closely, and he said, "How great a power have these robbers and it cannot be withstood!"

Now the prime minister's first thought had been to summon Sung Chiang and those with him and receive them back again into the imperial favor and so have peace, and put the glory upon the governor Liang and it would give himself some glory too. But now the day was lost and the thing could not be hid from the eyes of the Emperor and he must make war therefore.

So was the prime minister filled with great anger and he bade the messenger retire. On the next day at the fifth watch the bell sounded for the Emperor's audience. In the courts of the waiting halls there were gathered civil and military officials, and the prime minister led them and they went straightway to the Hall Of Audience and to the throne, and there the thing was told before the Emperor's face. Now when the Son Of Heaven read the memorial he fell into a fright. Then there came forward an imperial advisor whose name was Chao Ting, and he came out from the ranked officials and he said, "Aforetime we did always send out soldiers to fight against these robbers, and such as we sent were always vanquished and we lost many warriors so, because they did not know those lands and how they lay. According to my small stupid sight, better would it be if we forgave all the robbers and sent a royal mandate and bade them come back to the throne. Then could they be sent to the border to protect it and so be loyal soldiers for us."

Now the prime minister heard this and in great rage he shouted in rebuke, "You are an advisor of the imperial court, but you turn about and put an end to the order of the house of the Son Of Heaven, and you add power to these little petty robbers! Your crime is such that we should beg the Son Of Heaven to set death on you for punishment!"

And the Son Of Heaven said, "Let him be sent forth from the court straightway."

So at that very hour was the advisor's place taken from him and he was made into a common man again. When he was treated thus, then who dared speak more? Again the Son Of Heaven asked the prime minister, saying, "Since these robbers are so great as this now, whom can we send to seize them?"

Then the prime minister addressed the Emperor thus, "Your subject thinks for such little petty thieves in the grass as these why should we use great armies? I have two warriors to present; one is surnamed Shang and his name is T'ing Kuei, and the other is surnamed Wei and his name is Ting Kuo, and they are generals now of local soldiery in their own city of Ling Chou. Let the One Above send down a command that this very day these men shall come with all their soldiers and let a day be set for them when they must have swept the robbers' lair clean."

Then was the Son Of Heaven greatly pleased and straightway was a mandate written and a sign of a bamboo split for a sign of surety and it was commanded that those armies should be taken to the robbers' lair. Then the Son Of Heaven rose and went away, and all the governors left the Hall Of Audience.

But the governors smiled secretly.

The next day the prime minister gathered all his ministers and generals and one was chosen to bear the royal mandate and the bamboo pledge and go to Ling Chou.

Let it be told further of the robbers' lair. There Sung Chiang took all the gold and silver and treasure they had brought from Ta Ming Fu and with it he rewarded the three companies of robbers, and day after day horses were killed and cows also and a mighty feast was prepared to welcome Lu Chün I. Although there were no such dainties at the feast as dragons' livers and the brains of phœnix birds, yet truly were the meats piled mountain high and the wine flowed like a very sea. At last the chieftains had drunken until they were near to drunkenness and then Wu Yung said to Sung Chiang and the others, "Since we have vanquished the city because of Lu Chün I and have killed many people and robbed the city treasure and pursued the governor Liang and his generals until they had to escape for their lives, will he not write it all in a memorial and send it to the Emperor? Moreover, his wife's father is the prime minister and can he let this be an end? Surely will he send out armies and horsemen and come hither to wage war against us."

Sung Chiang replied, "What you are grieving over is very right, Sir Counselor, and why should we not send spies this very night to the city of Ta Ming Fu and hear the news? Then we can prepare."

But Wu Yung smiled and said, "This lowly brother has already sent such spies and it is near time for them to return now."

In the midst of their feasting before they had finished taking counsel together the spies were seen to return and they said, "The governor Liang of the city of Ta Ming Fu has truly told the Emperor and soldiers are to be sent hither to make war against us. There is an advisor Chao Ting who begged the Emperor to forgive us but the prime minister shouted out and cursed him, and so the advisor lost his place. Now the prime minister has told the Emperor that he will send to Ling Chou for two warriors there who are generals over the soldiers in that city and they are to bring their armies hither and make war with us."

Then Sung Chiang asked, "If they are to come like this, how shall we withstand them?"

Wu Yung answered, "Let us wait until they come and then we will seize them all together."

Now Kuan Sheng rose and he said, "Ever since I came up the mountain I have not put forth a half a particle of my strength. Those two warriors Shang T'ing Kuei and Wei Ting Kuo I know and I met them once in the city of P'u Ch'en, and very well I know that Shang ever wages war by opening a river or some water somewhere and drowning all his enemy, and men call him Swift In Water. As for that Wei Ting Kuo, he is most clever to use fire against his enemy, and when he wages war he trusts to fire alone for victory. For this is he called Warrior Of Fire. Now I have no skill at anything, but I would borrow of you five thousand horsemen and I will not wait until these two come but I will go upon the road to Ling Chou and there meet them. If they are willing to join themselves to us, I will bring them up the mountain with us. But if they be not willing then will I seize them and present them here before you. Nor need I trouble you, my Brother Chiefs, to take your spears and bows and use your strength and weary out yourselves. But I do not know what you, Honored Ones, think of this."

Then Sung Chiang was full of pleasure and he bade Hsüan Tsan and Hao Ssŭ Wen, these two chieftains, to go with Kuan Sheng. And Kuan Sheng led the five thousand horsemen and the next day he went down the mountain and at dawn Sung Chiang and the chieftains drank a last cup with him at the camp upon The Golden Sands, and Kuan Sheng and the two other chieftains led the horsemen and went on their way.

All the chieftains returned then to the Hall Of Righteousness And Loyalty and Wu Yung said to Sung Chiang, "Kuan Sheng goes forth this time but we cannot know the truth of what his heart is. Let us send another good warrior after him to spy upon him, and come to him as though to help him."

Sung Chiang answered, "But I see this Kuan Sheng is a very righteous man and he is loyal from the first to last. You should not doubt the man, Sir Counselor."

But Wu Yung said again, "I do but fear his heart is not one with yours, my Brother. Let us bid Ling Ch'ung and Yang Chi take men out and let Sheng Li and Huang Hsin be aides and let them take five thousand horsemen and straightway go down the mountain."

Then Li K'uei said, "I will go, too, in the morning."

But Sung Chiang replied, "This time we do not want you. Doubtless there are good warriors who seek for such glory."

At this Li K'uei said, "But if I am idle then surely I shall fall ill. If you do not bid me go, then I will go alone the once."

Then Sung Chiang shouted out, "If you do not hear my commands then will I have your head cut off!"

And Li K'uei heard this and he grew melancholy in his heart and he went out from the hall.

But it will not be told now of Ling Ch'ung and Yang Chi nor of how they led the horsemen down the mountain to be aid. On the second day a robber came to report and he said, "The Black

Whirlwind Li K'uei took his two axes last night at the second watch and we do not know whither he is gone."

And Sung Chiang heard this report and he could but cry bitterness and he said, "It was I who offended him with those few words of mine last night and now doubtless he has gone to some other lair."

But Wu Yung said, "Brother, it is not thus. Although he is but a coarse and stupid fellow yet he is very loyal and surely would he not turn elsewhere. Doubtless he will return again in a day or two. Let your heart rest, my Brother."

But Sung Chiang was afraid and he sent Tai Chung in pursuit first and after him he sent Shih Ch'ien, Li Yün, Yo Ho and Wang Ting Lu, these four great chieftains, and they were to go in four different roads and seek for Li K'uei.

Let it be told now of Li K'uei. On that night he took his two battle axes and went down the mountain and he went by small paths straight to the city of Ling Chou and as he went he thought to himself, "These two accursed warriors—and why should all these horsemen and chieftains be sent against them? I will rush into the city and kill them both with a blow apiece of my axes, and my elder brother Sung Chiang will take a fright himself, and so can I draw my breath freely before them all."

So he went for half a day and then he perceived his belly was empty and he felt himself at the waist; he had come down the mountain all impatient and full of haste and he brought no money with him! To himself he thought, "For a long time I have not done my business and now I will seek someone to vent my anger upon."

Even as he was walking thus he saw a village wine shop there beside the road and he went in and sat down there. He drank three measures of wine, one after the other, and he ate two catties of meat and when he had eaten he rose to go. But the keeper laid hold of him for the money, and then Li K'uei said, "Wait until I go ahead a way and find someone to rob, which is my business, and then I will come and pay you." And when he had said this he would have gone his way.

But suddenly he saw before him a great tall fellow like a tiger and he shouted to Li K'uei, "You black thing, how bold you are! Who opens this wine shop that you come and eat for nothing and will not give any money in return?"

Then Li K'uei opened wide his eyes and said, "This lord cares nothing where he eats and I always eat for nothing!"

Then that fellow cried, "If I should tell you who I am your water would pour out of you and all your waste, too! This good lord, who am I, is a robber of the great mountain lair and I am Han P'ai Lung and the money wherewith I opened this shop was given me by my elder brother Sung Chiang."

Now Li K'uei heard this and he laughed secretly in his heart and he thought, "And when did we ever know this cursed fellow in our lair?"

Now this Han P'ai Lung was a robber far and wide on river and lake and he would have joined himself to the great lair and he came to the chieftain Chu Kuei and he would have had him take him to Sung Chiang. But at that time Sung Chiang lay ill in bed with the wen upon his back and there was great ado in the lair then, sending chieftains hither and thither, and there was no time for aught else, and so the man had not his desire yet and so Chu Kuei bade him for the time to stay in the village and sell wine.

Now Li K'uei took out from his girdle one of his axes and he looked at Han P'ai Lung and he said, "I will leave this axe here for my bond."

Now Han P'ai Lung did not know that this was guile and he put his hand out to take it and Li K'uei brought the axe down full in his face and split it open. Pity was it that Han P'ai Lung had not gone up the mountain yet! There he died by Li K'uei's hand.

And the two or three serving men ran fast and did but curse their parents that they had given them only two feet apiece and they ran into the village and so away. As for Li K'uei, he robbed the inn for travel money and set fire to its thatched roof and burned it and he went again toward Ling Chou.

Now he had gone less than a day and he was in the midst of going when he saw a tall big fellow coming down the road and he stared at Li K'uei from head to foot, and Li K'uei saw that man's staring and he said, "And how is it such as you stares at a lord?"

Then that fellow answered, "And whose lord are you?"

Then Li K'uei rushed forward but that fellow lifted up his fist and Li K'uei sat suddenly and hard upon the ground. Then Li K'uei thought to himself, "How good a fist this fellow has, in truth!" And there he sat upon the ground and he lifted up his face and asked, "You Fellow, what is your surname, and what your name?"

Then that fellow said, "This lord has no surname and if you would do battle with me, then let us do it. Do you dare to rise?"

Then Li K'uei fell into a mighty rage and he was about to leap up when that fellow kicked him under the arm and he sat down again. Then Li K'uei cried out, "I cannot win over you!" and he crawled up and went away. But the fellow called to him and asked, "What is your surname, you Black Fellow, and what your name? And you are a man of what place?"

Then Li K'uei answered, "Today I have lost to you and I fain would not tell out who I am. Yet it is a pity, too, for you are so good a fellow that I would fain not deceive you. Well, then—I am that Black Whirlwind Li K'uei of the great robbers' lair—that one am I!"

The good fellow asked, "But are you truly he? Do not lie!"

Li K'uei replied, "If you do not believe it then look at these two battle axes that I have."

That fellow said, "But if you are truly a good fellow of the mountain lair then whither do you go alone?"

Li K'uei said, "I had a breath of anger with my elder brother and I would go to Ling Chou and kill those two surnamed Shang and Wei."

That fellow said, "But I have heard that there are already horsemen gone against the two from the robbers' lair, and chieftains too. Tell me, then, who they are."

And Li K'uei answered, "The first one who leads the company is The Great Sword Kuan Sheng, and after him are The Leopard Headed Ling Ch'ung and The Blue Faced Beast Yang Chi, and they are aides."

When that fellow heard this he bowed his head down and he made obeisance and Li K'uei said, "Tell me truly, then, what your surname is and what your name."

That man answered, "Once I was a man of the city of Chung Shan Fu. Our family has had a certain skill for three generations and we are wrestlers for our livelihood. This way I used my hand and foot just now was a certain way a father teaches to a son but never to a pupil. Yet I have ever been a man without honor among others, and wherever I go to seek for help I am ever refused. In the province of Shantung, in the province of Hopei, they all call me Chiao T'ing The Faceless. But today I heard that in the city of K'ou Chou there is a certain mountain named The Mountain Of The Dead Tree and on that mountain there is a robber and all his life he has loved to do nothing else than kill men. Men name him after that dreadful god whom to see is death. His surname is Pao and his name Su, and he lives on that mountain and robs the countryside and now I am turning thither to join myself to him."

Then Li K'uei asked, "If you have such a skill as this why do you not come and join my elder brother Sung Chiang?"

Chiao T'ing answered, "Long have I wished to come and join you at the great lair but there was no door by which I could enter and none I knew to present me. Today I have come upon you, my Brother Warrior, and I would follow you."

But Li K'uei said, "I have had a mouthful of anger with my elder brother Sung Chiang and I came down the mountain. If I do not kill someone how can I go back and empty-handed? Go with me to that Mountain Of The Dead Tree and let us entice that Pao Su that he go with us to Ling Chou and let us kill those two warriors Shang and Wei and then we can go back the better to the mountain."

Chiao T'ing said, "But that city is greater than several county seats and there are many soldiers and horsemen there. There are but two of us and though we had the most perfect skill yet would it not be enough for this. It would be to lose our lives for nothing. Better would it be only to go to The Mountain Of The Dead Tree and fetch Pao Su and then let us go and join the great lair. This would be the best plan."

While the two were in the midst of their speaking, behind them Shih Ch'ien hastened near and he cried out, "Our elder brother grieves most heartily because you came down the mountain and he invites you to return straightway. They have gone in four directions to follow after you."

Then Li K'uei led forward Chiao T'ing and made him known to Shih Ch'ien and Shih Ch'ien besought Li K'uei to return to the mountain and he said, "Our elder brother Sung Chiang waits for you."

But Li K'uei said, "Stay, I pray you. I have already taken counsel with Chiao T'ing and we shall go first to The Mountain Of The Dead Tree and seek out Pao Su and only then will we return."

Shih Ch'ien said, "This you shall not do. Elder Brother waits for you to come straightway to the lair."

But Li K'uei answered, "If you will not go with me, then go back to the lair alone and tell it so my elder brother will know that I shall soon come back."

Now Shih Ch'ien was in terror of Li K'uei and so he went back to the lair alone, and Chiao T'ing and Li K'uei went on to K'ou Chou and they went toward The Mountain Of The Dead Tree.

Now the story divides itself in two. Let it be told how Kuan Sheng and Hsüan Tsan and Hao Ssŭ Wen, leading their five thousand men, came near to Ling Chou. Let it be told also that the governor of that city had received the mandate from the imperial court at the eastern capital and the letter that the prime minister had sent with it, and he had invited the generals, and among them Shang and Wei, to come and take counsel with him. The two generals received the letter of the prime minister and straightway they counted out their soldiers and prepared all their weapons and they saddled the horses and prepared the food for man and beast, and on the day set they were about to depart when suddenly one came to tell them, saying, "The Great Sword Kuan Sheng, who was of P'u Tung, is leading soldiers thither to wage war and seize the city."

Now when the two generals Shang and Wei heard this they were full of mighty anger and they gathered together their armies and went out of the city to meet the enemy. Thus the two armies came near and they saw each other's drums and banners. Beneath his banners Kuan Sheng came out and from out the other ranks there came the sound of a drum beaten and there came forth a warrior also and he wore a square helmet of wrought iron, and on his head was a great black cockade as large as a bushel basket and made of the long hair of a certain kind of ox. He wore a robe of war made of seamed bear skin bound about the edges and oiled with a black oil and over it he wore a black silken short-sleeved jacket embroidered in a round pattern of green, and on his feet were boots diagonally marked, the threads tufted, and the heels were shaped like clouds. About his waist was bound a green leather studded girdle, and with the head of a lion in the front, invincible. He had a bow also and a quiver full of arrows. He rode a very black horse and he had a black-handled spear. In front of him one carried a banner and it was black, the hue of the watery north, and it was made of silk. Upon the banner were written seven letters and they were "Swift In Water Shang T'ing Kuei."

Then was seen to come out from the side where there was the sound of many horse bells, yet another warrior, and he wore a helmet of vermilion spotted with gold and fitting closely to his head, and on the top was a red cockade, as large as a broom, of ox's hair. He wore a robe of the spotted fur of a wild beast and over it a red silken coat embroidered with a design of clouds and strange flying beasts. On his feet were boots which were embroidered with green water birds and the faëry beast called Ch'i Lin, and on the seam in front was a pattern of clouds also, and at the back the hues of the rainbow. He carried a carven bow and his arrows were feathered with phœnix feathers, and the barbs were wolves' teeth, and he rode a horse as red as rouge. In his hand he had a sword of wrought steel. In front of him one carried a silken banner embroidered and it was red, the color of the south. Upon it were seven silver letters and they were "Warrior of Fire Wei Ting Kuo."

These two tiger-like warriors came both together to the front of the ranks and Kuan Sheng saw them and from his horse he cried, "Sir Warriors both, long have we been parted!"

Then the two warriors laughed loudly and they pointed with their fingers at Kuan Sheng and they cursed him, saying, "You lowest and most ignorant of men, you fool and rebel against the throne, above you have violated the grace of the Emperor, and below you have desecrated the blood of your ancestors, and yet you know no shame! You lead your fighting men hither and now what reason can you speak?"

Then Kuan Sheng answered, saying, "You are both wrong, Sir Warriors. It is the Emperor who is fool now, for the corrupt governors have taken all his power. If they are not relatives they will not give any high place to any, and those whom they accuse before the throne are only such as are their personal enemies. But my brother, Sung Chiang, is merciful, righteous, loyal and sincere and he works righteousness for Heaven and he has sent me for the one purpose of inviting both of you, Sir Warriors, to our lair. If you do not despise us, therefore, then come and join us and return with us thither now."

Now the two generals, Shang and Wei, heard this and mighty wrath filled them and they urged their horses on and they galloped forth together and the one came forth like a great black cloud and the other came forth like a mass of flame and they came as though winged before the ranks of their armies. But even as Kuan Sheng went forward to do battle with them, there flew out from his left the chief Hsüan Tsan and from the right there sprang forth Hao Ssŭ Wen and there the two pairs did combat between the ranks. Sword struck sword, and there burst forth ten thousand sparks of cold light, and spear struck spear and fury filled the heavens.

Kuan Sheng, grasping his sword, stood there and he watched for a long time and he could not cease from crying out his praise of the sight. But in the midst of the battle the two warriors of Water and of Fire both turned their horses' heads and returned to their own ranks and Hao Ssŭ Wen and Hsüan Tsan made haste to pursue them and they dashed into the enemy's armies. Then was the warrior Wei seen to come from the left and the warrior Shang from the right, and Hsüan Tsan pursued Wei and Hao Ssŭ Wen pursued Shang. To tell it is too slow, but the doing was swift.

Let it be said then that even as Hsüan Tsan pursued there were seen to come four or five hundred soldiers on foot all bearing red banners and wearing red coats of war and they all came forward in a line and they carried long-handled hooks and bore ropes for nooses and they all came forward together and they seized Hsüan Tsan and his horse, both alive.

Let it be told now of Hao Ssŭ Wen, who had given pursuit to the right. He saw five hundred soldiers coming also on foot and they wore all black robes of war and they bore black banners and they came in a line, too, and they came rushing from behind his band and they seized Hao Ssŭ Wen alive. Then some took these men into the city of Ling Chou and some charged forward as they flew on to wage further battle.

Then was Kuan Sheng frightened for a while, and his hands were in confusion and he knew not how to move and he retreated to the rear. Immediately the two generals Shang and Wei whipped up their horses and gave pursuit, and even as Kuan Sheng retreated he saw two warriors come charging forth. When Kuan Sheng looked at them the left was Ling Ch'ung and the right was Yang Chi and they came from the two sides and they dispersed the armies of the enemy. Then Kuan Sheng gathered together his own men and he greeted Ling Ch'ung and Yang Chi and they joined their men together. And Sheng Li and Huang Hsin gave their greeting, too, and they all made camp together.

Let it be further told of the two warriors of Water and of Fire who had taken alive the chieftains Hsüan Tsan and Hao Ssŭ Wen. Since they were victorious they returned again to the city. There the governor met them and he made a feast to honor them, and he bade prisoners' carts to be made and he put the two captives in them and he sent a lesser captain with three hundred soldiers to go on foot that same night and take them to the eastern capital and present them to the Emperor.

Let it be further told of the lesser captain and his three hundred soldiers who went to guard Hsüan Tsan and Hao Ssŭ Wen to the capital. They wound their way along as the road wound and they came to a certain place and there they saw a mountain covered with dead trees and the ground was all covered with little new young reeds. Suddenly there was heard the sound of drums and a company of robbers dashed out.

The first one held two battle axes and he roared out in a voice like thunder and it was indeed The Black Whirlwind Li K'uei from the robbers' lair. Behind him was that other goodly fellow, and it was The Faceless, Chiao T'ing.

These two goodly fellows led out their robber band and they stood across the road nor did they speak a word but they seized the prisoners' carts. The lesser captain was about to run away in all haste when suddenly another man came out from behind him. His face was as black as the bottom of a cauldron and his eyes hung out of his head round and fierce and wild. This goodly fellow was indeed that one who was like the god to look upon whom was death, and it was Pao Su. He came forward and he lifted up his dagger and struck the lesser captain from his horse and all those who were with the captain threw aside the carts and ran for their lives. Now when Li K'uei saw this he saw those in the carts were Hsüan Tsan and Hao Ssŭ Wen and he asked them how they came to such a pass and Hsüan Tsan asked Li K'uei also, "And how came you here as well?"

Then Li K'uei answered, "Because my elder brother would not let me come out for to kill I went secretly and alone down the mountain, and first I killed Han P'ai Lung and then I came upon Chiao T'ing and he led me hither and when I saw Pao Su it was as though I had met an old friend, and he would have me come up the mountain and he treated me as well as any ever could. Even now we did but take counsel together and were on our way to go and fight against Ling Chou when a little robber went up on the mountain and saw this company of soldiers guarding prisoners' carts and coming by this way. We guessed it must be imperial soldiers who had seized some robbers, but we did not think it was you two, Good Sirs."

Then Pao Su invited them to come up to his lair and there he killed an ox and poured out wine and so treated them well. Hao Ssŭ Wen said, "Brother, if you have the heart to go and join yourself to our lair then it is best to bring your men and join us there at Ling Chou and let us fight against that city together. This will be the best plan."

And Pao Su said, "Thus had I but now planned with this other brother chief, and rightly have you spoken, Noble Sir. I have here, too, in my lair some two or three hundred goodly horses and some five or seven hundred little robbers."

Thus the five good fellows all went against Ling Chou.

Let it now be told of the retreating soldiers and how they came hastening back to the city. There they went to the governor and they said, "There were robbers upon the way and they have taken the prisoners' carts and they have killed the captain."

The generals Shang and Wei when they heard this were filled with a great anger and they said, "This time if we catch any of the enemy we will kill them here."

Now at that very moment they heard that Kuan Sheng led his men outside the city and sought for battle and the general Shang T'ing Kuei forced his chance to go first and the city gate was opened and the drawbridge let down and he led his five hundred black-garbed soldiers forth and they flew out of the city. Now where the banners parted in the front of their ranks he went out and greatly did he curse that Kuan Sheng and he said, "You warrior who have shamed the throne and are already vanquished, why do you not come hither and be killed?"

This Kuan Sheng heard and he brandished his sword and whipped up his horse and dashed forward. The two had not fought fifty rounds when Kuan Sheng reined in his horse's head and went away in haste. Straightway did Shang T'ing Kuei pursue him and he pursued some three miles and more when Kuan Sheng turned his head about and shouted, "Such as you, you will not come down off your horse and follow me, and how long will you wait?"

Then Shang T'ing Kuei lifted up his spear and thrust it at the back of Kuan Sheng's heart, but Kuan Sheng used all his god-like power and caught the spear upon the back of his sword and at that moment he shouted, "Down!" And Shang T'ing Kuei fell from his horse.

Then Kuan Sheng came down from his horse and he went and lifted him up and said, "Sir Warrior, forgive me for my sin!"

Then Shang T'ing Kuei, half shamed, half fearful, bowed himself to the ground and he begged for his life and he promised to follow the robbers. And Kuan Sheng said, "I have already spoken well of you before our elder brother Sung Chiang's face and I came on purpose to seek for you two warriors."

Then Shang T'ing Kuei answered, saying, "Useless as I am, yet would I use this strength of mine, though it be but that of horse or dog, to serve you all and so together will we work righteousness for Heaven."

And when the two had finished speaking they went away together side by side upon their horses, and Ling Ch'ung went to meet the two and he asked how it came about thus that they came thus side by side. Then Kuan Sheng spoke neither of victory nor of vanquishment but he said, "There in a lonely place upon the mountain we talked of old times and of our present hearts of friendship and I sought him and I begged him to come with me."

Then were Ling Ch'ung and all the others greatly pleased and Shang T'ing Kuei went back to his ranks and called out in a great voice, "You five hundred black-garbed soldiers, come you all over with me!" As for the others, they went hurrying back to the city and in all haste they went to report it to the governor.

Now the general Wei Ting Kuo, hearing what had befallen, was filled with wrath and on the next day he took out his horsemen and they went out of the city to seek for battle. And Shang T'ing Kuei and Kuan Sheng and Ling Ch'ung came to the front of their ranks and there the banners in front of them were parted on the other side and forth came the Warrior Of Fire. When he saw Shang T'ing Kuei thus joined to Kuan Sheng he cursed mightily and he said, "You little useless man who have forgotten mercy shown you and have turned on your lord the Emperor!"

Kuan Sheng smiled a little and he whipped up his horse and went forward to meet the enemy. The two horses came together and the weapons of the warriors were raised, but they had fought less than ten rounds when Wei Ting Kuo went back to his own ranks. Kuan Sheng was about to pursue him when Shang T'ing Kuei called out in a great voice, "Sir Warrior, you may not go in pursuit!"

In great haste therefore Kuan Sheng held back his horse and before the other's words were finished there came flying out from the enemy's ranks the five hundred soldiers of fire, and they were robed in red, and in their hands were torches to set fire, and before and behind them there came forth fifty fire carts. Upon the carts were reeds and all things to make fire and upon the backs of the soldiers each had tied a gourd of iron filled with brimstone and nitre and fiery powders of five hues and these they all set alight and they came dashing out as though on wings. Wherever fire struck man, that man fell and wherever it struck horse, that horse fell mortally wounded. Kuan Sheng's men dispersed and scattered and they fled more than ten miles before he could restrain them again.

Then Wei Ting Kuo gathered his men together again and returned to the city. But suddenly he saw that city full of roaring flames and great clouds of smoke rose up. It came from that Black Whirlwind Li K'uei who with Chiao T'ing and Pao Su and all the robbers from The Mountain Of The Dead Tree had attacked the city from the rear and bursting open the north gate they had gone in and set the town afire, and they had robbed the granaries and the treasuries of state and set fire everywhere. And Wei Ting Kuo learned of this and he dared not enter into the city but he recalled his men. Then did Kuan Sheng press hard on him from the rear and pursued him killing as he went and those in front could not help those in the rear, nor those behind the ones in front. The city was already lost and Wei Ting Kuo could do naught but go away and he hastened to a place called Chung Ling, and in that city did he rest.

But Kuan Sheng came leading all his men and he encircled that city and he bade all his warriors come and attack it. Then Wei Ting Kuo closed the gates and would not come forth, and Shang T'ing Kuei said to Kuan Sheng and Ling Ch'ung and to the others, "This man has naught but his courage and if you press him hard he will die but he will not come forth. But if you treat him liberally he will forget this ever was. You can do nothing if you are impatient. I will therefore go into the city nor will I hide from his sword or weapon. I will use good words to entice him and I will seem to bind his hands so he will join with us and thus will we spare ourselves a battle."

Now Kuan Sheng, hearing this, was much pleased and straightway he told Shang T'ing Kuei to go himself alone upon his horse into that city and a little soldier went and told Wei Ting Kuo the other came. Then Wei Ting Kuo came out to meet him and Shang T'ing Kuei used good words and he said, "The Emperor nowadays understands nothing and there is confusion under all the Heaven. The Son Of Heaven is a fool and his ministers have wrested his power from him for their own ends. Let us therefore turn to Sung Chiang and let us for the hour at least live in the robbers' lair. Later when these evil ministers are overcome we will come forth again and again we will be loyal to the throne and it will not be too late, either."

And Wei Ting Kuo heard this and he was silent pondering awhile and at last he said, "If you would have me join the robbers it must be Kuan Sheng himself who comes to ask me and then will I join. If he will not come, I will choose to die but I will not join with you."

Then straightway did Shang T'ing Kuei mount his horse again and he went back and told Kuan Sheng and Kuan Sheng heard what he said and then replied, "But what is there about me that is so honorable that he should mistake me thus and hold me so high?"

Yet mounting his horse and grasping his sword he parted from them all and with Shang T'ing Kuei he went forth. Then Ling Ch'ung, seeing this, exhorted him and said, "Brother, hard it is to know a man's heart—think thrice on what you do!"

But Kuan Sheng said, "And what danger can come from an old friend?"

Thus he went straight to the county court of that city and there Wei Ting Kuo met him full of pleasure and he would make obeisance and follow him and talk with him of old times. And he had prepared a feast for Kuan Sheng to greet him. On that day he led out his five hundred fiery soldiers and they all went to the other camp, and they met with Ling Ch'ung and Yang Chi and all the chieftains. When each had greeted the other they all made haste and prepared to return to the mountain lair.

Now Sung Chiang had early sent Tai Chung forth to meet them and he said to Li K'uei, "It is because you stole down the mountain secretly that we have hunted for you all these miles, and now Shih Ch'ien, Yo Ho, Li Yün and Wang Ting Lu, these four, have already returned. Now I will go and tell our elder brother also and so spare him more anxiety."

Let it not be told now of Tai Chung and how he went first, but let it be told first of Kuan Sheng and his army. They returned to The Golden Sands and there the water robbers and the chieftains brought boats to meet them and they ferried the armies over.

But suddenly they saw a man come panting there in disarray, and when they all looked at him it was that Yellow Haired Dog, Tuan Ching Chu, and Ling Ch'ung asked him, "You and Yang Ling and Shih Yung went to the north to buy horses and why do you come hither in such fear and haste?"

Now before Tuan Ching Chu could say a few words and before he could shape a sentence it came to pass that Sung Chiang sent forth armies to attack a certain city. He took revenge for an old wrong and he wiped away his old hatred as clean as snow. Truly was it

A hook and line was this brief word—
Once more a long past wrong was stirred.

What words then did Tuan Ching Chu speak? Pray hear it told in the next chapter.

Chapter 67

SUNG CHIANG ATTACKS BY NIGHT THE VILLAGE OF THE CHEN FAMILY. LU CHÜN I SEIZES SHI WEN KUNG ALIVE

IT IS SAID: At that time Tuan Ching Chu came running thither and he said to Ling Ch'ung and to the other chieftains, "I and Yang Ling and Shih Yung went to the north to buy horses and when we reached there we chose out the strong firm-fleshed horses and those with fine thick hair and we bought more than twenty such noble beasts and we went back to Ch'ing Chou. But there was a company of robbers whose chief was called The Vanguard God, Ju Pao Ssŭ, and he had gathered more than two hundred men and they robbed all the horses from us and sent them to the village of the Chen family, and I do not know where Shih Yung and Yang Ling have gone. Only this lowly one came running here by night to make report of this matter."

Now Ling Ch'ung heard this and he said, "Let us go back to the lair and meet our elder brother and there take counsel on this thing."

So they all passed across the ferry and they all gathered in the Hall Of Righteousness And Loyalty and there they saw Sung Chiang, and Kuan Sheng led the generals Shang T'ing Kuei and Wei Ting Kuo before all the great chieftains of the lair and so they met. Then Li K'uei told of how he went down the mountain and killed Han P'ai Lung and came upon Chiao T'ing and Pao Su and how they went together and overcame the city of Ling Chou. Sung Chiang heard to the end and he heard that four good chieftains had been added to their number and he was there in the midst of them rejoicing when Tuan Ching Chu told of the robbing of the horses. Now when Sung Chiang heard this he raged in anger and he said, "They did steal my horses once before and to this day I have not revenged myself and they even killed our chieftain Ch'ao Kai, The Heavenly King! Now today they act again thus without any righteousness! If we do not go and destroy these things they will surely bring us to great shame and laughter before men."

Then Wu Yung said, "Spring comes soon and the warm days, nor have we aught else to do and it is a very good time to go out and wage a war and seek for joy. That other time our chief Ch'ao Kai lost his way but this time we must use guile to gain our victory. Pray bid Shih Ch'ien come, for he can fly from house to house and walk on walls and let him go and spy the news out, and come back and then we can talk counsel."

So Shih Ch'ien heard the command and went his way and in less than two or three days Yang Ling and Shih Yung came straggling back and they told all about that one Shi Wen Kung in the village of the Chen family and what great words he spoke and how he would fain compete with the robbers in the lair unto the end and see which one was left. When Sung Chiang heard this he would have sent out men but Wu Yung said, "Let us wait until Shih Ch'ien comes back and it will not be too late."

But Sung Chiang's anger filled his breast and he would have his revenge and he could not hold himself a single little hour. Again he sent Tai Chung flying forth to hear what he could and he bade him return straightway. In a few days it was Tai Chung indeed who first returned and he said, "This village of Chen would take revenge for Ling Chou and now they have gathered up their armies, and there is a great camp already there at the mouth of the village. And in a certain temple there, too, they have made their central camp, and the banners fly thick for a hundred miles about and I do not know by what road we shall enter in."

On the next day Shih Ch'ien returned to the lair and he made report, saying, "This younger brother, who am I, went to the village of Chen and I spied closely. There are now five camps made ready, and in front of the village two thousand men stand guard. Of all the camps the chief is Shih Wen Kung. In the northern camp Chen T'u is chief and aiding him is Shu Ting. In the south lair there is the second son, Chen Mi. In the west camp there is the third son, Chen So, and in the east camp there is the fourth son, Chen K'uei. In the central camp the fifth son is chief, who is Chen Sheng, and his father Chen Nung is there and they guard the camp. Now this man of Ch'ing Chou, who is named Ju Pao Ssŭ, is ten feet high in person and his waist is so great that several men cannot encompass it, and he is called The Vanguard God. All those horses of ours he robbed from us he feeds there in a temple."

And Wu Yung heard to the end and he called for a gathering of the chieftains and he said, "If there be these five camps then let us divide ourselves into five companies and we will go against them by five paths."

Then Lu Chün I rose up and said, "I was saved by mercy and brought hither up the mountain and yet have I not repaid anything of my strength for this. Today, therefore, would I dare my life and lead these companies forth, except I do not know what your honored purpose is."

Then Sung Chiang asked Wu Yung, saying, "If this most noble one will go down the mountain can we ask him to demean himself by being our vanguard?"

Wu Yung answered, "This most noble one has but just come to our lair nor has he passed through a war, and it will inconvenience him sorely to ride over hill and valley on his horse. We cannot let him be the vanguard. Let him take another company, therefore, and let him go first and find some smooth plain where he may ambush, and when he hears the sound of our fireballs bursting, then let him come and aid us."

And Sung Chiang was greatly pleased and so he bade Lu Chün I take Yien Ch'ing and they were to lead out five hundred men on foot and they were to wait in little paths on some plain and there listen for the sound of the fireballs.

In the great camp to the due south of the Chen village there were appointed as chief of the horsemen The Fire In The Thunder Clap Ch'ing Ming and with him Little Li Kuan Hua Yung, and to aid them The Magic Iron Flautist Ma Ling and The Red Eyed Lion Teng Fei, and they were to take with them three thousand fighting men. For the great camp to the due east of the village there was appointed as chief of the fighting men on foot The Tattooed Priest Lu Chi Shen and with him The Hairy Priest Wu Sung and to aid them The Curly Haired K'ung Ming and The Lone Fire K'ung Liang, and they were to lead out three thousand men in all. For the great camp to the due north of the village there was appointed as chief of the horsemen The Blue Faced Beast Yang Chi and The Nine Dragoned Shih Chin, and to aid him were The White Spotted Snake Yang Ch'un and The Gorge Leaping Tiger Ch'en Ta, and they were to lead out three thousand men. For the great camp to the due west of the village the chief of the men on foot was The Beautiful Bearded Chu T'ung and The Winged Tiger Lei Heng and those to aid them were Dragon Out Of The Wood Chou Yuen and The One Horned Dragon Chou Jun and they led out three thousand men in all. For the central camp the chief over all was Sung Chiang and the counselor Wu Yung and Dragon In The Clouds Kung Sun Sheng, and those chieftains who went with them for aid were The Lesser Duke Lü Fang and He Who Is Like Jen Kuei Of Old Kao Shen, The Double Headed Snake Hsieh Chen, The Double Tailed Scorpion Hsieh Pao, The Magic Messenger Tai Chung and Flea On A Drum Shih Ch'ien, and they led out five thousand fighting men. Of those fighting men who came on foot and brought up the rear the chief was The Black Whirlwind Li K'uei and that King Of The Devils Who Roil Earth Fan Lui. The chiefs to aid them were The Eight Armed Lo Chao Hsiang Ch'ung and The Heaven Flying God Li Kun and they led out men on horse and on foot to the number of five thousand. All the other chieftains stayed to guard the lair.

Let it not be told of Sung Chiang leading his five companies of men and warriors, but rather let it be told of the spies of the Chen village. They spied out the coming of the robbers and they told the news to the camps and Chen The Eldest heard of it and he asked the general Shi Wen Kung and Shu Ting to take counsel with him on the chief matters of the armies, and Shi Wen Kung said, "When the companies of robbers come from the robbers' lair then let us dig many pitfalls for only thus can we capture their strong men and fierce chieftains. And in truth for such little thieves as these pitfalls are the best guile."

Then Chen The Eldest appointed his tenants and laborers and such men to take their hoes and spades and go in and about the village and dig pits in many places and they covered the pits and put earth over the covers, and on all four sides were soldiers ambushed. So they did but wait until the enemy was come. Again they went to the road north of the village and there also they digged many pits and they waited until Sung Chiang and his men and horsemen came by. Then Wu Yung secretly sent Shih Ch'ien to spy out and when several days were past Shih Ch'ien came back and he made report, saying, "To the north and to the south of the village of Chen they have digged many pits and I do not know how many they have digged for they are countless, and they do but wait until our men and horsemen come by."

Wu Yung heard this and he laughed loudly and he said, "This is no strange thing."

Then the companies were led forward and when they were come near to the village it was high noon. Now that company in front saw a horse coming and about its neck was a ring of brass bells, and on its tail were tied pheasants' feathers. Upon the horse sat a man robed in white, and wearing a sky-blue hat and in his hand was a short spear. The company of robbers in front saw him and were about to pursue him when Wu Yung stayed them and he bade them make camp there. All about the camp they digged a deep pit and in the pit they put iron barbs and there was a command sent forth bidding each company to divide and make its own camp in the same fashion. There they lived three days and none came out from the village to do battle. Then Wu Yung bade Shih Ch'ien disguise himself like a little soldier spy upon a wayside and he bade him go and spy out in the village, for he did not understand what was their purpose. Shih Ch'ien was, moreover, to remember where all the pits were digged and how far they were from the camp and how many there were in all.

Shih Ch'ien was gone a day and he found out everything and secretly he made signs here and there and he went back and told the counselor.

On the next day Wu Yung sent forth a command and he commanded the first company of foot fighting men each to take a hoe and then the company was to divide into two parts, and then he took a hundred carts and hid them in the reeds near the central camp. On that night he sent out a command to all the chieftains, saying, "Tomorrow at the beginning of the morning at the fourth watch let the fighting men on foot begin the battle on the roads to the east and to the west."

And again he commanded Yang Chi and Shih Chin to fight together on the north of the village and he said, "Rank your horsemen in a straight line there and beat the drums and wave your banners and pretend that you are about to do battle, but assuredly you are not to move forward at all."

And when Wu Yung had sent forth these commands he said again, "Shi Wen Kung of the village of Chen does only wish to entice Sung Chiang's men to do battle and then pursue them into the digged pits. But the road in front of their camp is very narrow and if they must escape, where can they go?"

On the next day at the fourth watch there was heard the sound of a rocket bursting and the robbers, on foot and on horse, went in a great company to the south gate. After this there came one from the eastern camp of the village and he said, "There is a priest carrying crosswise a long iron staff and there is also a long-haired wandering priest brandishing two priestly knives and they are attacking us from front and rear."

Shi Wen Kung said, "These two are from the robbers' lair, and they are Lu Chi Shen and Wu Sung—but perhaps there will be trouble—" and he sent one to go to aid Chen K'uei.

Then was one seen coming from the western camp to make report and he said, "There is a great tall bearded fellow and another tiger-faced fellow on whose banners are written 'Chu T'ung The Beautiful Bearded' and 'The Winged Tiger Lei Heng,' and they have come together to attack us very fiercely."

And Shi Wen Kung heard this and again he appointed men to go in aid of Chen So. Again he heard a rocket burst in front of the camp and then he kept his soldiers still and did not bid them go forward, for he waited for the enemy to come and fall into the pits so that all the soldiers beneath the hill might rush forward together to seize them.

But Wu Yung had divided his companies in two parts and they came around the hill by small and crosswise paths until they met in front of the enemy's camp. There Shi Wen Kung's foot soldiers stood on guard not daring to go out, and the soldiers he had ambushed were in front of the camp. From the rear Wu Yung's men came dashing forward and they forced the soldiers bit by bit until they were forced into those very pits they had digged. Even as Shi Wen Kung was about to come out to battle Wu Yung waved the point of his whip aloft, and there arose the sound of drums from his companies and there came forth a hundred carts and they were all set on fire. Upon them were reeds and dried fuel and brimstone and nitre and it was all aflame, and the smoke and fire hid the heavens. When Shi Wen Kung led out his soldiers and horsemen they were held by this line of blazing carts, and so they could but retreat and hide. But even as he was about to recall his men in all haste Kung Sun Sheng made a magic movement with his dagger and there arose a mighty wind and the fire went rolling and blazing into the south gate and soon the watch tower on the gate and the wooden stockades were wholly burned, and it was already a victory.

Gongs were beaten, therefore, and the robbers recalled and they all returned each to his own camp and for that night they rested.

But in that night Shi Wen Kung mended the south gate of the village and he barricaded the gate within and without and on the next day Chen T'u planned a piece of guile and he said, "If we do not first kill the chief of these robbers, hard it will be to destroy them at all," and he said to The Instructor Of War, Shi Wen Kung, "Guard well the barricade."

Then Chen T'u led forth soldiers and horsemen and he put on his garb of war and he mounted his horse and he went outside the village to do battle. Now Sung Chiang was among his own ranks and he heard that Chen T'u was coming seeking combat, and he led out Lü Fang and Kao Shen to go with him to the front of the ranks. But before he had come out from his banners he saw Chen T'u and anger rose in his heart and he pointed at him with his whip and said, "Who will seize this thing for me first, and so revenge me for an old wrong?"

Then Lü Fang whipped his horse and lifting up his bladed spear with the carven handle he went straight to Chen T'u. The two horses came together, the two weapons were upraised, and when they had fought more than thirty rounds Kao Shen, watching from beneath the banners, saw that of these two one was soon to be vanquished. Now Lü Fang's skill was no match for Chen T'u's, and even in those thirty rounds he had not matched him and after the thirtieth round he was using his weapon anyhow and he could but shield, parry, dodge, and give way. And Kao Shen feared lest evil come to him and he galloped forward in front of the ranks and the two attacked Chen T'u together, and the three horsemen and horses were mingled together.

Now upon those bladed spears there had been hung the tails of leopards and Lü Fang and Kao Shen were about to seize Chen T'u and their two spears were upraised. But Chen T'u's eyes were quick and clear and he used his own spear and thrust the others to one side and the leopards' tails became entangled with the red plume of ox's tail upon his own weapon and however they pulled they could not pull apart. Each of the three was fain to pull his own weapon free to use it. Then Hua Yung, who saw this from the midst of the ranks where he stood, feared lest the two chiefs be vanquished and he urged on his horse and came forth. In his left hand was his eagle bow and in his right hand were his golden arrows, and he fitted the arrow to the bowstring and pulled the bow full and aiming at Chen T'u, he let it fly.

Now at this moment Chen T'u had just freed his weapon and the two leopard tails were yet entangled. To tell it is long but how swift it was in the doing! Chen T'u drew back his spear to thrust it into Lü Fang's neck between his shoulders when Hua Yung's arrow came first and it struck full into Chen T'u's left arm and he fell from his horse. Then Lü Fang and Kao Shen struck forward with both their weapons and thus did Chen T'u die by violence.

Now some ten-odd horsemen went as though winged to make report of this to Shi Wen Kung and he told it to the central camp, and when Chen T'u's father heard it he fell into mighty weeping. Then was a strong warrior seen to come forth from one side, who was Chen Sheng.

This man's skill in war was excelling and he used two winged swords and none dared come near him in battle. When he heard the news now he was filled with great wrath and he gnashed his teeth and he shouted forth, "Saddle me my horse and bring it hither, for I go to take revenge for my elder brother!"

The old general his father could not restrain him. He clothed himself in armor from head to foot and he seized his swords and leaped upon his horse and galloped to the front camp. There Shi Wen Kung met him and implored him, saying, "Young General, do not hold your enemy too lightly. Among the ranks of Sung Chiang's robbers there are many warriors who are brave and fierce. If you would know my stupid purpose we can but guard most closely our five camps and secretly send messengers to the city of Ling Chou and bid them beg the Emperor that with all haste he will choose out good generals and send many of the imperial soldiers to us and let us divide and attack the robbers from two sides, one to attack the robbers' lair, and the other to save our village, and thus will these robbers have no heart more to go on fighting here, and surely will they recall their men and return with all haste to their mountain. At that time, then, though I be a useless man, yet I will go with you and your brothers to pursue and to kill them and we will gain great glory thereby."

Before he had finished speaking the lesser general in the north camp came forward who was Shu Ting, and when he heard it said they were to stay within the camps and guard them well, he said also, "That thing in the robbers' lair who is Wu Yung, knows every sort of wicked guile and he is no small enemy. We can but retire and wait until those armies come who are to save us, and then we can plan some good way."

But Chen Sheng roared forth, saying, "They have killed my elder brother and if I do not take revenge now then am I but a robber, too! If we wait until they have nursed their strength yet greater then will it be and hard indeed to force them back," and neither of the other two could hold him. He leaped upon his horse and he led with him some ten-odd horsemen and he rushed flying out of the camp to seek battle.

Now Sung Chiang heard of it and he sent forth a command, saying, "Let those who are in the front ranks go forth against the enemy."

And Ch'ing Ming received the command and he whirled aloft his wolf-toothed club and even as he was about to come forth out of the camp to do battle he saw The Black Whirlwind Li K'uei, his two hands grasping his axes, hastening to the front of the armies. He cared for naught and he asked for nothing but he rushed out between the two ranks. Among the enemy there were those who knew him and they said, "This is The Black Whirlwind Li K'uei from the robbers' lair."

Chen Sheng heard this and he cried out, "Let fly your arrows!"

Now Li K'uei was one who always went naked to do battle and he trusted entirely to the shields of his two aides, Hsiang Ch'ung and Li Kun. But now he came running out alone and Chen Sheng let fly an arrow and it struck full into Li K'uei's leg, and his vast body fell, like the great T'ai mountain overturned. Then all the soldiers behind Chen Sheng went rushing forward. From among the ranks of Sung Chiang, Ch'ing Ming and Hua Yung came flying out on their horses to save Li K'uei and behind them came Ma Ling, Teng Fei, Lü Fang and Kao Shen and they all seized him and saved him and took him back. Then Chen Sheng, seeing how great were these warriors Sung Chiang had, dared fight no more and therefore he recalled his soldiers and returned into his own camp. And Sung Chiang recalled his men and they went into camp also.

On the next day Shi Wen Kung and Shu Ting did but repeat their will, which was to fight no more with Sung Chiang, yet how could they withstand Chen Sheng's urging them? He said again, "I will take revenge for my brother!"

So Shi Wen Kung had no recourse and he could but put on his armor and mount his horse. Now this horse was one he had robbed from Tuan Ching Chu, and it was such a horse as could go above three hundred miles a day, and its bones were like dragon's bones. It was pure white, so pure a white that in the night it shone forth like a lion made of white jade. When Sung Chiang parted the ranks and led forth his warriors, there from the ranks opposite him came forth Shi Wen Kung. Then Sung Chiang saw that fine horse and in his heart the anger burned and he sent forth the command that those in the front ranks should make ready for battle.

Ch'ing Ming received the command and he sat upon his horse and flew forth as though winged to meet the enemy. The two horses came together, the two weapons were raised aloft and they fought twenty rounds and more when Ch'ing Ming's strength failed him and he turned and galloped back into his ranks. Then Shi Wen Kung let free all his energy and he went in pursuit and that godlike spear that he carried went into the back of Ch'ing Ming's leg, and he fell straightway from his horse. Lü Fang, Kao Shen, Ma Ling and Teng Fei, these four warriors came forth and they risked their lives to save him, and although they saved Ch'ing Ming yet was it counted to the robbers as a vanquishment.

Then Sung Chiang recalled his vanquished men and they retired three miles and more from their camp and there made camp afresh. And Sung Chiang commanded that a cart be brought for Ch'ing Ming and he bade some take him back to the lair to nurse his wound. Then Sung Chiang took secret counsel with Wu Yung and he commanded The Great Sword Kuan Sheng and Ch'ü Ling, the bearer of the golden spear and the Warriors of Fire and Water, Shang T'ing Kuei and Wei Ting Kuo, these four, to come down the mountain, and they were to come together to aid them.

And Sung Chiang himself burned incense and made a prayer and he secretly asked an oracle of the god. Then Wu Yung looked at the eight signs and he said, "I congratulate you—there will come no injury to you from this great vanquishment. But tonight the enemy will come and attack our camp."

Then Sung Chiang said, "Let us early prepare that we may be ready."

Wu Yung said, "Pray, Brother, let your heart be at rest. Do you but send forth this command and tell it to the chieftains of the other companies. Tonight let us divide into two camps, east and west. Let Hsieh Chen be at the left and Hsieh Pao at the right. As for the other horsemen, let them be all round about."

Thus was it done. On that night the sky was clear and the moon white and there was no wind and the clouds stood still. Shi Wen Kung in his camp said to Chen Sheng, "The robbers have lost two warriors today and surely they are made afraid. Let us take this opportunity therefore to take their camp by surprise."

This Chen Sheng heard and he called, "Let Shu Ting of the north camp and Chen Mi of the south camp and Chen So of the west camp lead their soldiers forward and we will go together and seize the robbers' camp."

When the time of the second watch was near soldiers were sent out to spy, and the bells were taken from the horses' necks and the soldiers put on soft armor, and thus they came into the midst of Sung Chiang's camp. There they saw no one on any side and they knew what they had taken was but an empty camp. In great agitation they cried out, "We have fallen into a plot!" and they turned about and made away.

Then from the left side did there come forth that Double Headed Snake Hsieh Chen, and from the right there rushed forth The Double Tailed Scorpion Hsieh Pao, and behind them was Little Li Kuan Hua Yung and they all hastened forward together. With one thrust of his fork did Hsieh Chen pierce Chen So there in the dimness of the night and he fell dead from his horse, and then were fires lit.

Now there arose cries from the camp behind, and east and west, these two sides, sent their men to fight together. And a great cry came up from the rear camp also and from the two sides east and west the robbers all rushed forth and the battle waged in confusion through half the night. At last Shi Wen Kung forced a way and he returned and when the old lord heard that Chen So was killed also his grief and anxiety were a hundredfold greater than they had been before.

On the next day the old man would fain have written a letter saying they would give themselves up to Sung Chiang and Shi Wen Kung was also eight parts out of ten afraid, and so straightway the letter was written and sent forth speedily by a messenger who ran straight to Sung Chiang's great camp. And a lesser robber came and told of it, saying, "There is a letter come from out the village of Chen."

Then Sung Chiang sent forth a command and he bade the man come thither. And the robber brought the letter in and when Sung Chiang opened it and looked at it it was written thus, "I, the lord of the village of Chen, who am named Chen Nung, bow my head in obeisance and again I bow beneath the great banner of Sung Chiang chief of all the chieftains. Formerly my little sons had not wisdom and they thought highly of their small brave strength and they robbed the horses and they scorned a power great as a tiger's. Once The Heavenly King Ch'ao Kai came down the mountain and according to the right we should even then have turned ourselves to you. But who could have thought a worthless soldier of mine would let fly his arrow secretly and so make our guilt the heavier? Now though I had a hundred mouths, how could I deny the guilt mine? Yet when I ponder on it well I know these deeds were not what I desired to be done. Now those stupid dogs who were my sons are dead and therefore do I send my messenger to implore you that we may talk together of peace. If you will grant us the favor to fight no more and to recall your men I will return all those horses that were robbed and beyond this will I bring silver and gold and reward these companies of yours and so spare bloodshed to both sides. With all care do I send this letter and I pray examine my purpose if it be right or wrong."

When Sung Chiang had read this letter that was come he turned his eyes to Wu Yung and his face was full of anger and he tore the letter to pieces and he cursed, saying, "They have murdered my elder brother and how can I talk of such a peace as this? I shall but wait until I have killed this village clean, for this was my first purpose."

Then did the messenger who had brought the letter fall upon his face and he was in such terror he trembled without ceasing. In great haste Wu Yung exhorted Sung Chiang, saying, "Elder Brother, you are wrong. We waged battle with the village of Chen because there was anger on both sides. But now they have sent a messenger to us with a letter asking for peace and how can we because of one time's wrath break a great principle of right?" And straightway he wrote an answering letter and he brought out silver and gave it as a reward to the messenger and bade him return to his own village and let them read there the letter he brought back as answer.

Then the old lord Chen tore the letter open and gave it to Shi Wen Kung to see and upon it was written, "I, Sung Chiang, the great chieftain of the mountain lair, do with mine own hand write a letter down to the lord of the Chen village who is Chen Nung. From ancient times until now a country that is unstable, whose word cannot be trusted, is doomed for destruction and a man who does not live according to the principle must surely die. Treasure gained unlawfully shall be lost again, and a warrior without courage shall be vanquished. These principles are sure, and there is naught strange in their truth. We of the great lair and you of the village of Chen had no enmity before. You stayed within your walls, we within our boundaries. Assuredly was it because you did that one hour of evil has all this anger arisen. If you would speak of peace with us then must you return to us the horses you have twice robbed from us, and that wicked fierce man Ju Pao Ssŭ, who took them, we must have. Moreover, you must reward our men with white silver and with goods. If you would speak honest peace with us, then there shall not be one thing lacking in the accomplishment of this, for if you do lack but a little then will we have another way to use."

This letter the old lord Chen gave Shi Wen Kung to see and every man was grieved and frightened. On the next day the lord Chen again sent a messenger to Sung Chiang, saying, "If you want Ju Pao Ssŭ sent to you, then send us a man also as a hostage."

And Sung Chiang and Wu Yung straightway sent Shih Ch'ien and Li K'uei and Fan Lui and Hsiang Ch'ung and Li Kun, these five men, to go first with an answering letter. As they started Wu Yung called Shih Ch'ien to come near and he put his mouth to his ear and said, "If anything unforeseen comes, then do thus and thus . . ."

But let it not be told of the five men who went forth; rather let it be told of Kuan Sheng, Ch'ü Ling, Shang T'ing Kuei and Wei Ting Kuo who now came. At this time they saw all and they mingled their men among those of Sung Chiang.

Let it be told further of Shih Ch'ien and the other four good fellows who came to see the old lord Chen. Shih Ch'ien came forward and said, "I have received my elder brother's command and he has commanded me, Shih Ch'ien, to bring Li K'uei and these other four to come hither first and speak of peace."

And Shi Wen Kung replied, "If Wu Yung bids these five men come, doubtless there is some plot herein."

Then was Li K'uei in a mighty wrath and he laid hold of Shi Wen Kung and began to beat him. In great haste the old lord Chen exhorted him to stay his hand but Shih Ch'ien said, "Although Li K'uei is a coarse fellow and rude, yet he is one very loyal to our brother Sung Chiang and so he has been sent for a purpose and you need not doubt anything."

Now it was in the old lord Chen's heart to speak peace and he would not hear Shi Wen Kung, but he commanded that a feast be prepared for the robbers, and he invited them to go into the camp in the temple to rest, and appointed five hundred soldiers to guard them front and rear, and he bade Chen Sheng to lead Ju Pao Ssŭ to go to Sung Chiang's camp to speak peace. These two came before all the chieftains and straightway they returned the horses they had twice robbed and the silver and gold wherewith to reward the men. When Sung Chiang had seen all he said, "These horses are those who were robbed the second time and there is not among them that horse that Tuan Ching Chu brought, who goes three hundred miles in a day, whose bones are like a dragon's bones, and its color so pure a white that it shone forth in the night like white jade. How is it I do not see that you have brought this horse hither also?"

Then Chen Sheng replied, "It is the horse my general Shi Wen Kung rides and for this we did not bring it."

Sung Chiang said, "Write a letter with all speed and tell them to lead that horse hither straightway."

Then Chen Sheng wrote the letter and he bade one who had come with him to return with it and ask for that horse. Now when Shi Wen Kung heard this he made answer, "If other horses are taken it does not grieve me, but this horse I will not give him."

The messenger then went back and forth several times but Sung Chiang would have that horse though he died for it. At last Shi Wen Kung sent messengers to say, "If he will have this horse of mine then tell him to recall his men straightway and I will send it to him."

Sung Chiang heard this and he took counsel with Wu Yung but before they had decided anything suddenly there was one who came to make report, saying, "There come armies along the two roads from Ch'ing Chou and Ling Chou."

Then Sung Chiang said, "If those things know of it they will turn at once," and secretly he sent out a command and he sent Kuan Sheng, Shang T'ing Kuei and Wei Ting Kuo to go and meet the army from Ch'ing Chou, and Hua Yung, Ma Ling and Teng Fei he sent to meet the army from Ling Chou. Then he called out Ju Pao Ssŭ secretly and he used good words to comfort him and he used every grace and courtesy toward him and he said, "If you are willing to secure this glory I will bid you be a chief, too, in the lair. See, here is an arrow, and I break it in two for a sign that I forgive all that is past and it is all over. But if you do not hear and follow me then will I soon make this village into dust. Let it be now as your heart says."

Ju Pao Ssŭ heard these words and he willed to turn robber and he swore to follow Sung Chiang's command. Then Wu Yung taught him a certain guile and he said, "Do you seem to run away to the village and go back to your camp and say to Shi Wen Kung, 'I went with Chen Sheng to speak peace and there we heard the truth. Now is it Sung Chiang's great determination that he will steal this horse from you. He has not sure purpose to speak peace. If you give the horse to him then he will turn as he was before. Now he hears that there are two armies coming to save us from Ch'ing Chou and Ling Chou and his heart is in utmost terror and surely we can use this chance nor can we lose the hour.' If he believes you then have I a way."

Ju Pao Ssŭ received these commands and he went straight into Shi Wen Kung's camp and he told there of all that happened. And Shi Wen

Kung led Ju Pao Ssŭ to see the lord Chen, and he told all in detail and how Sung Chiang had no desire to speak true peace and how this hour might be seized to go secretly and take his camp! Then the lord Chen said, "There is that son of mine Chen Sheng still there. If we change now surely will he die for it."

But Shi Wen Kung answered, "But when we break into their camp we will save him out at all costs. Tonight send forth a command to all the camps that our soldiers are to rise and we shall first seize Sung Chiang's great camp even as one cuts off a serpent's head. Then will the others be left useless, and when we come back we will kill Li K'uei and these four and it will not be too late."

And the old lord Chen said, "I pray you use some good guile."

Then was a command sent forth to the north camp to Shu Ting, and to Chen K'uei in the south camp and to Chen Mi in the east camp, that they were all to go and seize the enemy camp together by surprise. And Ju Pao Ssŭ took this chance to run into the camp in the temple and he saw Li K'uei and the others, the five, and secretly he told Shih Ch'ien this news.

Let it be told further of Sung Chiang. He said to Wu Yung, "I do not know if this guile be good or not."

Wu Yung answered, "If Ju Pao Ssŭ does not return then will we suffer from my guile. If he comes this night and seizes our camp then let us divide and hide on both sides and let us bid Lu Chi Shen and Wu Sung take the men on foot and attack their east camp, and Chu T'ung and Lei Heng lead men on foot and attack their west camp, and Yang Chi and Shih Chin with horsemen to cut off the north camp. The plan of this guile is called Foreign Dogs Hiding In The Den. Though the guile be used a hundred times, yet it ever does succeed."

Let it be told now how on that night Shi Wen Kung led with him Shu Ting and Chen Mi and Chen K'uei and the men they had and they all went forth. Now on this night the moon was dimmed by clouds and the stars were darkened. Shi Wen Kung and Shu Ting went in the front and Chen Mi and Chen K'uei brought up the rear and they took the bells from the horses' necks and the men all wore soft armor and they came thus to the camp where Sung Chiang was. There they saw the door opened and within the camp there was no one nor was there sign of man or movement. Then straightway did they know they had fallen into a plot and in haste they turned to retreat to hasten again to their own camp.

But suddenly they heard the sound of drums beaten and rockets bursting in the village of Chen, and it was Shih Ch'ien who had climbed into the bell tower of the temple and now he beat the great bell there. At the gates to east and west there was the sound of fireballs and rockets and there was the mighty shouting of many voices, and truly it could not be counted how many men and horsemen came charging thither.

Let it be told further that in that temple Li K'uei, Fan Lui, Hsiang Ch'ung and Li Kun all began together to make an uproar and they came rushing out. Shi Wen Kung and the others returned with all haste to their camps but they could find no path of escape. Then the old lord Chen, seeing how great was the turmoil and hearing, too, that in two directions the robbers came hastening to attack, then and there hung himself in his own camp. Chen Mi rushed to the west camp and Chu T'ung killed him with a single thrust of his sword. When Chen K'uei would have hastened to the east camp he was crushed in the mud by the confused feet of the many horses. Shu Ting at the risk of his life ran through the north gate but there were the countless pitfalls and behind him were Lu Chi Shen and Wu Sung coming on to kill him, and in front of him he came upon Yang Chi and Shih Chin and by the arrows coming every way he was pierced to death and the galloping horsemen who followed him all fell into the pitfalls and there lying heaped upon one another none could know how many died.

Let it be told further of Shi Wen Kung. He went with speed because of his fine horse and he dashed out of the west gate and he was alone in a wilderness. At this time the dark mists hid the skies and he could not tell where the north lay and where the south. When he had gone six miles and more he did not know where he was, only he heard the woods behind him full of the sound of gongs, and suddenly there charged out some three to five hundred fighting men, and the warrior at their head held a club in his hand and he beat the legs of the horse that Shi Wen Kung rode. Now that horse was such an one as could run three hundred miles and more a day, a very dragon of a horse, and when he saw the club come down he leaped over the head of the one who held it. But even as Shi Wen Kung was thus about to escape he saw the black clouds coming toward him and cold mists wrapped his body around and as far as eye could see were the dark mists and a mighty wind rose and blew in gusts against him. On all four sides in midair did the souls of Ch'ao Kai envelop him and stay him. Then Shi Wen Kung turned back on his old path but he came full upon The Prodigal Yien Ch'ing. He turned again but he came upon that one called The Jade Ch'i Lin, Lu Chün I, and this one gave a shout and he cried, "You robber, whence do you turn?"

So saying he thrust his keen blade into Shi Wen Kung's thigh and Shi Wen Kung fell from his horse and he was bound with ropes and taken to the village of Chen. Yien Ch'ing then took that fine horse and went straightway to the great lair and Sung Chiang saw it and in his heart he was partly grieved and partly glad. But he killed Chen Sheng first there in the camp and then not one was left alive in that village of Chen. And all the money in the village and all the goods and treasure and food they put upon carts and they returned to the lair and there everything was divided among the chieftains and the lesser ones were each rewarded also.

Let it only be told further that Kuan Sheng led his horsemen and went toward the armies of Ch'ing Chou and he vanquished them and Hua Yung thus vanquished also the armies from Ling Chou and now they all returned. Of all the chieftains large and small, not one was lacking and they had also that dragon-boned, jade-white horse. Of all else they had naught need be said. Shi Wen Kung they placed in a prisoner's cart and they gathered together all the men and horsemen and returned to the great mountain lair, nor did they harm at all any of the great cities or lesser or the countryside through which they passed.

When they returned thither they went to the Hall Of Loyalty And Righteousness and they all went before the spirit tablet of Ch'ao Kai. Then Ling Ch'ung asked Sung Chiang to send forth a command to bid that one of greatest skill in letters, Siao Jang, to write the memorial essay, and every chieftain high and low put on mourning robes and every man lifted up his voice in weeping. Then the body of Shi Wen Kung was split open and his heart was taken out and offered as a sacrifice to the spirit of Ch'ao Kai. When this was done Sung Chiang there in the Hall Of Loyalty And Righteousness took counsel with all his brother chieftains of the affairs of the lair and Wu Yung said, "Elder Brother, you are first among us, and Lu Chün I is the second. As for the other brothers, let each take his former usual place."

But Sung Chiang said, "Formerly The Heavenly King Ch'ao Kai left this dying command and he said, 'If one seizes Shi Wen Kung, it matters not who he be, let him be the chief of the lair.' Now Lu Chün I took this robber alive and he came up the mountain and offered him as a sacrifice to our elder brother Ch'ao Kai and so has he fulfilled the old revenge and wiped away the old hatred, and truly ought he to be the first among us. There is naught to say else."

But Lu Chün I said, "What good I have done is very little, and my skill is very slight and how dare I take upon myself the weight of this high place. If I were given the last place of all yet would I hold it too much."

Again Sung Chiang said, "It is not that I would use overmuch courtesy but in three places I am not equal to Lu Chün I. The first one is that I am short in body and very black, and you, Lu Chün I, are tall and beautiful and your whole person is full of power, and there is not one among us all to match you. In the second place, I had but the small lowly position of a scribe in a magistrate's court and I committed a crime and escaped for my life and I give thanks that these my brethren did not despise me but let me be for a while in this high seat. But you, Sir, were born in a rich and powerful house and when you were grown to manhood, everywhere were you called Most Noble, nor are there any among us who can match you in this either. In the third place, my learning is not sufficient to save the throne, nor in skill of war can I save the people. My two hands are weak, so weak they can scarcely tie fast a fowl, and in our lair this body of mine has never let fly so much as an inch-long arrow. But your strength, Sir, is greater than ten thousand, and of present times you know all and of ancient times there is nothing you do not understand. All the more in this can none compare with you among us. With such ability, with such goodness, truly ought you to be the chief of the lair. In other times to come when we return to the Emperor, again you may work some glory and do some great deed for the Emperor, whether as a governor, or as some high nobleman, and so can we, your brothers, all find profit in your glory. As for me, my decision is made, and do not refuse me."

Lu Chün I then bowed himself to the ground and he said, "Elder Brother, however you speak yet is it all in vain. I will die, but I will not obey in this."

And Wu Yung said again, "Elder Brother, you shall be first and Lu Chün I shall be second, and this is as we all would have it. If you do so persist in giving up this seat again and again, then perhaps the hearts of all these will turn cold."

Now Wu Yung had already looked about on the faces of those who were there and so he spoke thus. Suddenly The Black Whirlwind Li K'uei was heard to shout out to Sung Chiang in a mighty voice, "I came with you from Chiang Chou, reckless of my body and careless of my life! All these others would let you have your way somewhat, but only I do not fear even Heaven! You are forever letting your seat to this one and to that, and why do you do all this cursed pretending? I will rise up and be angry and then we will all be scattered every man for himself!"

Now Wu Sung saw that Wu Yung had cast his eyes about to make a secret sign that men were to speak and he also came forward and shouted loudly, "Elder Brother, there be many now beneath you who once led armies, and they all were governors under the Emperor and they all acknowledge you, and how can they be willing to follow another?"

And Liu T'ang said, "We seven came up the mountain first and at that time we gave the first place to you, Elder Brother, and shall we today give it to one who came later?"

Then Lu Chi Shen cried out also in a mighty voice, "If you use all these many courteous ways, Elder Brother, then we will all scatter ourselves!"

At last Sung Chiang said, "You need not all keep on with your much speaking. I have yet another way. Let us see what the will of Heaven is for only then can we decide it."

Wu Yung asked, "What wise way have you? Pray tell it to us."

Sung Chiang answered, "There are two matters—"

Truly because of these two were two more heroes added to the lair and in the city of Tung P'ing there arose yet a more great and sorrowful turmoil. So was it

> The thirty-six most great among the stars
> were gathered to the lair,
> Of seventy-two, the lesser ones, not one was
> lacking there.

What two matters then were these of which Sung Chiang told? Pray hear it told in the next chapter.

Chapter 68

THE NINE DRAGONED THROUGH ACCIDENT IS IMPRISONED IN THE CITY OF TUNG P'ING. IN GREAT MERCY SUNG CHIANG SETS FREE THE WARRIOR OF THE TWO SPEARS

IT IS SAID: Now Sung Chiang would have fulfilled the dying command of Ch'ao Kai and given the first place to Lu Chün I, but all the others were not willing, and again Sung Chiang said, "Our treasure and our food in the lair is now but very scanty. Toward the east of us there are two cities larger than county seats which have money and food. One of these is the city of Tung P'ing, and one is the city of Tung Ch'ang. Since the beginning we have never disturbed the people of those two cities but let us go today and ask of them. Let two names be writ upon paper and Lu Chün I and I will each pluck up one of the papers, and whichever one seizes first his city let that one be the chieftain of the great lair. Is this a good plan?"

Wu Yung replied, "Somewhat well, too."

But Lu Chün I said, "Do not speak thus. Only you, my Elder Brother, shall be chieftain of the lair, and I will hear your commands."

Yet this time Lu Chün I was not given his way, and then that iron-faced one, P'ei Hsuan, was told to write down the names of these two cities and incense was lit and a prayer sent to Heaven and when this was done each took up a paper. Sung Chiang took the city whose name was Tung P'ing and Lu Chün I chose Tung Ch'ang, and none of the other men had a word to say.

On that day a feast was made and in the midst of their feasting Sung Chiang sent forth a command that men and horses were to be divided. In Sung Chiang's division there were Ling Ch'ung, Hua Yung, Liu T'ang, Shih Chin, Ch'ü Ling, Yien Shun, Lü Fang, Kao Shen, Han T'ao, P'eng Ch'i, K'ung Ming, K'ung Liang, Hsieh Chen, Hsieh Pao, Wang The Dwarf Tiger, The Ten Foot Green Snake, Chang Ch'ing, The Goodwife Sheng, Sheng Sing, The Goodwife Ku, Shih Yung, Ju Pao Ssŭ, Wang Ting Lu and Tuan Ching Chu, and there were in all, high and low, twenty-five chieftains, and with them there were ten thousand fighting men on foot. There were also three chieftains of the water, Juan The Second, Juan The Fifth and Juan The Seventh, and they led out boats and water men.

Lu Chün I led out these: Wu Yung, Kung Sun Sheng, Kuan Sheng, Hu Yien Shu, Chu T'ung, Lei Heng, So Ch'ao, Yang Chi, Shang T'ing Kuei, Wei Ting Kuo, Hsüan Tsan, Hao Ssŭ Wen, Yien Ch'ing, Yang Ling, Ou P'eng, Ling Chen, Ma Ling, Teng Fei, Shih En, Fan Lui, Hsiang Ch'ung, Li Kun, Shih Ch'ien, Pei Sheng, chieftains high and low, in all twenty-five, and they led out horsemen and foot fighting men to the number of ten thousand. There were also three chieftains of the water, who were Li Chün, T'ung Wei and T'ung Meng, and they were to lead out robbers of the water and boats and so aid Lu Chün I. All the other chieftains and all those who were wounded stayed to guard the lair.

When all were thus appointed to their places Sung Chiang and the chieftains went to attack the city of Tung P'ing and Lu Chün I went with his chieftains to attack the city of Tung Ch'ang. Thus all this mighty host of chieftains went down the mountain. Now this was the time of the first of the third month of the year and the sun was hot and the winds mild, and the grass was green and the sands soft to the foot, and indeed it was very perfect time to go forth to kill and to wage war.

Let it now be told of Sung Chiang. He led his company and went toward the city of Tung P'ing and when he was but a little more than ten miles from there he came to a market town called The Hill Of Peace and here he halted his men and horses. Then Sung Chiang said, "The magistrate of the city of Tung P'ing is named Ch'en Wan Li and there is a general he has and they are both men of a city called Shang Tang, east of the river. This general is surnamed Tung and his name is P'ing and he uses very well two spears and so is he called by men The Warrior Of The Two Spears nor can ten thousand men withstand him. Now although we go against his city yet must we be courteous with him, too. I will appoint two who shall bear a letter which shall declare our war and they shall go and give him the letter. If he is willing to follow me, then will we be spared a war, but if he will not then though we kill a host of people they cannot blame us. Who dares go first to take this letter for me?"

Then was Ju Pao Ssŭ seen to come forth from among the ranks on foot and he said, "This lowly one knows the city and I would take the letter."

Again was seen one to come forth from among the ranks on foot and it was Wang Ting Lu, and he said, "This younger brother is but newly come nor have I ever done anything for the mountain lair. Today therefore would I go forth the once."

Then was Sung Chiang much pleased and immediately he wrote the letter of war and he gave it to Ju Pao Ssŭ and Wang Ting Lu and the two went forth. In the letter there was no more than a request to borrow food.

Let it now be told of the magistrate Ch'en in the city of Tung P'ing. When he heard that Sung Chiang sent forth fighting men and horsemen and that they were come to The Hill Of Peace, he invited his general to come, The Warrior Of The Two Spears, and they took counsel of matters of war. Even as they sat thus in council the gatemen made report, saying, "Sung Chiang has sent men with a letter of war."

The magistrate Ch'en commanded that they be summoned thither and Ju Pao Ssŭ and Wang Ting Lu came into the great hall and there they met the magistrate face to face and they presented the letter. Ch'en the magistrate read the letter that was come and he said to his general Tung, "They would have food from our city, and what shall we do, therefore?"

The general Tung heard this and he was in a mighty rage and shouted that these two men were to be thrust out and killed straightway. But the magistrate Ch'en said, "This may not be. From ancient times until now it has not been permitted that when war came between two countries those who came and went as messengers could be killed, and according to this law it should not be. Only let them each be beaten twenty times for punishment and sent back whence they came and we will see what they will do."

But the general Tung's anger was not appeased and he shouted that the two men were to be bound and thrown down and they were beaten until their skin was split and their flesh burst forth and then they were cast out of the city. The two returned to the encampment and there they wept and said to Sung Chiang, "That thing Tung is without any principle at all and how deeply does he despise our great lair!"

And Sung Chiang saw how the two were beaten and his wrath filled his breast and he would fain have gone forth straightway to level that city to the earth. But first he bade the two messengers return to the mountain to nurse their wounds.

Then was The Nine Dragoned Shih Chin seen to stand forth and he said, "This younger brother, when I did live in this city of Tung P'ing, was friends with a certain courtesan, whose surname was Li and her name was Sleeping Orchid, and I went many times to her so that we know each other very well. Now let me take a goodly sum of money and go secretly into the city and to her house to rest, and I will fix a day and hour when you shall come against the city. When the time comes to do battle I will climb up into the Drum Tower and set fire to it. Thus will there be attack from without and confusion from within and so a great deed be done."

Sung Chiang replied, "An excelling good plan!"

Straightway then did Shih Chin make ready silver and gold and he placed them in his bundle and he hid a weapon on his person and he said farewell and prepared to set forth, and Sung Chiang said, "Brother, wait well until the chance comes. I will hold my men here and not move forward."

Let it be further told of Shih Chin. He went into the city and he went straight to that west house where Sleeping Orchid lived and there the old man, who was the courtesan's father, saw it was Shih Chin and he gave a start of fear and led him within and he bade his daughter come out to meet him. Then the Sleeping Orchid led Shih Chin upstairs to sit himself down and she asked him, "How is it that for so long I have not seen so much as your shadow? Moreover I have heard you are a robber now in Liang Shan P'o. The magistrates have put out a proclamation that you are to be seized and these two days the streets have been full of talk and they say Sung Chiang will come against our city and that he has asked to borrow food of us. How then have you come hither?"

Shih Chin answered, "Truly will I not deceive you. I am a chieftain now in Liang Shan P'o but I have gained no glory. Now my elder brother comes against the city and he would borrow food and I have told him all about your house and today I have come as spy, and I have a packet of gold and silver to give to you, but indeed you may not let the news leak out. When the deed is done another day I will take you and your house up the mountain and there may you be happy."

In her confusion Sleeping Orchid promised him and she took the silver and the gold and she prepared some wines and meats for him. Then she went and took counsel with her mother, saying, "He used to be a guest here once and he was a good man then and it mattered nothing whether he came or went from my house. But now he is evil and a robber and if this comes out that he is here then it is no matter of play, for my father says Sung Chiang of the robbers' lair is such an one as cannot be made angry safely, for whatever city he goes against it will surely fall. If some word comes out from us and one day the city is broken in and they come in, then will they surely reckon with us."

But the old woman began to curse her, saying, "You old stupid thing, and what do you know of anything on earth? From ancient times has it been said that if wasps crawl within the bosom and sting us, then must we open up our coat with all speed and pluck them out. This is a law everywhere under Heaven from old. If any has done evil and himself goes before the magistrate and makes it known, his sin is wiped away. Quickly then go to the magistrate's court and make this known therefore, and they will come and seize him. Thus will we spare ourselves evil later."

But the old man said, "Yet has he given my daughter a mighty heap of gold and silver and if we do not bear a burden for him, then for what has he bought us?"

Then the old woman cursed him also, saying, "You old beast, such talk as this is but to pass your wind! Have we not done evil to countless men already through this courtesan of ours and why should we care for this one man? If you do not go and make report then will I go myself to the court and howl it out and I will put you into it with him."

The old man replied, "Do not be so angry. Bid our daughter hold him courteously. Do not beat the grass and frighten the snake away, and so suffer him to escape. Wait until I go and make it known to the runners of the court and let them come and seize him and then we can go and accuse him before the magistrate."

Let it now be further told of Shih Chin. When he saw Sleeping Orchid come up the stair he noticed that the hue of her face was not fixed, but wavering between red and white and so he asked her, saying, "Is there not some trouble in your house? You seem startled and astounded."

Then Sleeping Orchid made reply, "Just now as I came up the stair I stepped upon an emptiness and not knowing it I fell over and for this my heart is startled and confused."

Thus the time passed, but not more than enough to drink a half a cup of tea, when steps were heard beside the stair and someone leaped up the stair and a shouting arose outside the window and some tens of runners from the court broke into the room and they bound Shih Chin until he looked like a crouching lion and thus bound they brought him down the stairs and they took him to the hall of the magistrate's court. When the magistrate Ch'en saw him he cursed him mightily, saying, "You thing, your gall is great enough to put your whole body in it! How dare you come alone and spy on us? If it were not that the old man Li, the father of

Sleeping Orchid, had come and told us, I would have lost the lives of all the good people in my city. Tell your tale, then, speedily. For what did Sung Chiang bid you come?"

But Shih Chin would not say a word. Then the general Tung said, "If you do not beat such robbers' bones as this how can he be willing to speak?"

So Ch'en the magistrate shouted, saying, "Beat this thing for me with all your strength!"

Then from the two sides came forth guards and gaolers and first they filled their mouths with cold water and spurted it on Shih Chin's legs and on each leg they beat a hundred strokes. Shih Chin let them beat and he let them question, but he spoke no word. Then the general Tung said, "Let a long rack be put upon this thing and let his hands be put into wooden handcuffs and let him be thrown into the gaol for those condemned to die and wait until we have taken Sung Chiang. Then we will put the two together and take them to the capital and there will they be beheaded."

Let it be told further. Now Sung Chiang at the time that Shih Chin went away wrote a letter and he told Wu Yung all, and Wu Yung read the letter that was come from Sung Chiang and he said, "Shih Chin has gone to the house of the courtesan Sleeping Orchid to be a spy," and he feared greatly. In all haste he told Lu Chün I and that very night he went to Sung Chiang and he asked, "Who bade Shih Chin go?"

Sung Chiang answered, "He was fain to go himself. He said, 'This courtesan Sleeping Orchid is an old courtesan of mine and we have loved each other greatly,' and because of this he went thither."

Then Wu Yung said, "Brother, you have lacked something in judgment here. Had I been with you, in truth I would not have let him go. Ever have courtesans been such hearts as welcome the new guest and speed the old, and they have harmed many a good man, and the more because the hearts of the courtesans are as unstable as water. Even though she had this mighty love to Shih Chin yet would it be hard for him to escape the toils of the old woman. Now that this man has gone thither, assuredly will he suffer for it."

Sung Chiang then asked Wu Yung what was now to be done and Wu Yung called The Goodwife Ku and he said, "I shall trouble you to go the once. Disguise yourself as an old beggar woman and go secretly into the city and there make yourself seem but one of the beggars. If any news of trouble comes, then return in all haste. If Shih Chin is thrown into gaol, then go and beseech the guard of the gaol and say only this, 'In memory of a mercy which he showed me of old, I would take a mouthful of food to him,' and thus find your way into the gaol and say secretly to Shih Chin, 'On the last day of the month near the time of twilight we will surely come against the city. Do you go to the latrine and there prepare to escape.' As for you, on that night do you set fires alight in the city, and from our side we will send soldiers and so shall we fulfill our plan.—Brother, you must first attack the little county seat of Wen Shang, and all the people will certainly hasten to Tung P'ing. At that time let The Goodwife Ku mingle with the fleeing crowds and so take the chance to enter the city and not one will know of it."

When Wu Yung had thus planned this guile he mounted his horse and went back to the city of Tung Ch'ang. Then Sung Chiang appointed Hsieh Chen and Hsieh Pao and they led forth more than five hundred men and they attacked Wen Shang together. Truly enough the people, supporting their old and leading their young, came out in all directions like rats and like wolves and they fled toward Tung P'ing.

Let it be told further. The Goodwife Ku, her hair scattered, her clothing in tatters, mingled in the midst of the crowd and thus she came near to the city, and she went about the streets begging and she came at last to the front of the magistrate's court. There she heard it told that truly enough Shih Chin was fast in gaol. On the next day, carrying her beggar's bowl, she went to the front of the gaol and there she went to and fro and waiting. At last she saw an old court runner and he came out from the gaol. When The Goodwife Ku saw him she made obeisance and her tears fell down like rain and the old runner asked her, "What are you crying about, you old beggar woman?"

The Goodwife Ku said, "The lord Shih who is locked fast in the gaol was my master once and since I parted from him ten years have already long passed. I thought he was a traveling merchant and I do not know why he is now in gaol, but surely there is not one to bring him any food. This old woman who am I have begged this mouthful of food here and there and I have brought it a-purpose so as to stave off his hunger. Elder Brother, pity me anyhow and take me in! Greater goodness will yours be than if you had builded a seven-storied pagoda!"

That old runner replied, "But he is a robber from the robbers' lair and he has committed a crime for which he ought to die. Who dares to take you in, therefore?"

The Goodwife Ku said, "Though he die by a blow of the axe or by slicing, then must he close his eyes and bear it. But have pity and let this old body go in with this mouthful of food and so show forth the kindness of old days!" And when she had finished speaking she wept again.

Now the old runner thought to himself, "If it were a man it would be hard to let her in. But what is there to fear about a woman?"

And so then he led The Goodwife Ku into the gaol and she saw Shih Chin and there was a heavy rack upon his neck and about his waist was bound an iron chain. Now Shih Chin saw The Goodwife Ku also and he gave a start of fear and he could not speak a word. Then did The Goodwife Ku on the one hand pretend to weep bitterly the while she gave the food to him. But the gaolers came running thither, shouting, "This is an evil man who ought to die, and not even a little wind can come into this gaol for him. Who let you come in then to bring him food? Go out as quickly as you can, and we will spare you a couple of blows!"

So The Goodwife Ku could stay no longer and she did but say to Shih Chin, "You are told to save yourself on the last night of the moon."

When Shih Chin would have asked her more the goodwife was beaten out of the gaol by the gaolers.

Shih Chin only heard the three words "last—night—moon." Now this third month was a long moon, and when the twenty-ninth day came Shih Chin in the gaol saw two gaolers talking together and he asked, "What day of the moon is this?"

Now the gaoler remembered wrongly what day it was and he answered, saying, "It is the last day of the moon. Soon we will buy some spirit paper to burn to wandering souls."

Shih Chin heard this and he was fain to have the night come. Now there was a little gaoler who had drunk himself half drunken and he led Shih Chin to the edge of the latrine and Shih Chin deceived the gaoler, saying, "Who is that behind you?"

Thus deceived, the gaoler turned his head and at that moment Shih Chin wrenched off his rack and with one blow with its fore part he struck the gaoler in the face so that the man fell upon the ground. Then he bent and took up a stone and broke open the bonds about his ankles and with his eyes opened enormous and wide he dashed into the courts of the chief gaoler. There were several runners all drunken and Shih Chin faced them and struck them, and some died and some ran away. Then he jerked open the gaol gate and he waited for those to come from without to save him, and he freed all those others also who were in the gaol, and there were fifty or sixty in all and they set up a great shouting at the gaol gate.

Now there were those who made report to the magistrate, Ch'en Wan Li, and he was in such terror his face turned the hue of clay. In haste he called his general to come and take counsel with him and the general Tung said, "There must be yet other spies here in the city. First send out many men and encircle this robber about and I will take this chance and lead my soldiers out of the city and go and seize Sung Chiang. Let the magistrate but stay here and guard the city with all care, and appoint many guards to guard the gaol gate and let that one not escape."

So the general Tung mounted his horse and he counted out his soldiers and went his way. The magistrate Ch'en then called all the gaolers and all his guards and his runners and each of them held weapon and staff and they went shouting to the gate of the great gaol. Shih Chin still in the gaol gate did not dare come forth alone, nor did the guards dare to come in. The Goodwife Ku could but cry bitterness.

Let it be further told. The general Tung counted out his soldiers and horsemen and at the fourth watch at early dawn he mounted his horse

SUNG CHIANG SETS FREE THE WARRIOR OF THE TWO SPEARS

and rushed toward Sung Chiang's camp and the robber spies made report to Sung Chiang and he said, "This must be that again The Goodwife Ku has suffered in the city. Since the enemy comes, let us go forth against him therefore." When this command had been given the robbers all rose up, and at this time the dawn was but barely come. It was the exact time to meet the enemy's army, and the two companies ranged themselves, and the general Tung came forth on his horse.

Now this general was ever a wily and able man in the three religions and in the nine wisdoms and there was nothing he did not understand, and in all music, whether of the flute or stringed instruments, there was not one he was not able to play. In the provinces of Shantung and Hopei all men called him The Warrior Of The Two Spears.

And Sung Chiang in front of his ranks saw what a fine and handsome man the general Tung was and as soon as he saw him he loved him. He saw also in his quiver that there was thrust a little banner and upon it a couplet was written which said,

> "The Hero, The Warrior Of The Two Spears,
> The Dandy, The Duke Of Ten Thousand."

Then Sung Chiang bade Han T'ao go forth to do battle. So Han T'ao grasped in his hand his iron-barbed spear and he went straightway against the enemy. Now the general Tung wielded his two spears in ways that were well-nigh magic they were so wondrous, and no man could withstand them. Therefore Sung Chiang commanded that warrior who used a golden spear, Ch'ü Ling, to use his hooked spear and go forward and rescue Han T'ao. So Ch'ü Ling let his horse fly and went forward and he met the general and did battle with him.

The two fought there in the ranks more than fifty rounds and it could not be told who was victor and who vanquished, and they fought for a long time. Then Sung Chiang, fearing lest Ch'ü Ling come to grief, bade the gongs be beaten and the men recalled and Ch'ü Ling reined in his horse and came back, and the general Tung, his spears upraised, gave chase straightway.

Then Sung Chiang took this opportunity and waved his whip. On all four sides the robbers encircled the enemy, and Sung Chiang galloped his horse to a high place to watch and there he saw the general Tung so encircled. When he went east Sung Chiang pointed the signal flag to the east, and the fighting men and horsemen went east and encircled him, and he rushed hither and thither and he fought all day with those two spears of his. From dawn until mid-afternoon he fought and at last he forced a way through nor did Sung Chiang give chase.

When the general Tung saw he had not conquered in battle he called his soldiers together that night and he went back into the city. But in the night Sung Chiang sent forth his men and they went straight to the city and there they encircled the whole city wall. But The Goodwife Ku in the midst of the city did not dare to set a fire, nor did Shih Chin dare to come forth and thus each waited for the other.

Now the magistrate Ch'en had a daughter who was beautiful beyond compare and the general Tung had no wife and he was continually sending messengers to beg for the maid for his wife, but the magistrate Ch'en would not promise her to him. Because of this the two, the magistrate and the general, were outwardly in accord but not so in their hearts.

On that night when the general led his soldiers into the city he sought out one who had borne such a message before to take advantage of the hour and go and ask the magistrate if he would give him his daughter or not. The magistrate sent back answer, saying, "I am a civil official and you are an official of war, and it is very fitting that you should come into my house as a son-in-law. But now the robbers have come to the very city and if I promise in such a dangerous hour men will laugh at me and shame me. Wait until these robbers are repulsed and the city made safe again and then if we speak of marriage, it will not be too late."

The messenger took this answer back to the general Tung and although the general said with his mouth that it was fair answer enough he pondered in his heart and he was not well pleased, fearing lest later the magistrate be not willing.

Thus by night did Sung Chiang attack the city the more ardently and the magistrate urged the general to go out and fight, and the general Tung was filled with great wrath. He put on his armor and he hung his bow and arrows on his person and he mounted his horse, and he led out his whole army and went outside the city to seek battle.

Now Sung Chiang himself was there beneath the gate banners of his ranks and he began to curse, saying, "There is only this little accursed warrior. How can you withstand these who are beneath my hand, ten thousand brave fighting men and a thousand doughty chieftains? If you had come long ago and followed me, then might we have spared you your death!"

At this the general Tung was filled with rage and he answered, "You little branded petty clerk! You wild rebel who ought to die! How dare you speak so foolishly?"

When he had thus spoken he raised aloft his two spears he held, and he charged straight upon Sung Chiang. To the left of Sung Chiang was Ling Ch'ung, to the right was Hua Yung, and the two warriors came forth together, and each brought his own weapons to do battle with the enemy. They fought some several rounds and then the two warriors turned and went away, and Sung Chiang's men made a feint of being vanquished, and they scattered in all directions.

Now the general Tung was fain at this time to show forth all his reckless, irrepressible valor and he whipped up his horse and went in pursuit, and Sung Chiang and his men fell back almost to the precincts of the city of Shou Ch'un and Sung Chiang went in front and the general Tung pursued until they were a few miles from the city proper. In front they came to a village and there were thatched houses on both sides of them, and in the middle ran the highway. And the general Tung did not know this was a plot and he gave heed to naught but to urge his horse on in pursuit.

Now Sung Chiang, seeing how mighty was the strength of the general Tung, had already the night before told Wang The Dwarf Tiger, The Ten Foot Green Snake, Chang Ch'ing, and The Goodwife Sheng, these four, to lead out something over a hundred men and ambush themselves in the thatched houses to the two sides of the highway, and then they tied several hidden ropes across that way and they covered them with a thin coat of earth. They did but wait until the enemy came to beat gongs for a sign, and then they would lift up the ropes. Thus did they prepare to seize the general Tung.

And as the general Tung was in full pursuit he came to this place. Then he heard behind him K'ung Ming and K'ung Liang give a great shout, saying, "Do not harm our lord!"

By now he had come full to the front of the thatched houses and there arose the beating of gongs, and the doors on both sides of the street flew open and the ropes were drawn up. The horse was about to turn about, but the ropes were drawn up already behind him and the horse fell. Then the general Tung fell with his horse, and from the left there rushed forth The Ten Foot Green Snake and Wang The Dwarf Tiger, and from the right there came forth Chang Ch'ing and The Goodwife Sheng, and they all came on him together and they seized him. His helmet, his armor, his two spears, and his horse were all taken from him, and the two women chieftains laid hold on general Tung and they took hempen ropes and tied his hands behind his back. Then each chieftainess took a steel knife and thus threatening him they forced him before Sung Chiang.

Let it be told now of Sung Chiang. He had passed the thatched houses and reined in his horse and he stood beneath the green willow trees, and he went forward to meet the two chieftainesses as they guarded the general Tung. Straightway did Sung Chiang bid the women begone, saying, "I bade you go and invite the general hither. Who bade you bring him bound like this?"

The two women fell back assenting hastily, and with all speed did Sung Chiang come down from his horse and he went himself to loose his enemy's bonds. He took the silken robe from his own body and gave it to the general Tung to put on and then he bowed his head to the ground in obeisance. In haste did the general Tung return the courtesy and Sung Chiang said, "If you do not despise ones so lowly as we are then I do invite you to come and be chieftain of our lair."

The general Tung answered, saying, "This small warrior is but a captive, and though I died ten thousand deaths, yet would it be light punishment. If I am forgiven and given safety it is ten thousand fortunes. But if I am bid to be the great chief there, then am I in no small terror."

Then Sung Chiang said, "Our miserable lair is lacking in food and so did we come especially to the city of Tung P'ing to borrow some food, and truly have we no other purpose than this."

The general Tung replied, "That thing of a magistrate Ch'en was once but a tutor in the house of T'ung Kuang and thus did he gain this good high place he has, and so he oppresses the people. If you, my Elder Brother, will let me return and deceive them into opening the city gates then let us dash into the midst of the city, and we can all find food and treasure. Thus do I repay your mercy to me."

Then was Sung Chiang full of joy and he commanded that the helmet, the armor, the spears and the horse were to be returned to the general and that he was to mount his horse as he was before. So the general went in front and Sung Chiang and his company went behind and they rolled up their banners and they all went to the city. The general's army was in front, and he shouted loudly, "Let those on the city wall open the city gate with all speed!"

Then the gatemen let the light of their torches shine forth and they recognized that it was the general and straightway they opened the gates and let down the drawbridge and the general Tung whipped his horse and went in first, and he burst asunder the iron lock. Behind him Sung Chiang and the others followed with all their company and so they dashed in and so did they all enter the city. Straightway was a command sent down that the people were not to be killed nor injured nor were their houses to be set on fire.

The general galloped straight to the court of the magistrate and he killed the magistrate and his whole house and he took the daughter. Sung Chiang then commanded that the great gaol be opened and that Shih Chin was to be saved out, and then the treasury was opened and all the silver and gold and precious things were taken out. The granaries were forced open also, and the grain and rice were placed on carts to be taken to the mountain lair, and men were appointed to guard it and take it thither, and it was given to the three chieftains, the Juan brothers, who took it up the mountain.

As for Shih Chin, he himself led men to the court of that courtesan Sleeping Orchid and he chopped into small pieces even that trollop and all her house.

And Sung Chiang took the goods of the magistrate's courts and gave it to the people and at the same time he had proclamations written and put everywhere to announce to the people what had been done, and the proclamation was written thus: "He who oppressed the people, the magistrate of this city, we have already killed. Let all good people here go each to his own business."

When this was proclaimed, Sung Chiang prepared to recall his men and the chieftains, great and small, returned to The Hill Of Peace where they had been encamped.

Suddenly they saw that one called Rat In The Daylight Pei Sheng come as though flying and he made report of the battle at Tung Ch'ang. When Sung Chiang had heard, his godlike eyebrows stood erect, and his strange fierce eyes grew round and he shouted in a mighty voice, "Let none of my brother chieftains return to the lair, but let them all follow me!"

Truly was it

Again did the brave warriors of the watery lair
Go forth once more against a city fair.

How then did Sung Chiang, leading forth his companies, save these others? Pray hear it told in the next chapter.

Chapter 69

THE FEATHERLESS ARROW LETS FLY STONES AGAINST THE HEROES. SUNG CHIANG DISCARDS THE GRAIN AND CAPTURES A WARRIOR

IT IS SAID: Sung Chiang thus captured the city of Tung P'ing and he recalled his men and retired to the village called The Hill Of Peace and even as he was about to return to the mountain lair he saw Pei Sheng come who made report, saying, "Lu Chün I went against the city of Tung Ch'ang and he has been vanquished twice. There is a very fierce warrior in that city surnamed Chang and named Ch'ing, and he was once a man of Chang Tê and he rose from out the ranks of horsemen. He has great skill in throwing flying stones, and out of a hundred stones he throws a hundred times he hits his mark. Men call him The Featherless Arrow. Beneath him he has two warriors who aid him. One is called The Spotted Necked Tiger, Kung Wang. He is tattooed all over with spots like a tiger skin, and on his neck is tattooed a tiger's head. From his horse he can fling forth darts. The other is called The Arrow Wounded Tiger, Ting Tê Sheng. On his face and on his neck to the back even of his head is he heavily scarred and he can let fly forked darts from his horse. Lu Chün I led his men to that place and day after day for ten days the enemy did not come forth to do battle. But the day before yesterday Chang Ch'ing came out for battle. Hao Ssŭ Wen urged on his horse and went out to meet the enemy and they had fought but a few rounds when Chang Ch'ing went away. Hao Ssŭ Wen pursued him and he was struck with a stone upon his forehead and he fell from his horse. Then did Yien Ch'ing let fly an arrow and he struck the horse on which Chang Ch'ing rode and only so was Hao Ssŭ Wen's life saved. Thus was one battle lost. On the next day King Of The Devils Who Roil Earth, Fan Lui, led out Hsiang Ch'ung and Li Kun and they carried shields and went to meet the enemy. They did not think that Ting Tê Sheng would let fly a forked dart from beneath his arm and it pierced Hsiang Ch'ung. Thus again did we lose a battle. The two men now lie upon their beds to nurse their wounds. Our chieftain sent me, this lowly one, on purpose to tell this news. We pray you, Elder Brother, to go thither soon and save us."

Sung Chiang heard this and he sighed before them all and he said, "How unfortunate has Lu Chün I been! I did bid Wu Yung the counselor and Kung Sun Sheng go on purpose to aid him, and I thought he would be finished in one battle and so could he sit in the highest seat. Who would have thought he would find his match! Since it is thus, let us all go, who are his brothers, and help him against the enemy."

Then Sung Chiang sent forth a command that the three companies were to go forth, and every chief was to mount his horse and come with him, and thus they went to the region of the city of Tung Ch'ang and Lu Chün I and the others met them and told them all, and then they went into camp. Even as they were in the midst of their counsel together there came a robber who made report, saying, "The Featherless Arrow Chang Ch'ing comes out to seek battle."

Then Sung Chiang led them all out and they went forth and there in the vast plain he set forth his men in rank, and the chieftains, high and low, all mounted their horses and they followed Sung Chiang beneath the gate banners. When the drums had been thrice beaten Chang Ch'ing upon his horse rushed back and forth like a wave upon the sea and the dust rolled high and he let his horse gallop to and fro. Beneath the gate banners to the left there came forth the one spotted like a tiger, Kung Wang, and from the right there came forth The Arrow Wounded Tiger Ting Tê Sheng. Their three horses came before the ranks of the soldiers and Chang Ch'ing pointed at Sung Chiang and cursed, saying, "You little thieves out of a mud puddle and wild grass, I am come to do battle with you!"

Then Sung Chiang asked, saying, "Who can go and fight against this man?"

From among his ranks he saw a warrior come forth filled with wrath and sitting upon his curvetting horse and in his hands he held a barbed spear and he came to the front of the ranks. When Sung Chiang looked at him it was he who bore the golden spear, Ch'ü Ling. Sung Chiang was secretly pleased and he said, "This man is truly a match for the enemy."

And Ch'ü Ling let his horse fly straight against Chang Ch'ing and the two horses came together and the two weapons were lifted together. They had fought less than five rounds when Chang Ch'ing retreated, and Ch'ü Ling pursued him. Now Chang Ch'ing held his weapon seemingly loosely, and with his right hand he felt in a silken bag and took hold of a stone and turning his body and seeing Ch'ü Ling's face come near he threw the stone and struck Ch'ü Ling between the eyebrows so that he turned over and fell from his horse. Kung Wang and Ting Tê Sheng came to seize him, but there were many among Sung Chiang's ranks and already Lü Fang and Kao

Shen had come forth on their horses with their bladed spears held up to thrust, and they saved Ch'ü Ling back into his own camp. Then was Sung Chiang full of great fear, and his face lost its usual hue, and again he asked, "What chieftain among you will carry on the battle?"

Sung Chiang's words were not finished when from behind his horse a warrior flew forth, and when he looked to see who this was, it was that Five Hued Tiger, Yien Shun. Sung Chiang was about to stay him but the horse had already galloped past. Yien Shun went to meet Chang Ch'ing and they fought but a few rounds when Yien Shun could not withstand the enemy and he turned his horse about and retreated. Chang Ch'ing followed after in pursuit and he brought out a stone and let it fly at the back of Yien Shun's heart and it hit full upon his back plate and it struck there like a bell. But Yien Shun bent low upon his saddle and went on.

Then did one cry loudly from among Sung Chiang's ranks, "What is there to fear about this one beast of a fellow?"

And he whipped up his horse and grasping his barbed club he dashed forward in front of the ranks. When Sung Chiang looked he saw it was that warrior victorious in a hundred battles, Han T'ao, and he was fain to show forth his valor before Sung Chiang and so he brought forth all his power to do battle with Chang Ch'ing. In less than ten rounds Chang Ch'ing went away, and Han T'ao doubted lest he might not let a stone fly and he did not go in pursuit. Chang Ch'ing, looking back, did not see him following and again he turned his horse and went forward again. Even as Han T'ao was about to raise his barbed club and go to meet him, Chang Ch'ing held secretly in his hand a stone. He raised his hand and the stone flew into the bridge of Han T'ao's nose. Then Han T'ao's red blood was seen to stream forth and he galloped back into his own ranks.

Now P'eng Ch'i saw all this and a mighty wrath rose in him and he did not wait for Sung Chiang's command. Raising in his hand his bladed, three-pointed spear he let it fly forth straight against Chang Ch'ing. But the two had not brought their horses face to face when Chang Ch'ing had already a stone hidden in his hand. He raised his hand and the stone flew upon P'eng Ch'i's cheek. He dropped his spear and hastened his horse to retreat into his own ranks again. Sung Chiang, seeing that now several of his warriors were defeated, felt fear in his heart and he would have recalled his company, when someone was heard to cry out in a mighty voice from behind Lu Chün I, saying, "Today, if we have lost all our power, how can we ever wage war again? See now if one of his stones can strike me or not!"

Sung Chiang looked and it was The Ugly Warrior Hsüan Tsan, and he whipped his horse and raised his sword and he came straight to Chang Ch'ing. Then Chang Ch'ing said, "One comes and one goes; two come and two run away. Do you know how I can let fly stones?"

Hsüan Tsan answered, "And though you can strike others, how can that make me afraid?"

Before he had finished speaking Chang Ch'ing had raised his hand and a stone struck beside Hsüan Tsan's mouth and he turned himself and fell from his horse. Kung Wang and Ting Tê Sheng were even about to come and seize him but how could they withstand the mighty number of Sung Chiang's men? These had already saved him back into the ranks. Now Sung Chiang saw this and his anger filled the very heavens. He drew forth the magic dagger and held it and he cut off the ends of his robe and he made a vow and he said, "If I do not seize this man, I do vow I will never return."

Hu Yien Shu saw Sung Chiang make this vow and he said, "Elder Brother, of what use are these words of yours to us, your brothers?"

And he whipped up his inky-black horse with the snowy hoofs and charged straight before the ranks and he cursed mightily and he shouted, saying, "Chang Ch'ing, a son gains his father's favor by strength and bravery! Do you know this great warrior, Hu Yien Shu?"

Then Chang Ch'ing said, "You shame to the Emperor, you vanquished warrior, you, too, have come against this poisonous hand of mine!"

Before his words were finished a stone came flying forth. Hu Yien Shu, seeing the flying stone, raised his jointed club, but the stone struck against his wrist, and he could not wield his club and he retired to his own ranks. Then Sung Chiang said, "All the chieftains of the horsemen are wounded. Who among the fighting men on foot dares to come forth to seize this thing?"

Then was Liu T'ang seen to come forth, in his

hand a sword, and he came boldly forth to battle. Chang Ch'ing saw him and laughed loudly and he cursed him, saying, "Your horsemen are all vanquished, and you are as nothing beside them."

Then was Liu T'ang filled with wrath and he hastened straight upon Chang Ch'ing. But Chang Ch'ing would not fight with him and he galloped his horse into camp. Liu T'ang pursued him, and then Chang Ch'ing turned his horse again and came to meet him. Now Liu T'ang's hand was impatient and he struck out with his sword and he struck the horse on which Chang Ch'ing rode. Then the horse kicked up his hind hoofs, and his tail struck against Liu T'ang's face so that his two eyes were dimmed. Soon did he also fall to the ground from a stone that Chang Ch'ing let fly. Even as he was about to clamber up there came forth soldiers from the enemy army and pulling and dragging him this way and that they dragged him into their camp. At this Sung Chiang cried in a mighty voice, "Who will go to save Liu T'ang?"

Then was seen that Blue Faced Beast, Yang Chi, and he raised his blade aloft and whipped his horse and he went out against Chang Ch'ing. Chang Ch'ing pretended to raise his weapon against him and come to meet him and as Yang Chi raised his sword to strike him down with a blow Chang Ch'ing bent clean to the footprints of his horse, and Yang Chi struck against emptiness. Then swiftly did Chang Ch'ing take a stone and crying, "Speed!" the stone flew out, but it flew beneath Yang Chi's arm.

Again Chang Ch'ing took a stone and there was a sound and it struck upon Yang Chi's helmet, and it so frightened Yang Chi that his gall was like to burst and his heart grew cold. He lay close to his saddle and returned to his ranks. Sung Chiang saw this and he pondered thus, "If today we lose our power of victory how can we return to our mountain lair?—Who will revenge me for my anger?"

Now Chu T'ung heard him and he looked at Lei Heng and he said, "It is not enough for one to go out alone. Let us two attack together, one in front and one behind."

So Chu T'ung went to the left and Lei Heng to the right and the two keen swordsmen dashed out from among the robber ranks. Chang Ch'ing laughed and said, "One cannot do it, and so they add another. And if there were ten come, what of it?" And his color did not change at all.

There on his horse he hid two stones in his hand. Lei Heng came first. Chang Ch'ing's hand rose and he looked like that seventh lord whose likeness is set upon treasury books, his hand raised aloft to beckon treasure. Already was the stone struck upon Lei Heng's forehead and he fell suddenly to the ground. Chu T'ung made haste to go and save him when again there was a stone and it flew upon the back of his neck.

Now in the ranks Kuan Sheng saw this heavy loss and he put forth his godlike power, and he lifted up his blue dragon sword and he urged on his fine red horse and he went forth to save Chu T'ung and Lei Heng. He had but just brought them back to their own ranks when again Chang Ch'ing let fly a stone. Kuan Sheng raised his sword to stay it, and it struck full on the sword and sparks flew out. But Kuan Sheng had not the heart to do battle with him more and so he turned his horse and retired.

Then did the chief who carried two spears Tung P'ing see this and he meditated secretly in his heart, "I have but come after Sung Chiang, and if I do not show forth my skill in war then when I go up the mountain surely will I have no great honor there." So grasping levelly his two weapons he let his horse fly forth from the ranks. Chang Ch'ing saw him and he cursed mightily, "Our cities are neighboring cities, close as lips and teeth, and we two worked together to destroy these robbers, and surely it is what we ought to have done. Then why have you this day turned against the throne? Do you yourself feel no shame, therefore?"

Then was Tung P'ing filled with a great wrath and he went straight against Chang Ch'ing. The two horses came near and the weapons of the warriors were raised aloft. The three weapons struck back and forth upon the battle ground and the four arms whirled about in circles. They had thus fought some five or seven rounds when Chang Ch'ing turned his horse and went away. Then Tung P'ing said, "Others may be wounded by your stones, but how can you make me afraid?"

Chang Ch'ing, holding his weapon in one hand, felt in his silken bag and brought forth a stone. His right hand had but just risen and already the stone had struck for its mark. But Tung P'ing's eyes were clear and his hand was quick, and he dashed the stone aside. Then Chang Ch'ing seeing he had not struck him brought out the second stone. Again Tung P'ing dodged it. Two stones did not strike him and Chang Ch'ing's heart began to tremble. One horse's mouth was against the other horse's tail and as Chang Ch'ing came to the left of the banners of the ranks Tung P'ing thrust his weapon toward the other's back. But Chang Ch'ing leaned over to the earth and Tung P'ing thrust into emptiness. Then did Chang Ch'ing's weapon thrust forth. Now was Tung P'ing's horse side by side with Chang Ch'ing's horse. Then Chang Ch'ing threw aside his spear and with his two hands he laid hold on Tung P'ing's weapon and all to pull him over, but he could not pull him over, and the two wrestled.

Now So Ch'ao from Sung Chiang's ranks saw all, and brandishing his great axe he came forth to save. Kung Wang in the enemy ranks opposite and Ting Tê Sheng came forth on their two horses also and they met So Ch'ao and fell to battle. Chang Ch'ing and Tung P'ing could not separate and So Ch'ao and Kung Wang and Ting Tê Sheng wrestled together also. Ling Ch'ung, Hua Yung, Lü Fang, Kao Shen, these four warriors all came forth and their weapons were two spears and the two moon-curved spears, and they came to save Tung P'ing and So Ch'ao.

Now Chang Ch'ing, seeing the outlook was evil, left Tung P'ing and galloped into his ranks. But Tung P'ing would not leave him and he plunged after Chang Ch'ing but he forgot to guard himself against the stones. Chang Ch'ing, seeing Tung P'ing pursue him, secretly hid stones in his hand, and he waited until his enemy's horse was near and he shouted out, "Speed!" Tung P'ing made haste to dodge and the stone flew past beneath his ear. Then Tung P'ing returned and So Ch'ao left Kung Wang and Ting Tê Sheng and hastened also into the ranks. Chang Ch'ing held his weapon and felt again for his stone and he let it fly to So Ch'ao. So Ch'ao dodged swiftly, but it was too late and it struck upon his face and the fresh red blood flowed forth. He took up his axe and returned to his ranks.

Let it be told further of Ling Ch'ung and Hua Yung. They held Kung Wang at one side. Lü Fang and Kao Shen also held Ting Tê Sheng at another side. Now Kung Wang's heart was full of fear and impatience. He threw his flying dart, but he did not strike Hua Yung or Ling Ch'ung and since he had no weapon, they seized him alive. On the other side Ting Tê Sheng whirled his darting fork, and reckless of his life he withstood Lü Fang and Kao Shen. But he was not prepared against Yien Ch'ing, who saw this from the gate of the camp, and to himself he thought, "We have lost from our side one after the other fifteen of our great chiefs. If we cannot even capture these little warriors, then what honor have we left?"

He put down his staff, and he took out his repeating bow and he tied fast the string and let fly an arrow. There was a twang and he struck Ting Tê Sheng's horse's hoof, and that horse fell and Lü Fang and Kao Shen seized Ting Tê Sheng. When Chang Ch'ing came to save him he could not withstand so many and he could but take Liu T'ang and return to the city of Tung Ch'ang.

There the magistrate himself stood upon the city wall, and he had seen how first and last Chang Ch'ing had overcome fifteen great robber chiefs of the robbers' lair and although they had lost Kung Wang and Ting Tê Sheng, yet they had captured this Liu T'ang. He went back to his court and poured forth wine to congratulate Chang Ch'ing, but first he commanded that a long rack be placed upon Liu T'ang and that he be placed in gaol. Then they took counsel again.

Let it be told further of Sung Chiang. He recalled his men and went back and first he sent Kung Wang and Ting Tê Sheng back to the mountain lair. Again did Sung Chiang say to Wu Yung and to Lu Chün I, "I have heard that in the time of the Five Dynasties in the country of Ta Liang there was a man surnamed Wang and named Yien Chang, and before the shadows cast by the sun had moved he had vanquished thirty-six warriors of the country of T'ang. Today Chang Ch'ing in no time at all has conquered fifteen of my great chieftains one after the other. Surely he is no less than that one of old. Truly is he a brave fierce warrior!"

Those about him had not a word to say. Again Sung Chiang said, "But I saw this man and I saw that he did trust altogether to Kung Wang and

Ting Tê Sheng. Now these two wings of his are taken from him, and let us therefore use good guile to seize him."

And Wu Yung said, "Elder Brother, let your heart rest. This lowly one has watched this warrior in his comings to and fro and long ago have I prepared the guile. Since this is so, let us return to the lair these wounded chieftains, and let us bid Lu Chi Shen, Wu Sung, Sheng Li, Huang Hsin, and Li Li lead forth all our water robbers, and all our carts and boats and horses, and let the fighting men of the water and the fighting men of the land go forward side by side, and let boats and horses go forth to meet him and thus deceive him into coming out. Then can the great deed be done."

So did Wu Yung appoint each to his place.

Let it be further told of Chang Ch'ing. In the midst of the city he took counsel with the magistrate and he said, "Although we have won twice in battle, yet we have not yet destroyed utterly the roots of these robbers. Let men go to spy and to listen what is false and true among them, and then we will plan further."

Then did the spies return and make report, saying, "Behind the camp to the northwest there is a vast amount of grain and rice and we do not know from whence it is come. There are some hundred carts full, and in the river there are grain boats, and great and small, there are more than five hundred of these boats. Upon the water and upon land they come forward together, the boats and the horsemen, and there are several chieftains who lead them."

The magistrate said, "These robbers have surely some plot and let us take care lest we suffer from their poisonous hands."

And again he sent forth men to spy, to see whether or not it was truly grain and hay or not. On the next day the spy came back and made report, saying, "It is truly grain and hay upon the carts, for grain is leaking from them. Upon the boats in the water, although they are covered over, yet on every boat can be seen the sacks of grain."

Chang Ch'ing said, "Tonight I shall go out of the city and first I shall seize these carts on the land and then I will go and seize those boats of theirs on the water. Pray the magistrate to help me in battle, so that in one beating of the drum for battle I may seize them."

The magistrate answered, "This plan is excellent, indeed, and do you but watch well your chance," and he commanded the soldiers to fill themselves with food and wine and to put upon themselves completest armor and carry with them silken banners.

And Chang Ch'ing took his long spear and he led out secretly a thousand soldiers.

On that night the moon was dim and the light of the stars filled the sky. They had gone but a little more than three miles when they saw a crowd of carts and upon the banners over them was written clearly, "The Grain Of The Righteous And Loyal Robbers' Lair."

This Chang Ch'ing saw and he saw Lu Chi Shen carrying his staff across his two shoulders and his priest's black robe was girdled about him and he strode on in front. Then Chang Ch'ing said, "This bald-headed donkey's skull I will break with a stone."

Now Lu Chi Shen came on carrying his staff and by now he had seen the enemy, but he pretended he had not. He did but walk on with great strides. But he forgot to be heedful of the stones. Even as he went, Chang Ch'ing shouted from his horse and a stone flew straight upon Lu Chi Shen's head and the red blood flowed out and he fell backward. Then did Chang Ch'ing's soldiers all shout together and they all came charging forward. In all haste Wu Sung raised aloft his two priest knives and at the risk of his life he rushed to save Lu Chi Shen and he deserted the carts of grain and ran away. Then Chang Ch'ing seized the carts of grain and he saw they were truly filled with rice and grain and he was pleased in heart, nor did he go in pursuit of Lu Chi Shen. But he guarded the carts and brought them into the city.

The magistrate saw them and was greatly rejoiced and himself he put them into store. Chang Ch'ing then would fain have gone and seized the grain upon the boats but the magistrate said, "General, do you watch your chance with all care!"

Then Chang Ch'ing mounted his horse and came around to the south gate, and there he saw in the canals the boats, countless in number, and he cried out that the city gate was to be opened and all shouting together they dashed to the brink of the canal. Now by this time the clouds had covered the sky and the dark mists were over all and when the horsemen and the soldiers turned to look at each other face could not see face. But this was magic that Kung Sun Sheng had made. Chang Ch'ing saw it and his heart was filled with fear and his eyes were darkened and he would have fain retreated, but there was no way to go either forward or backward, and there was the sound of confusion and shouting on all four sides.

Truly it was not to be seen from whence the fighting men came. Ling Ch'ung, leading horsemen encased in iron armor, forced Chang Ch'ing and his men all into the water. In the midst of the canal there was Li Chün, Chang Heng, Chang Shun, the three Juan brothers and the two T'ung brothers, these eight water chiefs, and there they stood in a line. Chang Ch'ing would now fain have escaped from them but he could not and he was laid hold upon by the three heroes, the Juan brothers, and they took ropes and bound him about and they brought him to their camp. Then the water chiefs flew as though winged to make report to Sung Chiang.

Then Wu Yung urged all the chieftains great and small that very night to attack the city. There the magistrate was alone and how could he stay the falling city and withstand them? When he heard the sounds of bursting fireballs on all four sides of the city and that the city gates were opened he was terrified and there was no road whereby he might escape. Then Sung Chiang and his companies charged into the city and first freed Liu T'ang and then opened the treasury and sent a portion straightway to the robbers' lair, and the other portion they gave to the people in the city.

As for the magistrate, since he was commonly a man just and not loving gain, him Sung Chiang forgave.

Now Sung Chiang and all his men were at that time in the magistrate's court and there they met face to face. The water chiefs were then seen to have already brought thither Chang Ch'ing, and there were many who had been wounded by him, and each of these gnashed their teeth and they would fain have dashed forward to kill Chang Ch'ing. But Sung Chiang, seeing him there, himself went to meet him and untied his bonds and he made apologies, saying, "In heedlessness have they broken your power, and I pray you will not hold it in your heart against them," and he invited him to come into the hall.

Before he finished speaking he saw Lu Chi Shen in front of the house, his head bound about with a kerchief, and he had his iron staff and he dashed forward with all his strength to do battle. But Sung Chiang parted them and he called to Lu Chi Shen continuously to withdraw. Chang Ch'ing, seeing how courteous Sung Chiang was in his behavior to him, bowed himself to the ground in obeisance and vowed his willingness to follow after him. Then did Sung Chiang pour out a bowl of wine upon the ground, and he took an arrow and broke it in two and made a vow, saying, "If you, my Brothers, will take your revenge thus then Heaven itself will no longer preserve you, and surely will you die beneath the point of the dagger."

All of them heard this, and who dared say a word more?

When Sung Chiang had made the vow thus everybody began to laugh loudly and everyone was pleased and they made ready their horses and men and prepared to go back to the lair. Then Chang Ch'ing was seen to come before Sung Chiang and he presented a certain physician of the city whose skill was in healing beasts, and his surname was double and it was Huang Fu and his name was Tuan. This man's greatest skill was with horses and he knew their ills of cold and heat and in giving medicine or piercing with needles he never did amiss and truly was he skilled like that one of old, Pei Yo. He had been formerly a man of Yu Chou, but because his eyes were green and his beard yellow, his face looked like a foreigner, and because of this he was called Purple Bearded Duke and Chang Ch'ing said, "If there is a use for him in the robbers' lair then let this man be called thither and let him bring his wife and his children and go with us up the mountain."

When Sung Chiang heard these words he was filled with pleasure and he said, "If Huang Fu Tuan is willing to come with us, then will my heart be filled with content."

Chang Ch'ing, seeing that Sung Chiang loved him well, straightway went and called this physician of beasts Huang Fu Tuan, and he made obeisance to Sung Chiang and to all the chieftains. Sung Chiang, seeing him to be a man of no common appearance and very noble in his looks, and how in each of his green eyes he had two black pupils and how his rounded beard grew far past his belly, could not cease in praising him. And Huang Fu Tuan, seeing how courteous was Sung Chiang, was truly pleased in his heart and he was very willing to follow after him. Then was Sung Chiang filled with pleasure and when he had comforted the people he sent forth a command that all the chieftains were to make ready the carts and the grain and the gold and the silver and they were to set forth all together and the treasure and the grain of these two cities were thus taken to the robbers' lair, and all the companies of the robbers from first to last marched forward.

There is naught to tell of the journey and they soon returned to the mountain lair and gathered there in the Hall Of Righteousness And Loyalty. Sung Chiang commanded, "Let Kung Wang and Ting Tê Sheng be freed and let them come thither," and he used kind words to comfort them and the two men bowed themselves down and swore allegiance. And Huang Fu Tuan was added to the lair also, and his duty was to heal such beasts as were ill. The generals Tung P'ing and Chang Ch'ing were also made chieftains in the lair. And Sung Chiang was pleased and he commanded in haste that a feast was to be prepared for congratulations and there they were all in the Hall Of Righteousness And Loyalty and each man sat in the seat of his rank.

Now Sung Chiang looked about upon the chiefs and there were exactly one hundred and eight men. Then he began to speak, saying, "My Brothers, we are met together here upon this mountain and wherever we have gone we have not lost one of our number. This mercy is by the protection of the gods in Heaven, nor is it accomplished by the power of man. Today you have come about me to aid me as your chief and I do trust altogether to your bravery and courage, and I have somewhat to say and I pray you all, my Brothers, to hear me."

And Wu Yung said, "We would ask you, our Elder Brother, to instruct us and govern us."

Then Sung Chiang opened his mouth and spoke his will and truly was it that the thirty-six great stars fulfilled their number and the seventy-two lesser stars fulfilled the prophecy.

What then did Sung Chiang say? Pray hear it told in the next chapter.

Chapter 70

THE HALL OF RIGHTEOUSNESS AND LOYALTY RECEIVES WORDS FROM HEAVEN UPON A TABLET OF STONE. THE HEROES OF THE ROBBERS' LAIR ARE FEARFUL BECAUSE OF AN EVIL DREAM

IT IS SAID: Sung Chiang the first time attacked the city of Tung P'ing and the second time the city of Tung Ch'ang and then he returned to the mountain lair and there he counted the chieftains, great and small, and there were in all one hundred and eight, and so was his heart filled with great joy. Straightway then did he say to these his brethren, "Since I made turmoil in the city of Chiang Chou and since I came up this mountain I have trusted to the courage of my brothers to aid me. I have been made first chieftain and today are we gathered together, one hundred and eight in all, and truly is my heart made glad. Ever since our elder brother Ch'ao Kai returned to Heaven we have done naught but go down the mountain and forth to battle, and beyond all hopes is it that we have been preserved safely and not one of us is lacking. Truly is it that Heaven has guarded us, and it is not by the power of man. Whether some have been bound in gaol or whether those who have been taken captive or whether they have returned heavily wounded, yet no harm came to any of them. To-day there are the hundred and eight of us and all are met here before my face. Truly is it a thing not heard of from ancient times even until now.

"Yet when in the past our fighting men went forth they killed many men and there is no way whereby we may atone for this. It is in my heart therefore to put forth this purpose and it is to have a great mass said to thank Heaven and Earth and all the gods, since they have thus protected us and shown us mercy. In the first place we will pray that our bodies and spirits may be kept happy and at peace, and second we will pray that the Emperor may soon show forth the light of his mercy and forgive us our great sin against Heaven so that each of us may with all our strength use our bodies even to die and that with all our loyalty we may guard our country, unto the very day of death. In the third place, let us pray the soul of our elder brother, The Heavenly King Ch'ao Kai, the more quickly to pass from Hell into Heaven so that as life wheels once more into life we may hope to meet again. And while we do this let us pray out of Hell also those who have died innocently by fire or water or have died untimely by violent end so that they also may all pass onward upon the happy way. This would I do, but I do not know what my brothers think of it."

Then all the chieftains agreed to this and they answered, "This is a deed bearing good fruit, and our elder brother's purpose is no whit wrong."

And Wu Yung said, "Let us ask our brother Kung Sun Sheng to be chief of the mass and let others be sent down the mountain to go in all places and seek such Taoists as are of highest virtue and knowledge and let them bring their chants and their objects of worship hither to our lair, and let men be sent everywhere to find everything of incense and candles and paper gods and flowers and fruits and gifts to place before the gods, and vegetable foods and dishes and clean foods and all things needed for the mass."

Thus they took counsel together and they decided upon the fifteenth day of the fourth moon for the day and the mass was to be for seven days and seven nights and money was brought forth in plenty and men were directed with all speed. Before the Hall Of Righteousness And Loyalty were hung four great banners of cloth. In the hall was erected a three-storied dais and there were placed upon it the seven precious things and the likenesses of three gods, and beside them were placed the twenty-eight god-like stars which govern the days of the moon and there were placed the likenesses of the twelve god-like beasts, which govern the moons of the year, and all the starry gods which take charge of masses chanted by men.

Outside the hall there were warrior gods and when all were placed and nothing lacking the Taoists came who had been invited and with Kung Sun Sheng there were forty-nine. On that day the sky was clear and fair and the air was neither hot nor cold and the moon was white and the winds mild. Sung Chiang and Lu Chün I went first and Wu Yung and the other chiefs followed after them and they all came to burn incense. Kung Sun Sheng was chief priest and he governed all that took place. He it was who gave forth the chants and who wrote the runes and he with the forty-eight others came thrice daily before the gods and said mass. On the seventh day the mass was finished and they scattered.

Now Sung Chiang thought to implore an answer from Heaven and for this purpose he bade Kung Sun Sheng alone to write red letters upon a green paper and place the paper upon fire that it might ascend to ask of God. Every day he did this thrice. On the seventh day at the third watch, when Kung Sun Sheng was upon the highest terrace of the altar and the other priests upon the second and Sung Chiang and the other chieftains were on the third, and all the lesser chiefs and captains were on the ground below they prayed with all their strength to Heaven and they bowed themselves down to the ground and they besought Heaven to give them some answer.

In the night of that day at the third watch they heard a sound in the sky and it was like the ripping of silk and it came from the northwest gate of heaven. When they all looked there was as it were a great plate of gold standing there, the two ends pointed and the center wide, and this is called The Opening Of The Gate Of Heaven and it is also called The Opening Of The Eye Of Heaven. The light from this place came forth in a beam and it smote the eyes of men and in that place floated fair clouds of every hue. Out of the center there came forth a flame, round at the top like a winnowing basket, and it came whirling to the foot of the altar. There it circled about the altar and it struck the earth at the full south of the altar. When they looked again The Eye Of Heaven was closed. All the Taoists came down from the altar and straightway Sung Chiang bade men fetch iron spears and hoes and open up the earth and search for the flame.

When they had dug not yet three feet into that earth they saw a stone tablet, and upon its face and upon its two sides were heavenly writings.

Then did Sung Chiang command that spirit paper be burned and that they all scatter. When dawn was newly come he caused a vegetable meal to be given to the priests and to each he gave gold, silver and treasure as well as money for the mass.

Only then did he fetch the stone tablet and look at it. Upon it were written dragon letters and phœnix writing, shaped like tadpoles, and such as no man can read. But among the Taoists there was one surnamed Ho and his priestly name was Hsüan T'ung, and he said to Sung Chiang, "In my house there has been left from the time of our ancestors a certain book and it is such as can explain the letters that are written in Heaven. Upon its pages are also these ancient letters shaped like tadpoles and because of this I know very well such letters as these. Let me translate them and then we will know what they are."

Sung Chiang heard this and he was filled with joy and in great haste he handed the tablet to the priest. The priest looked at it long and at last he said, "Here upon this tablet are all the noble names of the great chieftains in this lair and they are carved upon it. At the one side there are these four letters, 'Work Righteousness For Heaven.' On the other side are the four letters, 'In Loyalty And Righteousness Complete.' On the top of this tablet there are many stars, the stars of the north and the stars of the south. Beneath the stars are written your noble names that men call you. If it be not held to me for a fault, then I will read these letters aloud, from first to last."

Sung Chiang answered, "Ten thousand fold happiness is it that we have such wisdom to lighten our darkness, and great is our destiny to have met it. If we can be so taught, then will we be grateful truly for so great a favor. But if there is any rebuke from Heaven I pray that it be not hidden from us. Ten thousand times do I hope that every word will be told in fullest meaning and not a whit be lost."

Then Sung Chiang bade the scribe Siao Jang to write down all upon yellow paper and the priest began to speak and he said, "Upon the front of this stone there are thirty-six names and they are the names of thirty-six powerful and heavenly stars. On the back of the stone there are also seventy-two names and these are the names of the seventy-two fierce and powerful earthly stars. Beneath are the names and surnames of the heroes. Upon the front of the stone is written, 'The thirty-six fierce and powerful stars of heaven made manifest in men, which are

The chief star among the Stars Of Heaven called The Opportune Rain, Sung Chiang

The fiery powerful star among the Stars Of Heaven called The Jade Ch'i Lin, Lu Chün I

The wise star among the Stars Of Heaven called The Great Intelligence, Wu Yung

The idle star among the Stars Of Heaven called Dragon In The Clouds, Kung Sun Sheng

The brave star among the Stars Of Heaven called The Great Sword, Kuan Sheng

The fierce heroic star among the Stars Of Heaven called The Leopard Headed, Ling Ch'ung

The star of swift courage among the Stars Of Heaven called The Fire In The Thunder Clap, Ch'ing Ming

The majestic star among the Stars Of Heaven called The Double Clubs, Hu Yien Shu

The heroic star among the Stars Of Heaven called Little Li Kuan, Hua Yung

The lofty star among the Stars Of Heaven called The Little Whirlwind, Ch'ai Chin

The star of wealth among the Stars Of Heaven called Eagle Who Smites The Heavens, Li Yün

The star of abundance among the Stars Of Heaven called The Beautiful Bearded, Chu T'ung

The lone star among the Stars Of Heaven called The Tattooed Priest, Lu Chi Shen

The wounded star among the Stars Of Heaven called The Hairy Priest, Wu Sung

The standing star among the Stars Of Heaven

called The Warrior Of The Two Spears, Tung P'ing

The swift star among the Stars Of Heaven called The Featherless Arrow, Chang Ch'ing

The star of darkness among the Stars Of Heaven called The Blue Faced Beast, Yang Chi

The guardian star among the Stars Of Heaven called The Wielder Of The Golden Sword, Ch'ü Ling

The empty star among the Stars Of Heaven called The Swift Vanguard, So Ch'ao

The speedy star among the Stars Of Heaven called The Magic Messenger, Tai Chung

The strange star among the Stars Of Heaven called The Redheaded Devil, Liu T'ang

The murderous star among the Stars Of Heaven called The Black Whirlwind, Li K'uei

The lowly star among the Stars Of Heaven called The Nine Dragoned, Shih Chin

The penetrating star among the Stars Of Heaven called He Whom No Obstacle Can Stay, Mu Hung

The retreating star among the Stars Of Heaven called The Winged Tiger, Lei Heng

The long-lived star among the Stars Of Heaven called The Dragon Who Roils Rivers, Li Chün

The dagger star among the Stars Of Heaven called The God Of Swift Death, Juan The Second

The level star among the Stars Of Heaven called The Boatman, Chang Heng

The sinning star among the Stars Of Heaven called The Short Lived, Juan The Fifth

The broken star among the Stars Of Heaven called White Stripe In The Waves, Chang Shun

The vanquished star among the Stars Of Heaven called The Fierce King Of Devils, Juan The Seventh

The gaol star among the Stars Of Heaven called The Sick Kuan So, Yang Hsiung

The intelligent star among the Stars Of Heaven called The One Who Heeds Not His Life, Shih Hsiu

The savage star among the Stars Of Heaven called The Double Headed Snake, Hsieh Chen

The weeping star among the Stars Of Heaven, The Double Tailed Scorpion, Hsieh Pao

The clever star among the Stars Of Heaven called The Prodigal, Yien Ch'ing.

"Upon the back of the stone tablet is written, The earthly stars, which are seventy-two in number, and these are

The chief star among the Stars Of Earth called The Wily Warrior, Chu Wu

The savage star among the Stars Of Earth called He Who Rules Three Mountains, Huang Hsin

The brave star among the Stars Of Earth called The Sick Warrior, Sheng Li

The noble wise star among the Stars Of Earth called The Ugly Warrior, Hsüan Tsan

The heroic star among the Stars Of Earth called The Guardian Star God, Hao Ssŭ Wen

The majestic star among the Stars Of Earth, Victor In A Hundred Battles, Han T'ao

The courageous star among the Stars Of Earth called The Eye Of Heaven, P'eng Ch'i

The strange star among the Stars Of Earth called Swift In Water, Shang T'ing Kuei

The ferocious star among the Stars Of Earth called Warrior Of Fire, Wei Ting Kuo

The learned star among the Stars Of Earth called The Magic Scribe, Siao Jang

The guileless star among the Stars Of Earth called The Iron Faced, P'ei Hsüan

The eminent star among the Stars Of Earth called Eagle In The Clouds, Ou P'eng

The folding star among the Stars Of Earth called The Red Eyed Lion, Teng Fei

The strong star among the Stars Of Earth called The Five Hued Tiger, Yien Shun

The dark star among the Stars Of Earth called The Five Hued Leopard, Yang Ling

The axis star among the Stars Of Earth called Thunder That Shakes The Heavens, Ling Chen

The gathering star among the Stars Of Earth called The God Of Accounting, Chiang Ching

The aiding star among the Stars Of Earth called The Lesser Duke, Lü Fang

The helpful star among the Stars Of Earth, He Who Is Like Jen Kuei Of Old, Kao Shen

The clever star among the Stars Of Earth called The Magic Physician, An Tao Ch'uan

The beast star among the Stars Of Earth called The Purple Bearded, Huang Fu Tuan

The least star among the Stars Of Earth called The Dwarf Tiger, Wang Ying

The intelligent star among the Stars Of Earth called The Ten Foot Green Snake, The Goodwife Hu

The barbarous star among the Stars Of Earth called The God Of Death, Pao Su

The silent star among the Stars Of Earth called King Of The Devils Who Roil Earth, Fan Lui

The wild star among the Stars Of Earth called The Curly Haired, K'ung Ming

The ambitious star among the Stars Of Earth called The Lone Fire, K'ung Liang

The flying star among the Stars Of Earth called The Eight Armed Lo Chao, Hsiang Ch'ung

The walking star among the Stars Of Earth called The Heaven Flying God, Li Kun

The cunning star among the Stars Of Earth called The Jade Armed Warrior, Ching Ta Chien

The clear star among the Stars Of Earth called The Magic Iron Flautist, Ma Ling

The forward star among the Stars Of Earth called Crocodile Out Of The Hole, T'ung Wei

The retreating star among the Stars Of Earth called The Oyster That Turns The River Over, T'ung Meng

The full star among the Stars Of Earth called The Jade Banner Pole, Meng K'an

The fulfilled star among the Stars Of Earth called The Strong Armed Gorilla, Hou Chien

The complete star among the Stars Of Earth called The Gorge Leaping Tiger, Ch'en Ta

The hidden star among the Stars Of Earth called The White Spotted Snake, Yang Ch'un

The peculiar star among the Stars Of Earth called The White Faced Goodman, Chen T'ien Shou

The just star among the Stars Of Earth called The Nine Tailed Turtle, T'ao Chung Wang

The elegant star among the Stars Of Earth called The Iron Fan, Sung Ch'ing

The musical star among the Stars Of Earth called The Iron Whistle, Yo Ho

The quick star among the Stars Of Earth called The Spotted Necked Tiger, Kung Wang

The hasty star among the Stars Of Earth called The Arrow Wounded Tiger, Ting Tê Sheng

The suppressing star among the Stars Of Earth called The Lesser One Whom No Obstacle Can Stay, Mu Ch'un

The haltered star among the Stars Of Earth called The Dagger Devil, Ch'ao Cheng

The devil star among the Stars Of Earth called The Guardian God In The Clouds, Sung Wan

The magic star among the Stars Of Earth called Eagle Who Flutters Against The Sky, Tu Ch'ien

The obscure star among the Stars Of Earth called The Sick Tiger, Hsüeh Yung

The lonely star among the Stars Of Earth, The Warrior Who Wars Against Tigers, Li Chung

The empty star among the Stars Of Earth called The Little Tyrant King, Chou T'ung

The orphan star among the Stars Of Earth called The Gold Spotted Leopard, T'ang Lung

The finished star among the Stars Of Earth called The Devil Faced, Tu Hsing

The short star among the Stars Of Earth called Dragon Out Of The Wood, Chou Yuen

The corner star among the Stars Of Earth called The One Horned Dragon, Chou Jun

The prisoner star among the Stars Of Earth called The Dry Land Water Beast, Chu Kuei

The hoarding star among the Stars Of Earth called The Smiling Faced Tiger, Chu Fu

The hiding star among the Stars Of Earth called The Gold Eyed Tiger Cub, Shih En

The smooth star among the Stars of Earth called The Iron Armed, Ts'ai Fu

The wounded star among the Stars Of Earth called The Single Flower, Ts'ai Ch'ing

The serving star among the Stars Of Earth called The Pursuing God Of Death, Li Li

The searching star among the Stars Of Earth called The Blue Eyed Tiger, Li Yün

The fierce star among the Stars Of Earth called The Faceless, Chiao T'ing

The ugly star among the Stars Of Earth called The Stone Warrior, Shih Yung

The mathematic star among the Stars Of Earth called The Lesser Yü Tse, Sheng Sing

The shadowy star among the Stars Of Earth called The Female Tiger, The Goodwife Ku

The avenging star among the Stars Of Earth called The Gardener, Chang Ch'ing

The strong star among the Stars Of Earth called The Female Savage, The Goodwife Sheng

The inferior star among the Stars Of Earth called The Lively Female, Wang Ting Lu
The mighty star among the Stars Of Earth called The Vanguard God, Ju Pao Ssŭ
The rat star among the Stars Of Earth called Rat In The Daylight, Pei Sheng
The thieving star among the Stars Of Earth called Flea On A Drum, Shih Ch'ien
The dog star among the Stars Of Earth called The Yellow Haired Dog, Tuan Ching Chu."

Thus did the priest Ho make clear the meaning of all the writing upon the sacred tablet and Siao Jang was told to write it down. When he had finished writing and they all had read it, they were full of fear and wonder. Then Sung Chiang said to all the chieftains, "So small and mean and despicable an one as I to be chief among the stars! My brothers, you, too, were once all a host together. Today has Heaven shown it to us, that we ought by destiny to meet here. Today is our number fulfilled and we must appoint our numbers each in his rank. Let each chieftain take his place and let none strive to be higher than his place is. Heaven's command cannot be disobeyed."

Then did they all say, "It is the will of Heaven and of Earth and all has been decided by the reckoning of Heaven and Earth. Who can dare to disobey?"

And Sung Chiang brought forth fifty ounces of gold and he gave it in thanks to the priest. As for the other priests, each received bounty for his chanting. Then were the books and the things used for the mass gathered together and each parted from the other and they went down the mountain.

But let it not be told now of all those Taoists who returned to their homes. Let it rather be told now of Sung Chiang and of the counselor Wu Yung and of Chu Wu and of the others, and how they took counsel together. They were fain to set up a tablet in their hall upon which was written the letters "The Hall Of Loyalty And Righteousness." In The Pavilion Of Dividing Gold there was also a great tablet hung. Before the houses where they lived were built three passes, and behind the Hall Of Loyalty And Righteousness were built terraces in the shape of the flight of wild geese. Highest of all was built a great hall with lesser halls to the east and to the west. In the great hall which was to the memory of The Heavenly King Ch'ao Kai, was placed his spirit tablet. In the east house Sung Chiang and Wu Yung, Lü Fang and Kao Shen lived. In the western house there lived Lu Chün I, Kung Sun Sheng, K'ung Ming and K'ung Liang. On the second ridge of the mountain in the houses to the left there lived Chu Wu, Huang Hsin, Sheng Li, Siao Jang and P'ei Hsüan. In the houses to the right there lived Tai Chung, Yien Ch'ing, Chang Ch'ing, An The Physician and Huang Fu Tuan. To the left of the Hall Of Loyalty And Righteousness there were houses for the treasure and the granaries, both to take in and to give out, and there lived also Ch'ai Chin, Li Yün, Chiang Ching and Ling Chen. To the right lived Hua Yung, Fan Lui, Hsiang Ch'ung and Li Kun.

At the front of the mountain upon the south road the first pass was guarded by Hsieh Chen and Hsieh Pao. The second pass was guarded by Lu Chi Shen and Wu Sung. The third pass was guarded by Chu T'ung and Lei Heng. Upon the eastern mountain there was one pass, and Shih Chin and Liu T'ang guarded it. The pass upon the western mountain was guarded by Yang Hsiung and Shih Hsiu. The pass upon the northern mountain was guarded by Mu Hung and Li K'uei.

Outside of these six passes there were set eight camps, four on land and four on water. In the camp to the due south were Ch'ing Ming, So Ch'ao, Ou P'eng, Teng Fei. In the camp to the east were Kuan Sheng, Ch'ü Ling, Hsüan Tsan, Hao Ssŭ Wen. In the camp to the west were Ling Ch'ung, Tung P'ing, Shang T'ing Kuei, Wei Ting Kuo. In the north camp were Hu Yien Shu, T'ang Lung, Han T'ao, P'eng Ch'i. On the southeast camp upon the water were Li Chün and Juan The Second. In the southwest camp were Chang Heng and Chang Shun. In the northeast camp were Juan The Fifth and T'ung Wei. In the northwest camp were Juan The Seventh and T'ung Meng.

As for all the others, each had his work. The former banners were cast aside and new ones made. Upon the crest of the mountain was raised aloft a new banner, apricot yellow in hue, and upon it were written four letters, "Work Righteousness For Heaven." In front of the Hall Of Loyalty And Righteousness there were two banners embroidered. Upon one was written "The Righteous Guard Of Shantung." On the other was written "The Jade Ch'i Lin Of Hopei." Besides these three banners, others were made with designs of winged dragons, winged tigers, winged bears, winged leopards, and of the constellations of The Sky-Blue Dragon and of The White Tiger, and of the southern constellation of The Vermilion Bird and of that north constellation also which is called The Turtle. Besides these were prepared gold-edged axes and tasseled staves, and sky-blue banners and black umbrellas, flying streamers, and a great square black banner. These were all to be used in the chief army.

Beyond these banners were others with the stars of The Great Dipper and stars of the four directions and of the Center Heaven and of Heaven and Earth and Man and of all the nine elements of the skies, and of the twenty-eight chief stars of Heaven and of the sixty-four diagrams of life and of the nine divisions of Heaven. There were one hundred and twenty banners to govern the spirits of the mountain and these banners were all made by Hou Chien. Ching Ta Chien made all the despatches for the men and the sealed proofs and so all was completed.

Then was a fortunate good day chosen and cows were butchered and horses killed with which to do sacrifice to the gods of Heaven and Earth and the tablets that had been prepared for the halls were then hung and the new banner which was to announce righteousness worked for Heaven was raised.

On that day Sung Chiang had spread a mighty feast and himself he bore thither his own seal and his own despatch case and he announced these commands to all there assembled, and he said, "My Brothers, great and small, let each of you do that to which he is appointed and let each of you respect and obey the laws of our lair and let none disobey my command and so wound our brotherhood. If there is one who of his own wish disobeys my command he shall be judged according to the military law, nor shall he be lightly forgiven."

Then he read from a paper thus. "The two generals who shall be chiefs over all the fighting men are these, The Opportune Rain, Sung Chiang, and The Jade Ch'i Lin, Lu Chün I. The two who shall teach the ways of war are The Great Intelligence Wu Yung and Dragon In The Clouds Kung Sun Sheng, and there shall be one chieftain to take counsel and advise with them concerning all matters of war, who shall be The Wily Warrior Chu Wu. Two chieftains there shall be to govern the treasury and the granaries and they shall be The Little Whirlwind Ch'ai Chin and The Blue Eyed Tiger Li Yün. There shall be five tiger-like chieftains to govern the horsemen, The Great Sword Kuan Sheng, The Leopard Headed Ling Ch'ung, The Fire In The Thunder Clap Ch'ing Ming, The Double Clubs Hu Yien Shu and The Warrior Of The Two Spears Tung P'ing. Out of the great warriors among the horsemen I do choose eight to be vanguard, Little Li Kuan Hua Yung, The Wielder Of The Golden Sword Ch'ü Ling, The Blue Faced Beast Yang Chi, The Swift Vanguard So Ch'ao, The Featherless Arrow Chang Ch'ing, The Beautiful Bearded Chu T'ung, The Nine Dragoned Shih Chin and He Whom No Obstacle Can Stay Mu Hung. Among the lesser chieftains of the horsemen I choose sixteen who shall act as spies and as outposts in war, and they are He Who Rules Three Mountains Huang Hsin, The Sick Warrior Sheng Li, The Ugly Warrior Hsüan Tsan, The Guardian Star God Hao Ssŭ Wen, Victor In A Hundred Battles Han T'ao, The Eye Of Heaven P'eng Ch'i, Swift In Water Shang T'ing Kuei, Warrior Of Fire Wei Ting Kuo, Eagle In The Clouds Ou P'eng, The Red Eyed Lion Teng Fei, The Five Hued Tiger Yien Shun, The Magic Iron Flautist Ma Ling, The Gorge Leaping Tiger Ch'en Ta, The White Spotted Snake Yang Ch'un, The Five Hued Leopard Yang Ling and The Little Tyrant King Chou T'ung. Among those who fight on foot let there be ten chieftains, The Tattooed Priest Lu Chi Shen, The Hairy Priest Wu Sung, The Redheaded Devil Liu T'ang, The Winged Tiger Lei Heng, The Black Whirlwind Li K'uei, The Prodigal Yien Ch'ing, The Sick Kuan So Yang Hsiung, The One Who Heeds Not His Life Shih Hsiu, The Double Headed Snake Hsieh

Chen and The Double Tailed Scorpion Hsieh Pao. Among these on foot let there be also seventeen men, King Of The Devils Who Roil Earth Fan Lui, The God Of Death Pao Su, The Eight Armed Lo Chao Hsiang Ch'ung, The Heaven Flying God Li Kun, The Stone Warrior Shih Yung, The Gold Eyed Tiger Cub Shih En, The Lesser One Whom No Obstacle Can Stay Mu Ch'un, The Warrior Who Wars Against Tigers Li Chung, The White Faced Goodman Chen T'ien Shou, The Guardian God In The Clouds Sung Wan, Eagle Who Flutters Against The Sky Tu Ch'ien, Dragon Out Of The Wood Chou Yuen, The One Horned Dragon Chou Jun, The Spotted Necked Tiger Kung Wang, The Arrow Wounded Tiger Ting Tê Sheng, The Faceless Chiao T'ing and The Stone Warrior Shih Yung. There shall be eight chiefs among the four water camps, and these are The Dragon Who Roils Rivers Li Chün, The Boatman Chang Heng and White Stripe In The Waves Chang Shun, The God Of Swift Death Juan The Second, The Short Lived Juan The Fifth, The Fierce King Of Devils Juan The Seventh, Crocodile Out Of The Hole T'ung Wei and The Oyster That Turns The River Over T'ung Meng. In the four wine shops to spy out the news and greet guests there shall be eight chieftains who shall be, in the east wine shop The Lesser Yü Tse Sheng Sing and The Female Tiger The Goodwife Ku, in the western wine shop The Gardener Chang Ch'ing and The Female Savage The Goodwife Sheng, in the southern wine shop The Dry Land Water Beast Chu Kuei and The Devil Faced Tu Hsing, and in the north wine shop The Pursuing God Of Death Li Li and The Lively Female Wang Ting Lu. There shall be one who shall be chieftain of all the spies, who shall be The Magic Messenger Tai Chung. Chief among the men who shall go hither and thither to carry secret messages shall be four, The Iron Whistle Yo Ho, Flea On A Drum Shih Ch'ien, The Yellow Haired Dog Tuan Ching Chu and Rat In The Daylight Pei Sheng. There shall be two brave chieftains of the guard among the central army, and these shall be The Lesser Duke Lü Fang and He Who Is Like Jen Kuei Of Old Kao Shen, and there shall be two also from among the fighting men on foot, The Curly Haired K'ung Ming and The Lone Fire K'ung Liang. Two there shall be to govern executions, and these are The Iron Armed Ts'ai Fu and The Single Flower Ts'ai Ch'ing. Two horsemen warriors there shall be who shall govern the spies among all the companies, and they are The Dwarf Tiger Wang Ying and The Ten Foot Green Snake The Goodwife Hu. Those who shall seek out supplies shall be sixteen in number. One there shall be in charge of all commands sent forth and despatches and the like and it shall be The Magic Scribe Siao Jang. To judge of punishments and rewards there shall be one and it shall be The Iron Faced P'ei Hsüan. To count the treasure and the amounts of grain, both receiving and paying out, there shall be one, and he shall be The God Of Accounting Chiang Ching. He who shall govern the making of boats of war, both great and small, shall be one and he shall be The Jade Banner Pole Meng K'an. He who shall carve the seals and proofs of surety shall be one and he shall be The Jade Armed Warrior Ching Ta Chien. He who shall govern the making of banners and garments and the like shall be The Strong Armed Gorilla Hou Chien. He who shall govern those physicians who heal the ills of the beasts shall be one and he shall be The Purple Bearded Huang Fu Tuan. He who shall be physician for men, both internal and external, shall be one and he shall be The Magic Physician An Tao Ch'uan. He who shall govern the making of all metal things shall be The Gold Spotted Leopard T'ang Lung. He who makes all explosives, fireballs and rockets and the like, shall be Thunder That Shakes The Heavens Ling Chen. He who shall govern the building or repairing of houses shall be one, who is The Blue Eyed Tiger Li Yün. For the butchering of pigs and sheep and cows and all such beasts there shall be one who is The Dagger Devil Ch'ao Cheng. He who shall govern the spreading of feasts shall be The Iron Fan Sung Ch'ing. He who shall be in charge of the feasting shall be one who is The Smiling Faced Tiger Chu Fu. He in charge of the walls about the lair shall be The Nine Tailed Turtle T'ao Chung Wang. He who shall bear the chief banner in battle shall be Ju Pao Ssŭ.

"This is in the second year of the Emperor Hsuen Ho, in the fourth moon and on the twenty-second day, at the great gathering in the lair, when each man was appointed to his own place."

On that day when the great chieftain of the robbers' lair, Sung Chiang, had finished his commands and when he had appointed every chieftain to his own place, each took his own despatch and his own seal and when they had finished feasting everyone was in a mighty drunkenness and so each went to his own house. Among these there were some who were not appointed to a special task, and these all went to the goose-flight-shaped houses and there they waited for their orders and when these commands were given each obeyed.

On the next day Sung Chiang commanded the drums to be beaten to call the chieftains together and so they all came into the hall and there burned an urn of incense and again he said to them, "Today we are no longer as we have been. I have a few words to say. If we be the stars of Heaven and of Earth gathered here together then must we make a covenant with Heaven, and we must all have one heart and trust each other, whether living or dead, and we must all aid each other in any woe. Do you then all aid me, your chief, that we may lift our heads and make reply to Heaven."

Then were all who heard this filled with great joy and they all joined their voices together and they answered, "So be it!" And when each had burned incense they all knelt there in the hall and Sung Chiang knelt in front of them to make their vow, and he said, "In this second year of the Emperor Hsuen Ho in the fourth moon and on the twenty-third day the righteous heroes of Liang Shan P'o, Sung Chiang, Lu Chün I, Wu Yung, Kung Sun Sheng, Kuan Sheng, Ling Ch'ung, Ch'ing Ming, Hu Yien Shu, Hua Yung, Ch'ai Chin, Li Yün, Chu T'ung, Lu Chi Shen, Wu Sung, Tung P'ing, Chang Ch'ing, Yang Chi, Ch'ü Ling, So Ch'ao, Tai Chung, Liu T'ang, Li K'uei, Shih Chin, Mu Hung, Lei Heng, Li Chün, Juan The Second, Chang Heng, Juan The Fifth, Chang Shun, Juan The Seventh, Yang Hsiung, Shih Hsiu, Hsieh Chen, Hsieh Pao, Yien Ch'ing, Chu Wu, Huang Hsin, Sheng Li, Hsüan Tsan, Hao Ssŭ Wen, Han T'ao, P'eng Ch'i, Shang T'ing Kuei, Wei Ting Kuo, Siao Jang, P'ei Hsüan, Ou P'eng, Teng Fei, Yien Shun, Yang Ling, Ling Chen, Chiang Ching, Lü Fang, Kao Shen, An Tao Ch'uan, Huang Fu Tuan, Wang Ying, The Goodwife Hu, Pao Su, Fan Lui, K'ung Ming, K'ung Liang, Hsiang Ch'ung, Li Kun, Ching Ta Chien, Ma Ling, T'ung Wei, T'ung Meng, Meng K'an, Hou Chien, Ch'en Ta, Yang Ch'un, Chen T'ien Shou, T'ao Chung Wang, Sung Ch'ing, Yo Ho, Kung Wang, Ting Tê Sheng, Mu Ch'un, Ch'ao Cheng, Sung Wan, Tu Ch'ien, Hsüeh Yung, Li Chung, Chou T'ung, T'ang Lung, Tu Hsing, Chou Yuen, Chou Jun, Chu Kuei, Chu Fu, Shih En, Ts'ai Fu, Ts'ai Ch'ing, Li Li, Li Yün, Chiao T'ing, Shih Yung, Sheng Sing, The Goodwife Ku, Chang Ch'ing, The Goodwife Sheng, Wang Ting Lu, Ju Pao Ssŭ, Pei Sheng, Shih Ch'ien and Tuan Ching Chu, these with all their true hearts here together make a great vow. We do ponder on this, that once we were scattered far and wide, but now are we gathered together in this one hall, brethren according to the stars, and we point to Heaven and Earth as father and mother. One hundred and eight of us, each face differing from the other, yet each face noble in its way; one hundred and eight of us, each with his separate heart, yet each heart pure as a star; in joy we shall be one, in sorrow one; our hour of birth was not one, but we will die together. Our names are writ upon the Heavens, nor may the men of Earth despise us. In this day we unite our purpose, and until we die we will not be divided in it. If there be one among us who will not endure and who cuts asunder this high purpose, or answers yea only with his lips but in his heart says nay, or if among these is such an one who begins well and ends ill, then let the Spirit Of Heaven search among us and the Demons Of Earth encompass us, for surely this one will die by sword or arrow, or thunder will fall upon him to destroy him. Then let him lie forever in Hell, that in ten thousand cycles of life he may not come to life again. Let each have his clear reward for good or evil; let Heaven and all the gods together search our hearts!"

When Sung Chiang had thus vowed, all the host together shouted assent and they said, "We would but meet again, life after life, generation after generation, forever undivided, even as we are this day!"

On that day did they all mingle blood with wine and drink it and when they had drunk themselves to mighty drunkenness, they parted.

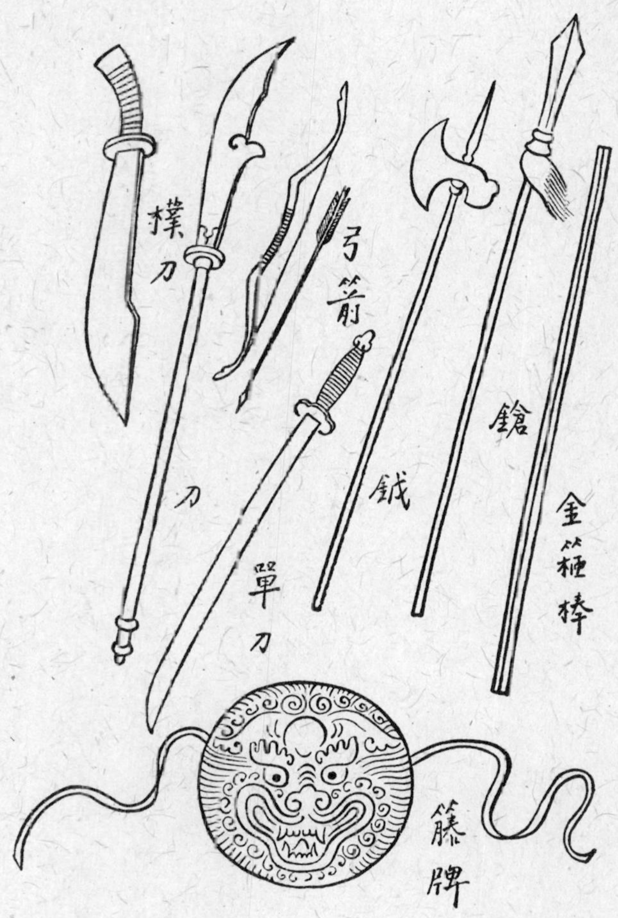

Of this edition of *All Men Are Brothers* fifteen hundred copies
have been made for the members of
The Limited Editions Club.
The composition of the text has been done
by Robert Dothard at the shop of E. L. Hildreth & Company
and the printing has been done by The Stratford Press.
The typography has been planned by Glenn Foss
and the calligraphic titles written by Jeanyee Wong.
The plates for the illustrations were made by Pioneer-Moss
and printed by The Aldus Printers,
the colors being applied by hand in the studio of Paul Baruch.
The paper was especially made by the Worthy Paper Company
and the volumes bound by Frank Fortney.

The illustrations were drawn by MIGUEL COVARRUBIAS
who here signs

Miguel Covarrubias

this copy, which is number 1090